Other Books by Drs. Freedman and Kaplan

COMPREHENSIVE TEXTBOOK OF PSYCHIATRY
Alfred M. Freedman and Harold I. Kaplan, EDITORS   1967

PSYCHOPATHOLOGY OF ADOLESCENCE
Alfred M. Freedman (with Joseph Zubin), EDITOR   1970

COMPREHENSIVE GROUP PSYCHOTHERAPY
Harold I. Kaplan (with Benjamin J. Sadock), EDITOR   1971

STUDIES IN HUMAN BEHAVIOR
Alfred M. Freedman and Harold I. Kaplan, GENERAL EDITORS
DIAGNOSING MENTAL ILLNESS: EVALUATION IN
PSYCHIATRY AND PSYCHOLOGY   1972
INTERPRETING PERSONALITY: A SURVEY OF
TWENTIETH-CENTURY VIEWS   1972
HUMAN BEHAVIOR: BIOLOGICAL, PSYCHOLOGICAL,
AND SOCIOLOGICAL   1972
TREATING MENTAL ILLNESS: ASPECTS OF
MODERN THERAPY   1972
THE CHILD: HIS PSYCHOLOGICAL AND
CULTURAL DEVELOPMENT   1972
VOL. 1: NORMAL DEVELOPMENT AND
PSYCHOLOGICAL ASSESSMENT
VOL. 2: THE MAJOR PSYCHOLOGICAL DISORDERS
AND THEIR TREATMENT

HUMAN
BEHAVIOR

HUMAN
BEHAVIOR

Biological, Psychological,
and Sociological

ALFRED M. FREEDMAN, M.D.

Chairman and Professor, Department of Psychiatry,
New York Medical College

AND

HAROLD I. KAPLAN, M.D.

Professor, Department of Psychiatry, New York Medical College

EDITORS

Studies in Human Behavior

New York ATHENEUM 1972

The editors express their appreciation to the following publishers and publications for permission to reprint portions of the works cited.

Basic Books, Inc., Publishers: W. C. Dement, Psychophysiology of Sleep and Dreams, *American Handbook of Psychiatry*, Silvano Arieti, editor, Vol. III, pp. 290–320, New York, 1966; Milton Rokeach, *The Open and Closed Mind*, New York, 1960.

Brooks/Cole Publishing Company: Fillmore Sanford, *Psychology: A Scientific Study of Man.* © 1961, 1965 by Wadsworth Publishing Company, Inc., Belmont, California 94002.

Holt, Rinehart and Winston, Inc.: A. Bachrach, *Learning, Case Studies in Behavior Modification*, L. P. Ullman and L. Krasner, editors, New York.

Random House, Inc.: F. S. Keller, *Learning: Reinforcement Theory*, 1954.

Science: S. S. Kety, A Biologist Examines the Mind and Behavior, Vol. 132, pp. 1861–70, December 23, 1960. Copyright 1960 by the American Association for the Advancement of Science.

University of Chicago Press: C. L. Hull, Conditioning: outline of a systematic theory of learning, *The Psychology of Learning*, 41st Yearbook, National Society for the Study of Education, Part II, Chicago, 1942.

Van Nostrand Reinhold Company: J. W. Atkinson, *An Introduction to Motivation.* Copyright © 1964, by Litton Educational Publishing Inc.

Preface

This book is one of a series of volumes based on the First Edition of the *Comprehensive Textbook of Psychiatry*, which we edited for use in medical schools. Dr. Helen S. Kaplan served as Assistant to the Editors of that edition. The *Comprehensive Textbook* resulted from our part in setting up the undergraduate and graduate programs in psychiatry at New York Medical College. New articles have been written for these volumes, and certain subjects have been updated or eliminated, in an effort to reach a wider audience.

The responsibility for teaching psychiatry has made us acutely aware of the whole spectrum of current progress in the continuing search for the causes of mental disorders. Recent scientific research has placed at the disposal of the clinical practitioner new knowledge that must be incorporated into existing theoretical and therapeutic methods. Our aim is to include in these volumes all such major contributions in the basic and social sciences that have an influence on the teaching and practice of psychiatry. We have attempted to derive a balanced and current summary of psychiatric thinking in a variety of fields.

The interaction with distinguished and creative colleagues in the preparation of the material contained in these volumes has been most gratifying. We have had a unique opportunity to engage in a stimulating exchange of ideas and to establish rewarding personal relationships as well.

Many people have given us dedicated and valuable help, and we wish to express our deep appreciation to them. We would mention in particular Lois A. Baken, Elaine Cohen, Pauline DeMarco, Margaret J. Davis, and Marian Hailey. And we give special thanks to Joan Welsh for her invaluable help in editing and styling this series.

A.M.F.
H.I.K.

Contents

AREA B

Basic Psychological Sciences

AREA C

Basic Sociocultural Sciences

Introduction

The science of human behavior is the main concern of psychiatry and of the many other scholarly disciplines, both theoretical and practical, that are allied with it. The psychiatrist draws on the results of the work of many other behavioral scientists and, in turn, contributes to their work. Of profound significance for the psychiatrist are the researches of the experimental psychologist, the neurophysiologist, the neurochemist, the sociologist, the anthropologist, and the scientists concerned with the increasingly sophisticated study of ethology, of which human behavior is merely a part. Without the underpinning provided by the work of students in these disciplines, the psychiatrist would be only a clinical technician, and the theoretical work of psychiatry would be supported far less strongly than it is today.

Admittedly, many of the data derived from the work of the basic behavioral scientists have not yet been effectively translated into psychiatric knowledge. Much remains to be done in the areas of interpretation, translation, and theoretical development. An immense amount of research has been undertaken in the basic behavioral sciences in the past twenty years, though it will doubtless be decades before the results of this research are fully assimilated into the field of psychiatry. Nevertheless, the data now available form the cornerstone of current psychiatric research. This research will, in turn, determine the future of the discipline.

Human behavior is a process of extraordinary complexity, reflecting the interaction of numerous variables. Its specific determinants are by no means fully understood yet; this is perhaps even more true of normal behavior than it is of abnormal behavior. The past decades have witnessed numerous complex modifications in the concepts and theories of psychic functioning. These modifications have been necessary to accommodate the rapid accumulation of data derived from increasingly intensive research in the basic behavioral sciences. Concurrently, it has become more and more apparent that the factors determining human behavior operate on several levels at once and that they must be considered within a sociocultural and psychological frame of reference as well as within a physiological one.

If the psychiatrist is to be effective in the treatment of his patients and if he is to advance the frontiers of his own discipline, he must acquire insight into the nature of the basic determinants that control human behavior. He needs more than just a knowledge of other disciplines allied to his own field and an awareness of their effect on psychiatry. He also needs some familiarity with the directions in which these fields are headed and with the ramifications of recent advances—their effect on the discipline as a whole and particularly on psychiatry.

For example, to plan community health services and social action for the prevention of mental illness, the psychiatrist must be aware of recent thinking about the social and cultural determinants of behavior, and he must appreciate the significance of such determinants. This appreciation depends on the psychiatrist's familiarity with the work concerning these determinants and on his theoretical outlook as well. Once he grants the significance of social and cultural determinants, he must assess such sociologically and anthropologically relevant phenomena as class structure, cultural influence on sexual role definition and on sexual mores, and cultural determinants directing patients toward treatment or away from it. He must take these determinants into account in dealing with the larger social context, with psychiatric theory, and with his patients, for patients with similar pathologies may react in quite different ways as a result of ethnic, cultural, or class variations.

Biological determinants play as vital a role as sociological and anthropological determinants. For example, basic concepts derived from research in psychopharmacology, neuroanatomy, and neurophysiology have provided the rationale for the application of psychoactive drug therapy, which has had a profound effect on the practice of psychiatry and on the status of the mentally disturbed. The use of this therapeutic modality requires knowledge of the undesirable side effects of specific drugs and of the drugs' basic effects on such psychological variables as motivation, affect, thought processes, and perception, and some knowledge about how these effects vary with specific psychopathological states.

Many research projects, including those designed to investigate the causes of specific psychiatric disorders, have failed to take into account some significant causative factors. Without considering all the variables, such as studies that point to a high incidence of certain disorders in certain population groups, research projects on the causes of mental diseases lose much of their meaning. A full survey of the factors that are believed to contribute to mental illness has to include comprehensive studies of affective and cognitive experiences in early childhood, the biochemical constituents of the brain, the family environment to which the patient was exposed in the past and that in which he functions at present, the social environment in which he participates and that has acted on him, changes in his social environment, ethnic and cultural differences, and perhaps even religious and economic factors.

This book on the basic behavioral sciences deals with some of the psychological, sociocultural, and physiological concepts that are fundamental for the understanding of psychiatry and human behavior. One area is devoted to the basic biological sciences—genetics, neurochemistry, psychopharmacology, neurophysiology, the study of sleep and dreams, and so on. These sciences underlie the study of psychiatry and have contributed much to therapeutic theory and practice. The operation of the brain and the central nervous system is described, and the chapter on psychopharmacology provides an outline of the operation and effects of the psychotropic and neurotropic drugs, the major and minor tranquilizers. The chapter on sleep and dreams summarizes the most recent findings in this field.

A second area is devoted to the basic psychological sciences, with individual chapters on perception, cognition, learning, motivation, ethology, and social communication. Much work has been done in these fields, and recent findings have great relevance to psychiatry. Communication engineering as an aid to the psychiatrist is discussed, and a survey of various learning theories is provided, as are surveys of the work done in perception and cognition.

The basic sociocultural sciences are featured in the third area, which includes discussions of the relations between anthropology and psychiatry and between sociology and psychiatry. Much work is yet to be done in integrating the findings of these disciplines with psychiatry, but it cannot be ignored that social interactions outside the immediate family may play a significant role in the cause and the progress of mental illness and in the direction that illness takes. Sociology can be of benefit in analyzing the causes of mental disorder and in modifying public attitudes toward the mentally ill, toward day care of mental patients, and toward psychiatry itself. This area also provides a discussion of the role of the family in psychiatry—family structure and dynamics, family pathology, and family functions, both individual and relational.

A fourth area covers other fundamental topics that play a significant role in psychiatry. One of these is sensory deprivation, a second is the hallucinogens, and a third is the related topic of experimental neurosis, its history and current findings. Psychiatric epidemiology is treated from the historic point of view and from the point of view of present knowledge of the field. One chapter discusses the use of computers in psychiatric study. Finally, there are two basic studies on another subject that underlies psychiatric theory and practice—the idea of normality. One is a general study, and the other focuses on normal psychosexual functioning. Both take account of new directions and new findings in the study of normal functioning.

Each chapter within the four areas presents its discipline's basic concepts, semantics, and methodology. Wherever relevant, the historical background of the discipline and variant concepts and methodologies are presented. In addition, there is a review of data derived from the field that are important to psychiatry. When feasible, this material is discussed in terms of its direct relevance to pathological behavior phenomena encountered in clinical practice.

To illustrate, the chapters on perception and cognition define the mechanisms of these functions as normal phenomena. In addition, perceptual and cognitive disorders that are characteristic of such psychiatric disorders as schizophrenia and mental deficiency are discussed, and concepts and methods derived from the study of perceptual and cognitive functions are applied to the clinical use of psychological test procedures. A survey of what is known about the neurophysiology of perception is provided. This survey can be read with reference to the larger discussion of neurophysiology that appears in another chapter. Normal relationships between personality and cognition are explored, as is the relationship between environmental stimulation and cognition. Thus, many of the chapters refer not just to a specific behavioral science but to other relevant behavioral science areas.

Similarly, ethology is discussed in terms of relevant data about the behavior of animals, with particular emphasis on the relationship of animal behavior to the developmental theories in child psychiatry. In addition, there is an exploration of the possible application to psychiatry of the methodological procedures employed in ethology and of the potential value of such application. This chapter also contains a history of ethological study.

The basic concepts of psychopharmacology and neurochemistry are discussed with specific reference to the clinical use of psychopharmacological agents. Chemical findings on mentally disturbed patients are presented, together with a discussion of the problems that arise in assigning a biological foundation to the causes of schizophrenia. There is, in addition, a survey of current research on the relationship between neurochemistry and behavior. The chapter on psychopharmacology discusses barbiturates, hallucinogenic drugs, and the psychotropic drugs that are frequently employed in psychiatric treatment. These chapters also present the accumulated biochemical data that are relevant to the behavioral manifestations of organic brain disorders and of patients suffering from psychotic states.

The chapter on learning theory is concerned with the manner in which pathological behavior is acquired and with the application of learning theory principles to the treatment of such psychopathology. This chapter includes a discussion of the history of learning theories and of their relationship to psychiatric therapy, particularly their relationship to behavioral therapy. Similarly, the chapters on anthropology and sociology focus on the application of the data derived from these disciplines to milieu therapy and community psychiatry, and on the value of the methodological procedures characteristic of these fields in the study of the causes of mental disorders.

Despite the fact that the relevance of some of this material to the complexities of human behavior and to clinical psychiatry is less precise at the present time than one would hope, there are compelling reasons to believe that findings in these areas will be translated into knowledge that will facilitate theoretic and therapeutic progress in psychiatry.

AREA A

Basic Biological Sciences

CHAPTER 1

Genetics and Psychiatry

JOHN D. RAINER, M.D.

INTRODUCTION

UNTIL THE EARLY 1930's, development in the fields of genetics and psychiatry followed separate paths. In the behavioral sciences, heredity and environmental factors were considered as separate, if not distinctly different, entities. Many psychiatrists were deeply concerned with the ancient dichotomy between nature and nurture and between mind and matter; as a result, they tended to separate the biological and the psychological disciplines.

For many years, the behavioral sciences were dominated by viewpoints similar to that expressed by J. B. Watson, who believed that one could produce any kind of human being if allowed to manipulate that individual's environment from an early age. Meanwhile, American psychiatry was under the constructive influence of Adolf Meyer, who considered mental disorder largely as a maladaptation in the face of environmental stresses. A number of family studies of the major psychoses were reported by Rosanoff, Pollock, Malzberg, and others, and biologists such as Raymond Pearl worked in the tradition of Galton and Pearson. But in the transplantation of psychoanalysis from Europe to the United States in the middle 1930's and its flourishing during and immediately after World War II, the attention that Freud and Ernest Jones had given to inborn differences was largely forgotten. Freudian psychoanalysis, particularly some of its offshoots in the United States, combined therapeutic zeal with exclusive attention to psychogenesis.

A few of that generation of psychoanalysts showed exceptions to this trend. Among these was Rado, who conceived of a unitary scheme of psychology with psychodynamics resting on the solid bases of genetics and physiology. The publication of Kallmann's Berlin family study and subsequently of his New York twin investigation in schizophrenia changed American psychiatry profoundly by calling attention to the importance of genetics in many psychiatric conditions. The area of Kallmann's work included schizophrenia, manic-depressive psychoses, homosexuality, mental deficiency, aging and longevity, tuberculosis, early deafness, and genetic counseling.

In the 1960's a more general shift in American psychiatry could be seen. Major advances in cytological and biochemical genetics not only captured the imagination of many psychiatrists but pointed to an understanding of the possible mechanisms of genetic influence. Experimental psychology was studying individual differences in various species from drosophila to dogs. The theory of interaction of genetic and ecological forces in human development became predominant, and the problems of population growth began to draw attention to important aspects of population genetics and human evolution. At the same time, on the basis of clinical observations, psychiatrists were beginning to be aware of the importance of family patterns, individual differences, and metabolic and pharmacological distinctions.

In considering the relation of genetics to psychiatry, we can conceive a series of organization levels: the molecular and cellular, the biochemical and neurophysiological, the psychodynamic, the demographic, and the social. In each of these areas, the continuous interaction of the organism with its surrounding forces determines its status at any given time; that is, there is an interplay of all the factors affecting human development—whether genetic, chromosomal, cytoplasmic, biochemical, embryological, metabolic, experiential, or social. The goal of psychiatric genetics as a science may be considered, in the broadest sense, to be the clarification of the mechanisms of cause, of effect, and of interaction not only in psychiatric disease but in normal behavior.

CLASSICAL GENETICS

Gregor Mendel's report on his garden pea experiments in 1865 paved the way for the modern theory of genetics. His observations led to the postulation that a genetic substance, which was not blended but rather remained intact during an individual's life, was transmitted in the form of stable units to his offspring. Mendel's ideas led to the description of populations in mathematical terms. The development of genetics later merged with that of the theory of evolution. Originally, Mendel's conclusions were statistical in nature. Counting the variations that he found in the progeny of certain matings, he inferred that each trait existed as if determined by paired particles (later called genes) in the germ plasm. From this inference, a number of general principles of inheritance were derived.

In classical genetics it is assumed that single genetic traits are determined by paired genes, one of which is derived from the male germ cell and the other from the female germ cell. One may speak of the total genetic constitution of the individual as his genotype and of his appearance at any given time as his phenotype. A person receiving a given gene from both parents is called a homozygote for that particular gene, and under proper environmental conditions he will be certain to show its characteristics. If an individual receives the given gene from one parent and a different gene at the corresponding locus from the other parent, he is known as heterozygote. In some cases, the heterozygote will display traits intermediate between those represented by homozygotes. In other cases he will display the trait as a homozygote does; in this instance, the trait is known as dominant. In still other cases, he will not display the trait; in this instance, the trait is known as recessive; that is, it is expressed only if both genes are present.

Mutant genes. If a single mutant gene can express itself against the genetic background of many other factors, its phenotype effect in most cases will tend to be pathological.

Simple dominant traits tend to be rare and incompletely expressed. When they appear, they are transmitted in the direct line of descent by inheritance from one parent. They may be easily studied in pedigrees, and they appear in approximately 50 per cent of the offspring of one affected parent (see Figure 1). Matings between two affected

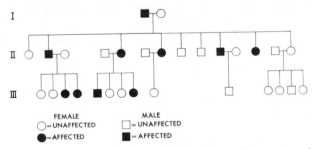

FIGURE 1. A pedigree of Huntington's chorea, illustrating dominant inheritance. (From the Department of Medical Genetics, New York State Psychiatric Institute.)

persons are rare, and a negligible role is played by consanguineous marriages.

In simple recessive traits, inheritance from both parents is necessary. The parents themselves are frequently unaffected, since they are usually heterozygotes. If two heterozygotes mate, each child has a 25 per cent chance of being a homozygote and, therefore, an affected individual (see Figure 2). In relatively rare disorders, consanguineous

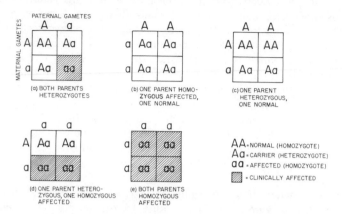

FIGURE 2. Diagram of theoretical expectations in simple recessive inheritance, such as for phenylketonuria. (From the Department of Medical Genetics, New York State Psychiatric Institute.)

marriages are apt to increase the chances of such affected offspring. Transmission of a simple recessive trait is usually along collateral rather than direct lines of descent.

Not all mutant genes in man conform to a simple mode of inheritance. A gene does not produce a given trait directly. It merely begins a long series of reactions that may be modified by environmental factors, both prenatal and postnatal, and by the action of other genes. Gene effects, therefore, may vary from complete expression to no apparent expression at all. There are genes that are neither completely dominant nor completely recessive but somewhere in between. Since recessive genes may express themselves mildly in heterozygotes, methods for their detection are of great importance in the practical application of genetic counseling.

Multiple genes. In addition to single-factor types of inheritance, certain traits are determined by the interaction of several or many genes. This type of inheritance is called multifactorial, with contributions made in a cumulative manner by a number of genes that by themselves produce only minor effects. Such genes are neither dominant nor recessive but are intermediate in their effect. Modifier genes may change the expression of a major gene, and suppressor genes may limit its effect entirely. For many traits—such as height, weight, intelligence, and perhaps personality variations that show small gradations within the range of normality—multifactorial inheritance may be at work.

HUMAN CYTOGENETICS

During the three decades in which Mendel's findings remained unnoticed, the discovery of the chromosomes in the cell nucleus took place. These specially staining threadlike bodies were observed to divide in the process of cell division and to be distributed as exact duplicates. But in the formation of germ cells, each cell received only half of the chromosomes in the parental cells. These facts turned out to be consistent with the statistical findings of Mendel, and thus it became possible to combine data derived from breeding experiments with the microscopic study of cells and chromosomes. For instance, if a gene is situated on one of the twenty-two pairs of autosomes, the type of inheritance is called autosomal, and the distribution of the trait between the sexes is equal. But if a gene is transmitted on the sex chromosomes, the inheritance is called sex-linked, and the distribution of the trait between the sexes is unequal. In recessive X-borne conditions, for example, males are more frequently affected than females because males have only one X chromosome, whereas females have two.

Nevertheless, the study of chromosomes in the human was long neglected. There was no agreement on such simple matters as the number of chromosomes and the mechanism by which sex was determined chromosomally. Most textbooks stated that the total number of chromosomes in each normal human cell is 48, a figure found to be incorrect in recent years. The number is now established as being 46. And, although it was known that females had two X chromosomes and males one X and one Y, it had been erroneously thought that the Y chromosome was inactive, sex being determined by the number of X chromosomes. Until recently, methodology was not advanced to the point where clinical abnormalities could be correlated with chromosomal aberrations.

SEX CHROMATIN AND NUCLEAR SEX DETERMINATION

In 1949 the first recent major discovery in human cytogenetics was made in Canada by Barr and Bertram, who uncovered an important difference between male and female cells while studying neurons of the cat. The investigators found a dark staining mass of chromatin in the nuclei of many cells. They soon made the crucial observation that it was the female cat that had this chromatin substance. Before long, this difference was shown to exist in other mammals, including man.

The determination of sex chromatin in the human is not a difficult procedure. It is done most easily by examining a smear made of buccal mucosal cells. The cells are scraped from the inside of the mouth, put on specially prepared slides, fixed and stained, and from one to two hundred cells are counted. The mass is seen plastered against the nuclear membrane. From 30 to 60 per cent of the cells of the normal woman show this dark staining mass, which is now referred to as sex chromatin or, after its

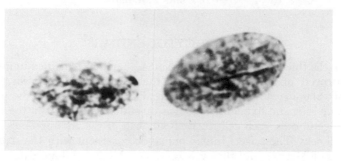

FIGURE 3. Sex chromatin in buccal mucosal cells (*left*, chromatin-positive; *right*, chromatin-negative). (From Cytogenetics Laboratory, Department of Medical Genetics, New York State Psychiatric Institute.)

discoverer, a Barr body (see Figure 3). The origin of the sex chromatin body is still not completely clear. Originally, it was believed that it consisted of parts of both X chromosomes. This theory was discarded in favor of one derived from the so-called Lyon hypothesis, which states that, in the early embryonic development of the female, one X chromosome in each cell is inactivated. Accordingly, the Barr body is thought to represent all or part of this inactivated chromosome.

In 1954 a second difference between male and female cells was discovered. A drumstick-like appendage attached to one of the lobes of the nucleus of polymorphonuclear leukocytes was consistently noted in more than 2 per cent of cells in females and in an insignificantly small number of cells in males.

Turner's syndrome. The technique of nuclear sexing soon led to the discovery of chromatin abnormalities in certain human sexual anomalies. In one of these, Turner's syndrome, cells were found to lack the Barr body. Girls with this syndrome are short and have infantile genitals, and their gonads are reduced to connective tissue streaks. There are other defects, such as webbed neck, short fingers, and shield chest. This anomaly appears in about 1 in 3,000 newborn females. Some patients with Turner's syndrome show intellectual impairment, but the condition is not usually associated with severe mental deficiency. Initially, these females were called "chromosomal males" because they lacked the chromatin patch.

Klinefelter's syndrome. Another syndrome studied on the basis of the presence or absence of sex chromatin was Klinefelter's syndrome. This condition occurs in males and includes small, atrophic testes, usually with sterility; notable gynecomastia; and increased excretion of gonadotrophin. It appears in 1 in 350 male births but accounts for 1 per cent of mentally retarded male patients in institutions. Klinefelter's syndrome was found to be associated with the presence of a Barr body, usually absent in the male, and for a time these patients were called "chromosomal females."

Development of Chromosome Technique

In 1956 improved methods of visualizing and counting human chromosomes promised to clarify many of these cytogenetic problems. Since chromosomes become visible and distinguishable only at the metaphase stage of a dividing nucleus, it was necessary to obtain cells in the process of division. Early investigations had been done with testicular tissue, and individual cells with visible and distinguishable chromosomes had been observed. However, these chromosomes clumped together and overlapped, rendering attempted counts inaccurate.

The problem of obtaining many cells in a dividing stage was dealt with by the use of tissue culture methods whereby cells from skin biopsy or from blood could grow and divide in vitro in tissue culture media. In order to arrest the cells at the metaphase stage, where the chromosomes may be distinguished, colchicine or other mitotic poisons were added to the culture medium shortly before the cells were harvested. In order to avoid clumping and overlapping of the chromosomes, the cells were suspended in a hypotonic solution in the stage before staining. This hypotonic solution swelled the nucleus and scattered the chromosomes over a larger area to make them discretely visible. Finally, the cells were centrifuged, spread on slides, dried, and stained.

Currently, most cultures are prepared with lymphocytes. They are stimulated to turn into large lymphocytes and to divide by the addition of a foreign antigen such as phytohaemagglutinin, a plant substance. The entire process of cell growth and harvesting takes about seventy-two hours.

Normal human karyotype. Tjio and Levan, in 1956, found by tissue culture methods that the number of chromosomes in man is 46. It soon became possible, by enlarging the photograph of the microscopic field and cutting each chromosome out, to arrange the chromosomes in descending order of size, thus producing a visual representation of the chromosome complement or karyotype. Since each chromosome is photographed at the stage in which it duplicates itself, the chromosomes have the appearance of a letter "X" or an inverted letter "V," each chromosome and its new partner remaining connected at one point, called the centromere. The chromosomes are distinguishable within size groups by the position of this centromere, which may be either median or toward one end. The median or submedian chromosomes are known as metacentric; the subterminal or terminal ones are acrocentric.

In 1960 the numbering system was standardized, the chromosomes being divided into seven groups (see Figure 4). Group A, made up of chromosomes 1 through 3, consists of large chromosomes with approximately median centromeres; these chromosomes may be easily distinguished from one another by their size and the location of the

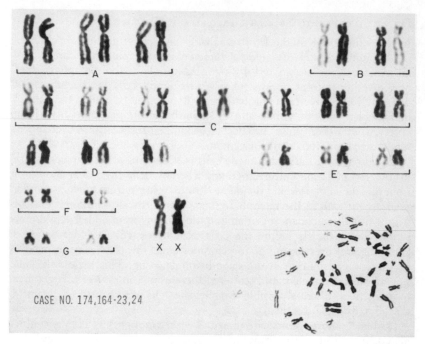

CASE NO. 174,164-23,24

FIGURE 4. Karyotype of normal woman. (From the Cytogenetics Laboratory, Department of Medical Genetics, New York State Psychiatric Institute.)

centromere. Group B, chromosomes 4 and 5, consists of large chromosomes with submedian centromeres; these chromosomes are more difficult to distinguish from one another. Group C, chromosomes 6 through 12, consists of medium-sized chromosomes with submedian centromeres; they are not easily distinguishable one from one another morphologically; the X chromosome resembles the larger chromosomes in this group. Group D, chromosomes 13 through 15, consists of medium-sized chromosomes with centromeres which are nearly terminal in location. Group E, chromosomes 16 through 18, contains rather short chromosomes with approximately median or submedian centromeres; chromosome 16 is easily distinguishable because its centromere is median, and it looks like a small letter "x." Group F, chromosomes 19 and 20, contains short chromosomes with approximately median centromeres. Group G, chromosomes 21 and 22, is made up of very short acrocentric chromosomes; the Y chromosome is similar to these in size.

Recent techniques of autoradiography, in which cells are grown in a labeled medium and the uptake of radioactive substance at various stages in chromosome replication is measured and visualized, indicate that in the various groups certain chromosomes replicate later than others. This characteristic serves to distinguish chromosomes that are difficult to recognize by appearance alone.

Chromosomal aberrations.

NONDISJUNCTION AND TRANSLOCATION. The three years after the correct description of the human karyotype were fruitful ones in cytogenetics. Even before the numbering system was standardized, a number of aberrations were described. One group of aberrations was marked by the presence of an extra chromosome, so that there were 47 rather than 46 chromosomes in the karyotype. The extra chromosome represented the presence of 3 rather than 2 of a given chromosome. Such an anomaly arises through a process of nondisjunction, usually in the formation of the sperm or the egg cell. In the splitting of the cell, 1 chromosome of each pair ordinarily goes to each of the daughter cells. If the 2 chromosomes of a given pair remain joined and migrate together to one of the daughter cells, that cell will have an extra chromosome. When that daughter cell combines in fertilization with a normal gamete, a zygote or single-cell-stage individual will be formed with the extra chromosome.

DOWN'S SYNDROME (MONGOLISM). Three viable types of nondisjunction causing trisomic conditions have been described. In these conditions the autosomes, as distinguished from the X and Y or sex chromosomes, are involved, and the affected chromosomes are triple instead of double. The first type described was the trisomy of a chromosome in group G in mongolism, better termed Down's syndrome, after the man who first described it in 1866. It had been known for a long time that most cases of this syndrome occurred in children born to older mothers. At the same time, however, the concordance rate in one-egg twins was close to 100 per cent. These findings foreshadowed an early germinal, possibly chromosomal, defect as the responsible agent. In 1959 Lejeune and others demonstrated by tissue culture methods the presence of an extra small acrocentric chromosome in patients with Down's syndrome. It is very likely that this condition arises by nondisjunction in the formation of the maternal ovum. The delicate balance of chromosomes is indicated by the fact that an extra one causes such widespread chemical, morphological, and psychological effects.

If the extra chromosome is lost through disjunction in the early cell divisions of the zygote, two cell lines may persist, one with 46 and one with 47 chromosomes. The individual will be known as a mosaic and may have an intermediate degree of symptomatology.

A third mechanism in mongolism was first postulated by Polani on the basis of the investigation of the chromosome complement in a mongoloid child born to a young mother. Chromosome count revealed the normal number of 46, but 1 of the chromosomes in group D turned out to be longer than normal. It was suggested that this oversized chromosome consisted of an extra G chromosome joined to the long arm of a D chromosome; in such cases there are, in effect, 3 G chromosomes. It has sometimes been found in these cases that the mother or the father has such a long D chromosome also, but the added unit is balanced by the absence of 1 of the unattached G chromosomes, leaving the individual with a total number of only 45 chromosomes. Such a parent is a carrier, and his children have approximately 1 chance out of 3 of being affected.

This interchange of chromosomal material is known as translocation. It may also occur in Down's syndrome between 2 chromosomes in the G group. The difference between trisomy and translocation is very important from a practical point of view. Most mothers who have a child with Down's syndrome have a small risk of producing a second one; the risk is no greater than for other women their age. At the highest, this risk is about 1 in 50 for mothers over 45. But if a mother is a translocation carrier, she has a risk of about 1 in 3 of having an affected child.

OTHER AUTOSOMAL TRISOMIES. A second autosomal trisomy syndrome is the trisomy 17–18 syndrome. Infants affected by this syndrome fail to thrive and live only a few months. Among the defects they show are apparent mental retardation, a small mandible, low-set ears, eyes wide apart, fingers flexed with a dorsal crossing or overlapping of the digits, and hypertonia. A third trisomy, of one of the chromosomes in group D, also results in failure to thrive, mental retardation with associated eye defect such as microphthalmia or anophthalmia, often a cleft palate and hare lip, polydactyly, and occasionally congenital heart disease.

Deletion. In addition to nondisjunction and translocation, a third mechanism causing chromosomal anomalies is that of deletion. In this condition part of a chromosome breaks off during cell replication, and future cells have a smaller-sized chromosome than usual. The *cri du chat* syndrome described by Lejeune is associated with a deletion of chromosome 5. Children displaying this syndrome fail to thrive; are mentally retarded; show microcephaly, hypertelorism, and low-set ears; and emit a characteristic mewlike cry similar to that of a kitten.

Abnormalities involving sex chromosomes. Contrary to the normal patterns, certain males show the sex chromatin patch, and certain females do not. Chromatin-positive male patients with Klinefelter's syndrome, once their karyotype is determined, are found to have 47 chromosomes. They do indeed have 2 X chromosomes, but they also possess a Y chromosome. The 2 X chromosomes are sufficient to cause the appearance of the Barr body, but the Y chromosome causes them to have male gonads and essentially male genitals. Such an anomaly may be brought about by the union of an abnormal XY sperm with a normal ovum or by the union of an abnormal XX ovum with a normal Y-bearing sperm. In each case, the abnormal gamete is the result of nondisjunction. Similarly, most girls with

Turner's syndrome and no Barr body are found to have a karyotype containing only 45 chromosomes; they have only 1 X chromosome, the other sex chromosome being missing. This condition is called the Xo condition, "o" referring to the absence of a chromosome that is normally present. In this case, a nondisjunction may result in a sperm cell or an ovum containing neither an X nor a Y chromosome; the union of such a deficient cell and an X-bearing gamete results in the given anomaly.

Another abnormality involving the sex chromosomes is seen in the "superfemale," who is actually sexually infantile and amenorrheic, having 47 chromosomes, with 3 X chromosomes and 2 Barr bodies.

The above findings and many variations thereof establish certain important principles in human sex determination. First, the presence of a Y chromosome appears to be both necessary and sufficient for the formation of male gonads, regardless of the number of X chromosomes the individual possesses. Individuals with XXXY or XXXXY karyotypes are basically males in spite of severe anomalies. Second, the sex chromatin pattern seems to be related in a simple way to the chromosome count; the number of Barr bodies is always one less than the number of X chromosomes.

Significance of chromosomal variations. It is too early to assess the value of chromosomal studies in unraveling the processes of human gene action. At present, such studies are valuable in the analysis of cases for genetic diagnosis and counseling. In the future, by correlating specific metabolic abnormalities with diseases involving certain chromosomes, it may be possible to further the localization of human genes and mapping of human chromosomes. A number of observations foreshadow this development. It is known, for example, that acute leukemia is frequently found in patients with Down's syndrome (trisomy G); at the same time, in patients with chronic myelogenous leukemia, one of the chromosomes in group G is abnormally small. It is likely, therefore, that some of the lesions in this type of leukemia may be traceable to genes located on this chromosome.

Chromosomal findings in psychiatric syndromes other than the mental deficiencies and sexual anomalies already described have thus far not been striking. A suggestive but not statistically significant correlation between sex chromosome anomalies and schizophrenia in large populations has been described, and many of the mental deficiency states associated with abnormal karyotypes evince psychotic types of behavior. It may someday be possible to localize some of the genetic mechanisms in human behavior. This has already been done in the fruit fly; strains of flies have been bred to travel either from or toward the light or away from or toward gravity. These strains have then been analyzed by cross-breeding experiments involving known markers to determine the contribution of the various chromosomes to their behavior.

BIOCHEMISTRY OF GENETIC SUBSTANCE

Structure of DNA. In the biochemical laboratory there have been outstanding advances in elucidating the nature of the genetic substance itself. By 1952 chemists had determined that the genetic material transferred from generation to generation and carrying genetic information is not protein, as had long been thought, but deoxyribonucleic acid (DNA). It was found possible to transform a bacterium of one type to another by injecting it into an animal together with pure DNA of the second type. It was also found that in certain viruses the effective part was DNA. Chromosomes are composed of DNA and protein, but DNA appeared to be the primary genetic material.

In 1953 the structure of this molecule was proposed by Watson and Crick. It had been known that DNA contains four nitrogenous bases—two purines (adenine and guanine) and two pyrimidines (cytosine and thymine)—that the amount of adenine equals the amount of thymine, and that the amount of guanine equals the amount of cytosine. Watson and Crick suggested that DNA consists of two chains of five-carbon sugars held together by phosphate bonds and that each of these chains is twisted in the form of a helix. From each sugar on one chain to a corresponding sugar on the other, there is a linkage between either adenine on one chain and thymine on the other or guanine on one and cytosine on the other, the linkage held together by hydrogen bonds. A DNA molecule may consist of thousands of such nucleotide linkages.

Functions of DNA. On the basis of this DNA structure, it is possible to explain the two main functions of the genetic material: (1) its ability to duplicate itself exactly and (2) its ability to transfer information to the cytoplasm of the cell and bring about the synthesis of unique enzymes or other proteins.

REPLICATION. If the two chains forming the double helix separate, breaking the linkages between the nucleotides, each half may then extract, from the surrounding nutrient material, substances with which to reconstruct a sister chain. In this process, the sequence of nucleotides on each sister chain must be complementary to that on the original half-chain. One is left with two double-helical chains, each of which is identical to the original.

PROTEIN MANUFACTURE. The process of protein manufacture is more complex and involves additional molecules. Basically, it is believed that a sequence of 3 nucleotide linkages is associated with the final production of a given amino acid. As there are 21 amino acids and 64 possible linkages of 3 nucleotides, there are more than enough different combinations, and some redundancy is probable. The process begins as the message on a portion of the DNA is message determines the production of enzymes or structural materials produced by the cell, and regulator and operator genes. The regulator and operator genes switch the structural genes on and off, depending on the presence and quantity of the substrate on which the genes act or of the product that the genes produce. Thus, a type of feedback mechanism ensures a regulation of the genes by their surroundings. More complex mechanisms may play a role in higher organisms. These may represent the basic prototypes of interaction, a concept of primary importance in psychiatric genetics.

INBORN ERRORS OF METABOLISM

One of the classic writings on genetics early in this century was the series of papers by Garrod, dealing with inborn errors of metabolism. Garrod foresaw the concept of genes determining enzyme production and conceived of the idea of metabolic blocks in which the absence of a necessary enzyme caused the intermediary metabolism of a certain substance to proceed in a faulty direction. His theory also foreshadowed the one gene-one enzyme hypothesis of Beadle and Tatum.

PHENYLKETONURIA

One example of a genetic defect in metabolism with notable effect on the brain is phenylketonuria. This condition was described in 1934 by Følling, who noted ten patients, some of them siblings, who were mentally deficient and who excreted phenylpyruvic acid. Jervis discovered the single autosomal recessive inheritance of this condition, observed large amounts of phenylalanine in the blood of these patients, and pinpointed the metabolic error as the absence of the enzyme, phenylalanine hydroxylase, which ordinarily oxidizes phenylalanine to tyrosine.

The heterozygous carriers, the parents of such children, have a reduced enzyme level, which is best detected by giving a test dose of phenylalanine and observing the plasma level one to four hours later. In this tolerance test the plasma phenylalanine concentration of the heterozygotes may be twice that of normals.

Clinical characteristics. As a recessive condition, phenylketonuria occurs, on the average, in one child out of four if both parents are heterozygotes. There is equal distribution of the condition between the sexes. Clinically, the first manifestations of mental retardation occur at about six months. Most patients develop to idiot level, a few develop to imbecile level, and a small number have borderline intelligence. Other characteristics of the disorder are seizures, psychotic symptoms consisting of destructive and noisy episodes and temper tantrums, skin manifestations consisting of eczema, dry or rough skin, and often blond hair and blue eyes. Patients with this disorder account for about 1 per cent of the population of institutions for mental defectives.

transferred to a single-stranded molecule known as ribonucleic acid (RNA), which then moves out into the cytoplasm of the cell. The sequence of nucleotides in the RNA is the same as in the DNA except that thymine is replaced by uracil. This RNA attaches itself to structures in the cytoplasm of the cell known as ribosomes.

Meanwhile, the amino acids derived from the diet and present in the cytoplasm attach themselves to a type of genetic molecule called transfer-RNA, a long chain bent like a hairpin and twisted into a helix. A given molecule of transfer-RNA is able to attach itself at its free end to one—and only one—of the amino acids. At the bend of the hairpin, a sequence of three nucleotides searches for its unique complementary sequence on the messenger-RNA and attaches itself thereto. In this manner, the messenger-RNA serves as a template that specifies how a sequence of amino acids, each accompanied by its appropriate transfer-RNA molecule, will line up. These amino acids form bonds, one with the other; the transfer-RNA molecules separate off, and the resulting chain of amino acids or polypeptide remains. These polypeptides form proteins, which may be enzymes or structural proteins, such as hemoglobin.

Mutations. Gene mutations represent changes in the genetic instruction so that new cells produce different substances than do the cells that preceded the mutation. If these mutations take place in germ cells, they may produce a change in the genetic information contained in the zygote and, depending on the locus of the mutation, a resultant particular enzyme deficiency or disease.

In the framework of the modern theory of gene action, a mutation may be considered as a change in the sequence of nucleotides in the DNA. Such changes may take place through a mistake in the replication process at the time the cell divides, possibly through the action of certain chemical compounds, or as a result of high energy radiation. The changes may consist of the addition of an extra nucleotide pair, the subtraction of a nucleotide, the substitution of one nucleotide for another, or various rearrangements of the nucleotide sequence. From then on, a changed message is sent via the messenger-RNA to the cytoplasm, and a different protein is produced.

Control of DNA function. One of the basic questions in this picture of gene action and protein synthesis is the problem of control or regulation. Every somatic cell in the body has the same 46 chromosomes, all of them descendants of those in the original one cell or zygote, but it is clear that cells differentiate and perform different functions. Not every chromosome, therefore, is transferring its total message at all times.

Various theories have been propounded to account for the control of gene action. One theory, propounded by Jacob and Monod on the basis of the study of bacteria, states that there exist both structural genes, which

Case detection. Until recently, phenylketonuria was detected by the ferric chloride test, in which a 5 per cent solution of ferric chloride added to fresh urine produces an olive green color, which fades within an hour or two. This test, however, frequently does not give a positive result until the infant is 4 to 6 weeks of age, when it may be difficult to follow up a child already discharged from the hospital. Recently, a simple test for detecting elevated phenylalanine levels in the blood of newborn infants was devised by Guthrie. At present, many states require that every newborn child be tested by this technique. Prior to the use of the Guthrie test, the incidence of phenylketonuria was thought to be about 1 in 25,000. Present determinations, excluding false positive results, yield an incidence of closer to 1 in 10,000.

Management. In line with the dictum that a genetic disease represents interaction between a gene-borne deficiency and the environment, Jervis found it possible to prevent the mental deficiency that develops in the phenylketonuric by supplying an environment relatively free of phenylalanine by means of a low-phenylalanine diet. Infants started on such a diet in the first few months of life may develop normally, even though the enzymatic deficiency is present. Indeed, such infants have been removed from these special diets at the age of 5 or 6 years; although the phenylalanine level in the blood subsequently rose, there was no effect on intelligence. This phenomenon represents an example of the relation of gene-borne deficiencies to time of life. A new problem is presented in the case of females who grow to adulthood and have children while their phenylalanine level is high. In these cases, placental transfer may cause brain damage in the child, even though the child is not a homozygote for phenylketonuria. It has been recommended that such women be returned to a low-phenylalanine diet before pregnancy.

Drug sensitivity. There is evidence that there may be inherited differences in response to drugs. This has given rise to a discipline known as pharmacogenetics. One example of an abnormality in this area with psychiatric implications is pseudocholinesterase deficiency. Individuals with a low concentration of this enzyme in the plasma and with an atypical form of the enzyme show a prolonged reaction to the drug succinylcholine. This skeletal muscle relaxant, acting at the neuromuscular junction, is usually destroyed by pseudocholinesterase and, therefore, has a very short duration of action. Succinylcholine is used in anesthesiology, particularly during endoscopic procedures and reductions of fractures and dislocations. It is used in psychiatry during electroshock treatment in order to avoid strong convulsions and muscular contractions that might cause bone fractures. In persons with atypical esterase, an excessive amount of the drug reaches the nerve end plate. Even a small test dose of the drug may cause 10 to 15 minutes of apnea in a patient with this metabolic disorder.

According to Kalow, this condition is determined by an autosomal gene. Persons homozygous for this gene have only atypical esterase; heterozygotes have mixtures of atypical and typical. Homozygotes account for about 1 person in 3,000; almost 4 per cent of the population may be heterozygotes. Determination of pseudocholinesterase activity in persons who are to receive electroconvulsive therapy and adequate provision for artificial respiration would reduce the seriousness of prolonged apneic reactions to succinylcholine.

PRINCIPLES OF POPULATION GENETICS AND EVOLUTION

Genetic factors determine important short- and long-range effects in human populations. A population may be defined as a group of individuals tending to mate among each other. Such a reproductive community shares a common gene pool, within which the relative frequencies of various genes may be specified. In a human population, other distinguishing features may be of a geographic, cultural, socioeconomic, ethnic, or psychological nature. These considerations may tend to isolate certain subpopulations within the main population. The changing stratification of such subpopulations exert a definite effect on the genetic composition of the given population groups.

HARDY-WEINBERG EQUILIBRIUM

The basis for a systematic approach to population genetics is a simple formula called the Hardy-Weinberg law. This law describes an equilibrium state in an ideal population that exists from generation to generation. It expresses, in terms of the gene frequencies, the expected values of the various genotypes if the following conditions are met: random mating, with every male individual having the same chance to mate with any female; no selective advantage or disadvantage of any one gene over the others at the same locus; and absence of mutations. In addition, the ideal Hardy-Weinberg equilibrium assumes a very large and geographically stable population.

The main importance of the law lies in the fact that it demonstrates a continuation of population variations from generation to generation rather than a trend toward increasing uniformity. If any of its conditions are not fulfilled, there is interference with the population equilibrium.

CAUSES OF DISEQUILIBRIUM

Interference with random mating. A change in the relative proportion of homozygotes and heterozygotes is brought about by any interference with random mating, such as consanguineous marriage, assortative mating, and the persistence or development of population isolates. Such practices result in an increase of recessive phenotypes, particularly in the case of relatively rare conditions, since there is an increased trend for two heterozygous carriers of recessive genes to mate and produce homozygous offspring.

Genetic drift. In small populations, even with random mating, there are chance variations in the relative frequency of genes from generation to generation. This phenomena, known as genetic drift, leads to fluctuations of gene frequencies, despite the absence of mutation, selection, and assortative mating.

Mutation and selection. Mutations, now understood in biochemical terms as a change in the DNA molecule, may be described in terms of calculable frequencies with definite effect on the gene pool for future generations. Mutations tend to cause changes not only in gene frequencies but also in the adaptiveness of individuals. In this process these individuals become subject to the action of selection, which may be defined as genetic advantage or disadvantage measured in terms of mean family size. If individuals of a certain genetic constitution produce an increased number of offspring, this is known as positive selection. A trend toward elimination of a trait due to a disadvantage is known as negative selection. To be sure, advantage is determined not only by the effect of individual genes determining unit characters but by general genetic aspects of fitness and adaptiveness to the environment, which may be determined by the action of many genes in both homozygous and heterozygous form. Selection may be mediated by differences in mating, fertility, emigration, and early mortality.

METHODS OF GENETIC INVESTIGATION

In genetic population studies, various approaches have been used, some favoring the analysis of the health problems of individual families, others studying entire populations. Since Mendelian ratios express only the average expectancy of a gene-controlled trait in a representative population sample, various statistical procedures are necessary to determine the validity of inferences drawn from individual observations.

PEDIGREE METHOD

Genetic data obtained from individual pedigrees or individual pairs of siblings or twins are useful in the study of rare pathological conditions that are fairly constant in their penetrance and clinical expression. Such data are not calculated to furnish conclusive proof about the operation of heredity or about the mode of inheritance involved. Since family histories are often published only if there is a concentration of affected individuals, the data are of limited value, since they are not statistically representative of the population.

CENSUS METHOD

Total population surveys by the census method are valuable but difficult to conduct. The populations must be sufficiently cooperative and not too large, and the traits under investigation must be relatively uncomplicated ones. Nevertheless, in certain special populations, particularly in regions of

Scandinavia, excellent psychiatric studies using this method have been produced.

FAMILY-RISK STUDIES

A very useful method of genetic investigation has been termed the contingency method of statistical prediction. The aim of this method is to compare the expectancy of a given medical condition developing among relatives of affected individuals with the expectancy in the general population. The condition in question must be well-defined so that a number of independent observers may accurately diagnose persons coming into the study. And the original group of patients whose relatives are to be investigated must be either a consecutively reported series representing a complete ascertainment or a random sample thereof. If this criterion is met, members of the group may be called index cases or probands. They generally represent all admissions to a given hospital system or clinic over a given period of time or at least a properly selected sample of such a list.

Not all the relatives who are free of symptoms will necessarily remain so if they live to an older age. For the relatives, therefore, one cannot simply consider the prevalence of the condition; one must also obtain a corrected figure known as the expectancy rate. A simple means of calculating this is Weinberg's abridged method. The number of observed cases among the relatives (the numerator) is related not to the total number of relatives but to all those who have survived the period in which the disease may be certain to be manifested plus one-half the number who are still within the age limits during which the disease may be manifested (the denominator). Persons who died before the earliest manifestation age of the given disease or who are still under that age are not counted as part of the denominator. This method yields morbidity risks that approach the average expectancy of developing the given condition in persons who remain alive through its manifestation period. These expectancy rates for various groups of relatives may be compared with one another and with the expectancy rates for the general population. General population rates have been obtained in many medical conditions through careful demographic studies of whole populations of small areas or of samples of populations of larger districts.

TWIN-FAMILY METHOD

The basic principles of the contingency method have been applied to an extended approach termed the twin-family method. The use of twins in genetic research was initiated by Galton and is based on the occurrence of two genetically different types of twins: those derived from one fertilized ovum and those derived from two fertilized ova. The former are always of the same sex (barring a rare sex chromosomal nondisjunction prior to the first cell division, which may result in a pair of identical twins comprising a normal male and a Turner's female); two-egg twins may be either of the same sex or of opposite sexes.

In the twin-family method, data are obtained on complete sibships of twin index cases and their parents. Comparisons are made between one-egg twins, two-egg twins of the same sex, two-egg twins of opposite sexes, full siblings, half-siblings, and step-siblings. This procedure provides a unique opportunity to investigate intrafamily variations with a minimum of uncontrolled variables. Comparisons can be made between one-egg twins brought up and living together and two-egg twins under the same conditions. It is more difficult to find one-egg twins who have been raised apart and who present a particular syndrome—at least in sufficient numbers to warrant drawing conclusions from concordance rates.

Certain significant misunderstandings concerning twin studies should be noted. Carefully stated hypotheses should not be questioned simply because pairs of dissimilar one-egg twins have been found. Genes actually determine a norm of reaction, the exact expression of which depends on many interactions taking place before, at, and after birth. Indeed, one-egg twins, especially those with a common chorion, are subject to more disparate influence before birth than are two-egg pairs, as a result of circulatory variations. There are many pathways from identical genetic structures to later expression of behavioral traits, and minor shifts in the process of interaction at crucial points may lead to wide divergence in phenotypes. Preconceived ideas on the locus of such crucial points often prove to be invalid. A spiral-like development toward marked dissimilarity in behavior may arise as a result of influences at all stages from the chromosomal to the postnatal ones. Conversely, similar development is often found to exist in two-egg twins.

The statistical value of investigating twins, with primary genetic factors maintained constant, does not preclude more intensive studies in the fields of biochemical and clinical investigation. One of these studies is represented by the co-twin control method in which data are obtained from a few selected pairs of one-egg twins. Their reactions and patterns are compared under different life conditions or in response to planned differences in management. In general, the careful study of discordant or dissimilar identical twin pairs may furnish important findings. Often the discordance turns out to be only a partial one, and much is learned about expressivity. In other cases the divergent development may be associated with certain key life factors.

PSYCHIATRIC GENETICS

Schizophrenia

In the early literature of psychiatric genetics, there are a number of case reports tending to confirm the common notion that psychoses tend to run in families. However, such studies, which were popular in the last century, are now thought to have limited value. At the time of their origin, the science of genetics itself had not yet been developed, and the reports themselves were usually restricted to families containing many cases and to observations that in no way ruled out intrafamilial causes other than those of a genetic nature.

Expectancy rates. In 1916, Rüdin, in Germany, insisted on the need for studying the genetics of schizophrenia in representative and clinically homogeneous samples. His school developed the methods of obtaining statistically corrected expectancy rates for schizophrenia in relatives of schizophrenics as compared with the general population. This method, the contingency method of statistical prediction, was applied first to siblings and half-siblings of schizophrenics. Other investigators studied cousins, nephews, nieces, and children of schizophrenics. Kallmann's first survey, the largest major study of the genetics of schizophrenia, was published in 1939 and represented work done in the 1930's. It focused on the expectancy of this condition in a large group of descendants of schizophrenics and their siblings. Meanwhile, improved methods for ascertaining rates of schizophrenia in the general population were devised by a number of English and Scandinavian workers. All these studies showed a significant difference between the incidence of schizophrenia in the families of schizophrenic patients and that in the general population. The range of expectancy rates found in these studies was as follows: general population, 0.85 per cent; half-siblings, 7 to 8 per cent; full siblings, 5 to 15 per cent; parents, 5 to 10 per cent; children of one index case, 8 to 16 per cent; children of two index cases, 53 to 68 per cent. The greater the genetic similarity to the schizophrenic, the greater was the expectancy rate. But the variations in the rates must be considered in light of the difficulties encountered in each investigation: the need to find missing family members, the differences between investigations based on hospital records and those based on direct diagnostic interviews, different diagnostic criteria in various countries, and diverse methods of age correction. Also, parental schizophrenia rates tend to vary from one population to another according to the chance of an adult becoming a parent despite certain signs of emotional instability. Most schizophrenic mothers have normal children, and many normal parents have schizophrenic offspring. There is no significant difference between the morbidity rates of the children of affected fathers and those of affected mothers. With all this, there has been widespread accord in finding that the various categories of relatives of schizophrenics show significantly higher expectancy rates than the general population.

Twin studies. As early as 1911 in the United States, twin studies were conducted with descriptions of the histories of interesting twin pairs as matters of curiosity. With progress in the accuracy of zygosity determination and psychiatric classification, data of more than historical interest were published by the early 1930's. These studies were limited in sample size. The first large-scale, unselected sample survey was planned by Kallmann in New York in 1936 and was followed by the European studies of Essen-Möller and Slater. The New York study, reported in 1946 and

1950, included 953 schizophrenic twin index cases. In this twin study the concordance rate for two-egg twins was 14.7 per cent, as compared to 14.3 per cent for full siblings, 7.1 per cent for half-siblings, and 85.8 per cent for one-egg twins.

Deafness and schizophrenia. Another study explored the effect of early total deafness, a severe sensory deprivation, upon the vulnerability to schizophrenia. Families of patients with both schizophrenia and deafness were studied. Although the schizophrenia rate among the general deaf population was no more than 2 per cent, that among the siblings of deaf schizophrenics was 12 to 14 per cent. This figure was significantly higher than that for the general population and was similar to that observed for the siblings of hearing schizophrenics. Of major importance was the fact that the schizophrenia rates between deaf siblings and hearing siblings did not differ significantly.

Mode of inheritance. Kallmann assumed that a single-unit factor was responsible for schizophrenia and that this factor was autosomal recessive in nature and subject to modification by other genes conferring a greater or lesser degree of resistance. Others have favored a simple dominant mode of inheritance. In either case, auxiliary hypotheses are needed. The diversity of the various theories seem to indicate that theories as to the exact mode of inheritance will remain inconclusive until the biochemical and physiological nature of the inherited vulnerability factor is identified.

Genetic studies and clinical psychiatry. The work of Sandor Rado and his school, based on the genetic theory of schizophrenia, has been directed at exploring the basic psychological organization of the genetically defined schizotype. The two most consistent factors he found were a defect in the utilization of pleasure and a proprioceptive deficit.

DEPRESSIVE ILLNESS

Manic-depressive psychosis. Twin-family studies have played an important role in both nosology and etiology of manic-depressive psychosis. In his classic investigation of this syndrome, Kraepelin observed large numbers of relatives who had the same illness, but he did not find an increase in dementia praecox among these relatives. The general population rate for manic-depressive psychosis in most European and American populations is not more than 0.4 per cent, though in a few special situations, such is isolated island populations, rates of 0.8 and up to 1.6 per cent have been found. In the case of parents, siblings, and children of manic-depressive index cases, the rates are much higher. Some of the earlier results indicated a range of 10 to 15 per cent in the parents and a similar range in siblings and children. Stenstedt, in Sweden, conducted a careful population study from 1949 to 1952 and found morbidity risks of 12.3 per cent for siblings, 7.4 per cent for parents, and 9.4 per cent for children.

The largest twin-family study, reported in 1950 by Kallmann in New

York, involved 27 one-egg and 58 two-egg pairs. In this series the expectancy of manic-depressive psychosis varied from 16.7 per cent for half-siblings to 22.7 and 25.5 per cent for siblings and two-egg co-twins, respectively, and 100 per cent for one-egg co-twins. Parents of index cases showed a rate of 23.4 per cent. The apparently perfect concordance rate of 100 per cent for one-egg twins was considered an artificial maximum value, since only patients admitted to a mental hospital, and hence the most severe cases, were included as index cases.

It was concluded by both Stenstedt and Kallmann that manic-depressive psychosis followed a dominant type of inheritance with incomplete penetrance and variable expressivity of a single autosomal gene. Although there were more females than males among the index cases in both studies, the sex ratio among siblings, parents, and children was no different from that of the normal population.

An important offshoot of the study of manic-depressive illness in families was the differentiation of depressive illness from schizophrenia. In no case was a pair of twins found with a schizophrenic psychosis in one partner and a cyclic psychosis in the other, and the morbidity risk for schizophrenia among families of manic-depressive index cases was not statistically different from that in the general population.

In attempting to define the psychological characteristics of the individual predisposed to manic-depressive psychosis, Rado described a tendency to emotional overreaction from infancy, a persistent alimentary dependent state, a strong craving for gratification from without, and an intolerance to pain. He considered the depressive spell the terminal link in an etiological chain stemming from the genotype.

Involutional psychosis. In one study Kallmann found no increase in involutional psychosis among the families of manic-depressives. In the families of ninety-six involutional twin index cases, the risk of involutional psychosis was increased (6.4 per cent for parents, 6 per cent for full siblings, 6 per cent for dizygotic co-twins, and 60.9 per cent for monozygotic co-twins). The risk for schizophrenia was somewhat elevated (5.5 per cent in parents and 4.2 per cent in siblings), but the risk for manic-depressive psychosis was hardly raised at all. Finally, the expectancy of involutional psychosis among the parents and siblings of schizophrenic twin index cases was increased to 6.6 per cent.

From these data it was concluded that the diagnostic category of involutional psychosis was more complex pathogenetically than schizophrenia and manic-depressive psychosis but that it was more closely associated with the group of schizoid personality traits than with manic-depressive psychosis.

Deafness and depressive illness. The modifying effect of incidental factors on depressive symptoms was indicated in the New York survey of persons with early total deafness. The survey showed no significant increase or decrease in manic-depressive or involutional psychosis, but it did show a decrease in symptoms of retardation, guilt, and depression in the presence of the early sensory deficit. Paranoid symptoms or anxious agitated states without depression appeared to take their place.

PSYCHONEUROSIS

In the case of psychoneurotic behavior, genetic studies have been hampered by problems of diagnosis and the need to develop quantitative methods. Reviewing the literature, Slater found an increase in neurotic illnesses and neurotic personality traits of a like kind among relatives of obsessional neurotics, anxiety neurotics, and persons diagnosed as hysterics, with the evidence much stronger in the first of these than in the last. The evidence supported a multifactor type of inheritance with continuous and probably multidimensional variation in traits.

Correlation tests have been conducted, with the use of various rating scales to measure neuroticism. In a twin sample tested with the Minnesota Multiphasic Personality Inventory, Gottesman found either a low genetic component or none in neuroses with hypochondriacal and hysterical elements, but he found a substantial genetic component in those with elements of anxiety, depression, obsession, and schizoid withdrawal.

CRIMINALITY

Some of the earlier findings in the area of criminal behavior indicated concordance rates of 14 per cent in opposite-sex pairs, 54 per cent in same-sex two-egg pairs, and 66 per cent in one-egg pairs, suggesting the importance of both family milieu and basic personality traits in shaping the habitual criminal. Unfavorable environmental influences appear to play a large part. Further studies measuring concordance as to specific personality traits likely to lead to a life of crime rather than criminal behavior itself seem to be indicated.

MALE HOMOSEXUALITY

The question of the genetic contribution to male homosexuality is presently under active debate, and more research is urgently needed. Early hypotheses in this field centered about the conception that male homosexuals may have a female chromosome structure. Certain investigators found a greater proportion of males among the siblings of male homosexuals than would be normally expected. However, with the onset of sex chromatin studies and karyotype analyses, no abnormalities in sex chromatin or sex chromosomes were discovered in male homosexuals. Nevertheless, Slater more recently found a later birth order and a high maternal age in a group of 401 consecutive admissions of male homosexuals. These findings were considered to suggest a chromosomal anomaly in some male homosexuals. Klinefelter's syndrome has been associated with a number of cases of homosexuality, transvestitism, and pedophilia, but these symptoms are not generally characteristic of the syndrome.

Twin studies. Some of the highest one-egg concordance rates have been those for homosexual behavior in the adult male. In Kallmann's series of forty-four male homosexuals, almost perfect concordance was found, whereas in fifty-one two-egg male homosexual twins, the degree of concordance in the co-twin was no higher than what might be anticipated on the basis of Kinsey's statistics for the general population.

These findings were interpreted as suggesting a gene-controlled disarrangement between male and female psychosexual maturation patterns. In this formulation, homosexuality would appear to be a part of the personality structure rather than directly determined by the gonadal apparatus. If this is so, the processes whereby this deviation develops may be studied within the interactional framework of psychiatric genetics. A normal rate of maturation of personality development and an ability to perceive and respond to sexual stimuli, to recognize satisfaction and success, and to utilize these experiences as integrating forces may be crucial to normal sexual role development. Vulnerability factors in these areas may render an individual susceptible to deviant behavior, which is then reinforced accidentally or by family or social surroundings.

A few one-egg twin pairs discordant for homosexual behavior have been discovered who also showed important similarities, principally in psychological test findings that indicated sexual confusion and body image distortion. Divergent patterns of experience may be influenced by such factors as differences in the twins' relationships with their parents, frustration in heterosexual contacts, and poor masculine identification in the case of the homosexual twin. The study of many additional cases of this kind may eventually yield a detailed interactional synthesis.

GENETICS OF BEHAVIOR

In the realm of general behavior, there has been a steady and increasing body of data, originating in psychiatric observation of basic differences among individuals, in which the clinician himself has been led to the hypothesis of genetic or constitutional uniqueness.

INTEGRATION OF GENETICS IN PSYCHODYNAMICS

The science of psychodynamics was always postulated by some psychoanalysts to be part of a unitary conceptual scheme in human biology. These psychoanalysts, such as Rado, analyzed behavioral variations in the gene-specific physiological (biochemical) context of the organism. In such a scheme the psychodynamic approach, focused on an understanding of motivation and emotional control, may uncover and delineate behavior problems that require for their complete explanation the clarification of the role of genetic transmission. Indeed, this approach was formulated in the writings of Freud. He always took into consideration both the constitutional and the accidental causes of neurotic disease, and he spoke of primary congenital variations in the ego and in the defense mechanisms an individual selects. And in an early essay on the study of twins, Hartmann wrote of personality structure as the result of interaction between heredity and environment. He considered the possibility of character *anlagen* that, in the course of development, differentiate into character traits. He felt that twin studies might throw light on the possible substitution of one trait for another.

Such an integrated approach may assume a central role in future psychodynamic work. In essence, this approach affords an opportunity to recognize fundamental genetic differences among individuals and to correlate these differences with various forms of developmental interaction both before and after birth. Although the role of genetics is not always made explicit in these studies, there are many advantages and potentialities within the scope of workers who combine the methods of both disciplines.

CHILD STUDIES

In the field of infant and child psychiatry, the integrated approach is becoming very fruitful and pertinent. Intrinsic differences among children have been found to be as powerful as maternal attitudes in determining final behavior patterns. These differences have been measured in various ways. Attention has been paid to sleep, feeding, and sensory responses; to activity types; to motor behavior; and to specific reaction patterns. Variations in drive endowment and reactions to stimuli have been shown to differ. The responses of neonates to various internal and external stimuli are under investigation. Genetic analysis will be the next step in studies of this kind.

GERIATRIC AND ANIMAL STUDIES

At the other extreme of human life, normal and pathological phenomena of senescence have been shown to have significant genetic components, as evidenced by studies of twins and their families. Finally, animal research has indicated variations between different strains in such species as mice, rats, and dogs and has applied selective breeding methods to produce extremes of behavioral characteristics.

DEMOGRAPHIC AND SOCIAL PROBLEMS

Many demographic problems fall within the scope and interest of the psychiatrist. Dysgenic trends in human population include wars, certain differential reproductive patterns, improvement in the efficiency of therapeutic procedures not accompanied by directed guidance as to reproduction, and such mutagenic procedures as exposure to radiation. The effects of migration, of socioeconomic drift, and of differential fertility are constantly in the forefront of discussions regarding trends in the prevalence of distribution of psychiatric disorder.

Reproductivity of Schizophrenics

There is current concern with the reproductivity of schizophrenic parents. Available data clearly indicate the increased risk of schizophrenia in the offspring of such parents, ranging from more than 10 per cent, if one parent is affected, to more than 50 per cent, if both are affected. Modern treatment methods in the past two decades have lessened the amount of time a schizophrenic patient remains in the hospital. At the turn of the century, the reproductivity rate of schizophrenic patients was about half that of the corresponding general population. This ratio increased only slightly through the 1930's. However, in a study of reproductivity changes between 1934 to 1936 and 1954 to 1956 (based on large samples of schizophrenic patients in New York), the rate in the earlier period was 58 per cent that of the general population, but in the later period it was 87 per cent that of the general population. Moreover, there seemed to be a similar increase in reproductivity for the siblings of the schizophrenic patients in the sample. About 2 per cent of the patient marriages were between two schizophrenic patients. If the reproductive rate of schizophrenics is approaching that of the general population, any selective disadvantage that schizophrenic illness may have had in terms of its evolutionary history may now be in the process of disappearing. This fact alone spurs the search for methods of preventing and treating this condition. Meanwhile, these data are available for marriage and parenthood counseling of the many families who request such guidance. The developmental hazards of children born into homes in which one or both parents are schizophrenic include overwhelming proportions of broken homes, displacements, and chaotic lives during many rehospitalizations of the parents, in which both the child and the parent are harmed. Many individual tragedies may be avoided if sound guidance is available when requested by patients and their families.

Genetic Counseling

In clinical practice the final common pathway of increased knowledge in the areas of genetics and family guidance is the responsible practice of marriage and parenthood counseling when there is a gene-borne condition present in one of the families concerned. When doubt exists regarding important and emotion-laden decisions as to marriage and parenthood, people must have access to trained professional advisers who are able not only to elicit the facts and evaluate them scientifically but also to resolve fears and misunderstandings and to be aware of the impact of their procedures upon their patients.

Genetic counseling may represent a short-term course of psychotherapy based on psychological understanding and conducted according to established techniques of psychiatric interviewing. The counselor must be well-versed in the medical, legal, and psychological implications of such procedures as contraception, sterilization, abortion, artificial insemination, and adoption. From the clinical point of view, responsible genetic counseling provides the most direct application of medical knowledge in the field of genetics to the patient and his family.

REFERENCES

Beadle, G. W. *Genetics and Modern Biology.* American Philosophical Society, Philadelphia, 1963.

Court Brown, W. M., Harnden, D. G., Jacobs, P. A., Maclean, N., and Mantle, D. J. *Abnormalities of the Sex Chromosome Complement in Man.* Her Majesty's Stationery Office, London, 1964.

Erlenmeyer-Kimling, L., Rainer, J. D., and Kallmann, F. J. Current reproductive trends in schizophrenia. In *Psychopathology of Schizophrenia*, P. H. Hoch and J. Zubin, editors. Grune & Stratton, New York, 1966.

Kallmann, F. J. The genetic theory of schizophrenia. Amer. J. Psychiat., *103:* 309, 1946.

Kallmann, F. J. Comparative twin study on the genetic aspects of male homosexuality. J. Nerv. Ment. Dis., *115:* 283, 1952.

Kallmann, F. J. *Heredity in Health and Mental Disorder.* W. W. Norton, New York, 1953.

Kallmann, F. J., editor. *Expanding Goals of Genetics in Psychiatry.* Grune & Stratton, New York, 1962.

Kallmann, F. J., and Rainer, J. D. Genetics and demography. In *The Study of Population*, P. M. Hauser and O. D. Duncan, editors, p. 759. University of Chicago Press, Chicago, 1959.

Kalow, W. *Pharmacogenetics.* W. B. Saunders, Philadelphia, 1962.

Knox, W. E. Phenylketonuria. In *The Metabolic Basis of Inherited Disease.* J. B. Stanbury, J. B. Wyngaarden, and D. S. Fredrickson, editors. McGraw-Hill, New York, 1960.

Neel, J. V., Shaw, M. W., and Schull, W. J., editors. *Genetics and Epidemiology of Chronic Diseases.* United States Department of Health, Education, and Welfare, Washington, 1965.

Rainer, J. D., Altshuler, K. Z., Kallmann, F. J., and Deming, W. E., editors. *Family and Mental Health Problems in a Deaf Population.* New York State Psychiatric Institute, New York, 1963.

Slater, E. *Psychotic and Neurotic Illnesses in Twins.* Her Majesty's Stationery Office, London, 1953.

Slater, E. Genetical factors in neurosis. Brit. J. Psychol., *55:* 265, 1964.

CHAPTER 2

Neurochemistry

WILLIAMINA A. HIMWICH, Ph.D., and HAROLD E. HIMWICH, M.D.

INTRODUCTION

ALTHOUGH ONE of the primary objectives of this textbook is to study the abnormal behavior of patients with mental disturbances, normal behavior must also be examined, if only to permit comparison of the normal individual with the disturbed patient. In the attempt to gain insight into behavior, neurochemical findings in the normal individual must be studied as well as biochemical changes accompanying abnormal behavior. We have not attempted to provide a complete survey of neurochemistry in this section, which is devoted to dealing with neurochemical data available on the human brain and to summarizing data too recently published to be available in textbooks.

NORMAL BRAIN CONSTITUENTS AND CEREBRAL METABOLISM

DEVELOPING BRAIN

The growth and development of the brain, including the attainment of the adult levels of metabolism and of the various chemical constituents, proceeds in all species of animals from the time of the appearance of the neural streak until maturity. The chronological relation of this maturation to events such as implantation, birth, and opening of the eyes varies in the different species of animals. There are some indications that the newborn human is more mature than the newborn rat, rabbit, cat, and dog. However, development after birth appears to proceed more slowly in man than in other species studied.

The changes in water, lipid, and protein composition that occur in the human brain during the first few years of life are similar to those in other animals (see Figure 1). The infant human brain reaches its adult level of deoxyribonucleic acid (DNA) at about 1 year of age. The percentage of ash in the cerebral hemispheres decreases progressively from the third month of conceptual life to birth. The development of succinic dehydrogenase and the ability of the human brain to maintain oxygen consumption during fetal life suggests the same neurophylogenetic pattern that has been established for other animals. Specifically, this means that the older parts of the brain—the medulla oblongata, for example—mature before the cerebral cortex. Although these data are only general indications, they suggest that the human brain develops in the same fashion as does that of the other animal species but not necessarily on the same time table.

The brain of the fetus shows a distinctive cerebroside pattern by the eighth fetal month. By the third fetal month the gangliosides show an adult type of pattern, which may be changed by birth trauma, with marked reduction of trisialogangliosides and disialogangliosides. This change is possibly due to a rapid liberation of sialic acid due to anoxemia.

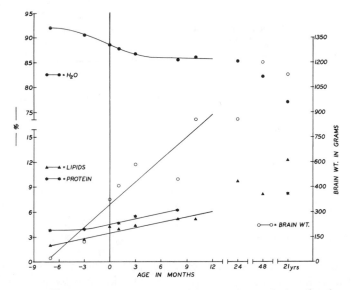

FIGURE 1. Changes in composition of human brain during development. The figures are combined from Tilney and Rosett, and MacArthur and Doisy. (Taken from Himwich, W. A. Biochemical and neurophysiological development of the brain in the neonatal period. In *International Revue of Neurobiology*, C. C. Pfeiffer and J. R. Smythies, editors, vol. 4, p. 117. Academic Press, Inc., New York, 1962.)

Bertler found both norepinephrine and 3, 4-dihydroxyphenlethyla-mine (dopamine) in the 5-month-old fetus, although dopamine was not present at the end of the first trimester. At 5 months of fetal life, dopamine was very low. By 8 months, dopamine had increased nearly to the level found in the adult human brain. Although norepineph-rine had also increased by 8 months, its rate of increase was not as high as that for dopamine. These data suggest a different maturation pattern for norepinephrine and dopamine. Hornykiewicz has sug-gested that the newborn human infant's relative development of the hypothalamus and related autonomic functions, as compared with the extrapyramidal motor functions, may account for the difference in the maturation patterns of norepinephrine and dopamine.

Mature Brain

Analyses of adult brains are more frequent than similar work on fetal brains. Of the many constituents of the adult brain that have been studied, variations in some appear to be particularly relevant to normal and abnormal behavior. Below is a brief review of the brain constituents for which there are analyses of human brain available.

MINERALS. In spite of the fact that the mineral content of the human brain would be expected to change slowly after death, there have not been many studies of adult human brains. Among the analyses that are available are those for copper, magnesium, rubid-ium, barium, silicone, strontium, phosphorus, and iron. Copper is of special importance because of its relation to Wilson's disease. This element reaches its peak concentration at about the same time brain growth is complete—that is, 19 or 20 years. In general, the copper content of gray matter is two to three times higher than that of white matter. The substantia nigra and the locus coerulous are particularly rich in copper.

LIPIDS. Table I gives the currently accepted classification of the lipids in the brain. Cerebrosides are typical myelin lipids, as shown by the predominant amount of cerebrosides in white matter as compared with the cortical gray matter. In the cerebral cortex, the localization of cerebrosides cannot be restricted to the few visible myelin sheaths. Undoubtedly, these substances are also localized in the membranes of myelin-free nerves and the membranes of nerve cells themselves. Cerebrosides also play a part in the formation of the cell membrane in the glial cells. Thus, they should be considered as membrane lipids. Gangliosides, on the other hand, are localized in the nerve cell bodies and probably also in dendrites and axons. It seems unlikely that gangliosides normally occur in glial cells.

The fatty acid composition of human cerebrosides from four re-gions of the brain shows that the content of these substances differs from region to region, as does the relative content of hydroxy acids. However, the distribution of acids within each class is independent of brain location. The normal saturated acids contain stearic and lignoceric as major acids, but fairly large amounts of C_{22}, C_{23}, and C_{25} acids are also present. The hydroxy-saturated acids are similar but

TABLE I

Classification of Lipids Found in the Nervous System[a]

A. Phosphatides (phospholipids)
  1. Glycerophosphatides (phosphoglycerides)
     Phosphatidylcholines (lecithins)
     Phosphatidylethanolamines
     Phosphatidylserines
     Plasmalogens (phosphatidylethanolamines)
     Cephalin B
  2. Inositol phosphatides (phosphoinositides)
  3. Sphingomyelins (phosphosphingosides) ⎤
B. Glycolipids   │
  1. Cerebrosides (glycosphingosides)   │
  2. Cerebroside sulfate esters (sulfatides) ⎬ Sphingolipids
  3. Mucolipids   │
     Gangliosides   │
     Strandin   ⎦
C. Nonsaponifiable lipids
  1. Sterols
  2. Hydrocarbons
D. Neutral fat (triglycerides)
E. Protein-bound lipids
  1. Proteolipids
  2. Phosphatidopeptides
  3. Lipoproteins

---

[a] Taken from Rossiter, R. J. Chemical constituents of brain and nerve. In *Neurochemistry*, K. A. C. Elliott, I. H. Page, and J. H. Quastel, editors, p. 10. Charles C Thomas, Springfield, Ill., 1962.

contain little hydroxystearic acid; the unsaturated acids of both classes contain the C_{24} acid as the major constituent.

Myelin has a higher lipid content than white or gray matter, 78 to 81 per cent as compared to 49 to 66 per cent and 36 to 40 per cent, respectively. This substance also contains higher percentages of cerebrosides and cholesterol and lower percentages of ethanolamine, glycerophosphatides, and choline glycerophosphatides than gray matter. The molar percentages of serine glycerophosphatides are reported to be about the same in each tissue. The extramyelin portion of white matter has a lipid composition similar to that of myelin but quite different from that of gray matter.

The fatty acid composition of sphingomyelins from gray matter is quite different from that of sphingomyelins from white. Before myelinization, C_{18}-saturated acid is the pre-dominating acid in both gray and white matter. The proportion of very long chain acids (C_{22} to C_{26}) in white matter increases with age and reaches about 70 per cent when the process of myelinization is complete.

O'Brien et al. analyzed brain lipids, especially cerebroside sulfate esters or sulfatides, in human gray and white matter. The major fatty acids are C_{24}-saturated, and C_{24}-monounsaturated. Odd chain fatty acids are present as well as monounsaturated acid of both odd and even chain fatty acids, but no polyenes were detected.

By far the most extensive work on the human brain throughout life has been by Bürger, who investigated 378 brains obtained from autopsies on individuals ranging in age from birth to 90 years. According to his data, the weight and the volume of the brain attains a maximum during the third decade, averaging 1,394 gm. in the male; at the age of 90 the volume of the brain is reduced to an average of 1,161 gm. As brain substances are lost, the percentage of nitrogen and protein falls (see Figure 2). DNA and ribonucleic acid (RNA), which form part of the liponucleoproteins, also diminish. The concentration of brain lipids is impaired in old age. This change applies to all lipid fractions with exception of a small one, the "rest lipid," which enlarges slowly to the eighth and ninth decades of life, at which time it composes about 8 per cent of the total lipids. This "rest" fraction appears to be made up in part of a yellow lipoprotein that accumulates and becomes widespread in old age. The water content of various brain parts reveals a phyletic order, the oldest areas being the driest. In addition to these differences, the decrease in water content in general throughout the early decades of life is reversed during the senium. The early fall may be ascribed chiefly to loss of extracellular water as myelin is laid down. The late increase is due mainly to an enlargement of the extracellular compartment, for the intracellular one probably decreases.

AMINO ACIDS AND PROTEINS. Relatively few analyses of human brain in regard to amino acid content or proteins per se have been made. Some information is available regarding the proteins that are contained in the lipoproteins. Data are also given on the total protein in human brain in Figures 1 and 2.

MISCELLANEOUS SUBSTANCES IN HUMAN BRAIN. Biotin is important because it appears to be involved in lipid metabolism. Disorders of lipid metabolism are among the most studied abnormalities of human neurochemistry. The differences in biotin content among brains tend to be greater than among regions in the same brain. When values are based on dry weight, the highest concentrations are found in gray matter. This difference disappears when values are placed on a fresh weight basis. The human brain has been shown to contain arabinose and xylose as well as glucose and galactose.

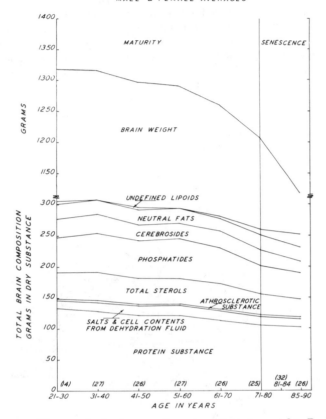

CHEMICAL BIOMORPHOSIS OF THE HUMAN BRAIN
MALE & FEMALE AVERAGES

FIGURE 2. Changes in brain constituents and brain weight. Brain constituents are calculated on a basis of dry weight, whereas the weights of the entire brain include all constituents plus water. (Adapted from Bürger. From Himwich, W. A., and Himwich, H. E. Neurochemistry of aging. In *Handbook of Aging and the Individual*, J. E. Birren, editor, p. 187. University of Chicago Press, Chicago, 1959.)

BIOGENIC AMINES. The distribution of the various catecholamines in the human brain suggests that dopamine plays an important part in the functioning of the extrapyramidal motor centers. This conclusion is based on these facts: (1) Dopamine occurs almost exclusively in the corpus striatum. (2) Its level is reduced in Parkinson's disease. (3) L-Dihydroxyphenylalanine (a precursor of dopamine) has a beneficial effect on the akinesia of Parkinson sufferers. Dopamine occurs principally in the structures related to involuntary motor function—for example, the basal ganglia and the substantia nigra (see Figure 3). Within the basal ganglia most of the material is found in the phylogenetically youngest part of these structures. Homovanillic acid, a metabolite of dopamine, exceeds 1 μg. per gram in the caudate nucleus, the putamen, the globus pallidus, and the substantia nigra. The data on dopamine and homovanillic acid for the globus pallidus suggest that a high dopamine turnover may occur in this region, though very little dopamine accumulation occurs.

The recent large body of work on the cellular localization of the monoamines, although done largely in the rat, contain suggestive data on how these substances exist and function in the central nervous system. Dopamine, noradrenaline (NA), and serotonin (5-HT) are present in specific neurons, largely in the mesencephalon. The fibers

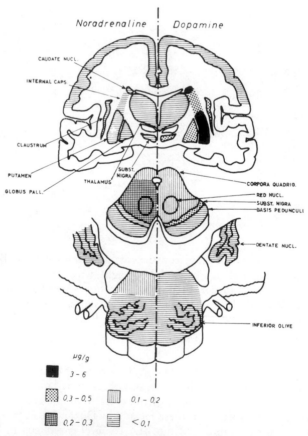

FIGURE 3. Noradrenaline and dopamine in the human brain. (From Bertler, A. Occurrence and localization of catecholamines in the human brain. Acta Physiol. Scand., 51: 97, 1961.)

arising from neurons containing dopamine go primarily anterior, those from NA neurons go both cephalad and caudad, and those from the 5-HT neurons go principally down the spinal cord. The NA and 5-HT fibers descend from the medulla and possibly higher levels. The localization of 5-HT nerve cells is entirely different from that of NA or dopamine nerve cells. The former are almost exclusively in the raphe nuclei; the latter cells are generally in a more lateral position.

ENZYMES. Enzyme studies have been particularly difficult to conduct in man because of the changes that occur after death. However, certain enzymes have been studied in the human brain. For example, the distribution of diphosphopyridine nucleotide-diaphorase in the human brain has been mapped by the excellent histochemical techniques of Friede. This enzyme shows a tendency toward a caudo-cranial differentiation in the chemical architecture of the brain. The thalamus and cerebral cortex are the most variable regions. The pattern of distribution of the diphosphopyridine nucleotide-diaphorase is almost identical with that of succinic dehydrogenase and of capillarization in the medulla oblongata. Previous material suggests a similar distribution of cytochrome oxidase and triphosphopyridine nucleotide-diaphorase. The patterns appear to follow the general gradations of tissue oxidation and energy metabolism. This knowledge can be applied to problems of neuropathology, since the mapping of the deposition of lipofuscin, a pigmented lipid in the aging human brain, shows that its extent is proportional to regional gradations of oxidative enzyme activity. This fact has led to the suggestion that the deposition of lipofuscin is proportional to the wear and tear in an area—that is, to the intensity of the oxidative energy metabolism.

The distribution of alkaline phosphatase, acid phosphatase, and nonspecific esterase in human nervous tissue shows that alkaline phosphatase is present in the vessel endothelium, the arachnoidal cells, and the external part of the first cortical layer. It is present in the cytoplasm, the nuclei being negative. Acid phosphatase and nonspecific esterase are seen in the cytoplasm and the processes of neurons and normal glial cells, and the nuclei are negative. Acid phosphatase in the human cerebellar cortex is found primarily in the cytoplasm of Bergmann cells. Some activity is also present perivascularly and in the cytoplasm of Purkinje cells, and in Golgi cells. Carbonic anhydrase in the human brain has been determined in thirty-two anatomical parts. The distribution in gray matter roughly parallels the metabolism of the area, as indicated by comparison with blood flow, rates of oxygen consumption, and distribution of succinic dehydrogenase. The high activity of carbonic anhydrase in subcortical white matter suggests a special function for this enzyme.

The distribution of acetylcholinesterase (AChE) and butyrylcholinesterase (BuChE) has been followed in the human brain by the

Warburg manometric technique and Koelle's histochemical method. the AChE activity is consistently higher than the BuChE activity in gray matter. AChE is active, in increasing order, in the cerebral cortex, cerebellar cortex, thalamus, globus pallidus, and caudate nucleus. The BuChE activity is higher in white matter than in gray matter, and the AChE activity is primarily present in a granular pattern in the protoplasm of the neurons. The distribution of cholinesterase activity in white matter is diffuse. The cholinesterases of human spinal fluid and the brain have also been studied by means of electrophoresis and chromatography. Three cholinesterases are present: two butyrylcholinesterases and one acetylcholinesterase. The electrophoretic mobilities of these cholinesterases, compared with those in plasma, suggest that the acetylcholinesterase in spinal fluid derives from the brain. No decision can yet be made as to the origin of the butyrylcholinesterases.

The highest activity of glutamic acid decarboxylase is also present in the extrapyramidal motor system. As yet, no data are available on the relationship of the enzyme to extrapyramidal motor syndromes.

Because of the uneven distribution of the biogenic amines, interest has grown in the patterns of concentration of the enzymes responsible for their elaboration and destruction. The activities of L-dihydroxyphenylalanine (L-dopa), decarboxylase, and monoamine oxidase do not correspond with the distribution of the respective amines.

These relatively sparse data indicate the areas of research in human brain chemistry of greatest interest at the present time. The data on lipids seem promising, as explanations of the various lipid degenerative diseases can be based on the abnormalities of lipid structure and composition. The biogenic amine distributions are important in clarifying neurological diseases such as parkinsonism. Moreover, the effects of psychotropic drugs on these compounds promise to aid in our understanding of their action and of the fundamental chemistry of the conditions in which they are effective.

CEREBRAL METABOLISM

The normal adult brain uses about 3.5 ml. of oxygen per 100 gm. of brain per minute. For a human brain of average weight, this is a total consumption of approximately 50 ml. of oxygen per minute or about 20 per cent of the basal oxygen requirement of the body as a whole. With age and degenerative disease there may be a decrease in cerebral metabolism (see Table II). The evidence is good that the intact brain utilizes glucose predominantly as a normal substrate for energy, with no evidence of significant utilization of other substrates for this purpose. Glucose is essential for the complete normal functioning of the human brain, and few substances, if any, can substitute for glucose in this respect, even under unusual cir-

TABLE II
Metabolism[a]

Subjects	Cerebral Blood Flow	Cerebral Oxygen Consumption	Cerebral Vascular Resistance	Arterial-Cerebral Venous Oxygen Difference	Respiratory Quotient	Mean Femoral Arterial Blood Pressure
	ml.	ml.	mm. Hg	volumes %		mm. Hg
Healthy young men[b]	54	3.3	1.6	6.3	0.99	86
Patients with hypertension[c]						
Various ages	57	3.5	2.8	6.2	0.90	153
61–70 yrs	50	3.2				
Patients 56–79 yrs[d]	44	2.9	2.4	6.5		97
Patients with senile psychosis[e]	41	2.8	3.0	6.8	0.95	121
Healthy 71-year-old men[f]	59	3.4	1.5	5.85	0.91	91.4

[a] Data given per 100 gm. of brain per minute. In order to compare the data obtained by the method of Kety and Schmidt with those of Scheinberg and Stead, in the case of the latter the values for the cerebral blood flow and oxygen consumption are decreased by 15 per cent, and the cerebrovascular resistance is increased by the same percentage. (From Himwich, H. E., and Himwich, W. A. Neurochemistry of aging. In *Handbook of Aging and the Individual*, J. E. Birren, editor, p. 187. University of Chicago Press, Chicago, 1959).

[b] Kety, S. S., and Schmidt, C. F. The effects of altered arterial tensions of carbon dioxide and oxygen on cerebral blood flow and cerebral oxygen consumption of normal young men. J. Clin. Invest., 27: 484, 1948. Scheinberg, P., and Stead, E. A., Jr. The cerebral blood flow in male subjects as measured by the nitrous oxide technique. Normal values for blood flow, oxygen utilization, glucose utilization and peripheral resistance, with observations on effect of tilting and anxiety. J. Clin. Invest., 28: 1163, 1949.

[c] Hafkenscheil, J. H., Crumpton, C. W., and Friedland, C. K. Cerebral oxygen consumption in essential hypertension. J. Clin. Invest., 33: 63, 1954.

[d] Scheinberg, P., Blackburn, I., Rich, M., and Saslaw, M. Effects of aging on cerebral circulation and metabolism. Arch. Neurol. Psychiat., 70: 77, 1953.

[e] Freyhan, F. A., Woodford, R. B., and Kety, S. S. Cerebral blood flow and metabolism in psychoses of senility. J. Nerv. Ment. Dis., 113: 449, 1951.

[f] Sokoloff, personal communication.

cumstances. Cerebral blood flow on an average in the normal alert subject is 54 ml./100 gm./minute; in the sleeping subject it is 65 ml./100 gm./minute. Glucose consumption is 5.4 mg./100 gm./minute. On the basis of whole brain, blood flow averages 750 ml. per minute, oxygen consumption 46 ml. per minute, and glucose consumption 7.6 mg. per minute.

DISORDERS AFFECTING BRAIN CONSTITUENTS
AND METABOLISM

ANOXIA

The brain is basically dependent on its supplies of glucose and oxygen. For this reason the two most important things that can affect the brain are anoxia and hypoglycemia.

Impairment of oxygen supply may be caused by a failure of any link in the long chain of events beginning with the inspiration of air and ending with a final utilization of oxygen by the tissues. It may occur because of (1) insufficient oxygen in the respired gases, as in high altitudes; (2) obstruction of respiratory passages; or (3) failure of the respiratory centers. The carriage of oxygen from the outside air to the tissues can be impaired by myocardial insufficiency, reduction of the oxygen carrying power of the blood, decrease of blood pressure (as in shock), relative cerebral ischemia, or enzymatic inactivation at the cellular level. Even if oxygen is available and all of the processes concerning it are normal, the requirement may be relatively excessive, as during convulsive seizures.

Anoxia results in an impairment of the energy supply to the brain. It can be withstood successfully for only about five minutes in the adult.

Anoxia is an important problem in the neonate. In fact, there is some tendency for all disorders of the newborn to be ascribed to anoxia or to birth injury. Chronic anoxia, often beginning in utero, may lead to various neurological disorders and to death. However, there are reports on one child who withstood anoxia for fourteen minutes with no apparent damage and on another child who recovered from a lack of oxygen after twenty-five minutes. It is difficult to distinguish between the effects of anoxia per se and of concomitant pathological processes of different origins in the fetus. Animal studies have cast some light on this problem, but it is still one that needs a great deal of research.

In any animal suffering from anoxia, survival depends largely on the release of energy from anaerobic processes. A small yield of energy is made available as substrates containing unsaturated hydrogen bonds accept hydrogen atoms from compounds that are thus oxidized to yield energy. Such compounds include unsaturated fatty acids and the sulfhydryl-containing compounds. Glycolysis—the anaerobic breakdown of carbohydrate, especially of glucose—is the most important source of anaerobic energy. In accordance with the Embden-Meyerhof scheme, glucose is broken to form pyruvic acid and, finally, lactic acid. Glycolysis is a wasteful process in comparison with oxidation; in glycolysis twelve molecules of carbohydrate supply approximately the same amount of energy as the oxidation of one molecule of that substance.

Another important anaerobic source of energy comes from the breakdown of energy-rich phosphate bonds, such as those contained in phosphocreatine and adenosine triphosphate. These and similar energy-rich compounds are built up by the energy derived from glycolysis, and the latter process is reversed as most of the lactic acid formed anaerobically is reconverted to carbohydrate by the energy released in oxidations. If glycolysis is stopped for any reason, energy-rich phosphate bonds are depleted as a secondary result. This depletion, however, is not complete; a small amount of energy-rich material remains.

Tews and Stone studied the effect of anoxia induced by the administration of 4.5 per cent oxygen in nitrogen for 12 to 13 minutes in adult dogs. There were significant increases in alanine, γ-aminobutyric acid (GABA), glutamic acid, leucine, tyrosine, and lactic acid, accompanied by decreases in aspartic acid. Remaining unchanged, however, were most of the free amino acids and related compounds (see Figure 4).

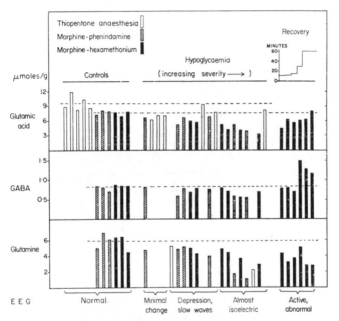

FIGURE 4. Changes in cerebral glutamic acid, GABA, and glutamine in relation to electrographic patterns during hypoglycemia and recovery. *Dotted lines* represent means control values. (Taken from Tews, et al. Chemical changes in the brain during insulin hypoglycaemia and recovery. J. Neurochem., *12*: 688, 1965.)

HYPOGLYCEMIA

In hypoglycemia the brain first makes use of the glycogen it has stored in the central nervous system. Figure 5 shows the changes in glycogen con-

Number of Experiment	Caudate	Corpora quadrigemmina	Cerebral gray	Thalamus	Cerebellum	Medulla	Cord
			Hypoglycemia				
1	8	26	56	45	40	35	46
2	12	28	33	40	32	26	14
3	8	32	21	27	33	24	14
4	1	8	16	8	30	49	122
5	20	0	11	18	18	36	45
6	12	13	19	20	8	19	16
7	6	15	10	8	1	31	43
8	0	0	2	0	1	31	32
9	0	2	6	0	6	13	26
			Normal				
Average	58	50	73	62	35	37	29
Range	44–71	37–60	45–108	41–68	23–46	21–47	15–31

FIGURE 5. Glycogen content of parts of the central nervous system of hypoglycemic dogs. Observations of nine experiments are presented here. A *line* has been drawn to separate the glycogen contents of the animals into two divisions. The *values to the left of the line* are significantly lower than the lowest values for the normal range for the same part. *Those to the right* are not significantly lower than the normal. In general, the upper parts of the brain lose their glycogen deposits before the lower areas are depleted. (Taken from Chesler, A., and Himwich, H. E. Effect of insulin hypoglycemia on glycogen content of parts of the central nervous system of the dog. Arch. Neurol. Psychiat., 52: 114, 1944.)

tent during insulin hypoglycemia in nine experimental dogs. In general, the upper parts of the brain lose their glycogen deposits before the lower areas are depleted. After the glycogen stores are gone, the brain then makes use of whatever material may be available for energy. The depletion of glycogen in the brain is followed by a reduction of material such as glutamic acid. Such a condition can be obtained only if the animals are given artificial respiration and have some means of maintaining their body temperature. The use of glutamic acid to supply energy does not, however, support the electrical activity of the cortex, even though 50 per cent of the glutamic acid remains. Other amino acids are also affected by hypoglycemia (see Figure 6). If the animal is kept alive long enough, functional and structural changes occur in the brain.

The changes that occur in insulin hypoglycemia have also been analyzed

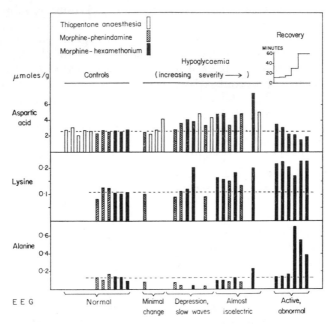

FIGURE 6. Changes in cerebral aspartic acid, lysine, and alanine in relation to electrographic patterns during hypoglycemia and recovery. *Dotted lines* represent mean control values. (Taken from Tews, et al. Chemical changes in the brain during insulin hypoglycaemia and recovery. J. Neurochem., *12*: 689, 1965.)

from the standpoint of the mineral content of the brain. Yannet, Geiger, and associates have shown that a marked loss of potassium and an increase in sodium occur with insulin hypoglycemia. The cats used by Yannet also had marked neurological defects. Acetylcholine is lowered in the brain in hypoglycemia.

CONVULSIONS

Convulsions are some of the most dramatic and interesting phenomena that the medical practitioner sees in his patients. Although there has been a great deal of clinical research in the field, relatively little if any work has been done on the changes in the human brain before, during, and after a convulsion. Most of the work in this area has been done with convulsions induced experimentally in animals.

With methionine sulfoxamine (MSO) at 6 mg. per kilogram, the dog does not always have convulsions, even though there is evidence of toxic reaction. Under these conditions there is the expected decrease in glutamate and glutamine, due probably to inhibition of glutamine synthetase.

The values for methionine and cystathione show a disturbance in methionine metabolism due to the MSO. The inhibition of glutamine synthetase by MSO leads to the reduction of protein synthesis in cerebral tissues, which can be reversed if methionine is given before or shortly after MSO treatment. The effects of the convulsive hydrazids seem to be related to GABA, glutamic acid decarboxylase, the GABA-α-ketoglutarate transaminase, and vitamin B_6. GABA is reduced in vivo by convulsive hydrazids whereas hydroxylamine raises the level and tends to reduce cerebral excitability. Five significant changes occur in cerebral constituents with these compounds: GABA is decreased, and its precursor, glutamate, shows a trend toward a higher value, although this difference is not statistically significant. Alanine, ammonia, lactate, and tyrosine are increased. The data by Tews and Stone are compatible with the suggestion that the seizures caused by drugs that inhibit glutamic acid decarboxylase or GABA-α-ketoglutarate transaminase result from the reduced rate of metabolism through the GABA pathway.

In animals treated with picrotoxin or pentylenetetrazol (Metrazol), neither of these convulsants produces a striking effect on the free amino acid content of a brain frozen while a seizure is in progress. Picrotoxin causes a slight reduction in aspartic acid; with Metrazol, the change is not significant. Animals given fluoroacetate and fluorobutyrate have also been studied, since both compounds cause violent seizures and alterations in the content of cerebral constituents. With both of these substances, significant changes are found for alanine, ammonia, citrate, lactate, leucine, and serine. Decreases are noted for aspartic acid, glutamate, and glycogen. These fluoro compounds block the tricarboxylic cycle prior to the ketoglutarate oxidase step and produce a decrease in glutamic and aspartic acids. Decreases in brain glycogen have been observed during seizures induced by fluoro compounds, in contrast with Metrazol, in the dog. Probably convulsions per se do not reduce brain glycogen, except in a transient fashion. If blood glucose and cerebral circulation are adequate, the normal value is soon restored.

In studying a group of epileptic and nonepileptic mice, Naruse and his co-workers showed that ammonia glutamate and glutamic acid were low in the brains of the epileptic mice, and GABA was 40 to 50 per cent higher. The level of total acetylcholine was 40 to 60 per cent higher than in the control strain, and the rate of resynthesis of acetylcholine was faster.

The human epileptogenic cerebral cortex has been studied by Tower. The biochemical lesion seemed to involve an inability to build up bound acetylcholine, a metabolic loss of glutamate in incubation in vitro, and reversal of normal potassium and sodium levels. These data were used as a basis for the treatment of epileptic patients.

Seizures have been linked to carbonic anhydrase by Millichap, who studied susceptibility to seizures in young animals as related to the activity of this enzyme. However, Robinson and Tizard pointed out that many other factors, such as dendritic development and myelinization, may be of equal importance in permitting the propagation of abnormal discharges. Nonetheless, a parallel can be demonstrated in adult animals between the degree of carbonic anhydrase inhibition and the degree of anticonvulsant activity.

Lipidoses

Lipidoses, abnormalities of lipid metabolism, are an enigmatic group of disorders that provide a fertile field for future study.

Tay-Sachs disease. A large study headed by Korey included both biochemical and electron microscopic analyses of brains of patients with Tay-Sachs disease. These patients were assessed clinically and then subjected to cerebral biopsy. These investigators found that the neuronal cytoplasm was crowded with distinctly laminated bodies that had no apparent association with normal cellular organelles. The macroglia pericytes and the endothelial cells contained degraded lipid. Myelin degeneration was of the Wallerian type, and the phagocytes contained myelin fragments and lipid bodies. Fibrous astrocytosis and an increase in extracellular space developed as the disease progressed. Biochemical studies of Tay-Sachs disease are complicated by the occurrence of the disease in a rapidly developing brain, showing both maturational changes and effects secondary to the primary pathology of the disease. Gangliosides were found to accumulate within the cells, not only in gray but also in white matter. An increased hexosamine content of cerebral tissues was also characteristic of the condition and possibly reflected the presence of asialo derivatives of gangliosides. In the early stages of the disease, brain slices showed normal respiration and lipid formation. A decrease in the free amino acid pool, however, occurred in the central nervous system, which may limit protein synthesis. Although the enzymes present in homogenates of diseased brains were capable of acting on normal brain, Tay-Sachs brain, or beef brain, there may be structural abnormalities in some of the gangliosides in Tay-Sachs disease that make them resistant to hydrolysis by enzymes in the diseased brain tissue. The membranous cytoplasmic bodies (MCB) have been isolated from homogenates of Tay-Sachs brain and analyzed for lipids. The data of Samuels and his colleagues, who attempted to form MCB in an artificial system, suggest that these bodies are neither lysosomes nor derivatives of normal organelles but may result from spontaneous aggregation of gangliosides, cholesterol, and phospholipids to form a molecular complex.

Leukodystrophy. Austin has described the biochemical changes in the globoid leukodystrophy (GLD), which is a fatal, genetically determined disorder of myelin that chiefly affects infants and children. The most consistent finding was an increase in the ratio of cerebrosides to sulfatides. But the data showed that GLD brains contain the usual amount of cerebrosides; the condition, therefore, is not, strictly speaking, a cerebroside lipidosis. However, the possibility of focal disproportional dyslipidoses should not be overlooked. This may appear as an increase in cerebrosides relative to sulfatides where there are islands of globoid elements. In the globoid bodies there were relative increases in cerebrosides identified as cerebron and kerasin. These increases were always in relation to a marked decrease in sulfatides and were usually evident in relation to the sphingomyelin as well. Fractions with higher globoid counts contained more than four times as much cerebrosides as sphingomyelins. The results suggest that the GLD fractions may share in the lipid imbalance in a manner similar to that of the globoid bodies.

Metachromatic leukodystrophy (sulfatidosis), studied by Svennerholm, shows a decrease of all lipids in the brain, especially cerebrosides, but an increase of sulfatides. The primary lesion may be the defective anabolism of cerebrosides with secondary increased formation of sulfatides.

Gaucher's disease and Niemann-Pick disease. In Gaucher's disease, a systematized storage disease of the reticuloendothelial system involving deposition of cerebrosides in liver and spleen, there are clinical signs of central nervous system involvement. Gaucher cells have been found in the adventitia of the blood vessels, but no increase has been detected in the brain. Niemann-Pick disease, on the other hand, involves storage of sphingomyelins in reticuloendothelial tissues. So far, analyses of the sphingomyelins found have shown no difference from the normal. Analyses of brains in both Gaucher's and Niemann-Pick diseases show a low concentration of myelin lipids, and the fatty acid analysis of sphingomyelins have an immature pattern.

DEMYELINATING DISEASES

The interest in lipidoses extends to the demyelinating diseases as well. Control glial fractions from advanced multiple sclerosis cases show relatively less sphingolipid than do glial fractions from GLD, whereas glial fractions from less-advanced diffuse disseminated sclerosis have relatively more. In multiple sclerosis there appear to be changes in the lipids of the brain; that is, there is a deficiency of the plasmalogens of the total phospholipids. Analyses of the carboxyl esters and the long-chain fatty acids reveal even-numbered saturated fatty acids in visually intact white matter. Phospholipids seem to be reduced in concentration, possibly because of a predemyelinating removal in the very early stages of degeneration. The appearance of cholesterol esters in the white matter of patients with multiple sclerosis is also of interest, since the appearance of these compounds is one of the earliest and most characteristic features of Wallerian degeneration.

EDEMA

Brain edema is thought to occur after neurosurgical procedures and in the areas adjacent to brain tumors in patients who have received electroshock.

Little can be done to study the human brain under these circumstances, and so the effects of edema on brain composition must be inferred from animal studies.

Anoxia produced in any way apparently causes rapid swelling of the brain, with an increase in intracranial pressure. When edema was produced by means of distilled water perfusion in monkeys and rabbits, the edematous brain contained more sodium and more water, especially in the white matter, but less potassium. Carbohydrate metabolites were altered in such a way as to indicate increased anaerobic glycolysis. The data obtained by Herschkowitz et al. suggest that the edema was mainly in the white matter, probably within the myelin sheath, and perhaps some in the extracellular space. When edema is produced by means of an experimental glioma in the mouse, the tissue adjacent to the implanted tumor becomes edematous, with an increase in water and sodium content. The chief alteration detected by electron micrography was a swelling of glial cell processes. It is suggested that there is altered membrane permeability or altered transport process.

Edema has also been produced in cats by a number of procedures, such as freezing treatment to the exposed dura and partial removal of brain tissue. Fluid did not accumulate as a result of reflection of the dura and simple exposure of the brain, but twenty-four hours after the production of a lesion by freezing, there was a decrease in dry weight, a fall in potassium, and an increase in sodium. These alterations occurred only in the white matter and persisted for at least five days. As far as the cortex as a whole is concerned, there were no changes. Three days after partial lobectomy, the same changes as with a freezing lesion were noted. A highly significant correlation occurred between sodium and potassium content. Cortisone apparently had no effect, although the authors were not able to rule out the possibility that the volume of tissue that was edematous was diminished in cortisone-treated animals.

NEUROCHEMISTRY IN PSYCHIATRIC DISORDERS

SOURCES OF INFORMATION

Only rarely does the opportunity arise to make neurochemical and other basic observations on the brains of patients with cerebral disorders. There is still too little application of the multidisciplinary approach, and, therefore, a dearth of basic observations on the various disorders of the brain and mind. And, unfortunately, there are limitations on the information available from the living patient. In the foreseeable future, researchers will find the greatest difficulty in obtaining biopsy materials for biochemical studies from the brains of living patients. Significant autopsy material is easier to obtain, but the information so obtained is similar in some ways to that available from neurohistological methods in general: The end results of a process can be seen, and the mechanisms may be inferred, but the various intermediary steps in that process cannot be observed and studied. But at least this inferential information presents suggestive leads. A step removed from the brain is the information to be obtained from the patients' blood and urinary constituents, which may be of indicative value. For example, in schizophrenic patients, an increase of urinary tryptamine foreshadows a worsening of schizophrenic symptoms, and a return to the usual tryptamine levels similarly precedes the cessation of the exacerbation. The increased urinary excretion of tryptamine only mirrors the increased levels of tryptamine in the blood, and since the blood-brain barrier is permeable to tryptamine, a rise in the brain concentration of tryptamine may be inferred.

The permeability of the blood-brain barrier to tryptamine has, however, been established by animal experimentation, and this leads us to another step still further removed from the primary source of the information sought, the human brain. In animal studies, researchers may try to imitate disease in man; for example, they may establish high levels of phenylalanine in an attempt to reproduce phenylketonuria and then study the effects of excessive phenylalanine on developmental behavior and changes in the brain constituents.

The following discussion examines all the aforementioned devices for examining the biochemical correlates of behavior; however, the most compelling data should be obtained from the brains of living patients.

CHEMICAL FINDINGS ON PATIENTS WITH DISTURBED MENTAL FUNCTIONING

Schizophrenia. Although the role of biological alterations in the pathogenesis of schizophrenia has been under investigation for many years, both experimental results and their interpretations remain controversial. One of the main problems is that schizophrenia is poorly defined and may cover a variety of pathogenic conditions. Even in individual patients, the clinical symptoms may vary greatly from time to time. Moreover, the dissimilar clinical responses to treatment with psychotropic drugs suggest that different biochemical situations may prevail in the various clinical states.

It is easy to understand why each new technique based on advances in the basic sciences is applied in turn to a study of schizophrenia, a prevalent disease that is emotionally crippling and costly, both financially and in interpersonal relationships. Many biochemical studies, however, not only failed to correlate the basic observations with the behavior of the patients but failed to use controls, including the important one of diet. Later work, done under improved conditions, indicated an impaired ability of the liver to detoxify psychotomimetic substances and a reduced turnover rate of some phosphate compounds in the blood of schizophrenic patients. Investigations have also disclosed dissimilarities in urine and blood constituents between schizophrenic patients and controls.

TRYPTOPHAN. One aspect of biochemical psychiatry is concerned with the relationship between schizophrenic behavior and the protein products contained in urine. Some studies on urinary derivatives of tryptophan have revealed abnormally high excretions of *indole substances* in patients with schizophrenia in comparison with nonschizophrenic individuals. But in other observations either no differences were found, or these products in the urine of patients with schizophrenia were abnormally low. It seems apparent, however, that the daily excretions of these urinary products exhibited a greater variability in schizophrenic patients than in normal controls. A series of studies on schizophrenia showed, not unexpectedly, that average values for urinary indoles were either within the normal ranges or somewhat higher than in controls. But when day-to-day correlations were made between the intensities of the psychotic symptoms and the levels of the urinary constituents, striking agreements were observed between the degree of psychotic activity and the daily output of tryptamine (see Table III) and of 3-indole acetic acid and 5-hydroxyin-

TABLE III

Urinary Tryptamine and Degree of Psychotic Activity[a]

The average of all observations lies within the normal range, but other averages, based on the degree of psychotic activity, reveal an increased output of tryptamine per day with greater degree of psychotic activity.

Degree of Psychotic Activity	No. of Patients	Days	Trpytamine[b]	
			Average	Range
			μg./day	
Apparently inactive	17	410	91.6	39–137
Slightly active	12	270	124.9	58–167
Moderately active	7	105	151.2	66–282
Active	6	40	202.8	153–292
Markedly active	2	10	382.5	180–585

[a] From Himwich, H. E. Loci of actions of psychotropic drugs in the brain. Fol. Psychiat. Neurol. Jap., 19: 217, 1965.

[b] Average, 118 μg. per day for 835 24-hour urinary specimens. Normal range, 36 to 120 μg. per day.

dole acetic acid. Tryptamine was the most sensitive indicator for the rise of the indole products in the urine. From one to five days before any signs of behavioral exacerbations were observed, indole substances began to increase in the urine. Levels continued high until rather precipitous falls were observed, usually beginning before the last day of active psychotic behavior. Examination of the results revealed that the increased indole products were endogenous. Such a conclusion was drawn partly on a basis of behavioral changes but chiefly on biochemical alterations. Behaviorally, some patients suffered a loss of appetite and simultaneously exhibited greater motor activity. Thus, caloric intake decreased at a time when caloric requirements were raised. Biochemically, the additional indole products in the urine were the result of the breakdown of body proteins.

Increases of urinary creatinine revealed that the breakdown of muscle protein was one source of the increased indole products. But another factor accounting for the endogenous origin must also be given serious consideration. Figure 7 shows the known pathways of tryptophan metabolism in the body. When the use of the pathway starting with formylkynurenine and ending with 1-N-methylnicotinamide is depressed, those of the indoles may show compensatory increases. Thus, two processes may be operative in the increased urinary excretion of indoles. But the diversion of

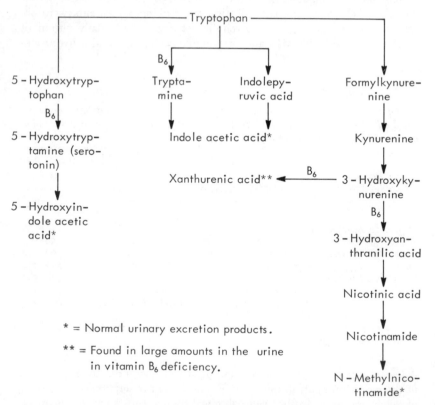

FIGURE 7. Known pathways of tryptophan metabolism in the body. Note that three of these pathways maintain the indole nucleus intact but that the fourth one, via kynurenine, does not. (Adapted from Figure 1 of Olson, R. E., Gursey, D., and Vaster, J. W. Evidence of a defect in tryptophan metabolism in chronic alcoholism. New Eng. J. Med., 263: 1169, 1960.)

tryptophan metabolism away from the formylkynurenine pathway and toward that of the indole amines does not exclude the increased breakdown of body protein as another source. In both cases greater amounts of tryptophan breakdown products would appear in the urine. A number of other amino acids, including methionine, may also be released from muscle. It is, therefore, possible that higher concentrations of indoles and methionine may give rise to an increased production of psychotogenic methylated indoles, thus accounting in part for the maintenance of the active psychotic behavior.

In a series of feeding experiments with methionine, tryptophan, and other amino acids, it was shown that, given by themselves, none of the amino acids evoked changes in the behavior of schizophrenic patients. Even with a monoamine oxidase (MAO) inhibitor, all but two were without effect. When, however, methionine was administered simultaneously with a monoamine oxidase inhibitor, significant changes occurred as the severity of symptoms increased. These changes were first observed by Pollin, Cardon, and Kety and were amply confirmed by other investigators. Tryptophan with an MAO inhibitor also aggravated the clinical picture but to a lesser degree. An important function of methionine is to make methyl groups available for the metabolic processes of the body. Since another methyl donor, betaine, also produced behavioral worsening when administered with an MAO inhibitor, it seemed that tryptophan metabolites and methionine might be involved in a common mechanism, a mechanism in which increases of indoles derived from tryptophan and elevated levels of methyl groups donated by methionine might facilitate the formation of methylated indoles with psychotogenic properties. It is worthy of note that N-dimethyltryptamine, similarly derived from tryptophan and methionine, is also psychotomimetic.

Thus, two factors may be involved in the mechanism of symptomatic deterioration of schizophrenic patients: the psychogenic action of methyl groups and the increased formation of indoles. Increases of tryptophan and methionine may act together to produce an endogenous metabolic factor by furnishing material for the production of a methylated psychotogenic indole. Such a psychotomimetic substance may be involved in this hypothetical cycle in an individual with a genetically determined schizophrenic reaction. From his hereditary nexus comes an unknown initiating component of the behavioral worsening, with loss of appetite as an early symptom. Next follows a breakdown of muscle protein and the release of amino acids, including tryptophan and perhaps methionine. In addition, more indole amines are formed from tryptophan, at the expense of the kynurenine metabolites. These amino acids, in turn, furnish materials for the formation of a methylated psychotogenic indole, an endogenous metabolic factor. Finally, the interactions of the endogenous factor and the schizophrenic hereditary component increase the severity of the psychotic symptoms.

CATECHOLAMINES. Phenylalanine and tyrosine are the sources

of all the catecholamines in the body, including dopamine, norepine-phrine (noradrenaline), and epinephrine (adrenaline) (see Figure 8). In-creases of urinary catecholamines usually accompany aggravations of psy-chotic symptoms but, unlike the indoles, do so on a somewhat different temporal basis. The indoles begin increasing *before* a sudden flare-up of symptoms and continue at high levels during psychotic activation. On the other hand, epinephrine and norepinephrine begin rising *simultaneously* with the increase of psychotic behavior.

Usually, exacerbations of schizophrenic symptoms are accompanied by increased motor activity, heightened tension, or both. In such instances, both urinary catecholamines and indole amines appear in greater amounts. But when signs of anxiety and tension increase in severity in the absence of marked worsening of schizophrenic symptoms, the catecholamine rise is not associated with a rise of the indoles. In the elevation of catechola-mines unaccompanied by an elevation of indoles during a period of re-duced psychotic activity, the relationship between the greater output of the catecholamines and the increased anxiety and muscular activity in schizophrenics does not appear to be different from the relationship be-tween the increased excretion of catecholamines and heightened tension and motor restlessness in nonschizophrenic individuals.

The methyl groups in the formation of psychotogenic indole amines have been stressed here, but a similar possibility exists with the catechola-mines. Osmond and Smythies suggested that a catecholamine related to mescaline may play a part in schizophrenia, and they included in their paper the remarks of Harley-Mason that such a catecholamine might arise as a result of faulty methylation. More recently, Friedhoff and Van Winkle have demonstrated that dimethoxyphenylethylamine (DMPEA), a catecholamine, is closely related in chemical structure to the well-known psychotomimetic agent, mescaline (trimethoxyphenylethylamine). And DMPEA occurs more frequently in the urine of schizophrenic patients than in nonschizophrenic populations. Much work has been done follow-ing this lead, which, however, like that of the psychotogenic indoles, is still regarded as controversial. Yet the conclusions of Friedhoff and Van Winkle have received much experimental support.

DMPEA may represent a nosological classification characteristic of cer-tain types of schizophrenia, and the increases in the other catecholamines —noradrenaline, adrenaline, and vanilmandelic acid—may correlate with hyperactivity and anxiety. But this correlation is not specific for patients with mental disease, since it also occurs in normal subjects. The altera-tions of the indole amines, on the other hand, seem to relate specifically to the worsening of the schizophrenic symptoms.

STEROID HORMONES. In some ways the changes in the urinary steroid hormones parallel those of the catecholamines. Sudden and severe exacerbations of schizophrenic symptoms are accompanied by rises in both 17-ketosteroids and 17-hydroxycorticosteroids. Ratings of the severity of

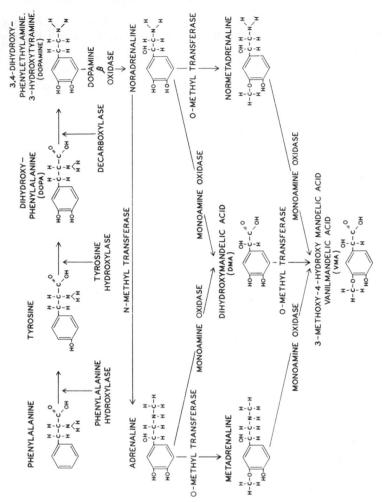

FIGURE 8. Pathways of catecholamine metabolism. The process starts with phenylalanine and goes on to tyrosine, dopa, and dopamine. Noradrenaline (norepinephrine) gives rise to adrenaline (epinephrine). At this point, there are two chief paths for the continuation of the metabolic process. In extraneuronal areas, these two substances are transformed into normetadrenaline (normetanephrine), metadrenaline (metanephrine), and reactions catalyzed by catechol (O-methyltransferase). Within the neuron, dihydroxymandelic acid is formed with the aid of monoamine oxidase. In both instances, however, these products are next acted on by the other one of these two enzyme systems so that, irrespective of the order in which the two enzymatic processes occur, the resulting product is the same, vanilmandelic acid. (Courtesy of H. E. Himwich.)

schizophrenic symptoms reveal that the levels of urinary steroid hormones may be associated with concomitant high degrees of motor activity and anxiety.

In a specific example (see Figure 9) a most severe exacerbation of

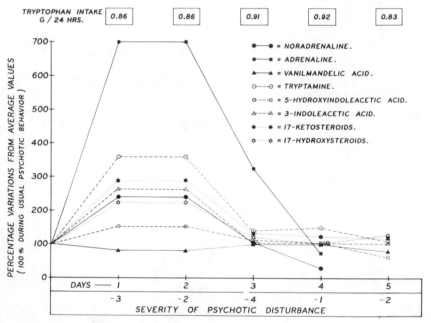

FIGURE 9. Excretion patterns. Urinary excretions of catecholamines, indole amines, and steroid hormones during periods of aggravation of schizophrenic symptoms in patient J. F. (From Berlet, H. H., Bull, C., Himwich, H. E., Kohl, H., Matsumoti, K., Pscheidt, G. R., Spaide, J., Tourlentes, T. T., and Valverde, J. M. Endogenous metabolic factor in schizophrenic behavior. Science, *144*: 311, 1964.)

schizophrenic behavior was accompanied by outbursts of violence, hostility, and hyperactivity. All urinary constituents studied, with the exception of vanilmandelic acid, rose during the behavioral worsening. The episode lasted for five days, with peak exacerbations on the first and second days, but psychotic symptoms were most severe on the third day.

These simultaneous observations of urinary indoles, catechols, and steroids during behavioral worsening have made it possible in many instances to separate psychotic symptoms in accordance with their relationships either to urinary indoles on one side or to urinary catechols and steroids on the other. One group of symptoms, characterized by rises in catechols and steroids, is composed of increased motor activity or motor restlessness, heightened tension, and anxiety. In contrast, a second group of symptoms is distinguished by increases of urinary indoles and is associated with such psychotic symptoms as intensifications of hallucinatory and delusional experiences, usually with mounting hostility. When to the latter group of symptoms are added motor restlessness and increased anxiety, either separately or together, all three classes of urinary products are significantly elevated in the urine. Perhaps the elevations of catecholamines and steroids indicate a total mobilization of the bodily resources to meet this grave emergency.

Affective disorders. The most prominent experimental concept on the affective disorders emanates from Kety's laboratory and indicates that some, if not all, depressions are associated with an *absolute or relative deficiency of catecholamines,* particularly of norepinephrine in the brain. Abnormal elation, conversely, may be accompanied by an excess of such amines. The experimental basis for the hypothesis is found in the work of Brodie and his associates, who correlated behavioral excitation in animals with increased levels of brain norepinephrine. Other workers were able to demonstrate that dopa, a catecholamine (but not serotonin), counteracts reserpine-induced sedation in animals. In the clinical field, Schildkraut also demonstrated that depressed patients treated with imipramine showed increased excretion rates of normetanephrine, a catecholamine metabolite, with clinical improvement. In contrast, according to some studies, sedation seems to be associated with a greater abundance of brain serotonin. However, other data do not support the hypothesis that fluctuations in catecholamines are the primary biochemical factors in depression.

An alternate dualistic approach—presented by Bueno, Pscheidt, and Himwich—suggests that *both catechol and indole amines* are involved in the biochemical basis of the affective disorders. This hypothesis accounts for several important clinical and experimental observations. The somatization of the depressive illness is adrenergic in quality and includes tachycardia, insomnia, anorexia, anxiety, and abnormalities in the digestive tract and in the sexual sphere. All these signs are strikingly similar to the amphetamine-induced organic psychoses. On the other hand, melancholia —with its depression of vital functions, lack of interest, decreased vitality, and delusional ideas of guilt and hopelessness—may be the result of disturbances in indole metabolism. Experimentally in animals, the dualistic hypothesis finds support in recent work using chronic treatment with MAO inhibitors, which block degradation of serotonin and catecholamines, combined with reserpine, which releases serotonin in its active form. These studies disclosed that behavioral and electroencephalographic activation can be related to disturbances in the *balance* between serotonin and norepinephrine; behavioral stimulation was associated with increases of brain serotonin while there was either a smaller rise or even a decrease in brain norepinephrine. Working with various mammalian species, different workers have also pointed out the importance of the equilibrium between both amines. Clinically encouraging results were obtained by Mendiguita and Penasco in the management of endogenous depressions using reserpine with an MAO inhibitor. Investigators have correlated clinical improvement in depressive patients, who improved with reserpine and imipramine but not with imipramine alone, with variations in indole metabolism and not in catechol turnover.

METABOLIC DISORDERS

Psychotic behavior and disorders of tryptophan metabolism have been observed not only with schizophrenia but also with a disorder of metabolism, Hartnup's disease. The similarities among the psychotic manifestations of Hartnup's disease, pellagra, and schizophrenia are worth noting. In this regard, a metabolic linking of homocysteinuria with schizophrenia has been suggested.

HARTNUP'S DISEASE. This disease is associated with intermittent and variable malfunctions, including psychosis, cerebellar ataxia, migraine headaches, and, occasionally, progressive mental retardation. Comparatively late, a dermatitis develops. Like the dermatitis in pellagra, it is a red, scaly rash occurring chiefly on surfaces exposed to the sunlight. Hartnup's disease is characterized by biochemical alterations, including a generalized amino aciduria, except that proline, cysteine, and taurine remain within normal limits. The excretions of other catecholamines are at least ten times the usual values. In the absence of elevated levels of these amino acids in the blood, this amino aciduria is ascribed to leakage through the kidney, probably due to defective reabsorption in the renal tubules.

A second biochemical defect is impaired absorption of tryptophan from the intestine. For that reason, tryptophan breakdown products (3-indole acetic acid, 3-indole acetylglutamine, and indican) accumulate in the intestinal lumen. These products are then absorbed in the blood stream and eliminated in the urine. A decrease of nicotinamide occurs as a result of the poor absorption of tryptophan. This may account for the pellagralike features of Hartnup's disease. During clinical remissions the metabolic abnormalities recede.

PELLAGRA. The multideficiency of pellagra includes lack of tryptophan, nicotinic acid, and perhaps other vitamins, including pyridoxine. The behavioral changes sometimes observed in pellagra may strikingly reproduce the clinical pictures of schizophrenia. Not long ago, patients with pellagra were sent to mental institutions with a diagnosis of schizophrenia. In man, pellagra is also linked to the genetically determined disorder of Hartnup's disease by changes in tryptophan; abnormally high urinary excretion rates of indole metabolites have been observed, and tryptamine has been isolated from the urine of pellagrins.

HOMOCYSTEINURIA. This syndrome is associated with the presence in the urine of homocysteine, a metabolite of methionine, and is characterized by such relatively constant features as mental retardation, fair hair, dislocated ocular lenses, malar flush, peculiar gait, and genu valgum. More variable features of this syndrome are excessively long extremities and digits, convulsions, thrombotic incidents, cardiovascular disorders, and fatty liver. Though resembling Marfan's syndrome in exhibiting pectus excavatum or carinatum, and ectopia lentis and arachnodactyly, it differs from Marfan's syndrome by the presence of mental retardation, malar flush, and osteoporosis.

Homocysteinuria is inherited as an autosomal recessive gene. Liver biopsies of homocysteinuric patients reveal that the enzymatic pathway fails to function because of a lack of activity of the enzyme cystathioninsynthase. In view of this close metabolic association between methionine and the other members of this pathway and in view of the observation that the administration of either methionine or cysteine to a schizophrenic patient receiving a MAO inhibitor worsens the schizophrenic symptoms, it is of interest to point out the pedigree of a homocysteinuric female patient. Her mother, brother, sister, maternal grandfather, maternal grand uncle, and maternal grand aunt were all probably schizophrenic. Another patient, who had been diagnosed as having schizophrenia, was found on further study to be suffering from homocysteinuria. At present, however, the question of whether metabolic relationships between methionine and homocysteine are of etiological importance in the schizophrenic patient can be regarded only as a suggestive lead for research.

WILSON'S DISEASE. This disease is also known as hepatolenticular degeneration; the latter name is descriptive of the morphological pathology, which usually includes degeneration of the corpus striatum with cirrhosis of the liver. The characteristic symptoms include difficulty in swallowing and in speech, irritability and explosive behavior, and a progressive organic dementia. The chemical pathology is concerned with an altered distribution of copper, with abnormally high amounts in the cerebrospinal fluid, urine, brain, liver, and kidney. Total blood copper is significantly lower than usual. Moreover, ceruloplasmin activity is reduced.

Wilson's disease is probably associated with a genetically altered ceruloplasmin; copper is no longer held tightly bound to ceruloplasmin, a serum globulin. Despite the fact that the copper loosely attached to serum albumin is above normal levels, a decrease in the total copper content of the blood occurs. The copper of the albumin fraction is excreted in the urine and also deposited in brain, liver, and other tissues where the affinity for copper is greater. The urine contains high levels of amino acids, tryptamine, 5-hydroxyindole acetic acid, 3-indole acetic acid, and other indole metabolites in addition to the catecholamines, epinephrine, and dopamine.

PHENYLKETONURIA. Phenylketonuria is a genetically determined condition involving a fault in the metabolism of phenylalanine, a failure in the conversion of that substance to tyrosine (see Figures 6 and 7). As might be expected, phenylalanine accumulates in all the fluids of the body, and metabolic products of phenylalanine are produced in excess. As with Hartnup's disease, excessively large amounts of 3-indole lactic acid, 3-indole pyruvic acid, 3-indole acetic acid, and indican are found in the urine; conversely, 5-hydroxyindole acetic acid is excreted at abnormally low levels.

These results may be explained by an inhibition exerted by phenylalanine on the absorption of tryptophan from the intestine. A similar explanation—impaired absorption of tryptophan—may apply to the low levels of serotonin observed in the brains of animals with experimental phenylketonuria. D. W. Woolley suggests that abnormalities of serotonin in the brain are linked to mental deficiencies and the psychoses. In addition to diminishing brain serotonin, excessive elevations of phenylalanine in the blood result in decreases in the concentrations of glutamic acid, glutamine, isoleucine, and GABA in the brain.

Another characteristic of patients with phenylketonuria is insufficient pigmentation, ascribed to an interference in the oxidation of tyrosine to dihydroxyphenylalanine, though only partial inhibition of this reaction has been demonstrated in phenylketonurics. Characteristically, patients with this disorder are blond and occasionally albino, even when they come from dark-complexioned Caucasian or Negro families.

The majority of victims have low intelligence quotients, and some never learn to talk or achieve toilet-training. On the other hand, there are a few authenticated cases with intelligence well within the normal range. Convulsions start in the first or second year of life and finally stop spontaneously. Abnormal electroencephalograms are observed in the absence of seizures. These electrical abnormalities are reversible with diet therapy. It is striking that records of mental institutions reveal that phenylketonurics are sometimes admitted with a diagnosis of childhood schizophrenia. Older children exhibit motor restlessness, are hyperactive, and may injure themselves.

For the normal development of intelligence, treatment consisting of an intake of phenylalanine reduced to about 4 to 5 per cent of the diet should be started in the first weeks of life. When the special diet may be stopped with impunity is not yet known, but it is known that a cerebral defect, once developed, is irreversible and probably involves permanent structural alterations of the central nervous system. The gray matter shows few abnormalities. In the white matter, in contrast, there are usually multiple areas of defective myelinization. In these patients, the pigmentation of the substantia nigra and the locus caerulus is decreased, although these areas are normally pigmented in albinos.

MAPLE SYRUP DISEASE. Maple syrup disease is so named because the urine of the patient has a striking odor similar to maple sugar. The nervous system deteriorates rapidly, and in most instances death occurs within the first month of life. The severe brain damage characteristic of this disorder is limited chiefly to the white matter, and myelination is defective. The inborn error of metabolism is transmitted as an autosomal recessive gene and is characterized by a failure in oxidative decarboxylation of four keto acids: α-ketoisocaproic acid, α-ketoisovaleric acid, α-keto-β-methyl-n-valeric acid, and, probably, α-ketobutyric acid. The metabolic deficiency occurs in the enzyme that catalyzes the conversion of α-ketoisocaproic acid to isovaleryl coenzyme A. In addition, there is a secondary rise in the keto acids and the respective amino acids, including leucine, isoleucine, aloisoleucine, and valine—all of which also appear in the urine.

BLOOD-BRAIN BARRIER

Knowledge of the blood-brain barrier is based almost entirely on animal experimentation. Hence the characteristics of the human blood-brain barrier can only be inferred from clinical studies and results on animals.

SELECTIVITY OF THE BARRIER

Although equilibrium is rapidly established between the vascular fluids and the interstitial fluids of most organs, many substances show a slow equilibration in the brain. Moreover, the brain is more accessible to certain substances if they are administered intrathecally than if they are given intravenously. An excellent example is the response to sodium ferricyanide. Given intravenously, this substance produces no symptoms, even in fairly high concentrations, nor can it be detected in the brain, although it penetrates all other tissues of the body. When, however, small amounts of ferricyanide are introduced into the cerebrospinal fluid, the animal develops pronounced symptoms and may die of convulsions. Thus, the intrathecal injection has circumvented a barrier between blood and brain. Consideration of the blood-brain barrier is of great importance in many problems, including the utilization of food stuffs by the brain, the therapeutic use of drugs, and the pathological effects of viruses and toxins on brain tissue. In discussing all these problems, the four fluid compartments in the brain and the barriers between them must be considered.

The acid aniline dyes (negatively charged) fail to enter the brain, although the basic aniline dyes (positively charged) do so readily. Not only the negatively charged dyes but also substances such as lactic acid and pyruvic acid, containing electronegative carboxyl groups, enter the brain slowly. The rate of entrance of these substances into the brain is considerably slower than that of glucose and is too slow to allow them to support brain metabolism. In contrast, observations on excised cerebral tissue reveal that lactic acid is as effective as glucose in maintaining brain metabolism. In excised tissues the blood-brain barrier is destroyed, and materials penetrate the brain easily at the cut surface.

Most ions, whether electropositive cations or electronegative anions, require a relatively prolonged period before equal concentrations are present in the blood and in brain tissue. Many studies have shown that anions such as bromide, iodide, thiocyanide, and chloride have a short equilibration period, usually only a few minutes, between the circulatory fluids of the vascular tree and the interstitial fluids of the various organs. Yet equilibration with the brain may not be complete after three hours. Sodium and potassium are the classical examples of cations that enter the brain slowly. Radioactive sodium concentration, for example, equalizes throughout the vascular and interstitial fluid of the various organs of the body within 11 minutes, and yet it requires sixty-two hours to attain equilibrium between brain and blood. Though potassium enters interstitial fluids more rapidly than sodium, this rate is slower for the brain than for other organs.

Only a few amino acids have been studied extensively in terms of their ability to pass the blood-brain barrier. These include glutamic acid, leucine, isoleucine, lysine, tyrosine, tryptophan, and phenylalanine. The ability of these substances to penetrate the brain is greater in the young animal than in the adult. Recently, it has been demonstrated that an increased blood level of one amino acid can influence the entrance of other amino acids into the brain. The most striking example is the inhibition of the uptake of tryptophan and tyrosine by a high blood level of phenylalanine.

VARIATIONS IN THE BARRIER

Not all parts of the brain are equally protected by the blood-brain barrier. A portion of the hypothalamus with the pituitary and pineal glands, the choroid plexus, and the area postrema are more permeable than other areas. Nor is the permeability of the blood-brain barrier a constant factor. The barrier appears to exert less influence, and that on fewer substances, at the time of birth and probably in fetal life than in later life. The physiological status of the brain is also important. Any injury to the brain tends to reduce the resistance of the blood-brain barrier to penetration. Inflammation facilitates the passage of substances. Considerable evidence has accumulated that an increase of carbon dioxide reduces barrier function. There is also the possibility that the rate of permeability may be regulated in part by nonnervous tissue. It has been found with the perfused brain of cats that the administration of glucose fails to revive the brain unless an extract of liver is added at the same time.

Nature of the Barrier

Many explanations have been offered for the existence of the blood-brain barrier. The current point of view is that what has been called the blood-brain barrier concept is not a generalized phenomenon. It is probably a summation effect of many factors, only some of which are integral parts of the boundary between blood and brain. The work in this field in the last fifteen years leads largely to the conclusion that there will be no generalized concept developed to fit all the phenomena and that each condition and each metabolite must be considered by itself.

Dobbing, however, has suggested a unified hypothesis that postulates a multiplicity of factors, including those the brain has in common with other tissues and those that make the brain the specialized tissue it is. In the first group Dobbing includes electrical charge, molecular size, degree of dissociation, extent of protein binding, and lipid solubility of the substances being considered. The second group consists of the negligible extracellular space in the brain, with consequent necessity for transcellular transport and the resistance to entry of substances into metabolically inert compartments. Brain metabolism, then, would dominate much of the transport of substances between blood and brain. Considered in this way, the blood-brain barrier is a reflection of, rather than a limiting factor in, in vivo cerebral metabolism.

ANATOMICAL EXPLANATION. Considerable research is still devoted to determining the exact location of the blood-brain barrier. Theoretically, the barrier could function at any one of several sites, beginning with the capillary wall, going outward to the peripheral lining of the perivascular space, and finally to the surface of the glial cells (see Figure 10).

The capillaries have again and again been implicated as the site of the blood-brain barrier phenomenon. Two possible elements are involved: the endothelial cells themselves and the matrix that binds these cells together. It is generally agreed that lipid-soluble substances —such as CO_2, O_2, urethane, and formaldehyde—diffuse easily through the endothelial cells. The portion of the capillaries traversed by lipid-insoluble substances—such as water, sodium chloride, and glucose—is still under dispute.

Two main camps have developed in the blood-brain barrier controversy. One supports the perivascular glial membrane theory and the other the capillary endothelial theory. At this time, experimental evidence exists in support of both positions.

In the last few years, attention has turned to the relative lack of extracellular space in the brain as a possible explanation for the blood-brain barrier phenomenon. The close packing of the cells in the brain results in a dearth of extracellular space, with a possible figure of less than 5 per cent being fairly well agreed on at this time. This situation means that material entering the brain has to enter a cell almost immediately, rather than entering the extracellular fluid. In contrast, in organs such as kidney and liver, the cells are surrounded by extracellular fluid, which may constitute 30 per cent of the organ. Astroglia function as a water ion compartment for the central nervous system; this compartment is involved in a selective transport of fluids and metabolites between blood and brain. These facts have led to the concept that the important factor in the blood-brain barrier may be a combination of glial cells and extracellular space, the so-called extraneuronal space.

TRANSPORT EXPLANATION. One of the most intriguing suggestions that has arisen from all the studies of the blood-brain barrier has been the concept that the barrier may have a functional rather than an anatomical localization and may depend on transport phenomena. An active transfer linked to metabolic processes has been suggested by Tschirgi to account for transfer between blood and brain, between brain and cerebrospinal fluid, and between blood and cerebrospinal fluid.

Figure 10 indicates the possibility that a net movement of water and solutes from the vascular compartment into the extravascular compartments in the central nervous system could be balanced, at least in part, by a net movement of water and solutes from the subarachnoid space through the arachnoid villi into the blood stream. Such fluid formation depends on the local elaboration of metabolic energy in order to explain the electrolyte composition of the cerebrospinal fluid. But the nature of this metabolic pump and its role in regulating the neuronal microenvironment are obscure.

Tschirgi has postulated a mechanism whereby sodium and chloride might be moved from plasma to the extravascular fluids of the central nervous system by an action of an exchange mechanism controlled by the carbon dioxide produced by metabolism.

This mechanism, according to his hypothesis, exists throughout the entire parenchymal perivascular membrane of the central nervous system, including the choroid plexus, with the exception of the arachnoid villi in the dural sinuses. The net influx of electrolytes in water is

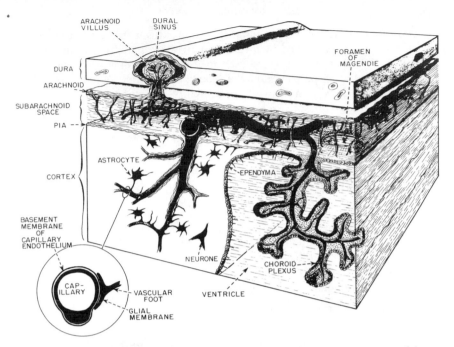

FIGURE 10. Semidiagrammatic section of central nervous system and investing membranes. This shows the relationships of various fluid compartments and barriers. The *enlargement at lower left* illustrates three probable sites of blood-brain barrier action: capillary endothelium, basement membrane, and perivascular glia. Note that invaginating pia does not accompany penetrating vessels beyond larger branches. Astrocytes form an 85 to 90 per cent complete sheath around blood vessels, although only a few are illustrated. (From Tschirgi, R. D. Chemical environment of the central nervous system. In *Handbook of Physiology*, J. Field, H. W. Magoun, and V. E. Hall, editors, section 1, vol. 3, p. 1865. American Physiological Society, Washington, 1960.)

seen as moving into the subarachnoid space and back into the blood stream largely through the arachnoid villi. Carbon dioxide, among other factors, would determine the rate. This mechanism for the transfer of sodium across the cellular membrane by exchange for metabolically produced hydrogen with the accompaniment of osmotically obligate water is essentially identical with that proposed for kidney tubular reabsorption of sodium. In the kidney, however, the pump is oriented to move sodium and water from the extravascular fluid into the plasma, whereas in the brain Tschirgi proposed that it is positioned to move these substances from the plasma into extracellular fluid.

The transfer of substances from the blood into the brain can be compared to the renal tubular transport apparatus in the case of glucose, which is reabsorbed by means of active transport from urine to blood. When organic acids are used to study overloading, they show various inhibiting potencies on the blood-brain barrier. A rough correlation can be drawn between their ability to inhibit blood-brain barrier transport and their maximal tubular rate of excretion.

The various factors that can influence the blood-brain barrier are shown in Table IV.

CURRENT RESEARCH IN NEUROCHEMISTRY AND BEHAVIOR

The early and voluminous work of Bennett and his group on cholinesterase and behavior or intelligence in rats has recently been confirmed by

TABLE IV
Summary of Blood-Brain Phenomena[a]

1. Lipophilic substances	Passive diffusion	No blood-brain barrier
2. Hydrophilic metabolites	Specific transport mechanisms[b]	
Nutrients (glucose, certain amino acids)	Blood → CNS	Partial blood-brain barrier (above transport capacity)
Waste products (organic conjugated ions, indicator dyes)	CNS → blood	Blood-brain barrier (countertransport)
3. Hydrophilic non-metabolized nonelectrolytes (inulin, sucrose, mannitol)	No transfer	Blood-brain barrier (passive)

Blood-Brain Barrier Phenomena and Effects of Injuries on It

1. Injuries	Causing free diffusion or flow (mechanical, necrotizing, or otherwise rupturing)
Indicators:	Detectable native or foreign blood constituents in general
2. Injuries	Causing functional alteration of specific transfer mechanism(s)
Indicators:	Substances presumed to be specifically handled by the actual mechanism(s)
Examples:	a. General transport inhibition: decreased CNS uptake of glucose, increased uptake (abnormal blood-CNS passage) of acid dyes
	b. Selective (overloading) inhibition of CNS-blood extrusion of waste acids: abnormal blood-CNS passage of acid indicators only

[a] From Steinwall, O. Blood-brain barrier dysfunction: Some theoretical aspects. Acta Neurol. Scand., 40: Suppl. 10, p. 25, 1964.
[b] Carrier-mediated, saturable (limited transport capacity), inhibitable by competitive overloading or by unspecific toxic influences.

Kling, Finer, and Nair in regard to the effects of handling and light stimulation on the developing rat brain. This work points out the importance of sensory stimuli on the biochemical development of the brain. This field will undoubtedly prove a fertile one for investigation and will also mean that workers in the field of brain development will have to check and control environmental stimuli if their data are to be evaluated properly. Levine and Alpert had earlier reported the effects of handling on the phospholipids of the developing brain.

The studies of the effects of learning on the RNA of the brain have been reported from Hydén's laboratory. Unfortunately, his elegant methods of nucleotide analysis have few practitioners, and his findings await confirmation from other laboratories. Work on memory and its relation to RNA and to the hippocampus is being pursued from a number of points of view. The transfer of memory of a learned task by administration of RNA or a fraction of the RNA from a trained animal to a naive one is being vigorously pursued. The probable low permeability of the blood-brain barrier to RNA as such increases the complexity of the problem. Flexner and his colleagues have used puromycin to destroy recent memory in the hippocampus. This approach appears quite promising.

Ever since γ-aminobutyric acid was described as an inhibitory substance, many attempts have been made to correlate its inhibitory effects with behavior. The most successful experiment was by Jasper, Khan, and Elliott. They were able to demonstrate that the fluid from the surface of the brain contained more GABA when the electroencephalographic pattern showed sleep spindles than when arousal tracings were seen. More recently Wiechert and Herbst were able to provoke convulsions by upsetting the balance between glutamic acid and GABA.

REFERENCES

Austin, J. H. Studies in globoid (Krabbe) leukodystrophy. Arch. Neurol., *9:* 207, 1963.

Bakay, L. Studies on blood-brain barrier with radioactive phosphorous; embryonic development of barrier. Arch. Neurol. Psychiat., *70:* 30, 1953.

Bennett, E. L., Rosenzweig, M. R., Krech, D., Ohlander, A., and Morimoto, H. Cholinesterase activity and protein content of rat brain. J. Neurochem., *6:* 210, 1961.

Bueno, J. R., Pscheidt, G. R., and Himwich, H. E. Hyperactivity and EEG altering with increase of brain serotonin. Trans. Amer. Neurol. Ass., *14:* 129, 1966.

Carter, C. H., editor. *Medical Aspects of Mental Retardation.* Charles C Thomas, Springfield, Ill., 1965.

Crossland, J., Elliott, K. A. C., and Pappius, H. M. Acetylcholine content of brain during insulin hypoglycemia. Amer. J. Physiol., *183:* 32, 1955.

Davison. A. N., and Wajda, M. Cerebral lipids in multiple sclerosis. J. Neurochem., *9:* 427, 1962.

Dobbing, J. The blood-brain barrier: some recent developments. Guy Hosp. Rep., *112*: 267, 1963.

Edström, R. Recent developments of the blood-brain barrier concept. Int. Rev. Neurobiol., *4*: 153, 1962.

Edström, R. F. S., and Essex, H. E. Swelling of the brain induced by anoxia. Neurology, *6*: 118, 1956.

Flexner, L. B., Flexner, J. B., De La Haba, G., and Roberts, D. B. Loss of memory as related to inhibition of cerebral protein synthesis. J. Neurochem., *12*: 535, 1965.

Friede, R., and Fleming, L. M. A mapping of oxidative enzymes in the human brain. J. Neurochem., *9*: 179, 1962.

Friedhoff, A., and Van Winkle, E. The characteristics of an amine found in the urine of schizophrenic patients. J. Nerv. Ment. Dis., *135*: 550, 1962.

Guroff, G., and Udenfriend, S. The uptake of aromatic amino acids by the brain of mature and newborn rats. In *Progress in Brain Research*, W. A. Himwich and H. E. Himwich, editors, vol. 9, p. 187. Elsevier, New York, 1964.

Herschkowitz, N., MacGillivray, B. B., and Cumings, J. N. Biochemical and electrophysiological studies in experimental cerebral oedema. Brain, *88*: 557, 1965.

Himwich, H. E. Carbohydrate metabolism in mental disease. In *Chemical Pathology of the Nervous System*, J. Folch-Pi, editor, p. 470. Pergamon Press, London, 1961.

Himwich, H. E., and Himwich, W. A. Anoxia and cerebral metabolism. Int. J. Neurol., *3*: 413, 1962.

Hoagland, H., Pennell, R. B., Bergen, J. R., Saravis, C. A., Freeman, H., and Koella, W. Studies of plasma protein factors that may be involved in psychoses. In *Recent Advances in Biological Psychiatry*, J. Wortis, editor, vol. 4, p. 329. Plenum Press, New York, 1962.

Hornykiewicz, O. The distribution and metabolism of catecholamines and 5-hydroxytryptamine in human brain. In *Comparative Neurochemistry; Proceedings of the 5th International Neurochemical Symposium*, p. 10. Hafner, Wolsgang, Austria, 1964.

Hydén, H. Biochemical and functional interplay between neuron and glia. In *Recent Advances in Biological Psychiatry*, J. Wortis, editor, vol. 6, p. 31. Plenum Press, New York, 1964.

Jasper, H. H., Khan, R. T., and Elliot, K. A. C. Amino acids released from the cerebral cortex in relation to its state of activation. Science, *147*: 1448, 1965.

Kety, S. S. Blood flow and metabolism of the human brain in health and disease. In *Neurochemistry*, ed. 2. K. A. C. Elliott, I. H. Page, and J. H. Quastel, editors, p. 113. Charles C Thomas, Springfield, Ill., 1962.

Kety, S. S., and Schmidt, C. F. The nitrous oxide method for the quantitative determination of cerebral blood flow in man: theory, procedure and normal values. J. Clin. Invest., *27*: 476, 1948.

Kety, S. S., and Schmidt, C. F. The effects of altered arterial tensions of carbon dioxide and oxygen on cerebral blood flow and cerebral oxygen consumption of normal young men. J. Clin. Invest., *27*: 484, 1948.

Klein, J. R., and Olsen, N. S. Effect of convulsive activity upon the concentration of brain glucose, glycogen, lactate and phosphates. J. Biol. Chem., *167*: 747, 1947.

Kling, A., Finer, S., and Nair, V. Effects of early handling and light stimulation on the acetylcholinesterase activity of the developing rat brain. Int. J. Neuropharmacol., *4*: 353, 1965.

Korey, S. R., Gonatas, J., and Stein, A. Studies in Tay-Sachs disease. III. Biochemistry: A. Analytic and metabolic aspects. J. Neuropath. Exp. Neurol., *22*: 56, 1966.

Lajtha, A., Lahiri, S., and Toth, J. The brain barrier system. IV. Cerebral amino acid uptake in different classes. J. Neurochem., 10: 765, 1963.

Leistyna, J. A. Lipid storage disorders of the central nervous system. Amer. J. Dis. Child., 104: 680, 1962.

Levine, S., and Alpert, M. Differential maturation of the central nervous system as a function of early experience. Arch. Gen. Psychiat., 1: 403, 1959.

Maynard, E. A., Schultz, R. L., and Pease, D. C. Electron microscopy of the vascular bed of rat cerebral cortex. Amer. J. Anat., 100: 409, 1957.

Mendiguita, R. C., and Lerma Penasco, J. L. *Psicofarmacologia de la Depression*, Paz Montalvo, Madrid, 1964.

Millichap, J. G. Development of seizure patterns in newborn animals. Significance of brain carbonic anhydrase. Proc. Soc. Exp. Biol. Med., 96: 125, 1957.

Naruse, H., Kato, M., Kurokawa, M., Haba, R., and Yabe, T. Metabolic defects in a convulsive strain of mouse. J. Neurochem., 5: 359, 1960.

O'Brien, J. S., Fillerup, D. L., and Mead, J. F. Brain lipids: I. Quantification and fatty acid composition of cerebroside sulfate in human cerebral gray and white matter. J. Lipid Res., 5: 109, 1964.

Osmond, H., and Smythies, J. R. Schizophrenia: a new approach. J. Ment. Sci., 98: 309, 1952.

Pappius, H. M., and Gulati, D. R. Water and electrolyte content of cerebral tissues in experimentally induced edema. Acta Neuropath., 2: 451, 1963.

Pollin, W., Cardon, P. V., and Kety, S. S. Effects of amino acid feeding in schizophrenic patients treated with iproniazid. Science, 133: 104, 1961.

Radin, N. S., and Akahori, Y. Fatty acids of human brain cerebrosides. J. Lipid Res., 2: 335, 1961.

Robinson, R. J., and Tizard, J. P. M. The central nervous system in the newborn. Brit. Med. Bull., 22: 49, 1966.

Rosenzweig, M. R., Krech, D., and Bennett, L. A search for relations between brain chemistry and behavior. Psychol. Bull., 57: 476, 1960.

Rossiter, R. J. Chemical constituents of brain and nerve. In *Neurochemistry*, ed. 2., K. A. C. Elliott, I. H. Page, and J. H. Quastel, editors, p. 10. Charles C Thomas, Springfield, Ill., 1963.

Schildkraut, J. J. The catecholamine hypothesis of affective disorders: a review of supporting evidence. Amer. J. Psychiat., 122: 509, 1965.

Smythies, J. R. *Schizophrenia*. Charles C Thomas, Springfield, Ill., 1963.

Spiro, H. R., Schimke, R. N., and Welch, J. P. Schizophrenia in a patient with a defect in methionine metabolism. J. Nerv. Ment. Dis., 141: 385, 1965.

Stallberg-Stenhagen, S., and Svennerholm, L. Fatty acid composition of human brain sphingomyelins: normal variation with age and changes during myelin disorders. J. Lipid Res., 6: 146, 1965.

Svennerholm, L. Lipidoses. In *Metabolism and Physiological Significance of Lipids*, R. M. C. Dawson and D. N. Rhodes, editors, p. 553. Wiley, New York, 1964.

Tanimukai, H., Inui, M., Hariguchi, S., and Kaneko, Z. Antiepileptic property of inhibitors of carbonic anhydrase. Biochem. Pharmacol., 14: 961, 1965.

Tews, J. K., and Stone, W. E. Free amino acids and related compounds in brain and other tissues: effects of convulsant drugs. In *Progress in Brain Research*, W. A. Himwich and J. P. Schadé, editors, vol. 16, p. 135. Elsevier, New York, 1965.

Tower, D. B. Nature and extent of the biochemical lesion in human epileptogenic cerebral cortex: an approach to its control *in vitro* and *in vivo*. Neurology, 5: 113, 1955.

Ungar, G., and Oceguera-Navarro, C. Transfer of habituation by material extracted from brain. Nature, 207: 301, 1965.

Weichert, P., and Herbst, A. Provocation of cerebral seizures by derangement of the natural balance between glutamic acid and gamma-aminobutyric acid.

J. Neurochem., 13: 59, 1966.

Woodbury, D. M., Koch, A., and Vernadakis, A. Relation between excitability and metabolism in brain as elucidated by anticonvulsant drugs. Neurology, 8: Suppl. 1, p. 113, 1958.

Woolley, D. W. *Biochemical Bases of Psychoses or the Serotonin Hypothesis about Mental Disease.* Wiley, New York, 1962.

Yannet, H. Changes in the brain resulting from depletion of extracellular electrolytes. Amer. J. Physiol., 128: 683, 1939–1940.

CHAPTER 3

Psychopharmacology

HAROLD E. HIMWICH, M.D.

INTRODUCTION

In this chapter the ameliorative effects of psychotropic drugs on the behavior of patients with disturbed mental functioning is discussed. These drug-induced changes in behavior are related to associated neurophysiological, neuropharmacological, and neurochemical changes. The actions of psychotomimetic agents receive a similar analysis.

The effects of drugs on human patients must be determined by observations made on man. However, electroencephalographic reactions in the structures of the limbic system must be ascertained by deep electrode implantation, and such applications on human beings are necessarily limited in number. Because it is difficult to obtain extirpations of human brain areas performed in order to explain biochemical changes induced by drugs during life, areas sensitive to psychotropic drugs have been analyzed in animal experiments. The results in infrahuman mammals cannot be extrapolated to man because differences in species may yield different results. But animal observations are suggestive in many instances. For example, a sufficient number of studies on members of many mammalian species, including man, have been performed to know that reserpine decreases brain amines in all mammals. This does not suggest a causal relationship between the brain changes produced by drugs in animals or man and the associated behavioral alterations in patients. It does, however, point out analogies between the specific effects of psychotropic drugs on the animal and human brain and the broader behavioral changes observed in patients —for example, whether the two different parameters indicate tendencies toward tranquilization. One may well take a pragmatic attitude toward the effects of drugs on patients with mental disease and compare the therapeutic values of psychotropic drugs with preparations for the control of diabetes, their dosage schedules revised in accordance with the severity of the symptoms. One need not go into the various debates as to whether psychotropic drugs cure the psychotic process or are chiefly of placebo value. The observed facts disclose the great symptomatic relief afforded to patients.

But what of the future? It is well known that, generally, the longer the patient stays in the hospital, the worse the prognosis. It would seem that the most optimistic attack on schizophrenia is the early application of psychotropic drugs to the patient in the hospital and rapid discharge to the outpatient clinic for continued chemotherapeutic supervision.

DRUGS USED IN THE TREATMENT OF SCHIZOPHRENIA
RESERPINE

This drug, one of the two original tranquilizers, is now to a certain extent replaced by the phenothiazines. Reserpine is recommended, however, in intensifying the action of antihypertensive agents and in the management of overactive, brain-injured children.

Action. Reserpine subserves an important neuropsychopharmacological action: It prevents the binding of noncholinergeric transmitters—for example, monoamines such as norepinephrine—to labile storage depots in intracellular granules. As a result of reserpine, the monoamines are not stored in the intracellular granules, and the concentrations of free neurotransmitters are temporarily increased. But as they are no longer protected from the action of the monoamine oxidase (MAO) enzyme, the neurotransmitters are rapidly metabolized, and the enduring effect of reserpine is to reduce the concentrations of free neurotransmitters.

These two different effects of reserpine on the concentrations of brain neurotransmitters are paralleled by biphasic actions on the electroencephalogram (EEG) and on behavior. About half an hour after the injection of a single intravenous dose of reserpine large enough to cause depletion of serotonin and norepinephrine in the brain (1 mg. per kilogram), the EEG begins to reveal activation (see Figure 1). But about four to five hours after the injection, a long-continued sleep pattern appears (see Figure 1*B*). The initial period of EEG alerting corresponds closely to the time interval during which free monoamines are increased as the stores in the granules are diminished by the action of the reserpine. The sleep pattern occurs when the concentrations of the monoamines decrease.

When reserpine is first administered to patients, it may produce a period of worsening in the psychotic symptoms, a period of turbulence that is usually more marked and longer than that evoked by the phenothiazine derivatives. It is not unlikely that the short period of the activation of the psychotic symptoms corresponds with the time when brain amines are increased above the usual levels and that the tranquilizing action is associated with the long-continued low levels of brain amines.

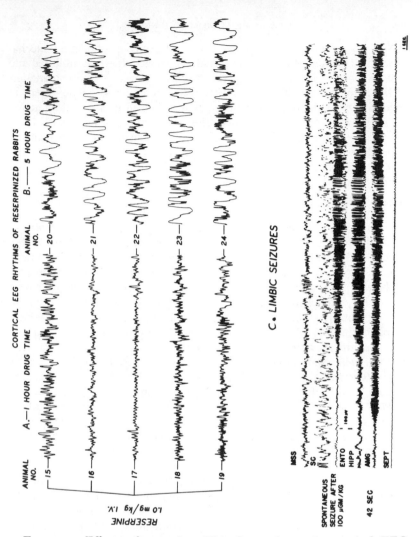

FIGURE 1. Effects of reserpine. This figure shows the cortical EEG tracings from 13 animals injected with reserpine (1.0 mg. per kilogram) before surgical preparation. Note the presence of EEG activation at one hour (A) and its absence at five hours (B). Electroencephalographic tracings were also recorded after the administration of 0.1 mg. of reserpine per kilogram (C). Note the spontaneous seizures of limbic structures. Recording leads are as follows: MSS, median suprasylvian gyrus; SC, sensory cortex; ENTO, entorhinal cortex; HIPP, hippocampus; AMG, amygdala; SEPT, septum. (A and B are unpublished observations. C is from Killam, E. K., and Killam, K. F. The influence of drugs on central afferent pathways. In *Brain Mechanisms and Drug Actions*, W. S. Fields, editor, p. 88. Charles C Thomas, Springfield, Ill., 1957.)

Site of action. The actions of reserpine on hypothalamic mechanisms are complex. It is true that noradrenergic activities are inhibited and that cholinergic activities are augmented, as observed in the constriction of the pupil and the bradycardia. One reason reserpine is not so potent in tranquilizing as the phenothiazines may be found in its stimulating action on limbic structures, which may exhibit spontaneous seizures with reserpine (see Figure 1C). The total effect of any medicament on behavior depends, of course, on the summation of all its influences on the brain, and with reserpine the result is less influential in the direction of tranquilization than with the phenothiazines.

Phenothiazines

The phenothiazine derivatives constitute the largest group of psychotropic drugs. From the clinical viewpoint there are important quantitative differences between their actions, but the qualitative similarities of the various phenothiazines facilitate their discussion as a group. Some important phenothiazine derivatives are chlorpromazine (Thorazine), triflupromazine (Vesprin), promazine (Sparine), methoxypromazine (Tentone), mepazine (Pacatal), piperacetazine (Quide), prochlorperazine (Compazine), perphenazine (Trilafon), trifluoperazine (Stelazine), fluphenazine (Prolixin, Permitil), acetophenazine (Tindal), carphenazine (Proketazine), and butyrylperazine (Repoise). They act on the mesodiencephalic activating system, including its caudal and rostral components; the reticular formation; and the diffuse thalamocortical projections.

Mesodiencephalic activating system. An important component of the mesodiencephalic activating system as a whole is cholinergic in function; and atropine, for example, can block EEG arousal caused by practically any kind of stimulus. These inhibiting effects occur because the rostral component of the mesodiencephalic activating system, arising in the diffuse thalamocortical nuclei with their thalamocortical projections, is cholinergic in part. On the other hand, the caudal portion, the reticular formation, responds to adrenergic stimuli. This response is probably not a direct action but is due to the effects of epinephrine and epinephrinelike substances on afferent collaterals to the reticular formation. The integrated activity of the caudal and rostral components are responsible for the EEG-alerting reactions. The blocking effect of phenothiazines on the EEG is in accordance with their cholinolytic action, even though it is much weaker than that of atropine. Figure 2 presents an example of the prevention of EEG arousal with a single dose of chlorpromazine. This blocking action may provide a basis for the alleviation of the distressing emotional cloak that surrounds noxious stimuli. It is well known that patients bear pain with less difficulty under phenothiazine therapy than without one of these drugs.

Reticular formation. Phenothiazine tranquilization also correlates with depression of the hypothalamus and midbrain reticular formation,

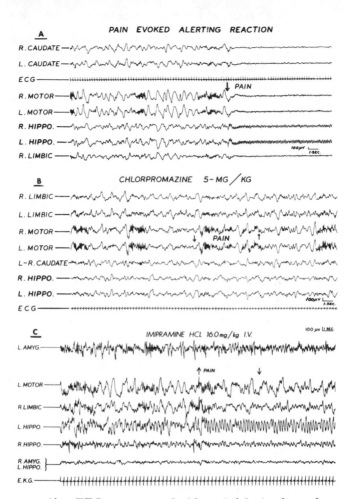

FIGURE 2. Alert EEG patterns evoked by painful stimulus and prevented by chlorpromazine and imipramine. A, bilateral leads taken from various cerebral structures as indicated: on *right side*, electroencephalographic control pattern of resting rabbit; on *left side*, the effects of pinching rabbit's leg. B, change produced by chlorpromazine (5 mg. per kilogram) in electroencephalographic pattern in response to pain. Note the absence of the alerting reaction to pain. C, effects of imipramine HCl on EEG arousal after peripheral pain stimulation. Note that the EEG arousal response to pain stimulation is blocked after the administration of imipramine HCl, 16 mg. per kilogram. (From Himwich, H. E. Anatomy and physiology of the emotions and their relation to psychoactive drugs. In *Scientific Basis of Drug Therapy in Psychiatry*, Proceedings of Symposium at St. Bartholomew's Hospital, London, September 7 and 8, 1964, pp. 3–24. Pergamon Press, London, 1965.)

areas containing relatively high concentrations of monoamine neurotransmitters, whose actions are inhibited by members of this group of drugs. This hypothalamic depression is attributed to an inhibiting effect on the α-adrenergic blocking action by chlorpromazine, thus preventing the response of the postsynaptic receptor to the monoamine neurotransmitter (see Figure 4). As the blood-brain barrier is permeable to the phenothiazines, there is no reason to doubt their penetration into the hypothalamus. In addition, it has been found that the phenothiazines reduce to some degree the excitability of the extrahypothalamic limbic structures. Therefore, the tranquilization produced by the phenothiazines seems to be associated with indirect influences on the hypothalamus and direct blocking action that prevents the reaction between the receptor sites and the monoamine neurotransmitters, norepinephrine and serotonin. Clinically, tranquilization is not specific in the treatment of schizophrenia; the drugs tranquilize irrespective of the diagnostic category and also relax people without mental disorders.

Thalamocortical projections. It is another question entirely to explain how hallucinations and delusions of schizophrenic patients are mitigated or eliminated by the phenothiazines. Because false sensory interpretations and unrealistic thinking in schizophrenic patients are favorably influenced, the therapeutic actions necessarily seem to involve neocortical functions. Because of the Papez circuit and similar reverberating feedbacks that involve both neocortical and limbic areas, the effect of the phenothiazines on the older brain parts may be indirectly brought to bear on functions allocated chiefly to the neocortex. Because of the drug-induced diminished intensity of the emotional reactions and the resulting decrease of anxiety, the defenses are no longer maintained.

HALOPERIDOL (HALDOL)

This drug, a butyrophenone, acts in many ways like a phenothiazine; small doses inhibit the mesodiencephalic activating system, probably in its rostral component. Larger doses, however, evoke EEG alert patterns. Clinically, the butyrophenone is more potent than the phenothiazines in general, but severe extrapyramidal disturbances are also exhibited with it, especially in excessive dosages. In observations on rabbit brain, smaller doses were required for the butyrophenone to block EEG arousal and evoke EEG alerting than were necessary for the phenothiazines. Similarly, both chlorpromazine and haloperidol enhance the accumulations of norepinephrine and catecholamine metabolites produced by the monoamine oxidase inhibitors in the brain.

DRUGS USED IN THE TREATMENT OF DEPRESSION

IMINODIBENZYLS

These antidepressant drugs, the psychostimulants or thymoleptics, are employed best in the management of psychotic depression of endogenous origin: melancholia and the depressive phase of the manic-depressive psychosis. The iminodibenzyl derivatives, initiated with the use of imipramine (Tofranil), soon included amitriptyline (Elavil), desmethylimipramine (Pertofrane and Norpramin), and opipramol (Ensidon). Two somewhat different chemical forms of desmethylamitriptyline (Nortriptyline and Vivactil) were also developed. The antidepressant effects of these drugs seem specific against endogenous depressions, and the stimulating actions on behavior of other kinds of depression and of nondepressed individuals are neither as marked nor as constant.

Monoamine Oxidase Inhibitors

These antidepressant drugs, the psychic energizers, secure their most favorable effects in atypical depressions in which either anxiety or hysteroid features are predominant. The monoamine oxidase inhibitors started with iproniazid (Marsilid) and now include isocarboxazid (Marplan), nialamide (Niamid), phenelzine (Nardil), and reversible ones like tranylcypromine (Parnate). Their therapeutic actions cannot be regarded as specific, for they exert euphorizing effects in individuals who are not depressed. The side reactions of the monoamine oxidase inhibitors are more dangerous and occur more frequently than those of the iminodibenzyls, but the untoward result can usually be prevented by lower dosages and appropriate medical treatment.

Phenothiazines

These drugs may exert antidepressant effects in addition to the tranquilization for which they are noted. Overall and his colleagues observed a paradoxical clinical result, a lifting of depression, with the phenothiazine thioridazine (Mellaril). A group of patients were selected on a basis of having depression as the major symptom, regardless of whether the psychiatric diagnoses fitted the usual depressive syndromes. Comparing the results of thioridazine with those of imipramine on these depressed patients, they found that there were essentially no significant differences in the salutary effects of these two drugs on the depressed patients.

Comparisons of the Drugs

A study of the EEG in animals reveals that under certain conditions the members of all three groups of drugs with clinical antidepressant actions may evoke EEG alerting. It is possible that this alerting may be associated with the antidepressant clinical effects of the iminodibenzyls as well as of the phenothiazines. In regard to tranylcypromine (Parnate), this monoamine oxidase inhibitor administered in 2 mg. per kilogram doses (see Figure 3C) twice in two hours evoked EEG alerting.

The phenothiazines and the iminodibenzyls have a common basis for their ability to evoke EEG alerting. In contrast to the blocking effects of the acute administration of phenothiazines or iminodibenzyls, EEG arousal results (see Figure 2) if the same dosage is given chronically, day

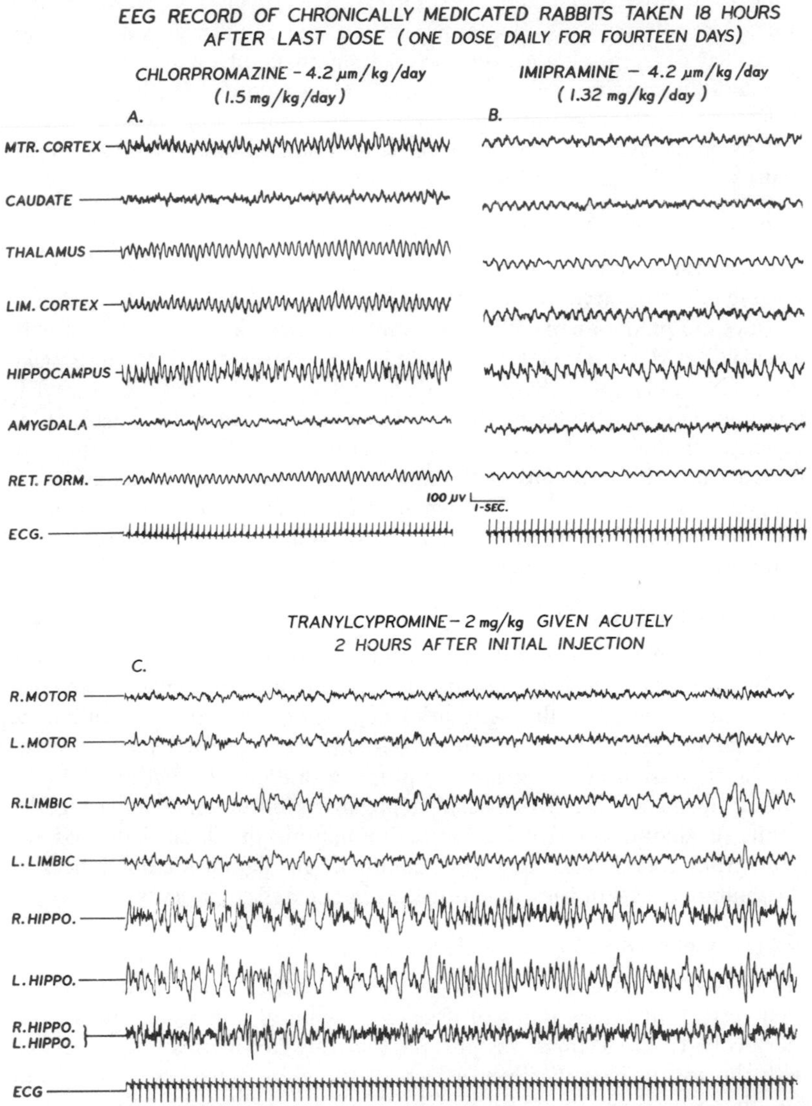

FIGURE 3. Effects of chlorpromazine, imipramine, and tranylcypromine. Spontaneous EEG activation resulted from chronic medication with chlorpromazine (A), imipramine (B), and tranylcypromine (Parnate) (C). (From Himwich, H. E. Loci of action of psychotropic drugs in the brain. Fol. Psychiat. Neurol. Jap., 19: 217, 1965.)

after day. Studies on chronic administration were made with four pheno-thiazines—chlorpromazine, triflupromazine, perphenazine, and trifluopera-zine—and two iminodibenzyls—amitriptyline and imipramine. EEG trac-ings were recorded eighteen hours after the last chronic dosage, and activated patterns were observed in the absence of any apparent stimula-tion. In most instances on the sixth day of chronic medication and in all animals at nine days, the EEG pattern exhibited increased spontaneous alerting. The percentage duration of alerting on these animals was greater than the percentage duration of alerting in unpremedicated animals. This EEG alerting reaction is not one of paradoxical sleep but is, rather, asso-ciated with wakefulness. Thus, in Figure 3 the effect of the chronic admin-istration of chlorpromazine (A) and imipramine (B) observed eighteen hours after the last dose revealed alerting.

The mechanism of action of the changes produced by chronic adminis-tration involves, among other factors, drug storage, especially in brain tis-sue, and the more rapid rate of metabolism of the drugs by increased amounts of the drug-metabolizing enzymes. These enzymes are contained in the microsomes, and the increased concentration of microsomes occur-ring with chronic dosage is referred to as enzyme induction. Enzyme induction, leading to a more rapid detoxication of the drugs, has been ob-served for various chemical agents and may also apply to the phenothia-zines and iminodibenzyls. Irrespective of the processes involved, the mem-bers of these three groups of drugs, when given chronically, all have the ability to facilitate the stimulating effects of EEG alerting.

Only the monoamine oxidase inhibitors have the power to elevate sig-nificantly the levels of brain neurohormones. But there are also differences between the phenothiazines and iminodibenzyls. In some ways the imino-dibenzyls exhibit stimulating effects not shared to any great extent by the phenothiazines. In contrast to the phenothiazines, six of the seven imino-dibenzyls studied evoked spikelike activity in the subcortical structures, particularly the olfactory bulb.

PSYCHOTROPIC DRUGS AND CELLULAR METABOLISM

To understand the clinical effects of these drugs, one might consider their pharmacological actions at the cellular level. Imipramine and chlorproma-zine have different effects on peripheral actions, as exhibited by changes in the degree of contractility of the nictitating membrane of the cat, whether produced by the direct stimulation of the cervical sympathetic nerve or by the injection of serotonin, norepinephrine, or epinephrine. Imipramine, as an example of the iminodibenzyls, increased the contraction of the nictita-ting membrane evoked by the injections of the neurohormones or by elec-trical stimulation. In contrast, chlorpromazine diminished these contrac-tions.

These different peripheral actions of chlorpromazine and imipramine are strikingly reminiscent of their chief behavioral effects—tranquilization by the phenothiazines and antidepression by the iminodibenzyls. Axelrod has shown that both groups of drugs inhibit the uptake of injected neurotransmitters and the return of the endogenously liberated norepinephrine to the sympathetic nerve endings. Thus, both groups of drugs prolong and intensify the effects of the neurotransmitters at receptor sites. This action to prevent the return of the monoamine to the presynaptic neuron is exerted on the neuronal membrane. Just as intracellular granules take up amines from the cell cytoplasm, so do cellular membranes take up amines into the cell from the extracellular spaces. Both chlorpromazine and imipramine inhibit this uptake from extracellular spaces, just as reserpine inhibits the uptake in the granules from the cell sap.

Chlorpromazine and imipramine also share another characteristic in common: They block receptor sites. Both drugs are α-adrenergic blockers and may thus prevent the stimulating effect of the neurotransmitter on the effector neuron. Both chlorpromazine and imipramine share α-blocking actions, and both drugs prevent the uptake of norepinephrine from the extracellular space. In the experiments on the cat, the α-adrenergic blocking effect is prepotent because the contractility of the nictitating membrane is reduced. On the other hand, with imipramine, the balance between the two actions is in favor of the blocking effect on the cell membrane, as revealed by the increased contractility. Perhaps this action—increasing the concentration of the adrenergic neurotransmitter at the receptor site—is responsible for antidepressant effects of this drug.

Figure 4 presents, in schematic form, a site of action of a representative of each of four groups of psychotropic drugs. Reserpine and the monoamine oxidase inhibitor evoke opposite effects. Reserpine diminishes the concentrations of the monoamines by preventing their incorporation into the labile fraction and thus exposes them to the monoamine oxidase enzyme. In contrast, the monoamine oxidase inhibitor increases neurotransmitter concentrations and, therefore, makes larger amounts of the free neurotransmitter available to react with the receptor site. Insofar as the pharmacological action at receptor sites is concerned, reserpine produces the same final effect as chlorpromazine, and the monoamine oxidase inhibitor evokes an action similar to that of imipramine.

The antidepressant ability of thioridazine, a phenothiazine, has been noted. Other observations have shown that imipramine, an iminodibenzyl, may act as a tranquilizer or antidepressant. Neuropsychopharmacological analysis discloses that they both exhibit complex behavioral actions. Perhaps these multifaceted behavioral actions, aiding in the management of the varying symptoms observed in psychotic patients, account for the clinical success of the phenothiazines on one hand and the iminodibenzyls on the other.

Unfortunately, the causes of the psychoses have not been elucidated. Therefore, direct therapy against the origins of these diseases cannot be

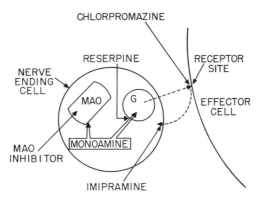

FIGURE 4. Principal sites of action and representatives of four groups of psychotropic drugs. This figure includes the schematic representation of a cell in a sympathetic nerve ending, an effector organ, and the gap between these two structures, through which the monoamine neurotransmitter, released from the nerve ending by a nerve impulse, finds its way to the receptor site and thus stimulates the effector organ. The structure of the mitochondrion is intimately bound with the monoamine oxidase activity of that enzyme. Monoamines are stored in granules (G) in a labile form. The monoamine liberated from the labile fraction may be utilized in four ways: (1) incorporated into a stable form, (2) released, after the nerve impulse, into the gap (*straight dotted line*), (3) reenter the nerve ending (*curved dotted line*), or (4) oxidized inside the cell by the MAO enzymes. (Published with permission of Arvid Carlsson. From Himwich, H. E. Loci of action of psychotropic drugs in the brain. Fol. Psychiat. Neurol. Jap., 19: 217, 1965.)

instituted. Experiences with the psychotropic drugs, however, indicate that patients with apparently similar clinical syndromes and the same diagnoses do not react the same way to a given drug. These patients may suffer from different chemical pathologies. Indeed, the Russian psychiatrist A. B. Snezhnevski has classified mental diseases in accordance with the reactions of the patients to various pychotropic drugs.

In this regard, the genetic background of the patients must be taken into consideration in order to explain why, when a depression of one member of a family is benefited either by an iminodibenzyl or by a monoamine oxidase inhibitor, another member of the family, when suffering from depression, is also likely to show salutary results with the same drug. A genetic explanation may also explain the different clinical results with use of butyrylperazine on patients in Germany and the United States. In America the results were poorer, despite the higher dosage required. Still another confusing phenomenon in the understanding of patients is that the same disease may have different modes of expression in people belonging to different cultures.

MINOR TRANQUILIZERS USED IN THE TREATMENT OF NEUROSES

For patients with grave forms of the neuroses, the same drugs are used as for patients with psychoses—namely, the major tranquilizers—but not for the same reason. In neuroses, the psychotropic drugs are given for the general calming action, an antianxiety effect, rather than as specifics. Nevertheless, in the milder forms of neuroses, including neurotic or reactive depressions, the minor tranquilizers bring strong adjunctive support to psychotherapy. By diminishing anxiety and tension, they help tide the patient over particularly bad periods, characterized by disabling anxiety, that may occur during psychotherapy. They may also be administered to overcome anxiety throughout the course of psychotherapy.

CHLORDIAZEPOXIDE (LIBRIUM)

In usual doses, chlordiazepoxide and the related diazepam (Valium) possess valuable assets in the amelioration of anxiety, whether or not associated with somatic complaints. Thiazenone and oxazepam (Serax) are similar medicaments. One action of these drugs, accounting for the antianxiety effect, is a polysynaptic depression, which releases muscular spasms and thus indirectly diminishes the muscular tension brought on by anxiety. In antispasmodic activity, diazepam is superior to chlordiazepoxide. Both drugs exert weak or no effects on the neocortex and neurotransmitter depots, but their antianxiety action seems to parallel their depressant influences on limbic structures—the septum, amygdala, and hippocampus. Such a depression may simulate to a certain degree the tranquilization observed with animals subjected to extirpations of these structures.

In experiments in which the amygdala was stimulated and evoked potentials taken off the hippocampus (see Figure 5), the administration of chlordiazepoxide or diazepam reduced the hippocampal responses. It is known that the amygdala and hippocampus may exert facilitatory influences upon behavior, and the elimination of such stimulation is produced by extirpation of these areas. A similar reduction of the sensitivity brought about by the depressant effects of chlordiazepoxide and diazepam may diminish the reactions to stressful influences, thus ameliorating anxiety. Such a desirable clinical response also parallels the ability of these drugs to inhibit, to a moderate degree, the alerting reaction to stimuli.

MEPROBAMATE (MILTOWN, EQUANIL)

Meprobamate calms the tense and nervous depressed patient, so frequently seen in general practice, and is also used to allay the anxiety occurring with neurotic depressions and depressed moods of exogenous or

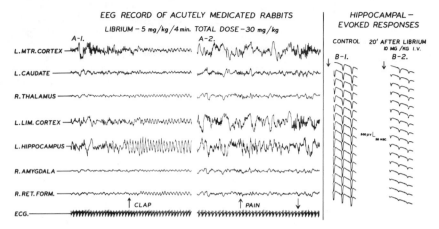

FIGURE 5. Effects of chlordiazepoxide (Librium) on spontaneous EEG recordings and evoked hippocampal responses after stimulation of the amygdala. A-1, control EEG, revealing the change from an alerting to a resting pattern (A-2), as the effect of the painful stimulus on EEG alerting is blocked by the administration of chlordiazepoxide. B-1, hippocampal responses to single shocks and repetitive stimulation of lateral nucleus of the amygdala. B-2, response to repetitive stimulation 20 minutes after intravenous injection of 10 mg. of chlordiazepoxide per kilogram. Note gradual impairment of evoked response. (From Himwich, H. E. Loci of actions of psychotropic drugs in the brain. Fol. Psychiat. Neurol. Jap., 19: 217, 1965.)

reactive origin. In usual doses this drug does not significantly influence the discriminative functions of the neocortex or those of either component of the mesodiencephalic activating system to affect EEG patterns. Neurotransmitter depots, moreover, are not altered.

On the other hand, meprobamate exerts potent effects on some limbic structures. In rats, meprobamate sets aside the irritability and savagery on tactile stimulation after the surgical production of septal lesions. Similarly, meprobamate has been found effective in rendering the hippocampus less sensitive to stimuli, as the after-discharge after electrical stimulation of that structure is first reduced and finally eliminated (see Figure 6). This reduction of hippocampal activity may bring on an attendant diminution of anxiety.

BARBITURATES

The superior effect of the psychotropic drugs, in comparison with the barbiturates, in the treatment of psychotic patients depends on the more specifically directed actions of the major tranquilizers. Vitro results on

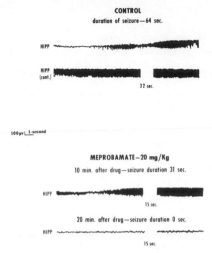

CONTROL
duration of seizure—64 sec.

HIPP

HIPP
(cont.)
32 sec.

100 μv⌐ 1-second

MEPROBAMATE—20 mg/Kg
10 min. after drug—seizure duration 31 sec.

HIPP
15 sec.

20 min. after drug—seizure duration 0 sec.

HIPP
15 sec.

FIGURE 6. Effect of meprobamate. It shortens duration of after-discharge produced in the hippocampus by local electrical stimulation. Control record prior to drug administration is presented as well as records made 10 and 20 minutes after administration of meprobamate. Each tracing begins at the end of a stimulation period. (From Kletzkin, M., and Berger, F. M. Effect of meprobamate on limbic system of the brain. Proc. Soc. Exper. Biol. Med., *100:* 631, 1959.)

brain tissue reveal that the most profound metabolic depression produced by pentobarbital is observed on the neocortex rather than on the subcortical areas. Similarly, in vivo, the barbiturates preferentially depress the primary sensory neocortical areas, a decrease associated with the deeper depression of neocortical metabolism. Further evidence is afforded by comparative studies of the distribution of the phenothiazines and the barbiturates in the brain. Chlorpromazine is concentrated in the neocortex to a lesser extent than in subcortical structures: hypothalamus, hippocampus, amygdala, midbrain, and medulla. In addition, chlorpromazine is found in high concentrations in the basal ganglia, thalamus, and pons. In contrast, barbiturates exhibit a nearly equal distribution in all parts of the brain.

In experimental studies of behavior, the barbiturates are less specific and extinguish both the conditioned and the unconditioned reflex responses with approximately similar dosages. The phenothiazines depress the conditioned reflex at levels significantly lower than those required for the unconditioned reflex. Thus, the barbiturates possess the more generalized actions exerted in all parts of the brain. Functionally important is the power of the barbiturates to depress significantly the mesodiencephalic activating system due to a direct action on its caudad component, the reticular formation. These drugs, therefore, block the EEG as seen in Figure 7, and the behavioral elements of arousal, both of which are medi-

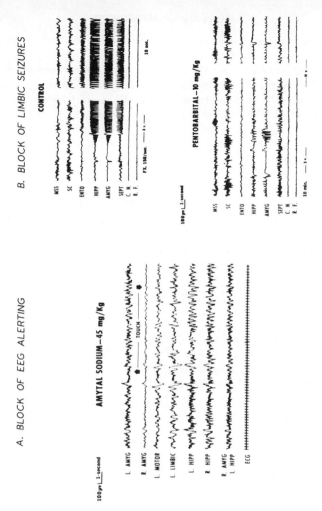

FIGURE 7. Blocking action of drugs. A, EEG alerting in response to touch is entirely eliminated by sodium Amytal as the reticular formation is inhibited. B, limbic-lobe seizures resulting from stimulation of the fornix were eliminated by pentobarbital. The blockng actions of pentobarbital on seizures were confined to the limbic lobe. Recordings were taken from median suprasylvian (MSS), sensory cortex (SC), entorhinal cortex (ENTO), hippocampus (HIPP), amygdala (AMYG), septum (SEPT), caudate nucleus (CN), and reticular formation of the mesencephalon (RF). (A, From Himwich, H. E. Tranquilizers, barbiturates and the brain. J. Neuropsychiat., 3: 279, 1962. B, From Killam, E. K., and Killam, K. F. The influence of drugs on central afferent pathways. In *Brain Mechanisms and Drug Actions*, W. S. Fields, editor, p. 71. Charles C Thomas, Springfield, Ill., 1957.)

ated in part by the midbrain reticular formation. Thus, behavioral re-
ponses to stimuli are diminished.

The barbiturates increase the neurohormonal stores moderately. This
increase, however, is secondary to central depression. Moreover, they directly diminish the excitability of the hypothalamic functions, including
the center for wakefulness. In addition, the limbic structures feeding into
the hypothalamus are rendered less sensitive to stimuli (see Figure 6). All
these depressant actions present possible sources of the sedative-hypnotic
powers of the barbiturates.

An even more significant difference between the tranquilizers in general
and the barbiturates as a group is that the barbiturates exert more widespread influences on the brain, including the neocortical areas, which are
associated with the so-called higher functions of the mind. For this reason,
the barbiturates interfere with therapeutic processes that require understanding and cooperation, especially important with neurotic patients. In
addition, in large doses, sometimes taken with suicidal intent, they present
the danger of death due to respiratory failure.

Thus, the more powerful psychotropic agents, especially the phenothiazines and the iminodibenzyls, used in the treatment of psychoses, exert
various actions at many sites, particularly on the structures forming the
limbic cortex, a broad and varied base. This situation is analogous to the
complex behavioral effects of these drugs and their successes in the management of the varied symptoms of psychotic patients. Moreover, the
clinical effects seem to be specific against such psychotic manifestations as
hallucinations and delusions. The minor tranquilizers, on the other hand,
are found to act in comparatively fewer limbic areas and to assume an
adjunctive role in the treatment of the neuroses, chiefly by their amelioration of the anxiety associated with the neurotic processes.

The more potent major tranquilizers, used in the treatment of the psychoses, also present stronger and more frequent side reactions. The minor
tranquilizers, employed with neurotic patients, exhibit fewer and milder
side effects.

When the psychotropic drugs as a group are compared with the barbiturates, both at the basic and clinical levels, it is seen that the actions of
the psychotropic group are more specifically directed in the treatment of
mentally disturbed patients than those of the barbiturates.

HALLUCINOGENS

MANIFESTATIONS

Catechol and indole groups. The actions of psychotomimetic drugs
belonging to the catechol or indole groups have been studied in controls
and in former opiate addicts and psychotic patients, chiefly schizophrenics, by Isbell and his associates. Though behavioral alterations vary from
person to person and even in a given individual, they are apt to include

anxiety and difficulties in explaining sensations, in concentrating, and in understanding; all of these alterations are accompanied by flights of ideas. Elation is more common than depression. Perceptual alterations are many. Greater sensitivity to touch; hyperacusis; changes in size, color, and depth vision; elementary kaleidoscopic visual variations; and true hallucinations are seen. In addition, depersonalization is frequently observed, and the patient thinks that the size, weight, shape, and appearance of various parts of the body change. More important, when these hallucinogens are not given in excessive doses, all these psychotic manifestations occur in a state of clear consciousness. The characteristics of the psychotic reactions appear to be within the same spheres in the addicts and in the controls.

In active schizophrenics studied by Hoch, however, greater accentuation of the psychotic symptoms is observed, with more marked disorganization of thought and less awareness of reality than in the controls, as the clinical profiles of the patients became more florid.

In burnt-out schizophrenics, visual hallucinations and disturbances of body image are also observed. But emotional apathy and indifference appear to a greater degree in them than in patients with more active symptoms. This difference suggests a phenomenon observed with schizophrenic patients receiving monoamine oxidase inhibitors with either methionine, tryptophan, or cysteine. The symptoms characteristic of a given schizophrenic patient are repeated in more exaggerated forms during the behavioral exacerbations brought on by these treatments.

Systemic reactions to psychotomimetic agents, studied quantitatively, reveal rises in rectal temperature, pulse rate, respiratory rate, systolic blood pressure, and pupillary diameter. In accordance with these signs of excitation, there is also a decreased threshold for the knee jerk.

Cholinolytics. In another group of drugs, including atropine and similar cholinolytics, are two agents, scopolamine and Ditran, an *N*-methyl-3-piperidylbenzilate studied by Abood and Meduna in 1958. Like the catechol and indole psychotomimetics, the cholinolytics produced gross distortions of visual perceptions, hallucinations, and paranoid ideation with ideas of grandeur in some patients. Others, however, exhibited chiefly a confusional state, delirium with faulty orientation, clouding of the sensorium, and memory disturbances.

This emphasis on the delirious state suggests that cholinolytics act by different mechanisms than the indole or catechol psychotomimetics.

TOLERANCE

The behavioral changes with the indole and catechol psychotomimetics seem to apply somewhat more closely than those with the cholinolytics to the symptoms of schizophrenia. The action mechanism in noncholinolytic psychotomimetics develops rapidly and is evident after three days of drug administration, both in systemic and in behavioral effects. The changes in knee jerks, blood pressure, and pupillary diameter are significantly diminished. Doses even quadruple the original do not restore the original severity of the mental changes. Tolerance is also rapidly lost, and the intensities of the reactions are fully restored three days after the discontinuation of lysergic acid diethylamide (LSD).

The spectrums of the objective and subjective reactions to the indoles— LSD, psilocin, and psilocybin—and to the catechol mescaline are strikingly similar. Because of this similarity, Isbell and co-workers suggested that all four drugs produce their effects by a common mechanism. They proceeded to test this hypothesis in studies of cross-tolerance. If the loss of sensitivity to the continued administration of LSD is called direct tolerance, then the tolerance to the subsequent administration of any other member of this group of four drugs is cross-tolerance. Isbell and colleagues demonstrated strong cross-tolerances among these drugs.

Mechanism of Action

The observations on cross-tolerance reveal that both the indole and the catechol psychotomimetics must be considered in the analysis of the mechanism of action, as in the experiments performed by Himwich and collaborators. A series of observations on rabbits to study indole psychotomimetics (psilocybin, psilocin, bufotenin, D-dimethyltryptamine, LSD) and catechols (mescaline and dimethoxyphenylethylamine) revealed that each of these drugs is capable of exciting EEG alerting in the intact animal but not in preparations with brain stem transected just below the midbrain. Thus, a structure in the lower brain stem affords a site for EEG arousal by these two groups of psychotomimetics. Though the nonpsychotomimetic congeners of these drugs also bring on EEG alerting in an animal with intact brain, a series of transections reveal that they depend on an area in the midbrain.

Chemical Structure

Another difference between the psychotomimetic and nonpsychotomimetic agents is evident in the chemical structure. The molecules of the psychotomimetic agents contain either N-dimethyl-(CH_3) or N-diethyl-(C_2H_5) groups in strategic sites, but the psychotomimetic catechols are O-methylated. The nonpsychotomimetics do not have either N-dimethyl or O-methyl groups (see Figure 8). The O-methylated catechols include mescaline and dimethoxyphenylethylamine; with the latter there is a direct connection between the screening studies of psychotomimetic drugs in rabbits and the clinical observations of Friedhoff and Van Winkle, as that compound appears in the urine of schizophrenic patients.

Limbic System Changes

Experiments also disclosed changes in the limbic system of the rabbit, especially in the hippocampus, with characteristic slow theta electrical potentials accompanying the EEG arousal patterns. Investigations of Mon-

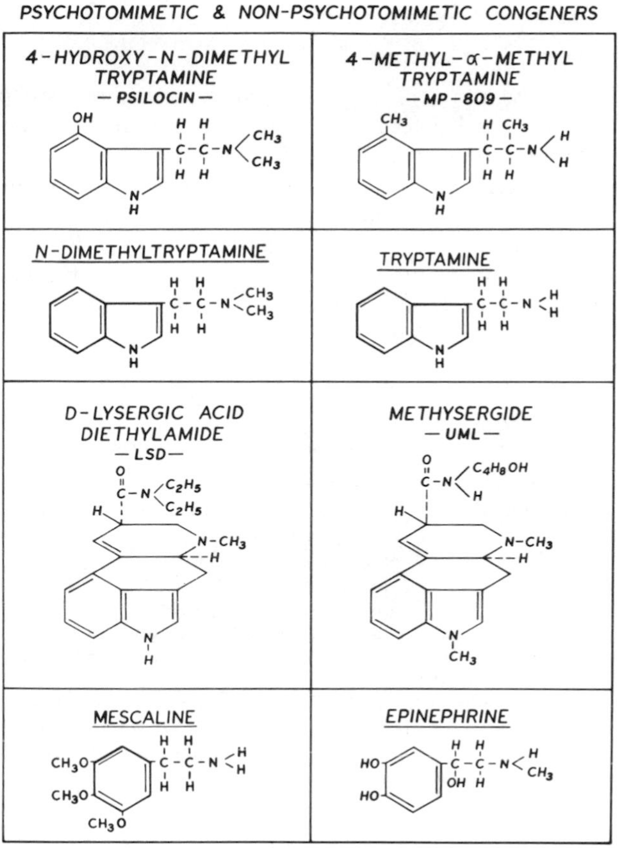

FIGURE 8. Psychotomimetic and nonpsychotomimetic congeners. Note that the indole psychotomimetics have either an N-dimethyl group (psilocin, N-dimethyltryptamine) or an N-diethyl group (LSD), but mescaline possesses O-methyl groups, and nonpsychotomimetic congeners are devoid of such groups. In contrast, 4-methyl-α-methyltryptamine and the other nonpsychotomimetic congeners—tryptamine and methysergide (UML, Sansert)—do not contain either N-dimethyl or N-diethyl groups, and epinephrine does not have O-methyl groups. (Prepared for this chapter by H. E. Himwich.)

roe and Heath have revealed the great sensitivity of the hippocampus, a sensitivity that appears to be specific, as seen in discriminative task performances of cats exposed to LSD. Stimulation of the reticular formation can evoke both EEG arousal with rapid low amplitude cortical waves and hippocampal theta rhythms, and stimulation of the posterior hippocampus can also cause EEG alerting, so it seems that these two processes are closely related phenomena.

BIOCHEMICAL CHANGES

A biochemical description of a mechanism of action of psychotogenic agents can be suggested. Because the indole amines and catecholamines are prominently represented in the limbic system, it has been suggested that the psychotogenic substances either interfere with the metabolic processes of the indoles and catechols in the brain or take the place of normal brain constituents and evoke abnormal reactions. By either process, aberrant behavioral results may be expected. The recent discoveries of the role of indoles and catechols in the urine of schizophrenic patients add substance to such a conception.

REFERENCES

Abood, L. G., and Meduna, L. J. Some effects of a new psychotogen in depressive states. J. Nerv. Ment. Dis., 127: 546, 1958.

Adey, W. R., Porter, R., Walter, D. O., and Brown, T. S. Prolonged effects of LSD on EEG records during discriminative performance in cat: evaluation by computer analysis. EEG Clin. Neurophysiol., 18: 25, 1965.

Axelrod, J. The uptake and release of catecholamines and the effects of drugs. In Progress in Brain Research, H. E. Himwich and W. A. Himwich, editors, vol. 8, p. 81. Elsevier, New York, 1964.

Berlet, H., Bull, C., Himwich, H. E., Kohl, H., Matsumoto, K., Pscheidt, G. R., Spaide, J. K., Tourlentes, T. T., and Valverde, J. M. The effect of diet on schizophrenic behavior. In Psychopathology of Schizophrenia, P. Hoch and J. Zubin, editors. Grune & Stratton, New York, 1966.

Berlet, H. H., Bull, C., Himwich, H. E., Kohl, H., Matsumoto, K., Pscheidt, G. R., Spaide, J., Tourlentes, T. T., and Valverde, J. M. Endogenous metabolic factor in schizophrenic behavior. Science, 144: 311, 1964.

Brune, G. G., and Himwich, H. E. Biogenic amines and behavior in schizophrenic patients. In Recent Advances in Biological Psychiatry, J. Wortis, editor, vol. 5, p. 144. Plenum Press, New York, 1963.

Himwich, H. E. Comparative neurophysiological studies of psychotomimetic N-dimethylamines and N-diethylamines and their nonpsychotomimetic congeners devoid of the N-dimethyl or N-diethyl configurations. Presented at Symposium on Amine Metabolism in Schizophrenia, Atlantic City, New Jersey, April 8–9, 1965.

Himwich, H. E. Loci of actions of psychotropic drugs in the brain. Fol. Psychiat. Neurol. Jap., 19: 217, 1965.

Hoch, P. H. Experimentally produced psychosis. Amer. J. Psychiat., 107: 607, 1950.

Isbell, H., Belleville, R. E., Fraser, H. F., Wikler, A., and Logan, C. R. Studies on lysergic acid diethylamide (LSD-25). Arch. Neurol. Psychiat., 76: 468, 1956.

Monroe, R. R., and Heath, R. G. Effects of lysergic acid and various derivatives on depth and cortical electrograms. J. Neuropsychiat., 3: 75, 1961.

Overall, J. E., Hollister, L. E., Meyer, F., Kimbell, I., and Shelton, J. Imipramine and thioridazine in depressed and schizophrenic patients. JAMA, 189: 605, 1964.

Sigg, E. B. Pharmacological studies with Tofranil. Canad. Psychiat. Assoc. J., *4:* Special suppl., p. S75, 1959.

Wolbach, A. B., Jr., Isbell, H., and Miner, E. J. Cross tolerance between mescaline and LSD-25 with a comparison of the mescaline and LSD reactions. Psychopharmacologia, 3: 1, 1962.

CHAPTER 4

Biogenic Amines and Emotion

JOSEPH J. SCHILDKRAUT, M.D., and

SEYMOUR KETY, M.D.

INTRODUCTION

THE HISTORIC STUDIES of Walter B. Cannon suggested that the biologically active amine "adrenaline" was secreted in response to stimuli which produced fear and rage reactions in animals (1); since then, the possible relationship of this and other biogenic amines to human emotions has generated considerable scientific interest. In the years following Cannon's work, the physiology and metabolism of the biogenic amines have been studied in various affective states, including normal and pathological anxiety, depression, elation, and anger. Research interest in this area was further stimulated during the past decade by the finding that many of the drugs used in the psychiatric treatment of patients with affective disorders (2–4) also caused significant changes in the metabolism and function of various biogenic amines, peripherally and centrally (5, 6).

Numerous recent reviews and symposia have covered many aspects of the extensive literature which may be pertinent to the relationship of biogenic amines to affect (5–15). The present review, which is more representative than comprehensive, concentrates primarily on studies in man, or on those studies in animals which appear relevant to interpretations of clinical phenomena. Several possible animal models of human affective states are also described, since these may prove to be of heuristic value, despite obvious differences between these behavioral analogs of emotion in animals and affective states in man.

This manuscript was prepared while one of us (J.J.S.) was a recipient of National Institute of Mental Health special fellowship No. MH-28, 079–01.

BIOLOGY OF THE BIOGENIC AMINES

The catecholamines, norepinephrine and dopamine, and the indole amine, serotonin, are the brain monoamines on which interest has focused. Norepinephrine is present in many areas of the brain, but the highest concentrations are found in the hypothalamus. Epinephrine, present peripherally in the adrenal medulla, occurs in the brain in very low concentration compared to the concentrations of norepinephrine. Highest concentrations of dopamine are found in the basal ganglia, and only lower concentrations of this amine are found in most other brain areas. Serotonin, while found in high concentration in various peripheral tissues, is also present in the brain in appreciable amount and is generally similar to norepinephrine in its distribution (16, 17). Regional distribution of biogenic amines in the brain has been extensively studied by the recently developed histochemical fluorescence method, and monoamine-containing neurons have been described (18, 19). High densities of such neurons have been found in the limbic system, which includes the hypothalamus and other functionally related brain structures which may be concerned with emotional state.

While norepinephrine functions as a chemical transmitter substance at the terminals of the peripheral sympathetic nervous system (20), the role of this and other amines in the central nervous system is far from clear. It is thought that, at synapses, which are the junctions of two adjacent neurons, the chemical transmitter released from the presynaptic nerve endings causes changes in the postsynaptic neuronal membrane potential, which may thereby generate a nerve impulse. It has been suggested that norepinephrine, dopamine, and serotonin may each function directly as a transmitter substance in the central nervous system. None of the biogenic amines has yet been definitively established as a chemical neurotransmitter in the brain, however, and some investigators have suggested (17, 19, 21–23) that one or more of these amines may act instead as modulators or regulators of synaptic transmission mediated by some other chemical transmitter—for example, acetylcholine.

Norepinephrine is synthesized from the amino acid tyrosine, through the intermediates 3,4-dihydroxyphenylalanine (dopa) and dopamine; it is stored within the nerve in intraneuronal granules. These granules have been observed by electron microscopy to occur at presynaptic nerve endings, and their contents may be released into the synaptic cleft in response to nerve impulses. Norepinephrine discharged from neuronal endings in physiologically active form, by either nerve impulses or the action of sympathomimetic drugs, is inactivated mainly by cellular re-uptake or by enzymatic conversion by catechol-O-methyltransferase to form normetanephrine. Norepinephrine released intracellularly, either spontaneously or by reserpine-like drugs, may be inactivated mainly by mitochondrial monoamine oxidase, forming deaminated catechol metabolites—for example,

3,4-dihydroxymandelic acid—before leaving the cell; monoamine oxidase may thus regulate tissue levels of norepinephrine (see Figures 1 and 2) (10, 21, 24–26). Secondary O-methylation or deamination reactions involved in the formation of 3-methoxy-4-hydroxymandelic acid (vanillyl-mandelic acid, or VMA), the major urinary metabolite of norepinephrine and epinephrine in man, presumably can occur in the liver or kidney as well as in the nervous system (see Figure 2). While most of these concepts derive from studies of peripheral sympathetic nerves, similar patterns of metabolism appear to occur in the brain (21, 27, 28).

Epinephrine is synthesized from norepinephrine in the adrenal medulla by enzymatic methylation of the amine nitrogen. Activity of phenyletha-nolamine-N-methyltransferase, the enzyme involved in this reaction, has recently been shown to be enhanced by adrenocortical steroids (29).

Serotonin is synthesized from the precursor amino acid 5-hydroxytryp-tophan by decarboxylation and, like norepinephrine, may exist in the neuron in a bound and a free form. Serotonin is metabolized by monoamine oxidase, forming 5-hydroxyindoleacetic acid (30, 31).

Various aspects of the extensive literature on biogenic amine metabolism have been well reviewed recently, and the reader is referred to these summaries for more comprehensive coverage (9, 24, 30, 32).

PERIPHERAL CATECHOLAMINES AND AFFECTIVE STATE

Some time after Cannon's work, norepinephrine was found to be secreted at sympathetic nerve endings (20) and was identified as a neurotransmitter at the terminals of the peripheral sympathetic nervous system. Epinephrine, however, was found to derive almost exclusively from adrenal medullary secretion in man (33). Norepinephrine appears not to cross the blood-brain barrier to an appreciable extent (34, 35): thus it is unlikely that the brain can be a significant source of circulating norepinephrine.

Attempts have been made by numerous investigators to relate secretion of norepinephrine or epinephrine to specific emotional states. From polygraphic measurements, Ax (36) concluded that the physiological response during anger resembled the reaction to an injection of norepinephrine alone, whereas the response during fear resembled the reaction to an injection of both norepinephrine and epinephrine. Funkenstein (37), in an extensive study of the cardiovascular responses of psychiatric patients and normal subjects under psychological stress, found blood pressure changes associated with angry and aggressive states to be similar to those occurring during norepinephrine infusion, whereas the cardiovascular responses in states of anxiety or depression were similar to those observed during epinephrine infusion. In these studies, inferences concerning catecholamine secretion were made from data on physiological responses. In more recent investigations, catecholamines have been measured chemically. Mason et al. (38) have found, in the rhesus monkey, that increases in blood levels

A
B
C
NE
MAO
DCM
COMT
NMN
1
2
3

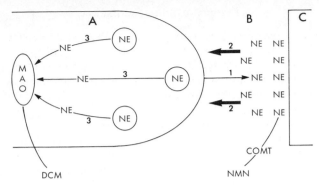

Figure 1. Schematic representation of (*A*) a noradrenergic nerve ending, (*B*) synaptic cleft, and (*C*) receptor. *NE*, norepinephrine; *NMN*, normetanephrine; *DCM*, de-aminated catechol metabolites; *COMT*, catechol O-methyltransferase; *MAO*, monoamine oxidase (within a mitochondrion); 1, discharge of norepinephrine into synaptic cleft and onto receptor; 2, reuptake of norepinephrine from synaptic cleft; 3, intracellular release of norepinephrine from storage granules into cytoplasm and onto mitochondrial monoamine oxidase.

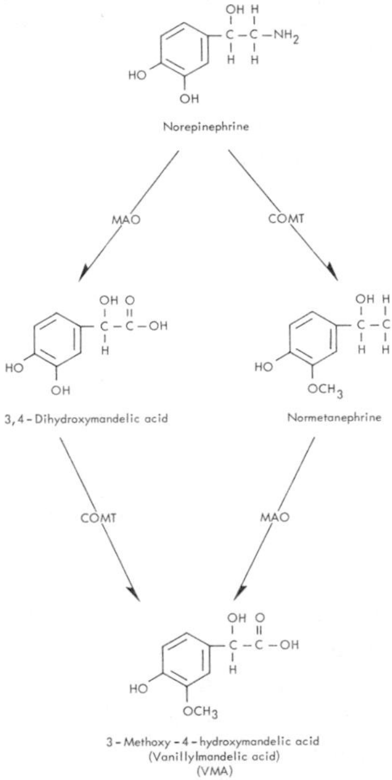

Norepinephrine
MAO
COMT
3,4-Dihydroxymandelic acid
Normetanephrine
COMT
MAO
3-Methoxy-4-hydroxymandelic acid
(Vanillylmandelic acid)
(VMA)

Figure 2. Pathways of metabolism of norepinephrine (simplified). *COMT*, catechol O-methyltransferase; *MAO*, monoamine oxidase.

of epinephrine occurred in situations which combined uncertainty or unpredictability with the threat of noxious stimuli and anticipation of the need for coping behavior. Release of norepinephrine without concurrent elevation of the epinephrine level occurred when the conditions associated with administration of the noxious stimuli were familiar, unambiguous, and predictable.

Although momentary blood levels of the catecholamines may reflect with greater sensitivity their release in response to transient situations, the concentrations involved are low and the methods are fraught with difficulty, so that most investigators, when studying man, have relied upon urinary excretion for their measurements. Elmadjian et al. (39) found increases in norepinephrine excretion, with smaller increases in epinephrine excretion, in hockey players during active competition and in psychiatric patients showing aggressive emotional outbursts. Increases in epinephrine excretion alone were found in players who observed but did not participate in the game and in psychiatric patients during staff conferences. Euler and Lundberg (40) have observed increased excretion of both norepinephrine and epinephrine in aircraft pilots during moderately stressful flights; epinephrine excretion alone was increased in military personnel being transported by airplane as passengers. The effects of a variety of other stresses upon catecholamine excretion have been studied in Euler's laboratory, and these findings are summarized in a recent publication (12).

The psychological and physical effects of centrifugation on catecholamine excretion have been studied by Goodall (41). During the period of anticipation prior to centrifugation there was an increase in epinephrine but not in norepinephrine excretion, whereas, during centrifugation, the excretion of both amines was elevated. Silverman et al. (42) have found epinephrine excretion to be preferentially increased in anxious subjects, while norepinephrine excretion was relatively greater in angry or aggressive subjects who were studied under various experimental conditions.

During work performed under conditions of stress, improved performance was correlated with increased excretion of norepinephrine but not of epinephrine (43). In a study of catecholamine excretion in subjects viewing motion pictures selected to induce a variety of emotional states, Levi (44) found that bland, scenic films were associated with a reduction in urinary epinephrine and norepinephrine, whereas excretion of both amines was increased during emotionally evocative films (comedies or tragedies).

Although changes due to alterations in motor activity cannot be excluded in some studies (12, 42) and definitive interpretations of these findings may be limited by the relative lack of specificity of the catecholamine assay procedures, particularly in earlier investigations, these data seem generally compatible with the hypothesis that psychological and situational factors may differentially affect the relative excretion of epinephrine or norepinephrine. Increased epinephrine excretion seems to occur in states of anxiety or in threatening situations of uncertain or unpredictable nature in which active coping behavior may be required but has not been achieved. In contrast, norepinephrine excretion may occur in states of anger or aggression or in situations which are challenging but predictable and which allow active and appropriate behavioral responses to the challenge. Under various conditions, increase of either epinephrine or norepinephrine or of both of these catecholamines may represent specific adaptive responses; this appears to be an area where the conjunction of psychosocial, physiological, and biochemical investigation may be particularly rewarding (8, 45). The recent finding, in animals, that adrenocortical steroids enhance the activity of the enzyme which converts norepinephrine to epinephrine in the adrenal (29) may stimulate further study of possible functional interrelationships of these hormones in man.

The findings of changes in excretion of endogenous norepinephrine or epinephrine with various affective states are supplemented by data from studies of the psychological effects occurring with the exogenous administration of the catecholamines. Since the early studies of Wearn and Sturgis (46), investigators who have given human subjects infusions of epinephrine have reported the occurrence of subjective symptoms resembling anxiety (47–50). In many instances, however, these epinephrine-induced "anxiety states" have been clearly differentiated from true emotions by some experimental subjects, who reported feeling "as if" they were anxious, and these states were designated "cold" emotions by Maranon (51). Emotions other than anxiety after the administration of epinephrine have also been reported, and some subjects have experienced no emotional changes (46, 48, 52, 53). In contrast to the effects of epinephrine, less pronounced effects on emotion after the administration of norepinephrine have been reported (49, 54, 55).

It has been suggested that epinephrine infusion may produce a nonspecific state of arousal and that the past experiences of the individual subject and the characteristics of the experimental situation may be the factors which determine the quality and intensity of the elicited emotions. The limited data available from studies, relatively uncontrolled with respect to these variables, are compatible with this plausible hypothesis (11, 47, 52, 54). Schachter and Singer (52), in one of the few studies in which environmental cues have been controlled, have shown that, in experimental situations designed to produce either euphoria or anger, each mood was accentuated by administration of epinephrine but not by administration of a placebo. The relative passivity or activity of the subject, particularly with respect to the opportunity for effective expression of affect in the experimental situation, may also be of importance in determining whether anxiety or either anger or euphoria will be elicited (52, 53). More systematic and controlled studies of these intraindividual and situational factors will be required to test these hypotheses.

The blood-brain barrier effectively prevents the entry of epinephrine into the brain, except possibly in the region of the hypothalamus (34). Unresolved is the question of whether epinephrine, administered or released peripherally, produces changes in affective state by a direct action on the hypothalamus or through subjective perception of its peripheral effects, which resemble those of anxiety. This controversy can be traced back to the original James-Lange theory of the visceral origin of emotions (56) and to Cannon's criticism of this formulation (57), which has been reviewed recently by Breggin (11).

PHARMACOLOGICAL STUDIES

During the past decade, a significant contribution to our understanding of the possible relationship of the biogenic amines to affective state has come from studies of the changes in metabolism of brain monoamines produced by clinically active psychotropic drugs. These studies have been the subject of several recent reviews (6, 13, 45, 58).

RESERPINE AND RESERPINELIKE AGENTS

Reserpine, which was used in psychiatry in the treatment of mania and excitement prior to the introduction of the phenothiazines and is used in general medicine in the treatment of hypertension, has been reported to produce severe depression of mood in some patients, particularly hypertensive patients treated with relatively large doses (4, 59). Discontinuing administration of the drug generally leads to remission of the depression. Depression has also been observed in patients given tetrabenazine, a drug which is similar to reserpine in its effects on biogenic amine metabolism (60). Such drug-induced depressions have been regarded by most observers as indistinguishable from naturally occurring depressive disorders, although this opinion has been questioned by some investigators (61).

The effects of reserpine have been extensively studied in experimental animals and in in-vitro systems (62). By a mechanism which has not yet been elucidated, reserpine interferes with the intraneuronal binding of the catecholamines and serotonin (62). With impairment of the binding mechanism by reserpine, these amines may diffuse freely through the cytoplasm and onto mitochondrial monoamine oxidase. This results in their inactivation by deamination and, thus, in depletion of tissue amine stores (24, 25, 63).

In animals, reserpine induces sedation, a state which has been proposed by some investigators as a possible animal analog of depression in man (13). This model has found practical application in the screening of potential antidepressant drugs. Reserpine-induced sedation in animals is associated with decreased brain levels of norepinephrine, dopamine, and serotonin (58, 64). Several congeners of reserpine have been prepared, and these show a good correlation between sedative action and the ability to reduce cerebral amines (65).

Since a fraction of the monoamines present in brain may be contained in reservoir pools, changes in the levels of the monoamines need not necessarily be associated with an alternation in function. Haggendal and Lindqvist (66), through long-term administration of reserpine in animals, depleted what are presumed to be the reservoir pools without producing chronic sedation. Having thus reduced the concentrations of monoamines in brain to about 10 per cent of normal, these investigators then found an excellent temporal correlation, after each dose of reserpine, between the behavioral effects and the changes in the residual (possibly functional) pools of the three monoamines studied: norepinephrine, dopamine, and serotonin (66). Consistent with these findings have been the reports of a temporal association between the return of normal motor behavior in animals sedated with reserpine and the restoration of the brain's capacity to accumulate both norepinephrine injected into the cerebral ventricles and serotonin synthesized from the exogenously administered precursor 5-hydroxytryptophan (67, 68). These findings thus support the hypothesis that reserpine-induced sedation is related to impairment of the binding of monoamines; but the data do not allow separation of the effects of catecholamine depletion from those of serotonin release or depletion.

Further relevant data come from studies in which the amino acid precursors of catecholamines and serotonin have been administered to animals previously given reserpine. These precursor amino acids, unlike the monoamines, can cross the blood-brain barrier in animals and raise the concentrations of the respective monoamines in the brain (69). Administration of dihydroxyphenylalanine, the catecholamine precursor, reverses reserpine-induced sedation in animals and restores gross behavior and the conditioned avoidance response to approximately normal levels. The serotonin precursor, 5-hydroxytryptophan, however, does not restore normal functioning (22, 69, 70). Moreover, in one study involving human subjects, dihydroxyphenylalanine has been reported to counteract the psychological effects of reserpine (71). These findings suggest the importance of catecholamine depletion in reserpine-induced sedation in animals and, possibly, also in reserpine-induced depression in man.

The role of serotonin in the reserpine syndrome has been stressed by a number of investigators (72, 73). Some have suggested that serotonin produces central excitation and that depletion of serotonin contributes to the reserpine syndrome (72). Brodie et al. (68), however, have hypothesized that serotonin and norepinephrine exert antagonistic effects centrally and that free serotonin in the brain causes sedation. On the basis of kinetic considerations and other data they have concluded that the impairment of amine-binding by reserpine increases the free (unbound) serotonin available to occupy brain receptor sites and that this causes sedation in animals given reserpine; but this formulation has aroused some controversy (21).

The findings of recent studies with drugs which block the synthesis of serotonin or norepinephrine raise questions concerning the importance of serotonin in reserpine-induced sedation. The enzymatic hydroxylation of tryptophan is blocked by p-chlorophenylalanine, and brain levels of serotonin in animals have been reduced to less than 10 per cent without changes in norepinephrine content. Sedation was not observed, under these conditions (74, 75). After administration of reserpine, however, animals whose brain levels of serotonin had previously been depleted through administration of p-chlorophenylalanine became sedated (74).

Catecholamine synthesis in the brain may be inhibited by α-methylparatyrosine, as discussed below, and norepinephrine levels may thereby be reduced without alteration in the serotonin levels (76). Spector et al. (76) observed sedation in animals when norepinephrine synthesis was interrupted by administration of α-methylparatyrosine. This finding has been confirmed (68), but not in all studies (77).

Some of the problems involved in establishing definitive evidence in this area have been discussed elsewhere (45). Much of the biochemical evidence has depended upon measurement of the total brain content of one or another amine, or upon studies involving administration of precursor amino acids. The histological localization of the several endogenous pools of each of these amines (free and bound) has not been clarified, and there is now evidence, at least for norepinephrine in peripheral tissues, supporting the earlier speculation (45) that function may depend, not on the total content of an amine, but on the presence of a very small, but probably specifically localized, fraction (21, 66, 78), which may represent the newly synthesized amine. The distribution of amines formed from exogenously administered precursors, moreover, is not necessarily identical with the distribution of the endogenously formed amines (79). With these gaps in our basic knowledge, it is not surprising that, even after almost a decade of investigation, the problem of relating the phenomenon of reserpine-induced sedation to an effect of one or another specific amine, or their interaction, remains unresolved.

Monoamine Oxidase Inhibitors

Since the initial observation nearly ten years ago of the antidepressant effects of iproniazid, a drug which inhibits the enzymatic activity of monoamine oxidase (2), numerous other monoamine oxidase inhibitors have also been reported to be effective in the treatment of depression (80, 81). Recent studies have indicated a correlation between clinical improvement in depressed patients and the degree of monoamine oxidase inhibition achieved during drug administration (82). Controlled studies of the clinical effectiveness of these compounds are limited, however, and there is some controversy concerning the relative clinical effectiveness of some of the monoamine oxidase inhibitors and the specific subgroups of depressed patients for whom these drugs are most indicated (80, 81).

In some animal species the monoamine oxidase inhibitors produce both behavioral excitation and elevated brain levels of norepinephrine and serotonin. This elevation of brain levels of monoamines presumably results from impairment by the enzyme inhibitor of normal metabolic inactivation by deamination. There has been some controversy over attempts to relate the behavioral excitation to increased concentrations of a specific amine (5). Spector and his co-workers, however, were able to separate these effects by using various inhibitors, doses, and animal species. They found that, in those species where the monoamine oxidase inhibitors elevated the levels of both norepinephrine and serotonin, the observed behavioral excitation was temporally correlated with the increase in levels of norepinephrine, whereas, in species in which there was an increase in serotonin without an increase in norepinephrine, no behavioral excitation was observed (83).

The monoamine oxidase inhibitors have also been found to counteract reserpine-induced sedation in animals (58, 83–85), and this behavioral change has also correlated better with changes in brain levels of norepinephrine than with changes in brain levels of serotonin (21, 83). Although definitive interpretation of such data on total brain content of amines is subject to the limitations discussed above, it seems plausible to hypothesize that the excitation which follows administration of monoamine oxidase inhibitors may be associated with the spillover of free norepinephrine onto receptor sites (83).

Reserpine-induced sedation is antagonized by prior treatment with monoamine oxidase inhibitors, and animals previously treated with a monoamine oxidase inhibitor show excitation and not the usual sedation after administration of reserpine (84). This has been ascribed to an accumulation of free active amines which are released by reserpine and cannot be inactivated by deamination.

IMIPRAMINE AND THE TRICYCLIC ANTIDEPRESSANTS

Imipramine and other related tricyclic derivatives have been found to be the most clinically effective of the antidepressant drugs (41, 81). Although imipramine does not chemically inhibit either monoamine oxidase or catechol O-methyltransferase, it has been found to potentiate both the response to sympathetic nerve stimulation in several experimental systems and many of the peripheral effects of exogenously administered norepinephrine in animals and in man (14, 86, 87). Potentiation, by imipramine, of the effects of serotonin in animals has also been reported (86, 88).

Hertting et al. (89) have found, in animals, that imipramine interferes with the uptake of infused norepinephrine into peripheral tissues, and have suggested that imipramine may decrease the cell-membrane or storage-granule-membrane permeability to this amine. Potentiation of the effects of norepinephrine by imipramine may thus result, in part, from impairment of the inactivation of free norepinephrine at the synapse by cellular re-uptake. This process would provide a mechanism for the "sensitization of central adrenergic synapses" which Sigg (90) had proposed to account for the antidepressant action of imipramine. Experimental evidence that imipramine inhibits norepinephrine uptake in the brain as it does in peripheral tissues has been reported recently by Glowinski and Axelrod (91). They, moreover, found that the chemically related tricyclic antidepressants desmethylimipramine and amitriptyline also inhibited norepinephrine uptake in the brain.

Following the intracisternal administration of H^3-norepinephrine into rat brain, Schanberg et. al. (92) found that imipramine and desmethylimipramine increased brain concentrations of the O-methylated metabolite, H^3-normetanephrine, whereas chlorpromazine, a tranquilizer, did not. It has been suggested by a number of investigators that physiologically active norepinephrine which has interacted with receptors may be inactivated by O-methylation, but evidence supporting this plausible hypothesis is limited (21, 93). Eisenfeld et al. (94) have found, in peripheral tissues, that drugs which block adrenergic receptors decrease the formation of normetanephrine.

Prior treatment with imipramine can prevent reserpine-induced sedation in animals. This phenomenon has been shown, by Sulser et al. (95), to depend upon the availability and rate of release of catecholamines. When animals are first partially depleted of norepinephrine stores by administration of α-methylmetyrosine, prior treatment with imipramine does not prevent reserpine-induced sedation. Scheckel and Boff (96) have found that small nondepressant doses of tetrabenazine caused excitation in animals previously treated with imipramine. This effect, too, can be prevented if catecholamine stores are first depleted by administration of α-methylmetatyrosine. These data seem compatible with the hypothesis that imipramine may exert its antidepressant action through potentiation of catecholamines at adrenergic receptor sites in the brain (6, 7, 13, 90, 95, 96).

AMPHETAMINE

Amphetamine is a short-acting sympathomimetic psychic stimulant which has been used for many years with variable results in the treatment of depression (97). There is evidence that amphetamine may both release physiologically active norepinephrine from nerve cells and block the inactivation of norepinephrine by cellular re-uptake (28, 98). In studies of the metabolism of H^3-norepinephrine in the brain, Glowinski and Axelrod (28) have found that amphetamine increases concentrations of H^3-normetanephrine and decreases the content of deaminated tritiated catechols. Many of the behavioral effects of amphetamine are potentiated by imipramine (96, 99).

Large doses of amphetamine significantly lower the concentration of brain norepinephrine in animals (100), and amphetamine accentuates the decrease in brain norepinephrine induced by stress (101). Tachyphylaxis, a diminishing effect with repeated dosage, has been observed clinically, and the period of acute stimulation by amphetamine, particularly after large doses, is often followed by a "rebound period" of mental depression and fatigue (97). These observations may reflect a temporary depletion of norepinephrine stores available for continued release. While many observations suggest that amphetamine may release norepinephrine and potentiate the effects of this catecholamine at receptor sites, there is evidence that amphetamine may also exert a direct action at receptors (102).

LITHIUM SALTS

Lithium salts have been used in the treatment of elations (hypomania and mania) over a number of years, and their clinical effectiveness has been fairly well established (103). Schildkraut et al. (104; see also 92) have recently found that lithium salts alter the metabolism of H^3-norepinephrine in the brain; concentrations of tritiated normetanephrine are decreased, while those of deaminated catechols are increased. It is unlikely that these changes are due to an inhibition of catechol O-methyltransferase, since lithium did not alter the activity of this enzyme in vitro (92). The changes in H^3-norepinephrine metabolites with administration of lithium are opposite to those observed with the euphoriant drug amphetamine (28). These findings are compatible with the hypothesis that lithium, a drug effective in the treatment of elations, may increase the intracellular deamination of norepinephrine and decrease the norepinephrine available at adrenergic receptor sites.

ALPHA-METHYLPARATYROSINE

Spector et al. (76) have found that α-methylparatyrosine interrupts the synthesis of norepinephrine by inhibiting activity of the enzyme which converts tyrosine to dihydroxyphenylalanine. Sedation and impairment of motor activity have been reported to occur in animals when norepinephrine synthesis is interrupted through administration of α-methylparatyrosine (76; see also 68) and Hanson (105) has reported disruption of conditioned avoidance behavior, which can be restored by treatment with dihydroxyphenylalanine; escape behavior was not impaired. Weissman et al. (77, 106) observed no sedation or disruption of conditioned avoidance behavior after animals were treated with α-methylparatyrosine, but found that the usual stimulation, by amphetamine, of gross behavior as well as of conditioned avoidance responding was blocked by α-methylparatyrosine and that the impairment of conditioned avoidance behavior by chlorpromazine was potentiated by α-methylparatyrosine. Differences in species or dosages may account for apparent discrepancies in these findings.

The pharmacological effects of this drug in man are currently under investigation. Preliminary study suggests that some patients receiving α-

methylparatyrosine may experience transient sedation as dosage is increased and hypomanic-like reactions as the drug is withdrawn (107).

POSSIBLE MODELS FOR THE STUDY OF AFFECTIVE STATES

In the self-stimulation technique of Olds and Milner (108), an animal may, through implanted electrodes, deliver an electrical stimulation to its own brain by making some arbitrarily selected response such as pressing a lever. When electrodes are implanted in the lateral or posterior hypothalamus or certain other areas of the brain, animals will repetitively respond and induce brain stimulation without administration of external rewards. From these findings, a number of investigators have generated the hypothesis that a neuronal system for reward or pleasure may exist within the brain (109). Stein and others (110, 111) have suggested a possible relationship of this system to human affective experiences. While of heuristic value, this speculative formulation must be interpreted cautiously.

The technique of self-stimulation has been used to study the effects of psychoactive drugs. Stein has demonstrated (111, 112) an increase in the rate, and a lowering of the threshold, of self-stimulation in rats treated with amphetamine. These effects of amphetamine are potentiated by monoamine oxidase inhibitors or imipramine and counteracted by chlorpromazine. The effects of amphetamine are mimicked by phenylethylamine when inactivation of this substance is prevented by prior treatment with a monoamine oxidase inhibitor. After depletion of norepinephrine levels through treatment with reserpine or with α-methylparatyrosine, the inhibitor of tyrosine hydroxylase, the effects of amphetamine on self-stimulation are reduced (111, 113). Decrease in the rate of self-stimulation was observed after administration of tetrabenazine, a drug which releases, and depletes levels of, norepinephrine and other amines, but an increase in the rate occurred when tetrabenazine was administered to animals previously treated with a monoamine oxidase inhibitor (114).

These data seem compatible with the hypothesis that norepinephrine may function as a transmitter or modulator in the neuronal systems which are involved in the phenomenon of self-stimulation. Decreased norepinephrine content in the brain and decreased epinephrine levels in the adrenal following rage reactions induced by electrical stimulation of the amygdala in cats have also been reported. When electrical stimulation did not produce rage responses, catecholamine levels were unaffected (115).

These techniques of electrical stimulation of the brain may provide valuable approaches for the biochemical study of behavioral analogs of emotion in animals. Further investigation will be required, however, before these may be accepted as adequate models for human affective experience.

CLINICAL STUDIES IN PATIENTS WITH
AFFECTIVE DISORDERS

Catecholamine metabolism in patients with affective disorders (depressions and elations) has been studied by a number of investigators. Strom-Olsen and Weil-Malherbe (116) found urinary excretion of norepinephrine and epinephrine to be greater during the manic phase than during the depressed phase in patients with manic-depressive disorders. Shinfuku et al. (117) reported a similar increase in norepinephrine excretion during mania in a single patient with regular manic-depressive mood changes. Norepinephrine and epinephrine excretions were elevated in a large series of manic patients reported by Bergsman (118). No significant change in the excretion of either amine was observed in the group of patients with endogenous depressions, but the patients with retarded depressions were not separately characterized (118). Increased urinary excretion of norepinephrine in depressed patients has also been reported (119).

In a longitudinal study of affective disorders, Schildkraut et al. (120) have observed a gradual rise in normetanephrine excretion during the period of definitive clinical improvement in depressed patients treated with imipramine. Normetanephrine excretion was found to be significantly lower, in patients with retarded depression, before treatment than after treatment with imipramine when clinical improvement occurred. Increased normetanephrine excretion was observed in one patient studied during a hypomanic episode, which occurred without drug administration. The magnitude of the increase in normetanephrine excretion appeared to be related to the clinical severity of the hypomanic symptoms. In their studies of the effects of reserpine and sympathomimetic drugs on H^3-norepinephrine metabolism in animals, Kopin and Gordon (25) have adduced evidence compatible with the hypothesis that normetanephrine excretion may reflect noradrenergic activity. If this relationship also applies in man, the data on normetanephrine excretion in patients with affective disorders would suggest that increasing noradrenergic activity may be associated with the period of definitive clinical improvement from depression, and that noradrenergic activity may be relatively decreased in retarded depressions and increased in mania (120).

Caution must be exercised, however, in interpreting such data on the urinary excretion of norepinephrine and metabolites, since factors other than affective state—for example, muscular activity—may produce significant changes (121). Moreover, a blood-brain barrier to normetanephrine similar to that known to exist for norepinephrine has recently been described in animals (27). It is, therefore, probable that only a small fraction of urinary norepinephrine or normetanephrine derives from the brain. Nonetheless, such data on the urinary excretion of norepinephrine and metabolites are of interest, since biochemical changes in catecholamine metabolism in the periphery may reflect similar changes occurring centrally, and an increase in peripheral sympathetic activity may reflect increased central noradrenergic activity.

In studies of the urinary metabolites of infused radioactive norepinephrine in psychiatric patients, Rosenblatt and Chanley have reported (122) an elevated ratio of amines to deaminated acid metabolites in a subgroup of patients with retarded depression whom they classified as manic-depressive. The definitive interpretation of this finding, however, is not immediately apparent in the light of the studies on endogenous norepinephrine and metabolites.

A number of studies (7, 123) have shown that clinically effective doses of the monoamine oxidase inhibitors decrease excretion of 3-methoxy-4-hydroxymandelic acid (VMA) and 5-hydroxyindoleacetic acid in man. Decreased excretion of 3-methoxy-4-hydroxymandelic acid has, moreover, been found in depressed patients during treatment with imipramine or with monoamine oxidase inhibitors (7, 124). It has been suggested that imipramine, which inhibits cellular re-uptake of norepinephrine, possibly by decreasing membrane permeability to norepinephrine, might also inhibit the spontaneous intracellular release and deamination of norepinephrine. Inhibition of norepinephrine synthesis may also occur. Decrease in excretion of 3-methoxy-4-hydroxymandelic acid during short-term and long-term treatment with chlorpromazine has also been reported (125).

Alterations in the metabolism of the indole amines have been reported in patients with affective disorders. Ashcroft and Sharman observed a decrease in the concentration of 5-hydroxyindoles in the cerebrospinal fluid of depressed patients (126). A decreased rate of liberation of $C^{14}O_2$ from administered carboxy-labeled 5-hydroxy tryptophan was found by Coppen et al. (127). These investigators have recently reported urinary tryptamine excretion to be relatively decreased in depressed patients prior to treatment, and increased to approximately normal levels following clinical improvement. Most urinary tryptamine is probably not of central origin but may derive from the decarboxylation of tryptophan in the kidney (128).

The amino acid precursors of serotonin and norepinephrine will cross the blood-brain barrier; these have been administered to human subjects and their effects on mood studied. Of the several amino acids administered in conjunction with a monoamine oxidase inhibitor, tryptophan was the only one found to produce mood elevation in chronic schizophrenic patients (129). On that basis, tryptophan was tested by other investigators and found to potentiate the therapeutic effects of monoamine oxidase inhibitors in depressed patients (130). Tryptophan administered alone to normal subjects has been found to produce various clinical signs and symptoms, including euphoria and drowsiness (131). The antidepressant activity of monoamine oxidase inhibitors has also been reported (132) to be potentiated by 5-hydroxytryptophan, but this effect could not then be replicated in a subsequent study, and other investigators have not observed

TABLE I

Summary of the Pharmacological Observations Compatible with the Catecholamine Hypothesis of Affective Disorders

Drug	Effects on Mood in Man	Effects on Behavior in Animals	Effects on Catecholamines in Brain (Animals)
Reserpine	Sedation Depression (in some patients)	Sedation	Depletion (intracellular deamination and inactivation)
Tetrabenazine	Sedation Depression (in some patients)	Sedation	Depletion (intracellular deamination and inactivation)
Amphetamine	Stimulant	Stimulation Excitement	Releases norepinephrine (? onto receptors) Inhibits cellular uptake (and inactivation) of norepinephrine
Monoamine oxidase inhibitors	Antidepressant	Excitement Prevents and reverses reserpine-induced sedation	Increases levels
Imipramine	Antidepressant	Prevents reserpine-induced sedation Potentiation of amphetamine effects	Inhibits cellular uptake (and inactivation) of norepinephrine ? Potentiates action of norepinephrine (as in periphery)
Lithium salts	Treatment of mania		? Increases intracellular deamination of norepinephrine ? Decreases norepinephrine available at receptors
α-Methylparatyrosine	Sedation (transient) with hypomania upon withdrawal	Sedation (in some studies)	Inhibits synthesis

this effect with 5-hydroxytryptophan (133).

Dihydroxyphenylalanine, the precursor of norepinephrine, administered alone or with a monoamine oxidase inhibitor, was not found to be effective in the treatment of depression by either Pare and Sandler (133) or Klerman et al. (134). More recently, Turner and Merlis (135) have reported mood elevation in a group of patients treated with a monoamine oxidase inhibitor and dihydroxyphenylalanine, and Matussek (136) has observed transient improvement in depressed patients following short-term administration of dihydroxyphenylalanine. The possible therapeutic effectiveness of dihydroxyphenylalanine and monoamine oxidase inhibitors in the treatment of depression, therefore, merits further careful study. It must be noted, however, that this combination of drugs may produce severe hypertension and cardiac arrhythmias (137).

Corresponding to the finding that reserpine-like agents produce excitement in animals previously treated with imipramine, clinical improvement has been observed when reserpine or tetrabenazine has been added to the therapeutic regimen of a small number of depressed patients who had failed to respond to tricyclic antidepressants alone (138). Further study, however, will be required to document this important finding.

Electroconvulsive therapy, well established as an effective treatment for some depressed patients, has been studied by several investigators in an effort to determine whether the clinical effects were associated with an alteration in amine metabolism (139). Increases in plasma and urinary concentrations of norepinephrine and epinephrine after unmodified electroconvulsive therapy have been reported, but these changes are markedly diminished when barbiturates or muscle relaxants are used. It has been suggested (140) that, in animals, increased permeability of the blood–cerebrospinal-fluid barrier to norepinephrine occurs after electroconvulsive therapy.

CONCLUSION

The studies discussed here have shown a fairly consistent relationship between the effects of drugs on biogenic amines, particularly norepinephrine, and affective or behavioral states. Those drugs which cause depletion and inactivation of norepinephrine centrally produce sedation or depression, while drugs which increase or potentiate brain norepinephrine are associated with behavioral stimulation or excitement and generally have an antidepressant effect in man (see Table I). From these findings, a number of investigators have formulated the concept, designated the catecholamine hypothesis of affective disorders (6), that some, if not all, depressions may be associated with a relative deficiency of norepinephrine at functionally important adrenergic receptor sites in the brain, whereas elations may be associated with an excess of such amines.

It is not possible either to confirm or to reject this hypothesis on the basis of currently available clinical data. Although there does appear to be a fairly consistent relationship between the effects of pharmacological agents on norepinephrine metabolism and on affective state, a rigorous extrapolation from pharmacological studies to pathophysiology cannot be made. Confirmation of this hypothesis must ultimately depend upon direct demonstration of the biochemical abnormality in the naturally occurring illness.

It should be emphasized, however, that the demonstration of such a biochemical abnormality would not necessarily imply a genetic or constitutional, rather than an environmental or psychological, etiology of depression. Whereas specific genetic factors may be of importance in the etiology of some, and possibly all, depressions, it is equally conceivable that early experiences of the infant or child may cause enduring biochemical changes and that these may predispose some individuals to depressions in adulthood.

It is not likely that changes in the metabolism of the biogenic amines alone will account for the complex phenomena of normal or pathological affect. Whereas the effects of these amines at particular sites in the brain may be of crucial importance in the regulation of affect, any comprehensive formulation of the physiology of affective state will have to include many other concomitant biochemical, physiological, and psychological factors. Although in this review of the relationship of biogenic amines to affective state relatively little has been said concerning the intricate set of environmental and psychological determinants of emotion, the importance of these factors must be stressed.

The normally occurring alterations in affective state induced by environmental events is well known to all, from personal experience. The interactions between such environmental determinants of affect, various physiological factors, and the complexity of psychological determinants, including cognitive factors derived from the individual's remote and immediate past experiences, have received only limited study under adequately controlled conditions. It may be anticipated, however, that this will prove to be a particularly fruitful area for future research, for only within such a multifactorial framework may one expect to understand fully the relationship of the biogenic amines to emotional state.

REFERENCES

1. W. B. Cannon. *Bodily Changes in Pain, Hunger, Fear and Rage.* Appleton, New York, 1915.
2. J. O. Cole, R. T. Jones, G. L. Klerman. Progr. Neurol. Psychiat., 16: 539, 1961. H. P. Loomer, J. C. Saunders, N. S. Kline. Psychiat. Res. Rep. Amer. Psychiat. Assoc. 8: 129, 1957; G. E. Crane. Psychiat. Res. Rep. Amer. Psychiat. Assoc. 8: 142, 1957.

3. R. Kuhn. Amer. J. Psychiat., 115: 459, 1958; N. S. Kline. Res. Publ. Assoc. Res. Nervous Mental Disease, 37: 218, 1959.
4. T. H. Harris. Amer. J. Psychiat., 113: 950, 1957.
5. S. S. Kety. Res. Publ. Assoc. Res. Nervous Mental Disease, 40: 311, 1962.
6. J. J. Schildkraut. Amer. J. Psychiat., 122: 509, 1965.
7. ──── J. J. Schildkraut, G. L. Klerman, R. Hammond, D. G. Friend, J. Psychiat. Res., 2: 257, 1964.
8. S. S. Kety. Pharmacol. Rev., 18: 787, 1966.
9. J. Axelrod. In *The Clinical Chemistry of Monoamines*, H. Varley and A. H. Gowenlock, editors, p. 5. Elsevier, Amsterdam, 1963. S. Eiduson, E. Geller, A. Yuwiler, B. T. Eiduson. *Biochemistry and Behavior*. Van Nostrand, Princeton, 1964. H. E. Himwich and W. A. Himwich, editors. *Progress in Brain Research*, vol. 8, *Biogenic Amines*. Elsevier, Amsterdam, 1964.
10. E. Costa and B. B. Brodie. In *Progress in Brain Research*, vol. 8, *Biogenic Amines*. H. E. Himwich and W. A. Himwich, editors, p. 168. Elsevier, Amsterdam, 1964.
11. P. R. Breggin. J. Nervous Mental Disease, 139: 558, 1964.
12. U. S. von Euler. Clin. Pharmacol. Therap., 5: 398, 1964.
13. B. B. Brodie. In *The Scientific Basis of Drug Therapy in Psychiatry*. Pergamon, Oxford, 1965.
14. G. L. Klerman and J. O. Cole. Pharmacol. Rev., 17: 101, 1965.
15. J. Durell and J. J. Schildkraut. In *American Handbook of Psychiatry*, S. Arieti, editor, vol. 3, p. 423. Basic Books, New York, 1966. D. X. Freedman and N. J. Giarman. In *EEG and Behavior*, G. A. Glaser, editor, p. 198. Basic Books, New York, 1963. A. J. Prange, Jr., Diseases Nervous System, 25: 217, 1964. J. de Ajuriaguerra, editor. *Monoamines et Systeme Nerveux Central*. Georg, Geneva, 1962. A. Bergsman. Acta Psychiat. Neurol. Scand. Suppl., 133: 1, 1959. R. A. Cohen, W. F. Bridgers, J. Axelrod, H. Weil-Malherbe, E. H. LeBrosse, W. E. Bunney, P. V. Cardon, S. S. Kety, Ann. Intern. Med., 56: 960, 1962. Symposium on catecholamines, section V. Pharmacol. Rev., 11: 483, 1959. D. X. Freedman. Amer. J. Psychiat., 119: 843, 1963.
16. M. Vogt. J. Physiol. London, 123: 451, 1954. A. Carlsson, M. Lindqvist, T. Magnusson. In *Adrenergic Mechanisms*, J. R. Vane, G. E. W. Wolstenholme, M. O'Connor, editors. Little, Brown, Boston, 1960. T. B. B. Crawford. In *5-Hydroxytryptamine*, G. P. Lewis, editor. Pergamon, London, 1958. H. McLennan. *Synaptic Transmission*. Saunders, Philadelphia, 1963.
17. J. Crossland. In *The Clinical Chemistry of Monoamines*, H. Varley and A. H. Gowenlock, editors. Elsevier, Amsterdam, 1963.
18. N. A. Hillarp, K. Fuxe, A. Dahlstrom. Pharmacol. Rev., 18: 727, 1966.
19. B. Falck. In *Progress in Brain Research*, vol. 8, *Biogenic Amines*, H. E. Himwich and W. A. Himwich, editors, p. 28. Elsevier, Amsterdam, 1964.
20. U. S. von Euler. *Noradrenaline*. Charles C Thomas, Springfield, Ill., 1956.
21. A. Carlsson. In *Progress in Brain Research*, vol. 8, *Biogenic Amines*, H. E. Himwich and W. A. Himwich, editors, p. 9. Elsevier, Amsterdam, 1964.
22. P. L. McGeer, E. G. McGeer, J. A. Wada. Arch. Neurol., 9: 81, 1963.
23. N. J. Giarman. Yale J. Biol. Med., 132: 73, 1959. V. P. Whittaker. In *Progress in Brain Research*, vol. 8, *Biogenic Amines*, H. E. Himwich and W. A. Himwich, editors, p. 90. Elsevier, Amsterdam, 1964. M. H. Aprison. Recent Advan. Biol. Psychiat., 4: 133, 1962.
24. I. J. Kopin, Pharmacol. Rev., 16: 179, 1964.
25. I. J. Kopin and E. K. Gordon. J. Pharmacol. Exp. Therap., 138: 351, 1962. I. J. Kopin and E. K. Gordon. J. Pharmacol. Exp. Therap., 140: 207, 1963.
26. J. Axelrod. In *Progress in Brain Research*, vol. 8, *Biogenic Amines*, H. E. Himwich and W. A. Himwich, editors, p. 81. Elsevier, Amsterdam, 1964. L. T. Potter and J. Axelrod. J. Pharmacol. Exp. Therap., 140: 199, 1963.

27. J. Glowinski, I. J. Kopin, J. Axelrod. J. Neurochem., *12:* 25, 1965.
28. J. Glowinski and J. Axelrod. J. Pharmacol. Exp. Therap., *149:* 43, 1965.
29. R. J. Wurtman and J. Axelrod. Science, *150:* 1464, 1965.
30. S. Garattini and L. Valzelli. *Serotonin.* Elsevier, Amsterdam, 1965.
31. S. Udenfriend. In *5-Hydroxytryptamine,* G. P. Lewis, editor. Pergamon, Oxford, 1958. N. J. Giarman and S. M. Schanberg. Biochem. Pharmacol., *1:* 301, 1958. S. M. Schanberg and N. J. Giarman. Biochem. Pharmacol., *11:* 187, 1962. H. Blaschko. In *5-Hydroxytryptamine,* G. P. Lewis, editor. Pergamon, Oxford, 1958.
32. G. P. Lewis, editor. *5-Hydroxytryptamine.* Pergamon, Oxford, 1958. R. J. Wurtman. New Engl. J. Med., *273:* 637, 1965. R. J. Wurtman. New Engl. J. Med., *273:* 693, 1965. R. J. Wurtman. New Engl. J. Med., *273:* 746, 1965. G. H. Acheson, editor. *Second Symposium on Catecholamines.* Williams & Wilkins, Baltimore, 1966. U. S. von Euler, S. Rosell, B. Uvnas, editors. *Mechanisms of Release of Biogenic Amines.* Pergamon, Oxford, 1966.
33. U. S. von Euler, C. Franksson, J. Hellstrom. Acta Physiol. Scand., *31:* 1, 1954.
34. H. Weil-Malherbe, J. Axelrod, R. Tomchick. Science, *129:* 1226, 1959.
35. J. Glowinski, I. J. Kopin, J. Axelrod. J. Neurochem., *12:* 25, 1965.
36. A. F. Ax. Psychosomat. Med., *15:* 433, 1953.
37. D. H. Funkenstein and L. W. Meade. J. Nervous Mental Disease, *119:* 380, 1954. D. H. Funkenstein. Sci. Amer., *192:* 74, 1955. D. H. Funkenstein, S. H. King, H. Stanley, M. E. Drolette. *Mastery of Stress.* Harvard University Press, Cambridge, 1957.
38. J. W. Mason, G. Mangan, J. V. Brady, D. Conrad, D. Rioch. Psychosomat. Med., *23:* 344, 1961.
39. F. Elmadjian, J. M. Hope, E. T. Lamson. J. Clin. Endocrinol., *17:* 608, 1957.
40. U. S. von Euler and U. Lundberg. J. Appl. Physiol., *6:* 551, 1954.
41. M. Goodall. J. Clin. Invest., *41:* 197, 1962.
42. A. J. Silverman and S. I. Cohen. Psychiat. Res. Rep. Amer. Psychiat. Assoc., *12:* 16, 1960. A. J. Silverman, S. I. Cohen, B. M. Shmavonian, N. Kirschner. Recent Advan. Biol. Psychiat., *3:* 104, 1961.
43. M. Frankenhaeuser and P. Patkai. Perceptual Motor Skills, *19:* 13, 1964.
44. L. Levi. Psychosomat. Med., *27:* 80, 1965.
45. S. S. Kety. In *Ultrastructure and Metabolism of the Nervous System,* S. R. Korey, A. Pope, E. Robins, editors, p. 311. Williams & Wilkins, Baltimore, 1962.
46. J. T. Wearn and C. C. Sturgis. Arch. Intern. Med., *24:* 247, 1919.
47. H. Basowitz, S. J. Korchin, D. Oken, M. S. Goldstein, H. Gussack. A.M.A. Arch. Neurol. Psychiat., *76:* 98, 1956.
48. E. Lindemann and J. E. Finesinger. Psychosomat. Med., *2:* 231, 1940.
49. D. R. Hawkins, J. T. Monroe, M. G. Sandifer, C. R. Vernon. Psychiat. Res. Rep. Amer. Psychiat. Assoc., *12:* 40, 1960.
50. H. Cantril and W. A. Hunt. Amer. J. Psychol., *44:* 300, 1932. D. Richter. Proc. Roy. Soc. Med., *33:* 615, 1940.
51. G. Maranon. Rev. Franc. Endocrinol., *2:* 301, 1924.
52. S. Schacter and J. E. Singer. Psychol. Rev., *69:* 379, 1962.
53. W. Pollin and S. Goldin. J. Psychiat. Res., *1:* 50, 1961.
54. A. B. Rothballer. Pharmacol. Rev., *11:* 494, 1959.
55. B. D. King, L. Sokoloff, R. L. Wechsler. J. Clin. Invest., *31:* 273, 1952. H. J. C. Swan. Brit. Med. J., *1952–I:* 1003, 1952.
56. W. James. *Principles of Psychology.* Holt, New York, 1890.
57. W. B. Cannon. Amer. J. Psychol., *39:* 106, 1927.
58. A. Carlsson. Neuropsychopharmacol., *2:* 417, 1961.

59. J. C. Muller, W. W. Pryer, J. E. Gibbons, E. S. Orgain. JAMA, 159: 836, 1955. R. W. P. Achor, N. O. Hanson, R. W. Gifford, Jr., JAMA, 159: 841, 1955. G. Lemieux, A. Davignon, J. Genest. Can. Med. Assoc. J., 74: 522, 1956.
60. O. Lingjaerde. Acta Psychiat. Neurol. Scand. Suppl., 170: 1, 1963.
61. S. Bernstein and M. R. Kaufman. J. Mount Sinai Hosp., 27: 525, 1960. F. J. Ayd, Jr. N. Y. J. Med., 58: 354, 1958.
62. M. Holzbauer and M. Vogt. J. Neurochem., 1: 8, 1956. A. Bertler, A. Carlsson, E. Rosengren. Naturwissenschaften, 22: 521, 1956. L. L. Iversen, J. Glowinski, J. Axelrod. J. Pharmacol. Exp. Therap., 150: 173, 1965. A. Pletscher, P. A. Shore, B. B. Brodie. Science, 122: 374, 1955. P. A. Shore, A. Pletscher, E. G. Tomich, A. Carlsson, R. Kuntzman, B. B. Brodie. Ann. N. Y. Acad. Sci., 66: 609, 1957. P. A. Shore. Pharmacol. Rev., 14: 531, 1962.
63. A. Carlsson, E. Rosengren, A. Bertler, J. Nillsson. In Psychotropic Drugs, S. Garattini and V. Ghetti, editors, p. 363. Elsevier, Amsterdam, 1957.
64. B. B. Brodie and P. A. Shore. Ann. N. Y. Acad. Sci., 66: 631, 1957.
65. B. B. Brodie, K. F. Finger, F. B. Orlans, G. P. Quinn, F. Sulser. J. Pharmacol. Exp. Therap., 129: 250, 1960.
66. J. Haggendal and M. Lindqvist. Acta Physiol. Scand., 60: 351, 1964.
67. J. Glowinski, L. Iversen, J. Axelrod. J. Pharmacol. Exp. Therap., 151: 385, 1966.
68. B. B. Brodie, M. S. Comer, E. Costa, A. Diabac. J. Phamacol. Exp. Therap., 152: 340, 1966.
69. A. Carlsson, M. Lindqvist, T. Magnusson. Nature, 180: 1200, 1957.
70. J. A. Wada, J. Wrinch, D. Hill, P. L. McGeer, E. G. McGeer. Arch. Neurol., 9: 69, 1963.
71. R. Degkwitz, R. Frowein, C. Kulenkampff, U. Mohs. Klin. Wochschr., 38: 120, 1960.
72. D. W. Woolley. The Biochemical Bases of Psychoses or the Serotonin Hypothesis about Mental Disease. Wiley, New York, 1962.
73. P. A. Shore, A. Pletscher, E. G. Timich, A. Carlsson, R. Kuntzman, B. B. Brodie. Ann. N. Y. Acad. Sci., 66: 609, 1957.
74. B. K. Koe and A. Weissman. Federation Proc., 25: 452, 1966.
75. M. A. Lipton and S. Udenfriend. Personal communication.
76. S. Spector, A. Sjoerdsma, S. Udenfriend. J. Pharmacol. Exp. Therap., 147: 86, 1965.
77. A. Weissman, B. K. Koe, S. S. Tenen. J. Pharmacol. Exp. Therap., 151: 339, 1966.
78. A. Carlsson, J. Jonasson, E. Rosengren. Acta Physiol. Scand., 59: 474, 1963. G. Sedvall and J. Thorson. Acta Physiol. Scand., 64: 251, 1965. N. E. Anden. Life Sci., 3: 19, 1964.
79. H. Green and J. L. Sawyer. In Biogenic Amines, H. E. Himwich and W. A. Himwich, editors, p. 150. Elsevier, Amsterdam, 1964. P. L. McGeer, E. G. McGeer, J. A. Wada. Arch. Neurol., 9: 91, 1963.
80. J. O. Cole. J. Amer. Med. Assoc., 190: 448, 1964.
81. A. Hordern. New Engl. J. Med., 272: 1159, 1965.
82. A. Feldstein, H. Hoagland, M. R. Oktem, H. Freeman. Intern. J. Neuropsychiat., 1: 384, 1965. E. Dunlop, E. DeFelice, J. R. Bergen, O. Resnick. Psychosomatics, 6: 1, 1965. J. W. Shaffer, W. R. Freinek, J. K. McCusker, E. A. DeFelice. J. New Drugs, 4: 288, 1964.
83. S. Spector, C. W. Hirsch, B. B. Brodie. Intern. J. Neuropharmacol., 2: 81, 1963. S. Spector, P. A. Shore, B. B. Brodie. J. Pharmacol. Exp. Therap., 128: 15, 1960.
84. M. Chessin, E. R. Kramer, C. T. Scott. J. Pharmacol. Exp. Therap., 119: 453, 1957.
85. L. Stein and O. S. Ray. Nature, 188: 1199, 1960.

86. E. B. Sigg, L. Soffer, L. Gyermek. J. Pharmacol. Exp. Therap., *142:* 13, 1963.
87. R. W. Ryall. Brit. J. Pharmacol., *17:* 339, 1961. H. Thoenen, A. Huerli-mann, W. Haefely. J. Pharmacol. Exp. Therap., *144:* 405, 1965. S. Gershon, G. Holmberg. E. Mattsson, N. Mattsson, A. Marshall. Arch. Gen. Psychiat., *6:* 96, 1962.
88. L. Gyermek and C. Possemato. Med. Exp., *3:* 225, 1960.
89. G. Hertting, J. Axelrod, L. G. Whitby. J. Pharmacol. Exp. Therap., *134:* 146, 1961.
90. E. B. Sigg. Can. Psychiat. Assoc. J., *4:* suppl. 1, 75, 1959.
91. J. Glowinski and J. Axelrod. Nature, *204:* 1318, 1964.
92. S. M. Schanberg, J. J. Schildkraut, I. J. Kopin. Biochem. Pharmacol., *16:* 393, 1967.
93. I. J. Kopin. Pharmacol. Rev., *18:* 513, 1966.
94. A. J. Eisenfeld, L. Krakoff, L. L. Iversen, J. Axelrod. Nature, *213:* 297, 1967. A. J. Eisenfeld, J. Axelrod, L, Krakoff. J. Pharmacol. Exp. Therap., in press.
95. F. Sulser, M. H. Bickel, B. B. Brodie. J. Pharmacol. Exp. Therap., *144:* 321, 1964.
96. C. L. Scheckel and E. Boff, Psychopharmacologia, *5:* 198, 1964.
97. L. S. Goodman and A. Gilman. *The Pharmacological Bases of Therapeutics,* ed. 2. Macmillan, New York, 1955.
98. L. L. Iverson. J. Pharm. Pharmacol., *16:* 435, 1964.
99. L. Stein. In *Psychosomatic Medicine,* J. H. Nodine and J. H. Moyer, editors, p. 297. Lea and Febiger, Philadelphia, 1962. P. L. Carlton, Psychopharmacologia, *2:* 364, 1961. A. Weissman. Pharmacologist, *3:* 60, 1961.
100. K. E. Moore and E. W. Lariviere. Biochem. Pharmacol., *12:* 1283, 1963. C. B. Smith. J. Pharmacol. Exp. Therap., *147:* 96, 1965.
101. K. E. Moore and E. W. Lariviere. Biochem. Pharmacol., *13:* 1098, 1964.
102. J. M. Van Rossum, J. B. Van Der Schoot, J. A. T. M. Horkmans. Experientia, *18:* 229, 1962. C. B. Smith, J. Pharmacol. Exp. Therap., *142:* 343, 1963.
103. F. Cade. Med. J. Australia, *2:* 349, 1949. M. Schou. Psychopharmacologia, *1:* 65, 1959. S. Gershon and A. Yuwiler. J. Neuropsychiat., *1:* 299, 1960.
104. J. J. Schildkraut, S. M. Schanberg, I. J. Kopin, Life Sci., *5:* 1479, 1966.
105. L. C. F. Hanson. Psychopharmacologia, *8:* 100, 1965.
106. A. Weissman and B. K. Koe. Life Sci., *4:* 1037, 1965.
107. A. Sjoerdsma, K. Engleman, S. Spector, S. Udenfriend. Lancet, *1965-II:* 1092, 1965.
108. J. Olds and P. Milner. J. Comp. Physiol. Psychol., *47:* 419, 1954.
109. J. Olds. Physiol. Rev., *42:* 554, 1962. L. Stein. In *The Role of Pleasure in Behavior,* R. G. Heath, editor, p. 113. Harper & Row, New York, 1964.
110. L. Stein. Recent Advan. Biol. Psychiat., *4:* 288, 1962. B. P. H. Poschel and F. W. Ninteman. Life Sci., *3:* 903, 1964.
111. L. Stein. In *Antidepressant Drugs,* S. Garutini and M. N. G. Dukes, editors. Excerpta Medica Foundation, Amsterdam, 1967.
112. L. Stein and J. Seifter. Science, *134:* 286, 1961.
113. L. Stein. In *Psychosomatic Medicine,* J. H. Nodine and J. H. Moyer, editors, p. 297. Lea and Febiger, Philadelphia, 1962. L. Stein. Federation Proc., *23:* 836, 1964.
114. B. P. H. Poschel and F. W. Ninteman. Life Sci., *2:* 782, 1963.
115. D. J. Reis and L. M. Gunne. Science, *149:* 450, 1965.
116. R. Strom-Olsen and H. Weil-Malherbe. J. Mental Sci., *104:* 696, 1958.
117. N. Shinfuku, D. Michio, K. Masao. Yonago Acta Med., *5:* 109, 1961.
118. A. Bergsman. Acta Psychiat. Neurol. Scand. Suppl., *133:* 1959.

119. G. C. Curtis, R. A. Cleghorn, T. L. Sourkes. J. Psychosomat. Res., 4: 176, 1960.
120. J. J. Schildkraut, E. K. Gordon, J. Durell. J. Psychiat. Res., 3: 213, 1965. J. J. Schildkraut, R. Green, E. K. Gordon, J. Durell. Amer. J. Psychiat., 123: 690, 1966.
121. N. T. Karki. Acta Physiol. Scand. Suppl., 132: 1, 1956.
122. S. Rosenblatt and J. D. Chanley. Arch. Gen. Psychiat., 13: 495, 1965.
123. W. Studnitz. J. Clin. Lab. Invest., 11: 224, 1959. R. R. Schopbach, A. R. Kelly, J. S. Lukaszewski. In Progress in Brain Research, vol. 8, Biogenic Amines, H. E. Himwich and W. A. Himwich, editors, p. 207. Elsevier, Amsterdam, 1964. A. Sjoerdsma, L. Gillespie, Jr., S. Udenfriend. Lancet, 1958-II: 159, 1958.
124. J. J. Schildkraut, E. K. Gordon, J. Durell. J. Psychiat. Res., 3: 213, 1965.
125. R. K. McDonald and V. K. Weise. J. Psychiat. Res., 1: 173, 1962. A. Allegranza, R. Bozzi, A. Bruno. J. Nervous Mental Disease, 140: 207, 1965.
126. G. W. Ashcroft and D. F. Sharman. Nature, 186: 1050, 1960.
127. A. Coppen, D. M. Shaw, A. Malleson. Brit. J. Psychiat., 111: 105, 1965.
128. A. Coppen, D. M. Shaw, A. Malleson, S. Eccleston, G. Gundy. Brit J. Psychiat., 111: 993, 1965.
129. W. Pollin, P. V. Cardon, Jr., S. S. Kety. Science, 133: 104, 1961.
130. A. J. Coppen, D. M. Shaw, J. P. Farrell. Lancet, 1963-I: 79, 1963. C. M. B. Pare. Lancet, 1963-II: 527, 1963.
131. B. Smith and D. J. Prockop. New Engl. J. Med., 267: 1338, 1962.
132. N. S. Kline and W. Sacks. Amer. J. Psychiat., 120: 274, 1963. N. S. Kline, W. Sacks, G. M. Simpson. Amer. J. Psychiat., 121: 379, 1964.
133. C. M. B. Pare and M. Sandler. J. Neurol. Neurosurg. Psychiat., 22: 247, 1959.
134. G. L. Klerman, J. J. Schildkraut, L. L. Hasenbush, M. Greenblatt, D. G. Friend. J. Psychiat. Res., 1: 289, 1963.
135. W. J. Turner and S. Merlis. Diseases Nervous System, 25: 538, 1964.
136. N. Matussek. Personal communication.
137. J. J. Schildkraut, G. L. Klerman, D. G. Friend, M. Greenblatt. Ann. N. Y. Acad. Sci., 107: 1005, 1963.
138. W. Poldinger, Psychopharmacologia, 4: 308, 1963. P. Dick and P. Roch. In Antidepressant Drugs, S. Garutini and M. N. G. Dukes, editors. Excerpta Medica Foundation, Amsterdam, 1967.
139. G. Holmberg. Intern. Rev. Neurobiol., 5: 389, 1963. L. L. Havens, M. S. Zileli, A. DiMascio, L. Boling, A. Goldfien. In Biological Psychiatry, J. H. Masserman, editor, vol. 1, p. 120. Grune & Stratton, New York, 1959. H. Weil-Malherbe. J. Mental Sci., 101: 156, 1955. B. Cochran, Jr., and E. P. Marbach. Recent Advan. Biol. Psychiat., 4: 154, 1962.
140. S. Rosenblatt, J. D. Chanley, H. Sobotka, M. R. Kaufman. J. Neurochem., 5: 172, 1960.

CHAPTER 5

Sleep and Dreams

WILLIAM C. DEMENT, M.D., Ph.D.

INTRODUCTION

SLEEP MAY be briefly characterized as a readily reversible suspension of sensorimotor interaction with the environment, usually associated with recumbency and immobility. As such, it appears to interrupt wakefulness periodically in vertebrate organisms, but its presence may become difficult to establish in lower organisms and plants, where it blurs with transitory intervals of inactivity resulting from environmental influences; or in higher organisms, where it is difficult to differentiate from such borderline conditions as hibernations, anesthesia, trance, and coma.

Sleep has great practical interest for biologists and psychiatrists from several points of view: (1) It provides a basal background state against which arousal or vigilance mechanisms may be superimposed and studied; (2) it poses problems related to its seeming obligatory universality; (3) it provides the physiological background for the experience of dreaming; and (4) it has clinical implications, especially in regard to sleep disturbances and the relationship of sleep to psychopathology.

The field of sleep research has been unusually active in the last few years. As a consequence, there is no simple answer to the question, "What is sleep?" The major complication in answering this question, even from a descriptive viewpoint, is the recent finding that sleep is not one thing but at least two entirely different things. It is now generally accepted that there are two kinds of sleep, which are sufficiently disparate to raise the question of whether the term "sleep" should, in fact, apply to both. Moreover, within each of these major divisions, there are variations of one sort or another. It appears that our understanding of sleep mechanisms has developed to a point where no unitary explanation will suffice for all the phenomena that have been observed.

Unfortunately, there is no standard nomenclature for the two kinds of sleep, and a bewildering array of names have been used. The single term "sleep" served to cover all eventualities, with the exception of borderline states, until 1953, when Aserinsky and Kleitman at the University of Chicago reported the occurrence of rapid eye movements in sleeping subjects. It is now known that these rapid eye movements occur during a specific state, to which the term rapid eye movement (REM) sleep has been applied by some workers. In line with this, the remainder of sleep has been designated as non-rapid eye movement (NREM) sleep. A number of other labels have been applied. For example, REM sleep is also called "dreaming sleep," "paradoxical sleep," "fast sleep," "deep sleep," and "rhombencephalic sleep." NREM sleep has been called "slow sleep," "neocortical sleep," "light sleep," and "classical sleep."

Prior to the discovery of rapid eye movements, there was no suspicion that sleep was more than one thing. In general, it was felt that organisms with complex nervous systems existed on a sort of vertical continuum of sleep and wakefulness. It was assumed that, depending on the degree of central nervous activity, the organism would shift about on this continuum, through a range extending from deep sleep to a highly alert state. Thus, sleep was essentially a uniform state, varying only in intensity or depth. A great deal of early data was derived from single observations that were generalized to include the entire sleep period, the investigator feeling no need to repeat his observations in other segments of this presumably uniform state. Furthermore, some experimental studies must have confounded the two states. In the case of total sleep deprivation, for example, the organism is being simultaneously deprived of two entirely different things.

For a variety of reasons, the probability that most observations on sleep actually dealt with NREM sleep is quite high. The current situation is somewhat analogous to a Newtonian versus an Einsteinian view of physical systems. The latter does not invalidate the former; it is, rather, an extension. If most of the information obtained on sleep prior to the discovery of rapid eye movements is assumed to apply to NREM sleep, the more recent findings on both kinds of sleep simply fill out and extend the picture.

NREM SLEEP

Ordinarily, the normal adult mammal, in going to sleep, passes from wakefulness into that state now known as NREM sleep. With occasional exceptions, this process is closely associated with a marked behavioral change from movement and uprightness to stillness and recumbency. Humans—but probably not animals—can mimic many of the gross behavioral aspects of sleep. Such things as eye closure, stillness, and regular breathing can be easily simulated. Other attributes of sleep may be brought about by relaxation and recumbency alone. Because of these factors, more penetrating measures have been utilized to establish the presence of sleep. Of these, perhaps the most widely used is the electroencephalogram (EEG), which has been particularly well studied in the human.

EEG

For all practical purposes, the electroencephalogram (EEG) defines the presence of NREM sleep in the human. Actually, a small sample of brain waves contains a highly complex mixture of amplitudes and frequencies, but certain ones usually predominate and may serve to characterize the sample. It has been possible to divide the continuum of change in EEG rhythms through wakefulness and NREM sleep into several easily recognized stages. Interestingly enough, the widest range of gross variation occurs in NREM sleep, not in wakefulness. A typical categorization is illustrated in Figure 1. These definitions are strictly valid only for the human adult. In younger age groups, the overall frequency spectrum of the EEG is shifted toward the slow side, and classification must be altered to take this into account.

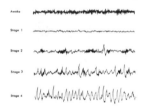

FIGURE 1. EEG tracings of sleep stages. These sample tracings of a subject's brain waves were made during a single night. The recording paper was moving under the pens at one-third the standard speed, which means that the waves are somewhat pushed together. The top line shows the 10-per-second alpha waves characteristic of the awake EEG. Their mean amplitude is about 50 microvolts. The stage 1 tracing shows a mixture of low-voltage, irregular, relatively fast waves. The stage 2 tracing shows the characteristic waxing-waning bursts of regular waves (sleep spindles) lasting one to two seconds. The frequency of the spindle waves is about 12 to 14 a second, which causes them to be somewhat blurred at this paper speed. Nonetheless, they stand out sharply from the low-voltage, irregular background rhythms. A moderate amount of high-voltage, slow-activity waves is seen in the stage 3 tracing. Stage 4 is characterized by continuous high-voltage, slow-activity waves. Their frequency is about one a second. (From Dement, W. C. An essay on dreams. In *New Directions in Psychology*, vol. 2. Holt, Rinehart and Winston, New York, 1965.)

Figure 2 shows the plots of all-night recordings for three representative nights of sleep. The dark bars represent REM sleep, which is discussed below. The time spent in the various stages and their periodicity are relatively constant from night to night in human subjects. These EEG stages have been presumed to indicate the depth of sleep, with the high-amplitude, slow-wave phase representing the maximum depth. It should be noted that stage 4, the high-voltage, slow-activity period, occurs mostly in the early hours of the night.

Prolonged sleep deprivation does not change the amplitude or frequency of stage 4 patterns. If amplitude and frequency are taken as some measure of depth of sleep, no increase in depth follows even as much as eleven days of total sleep deprivation. There is every likelihood that the various predominant wave patterns of these stages are produced by specific neural mechanisms and remain constant in their form, unless the mechanisms are altered by serious damage.

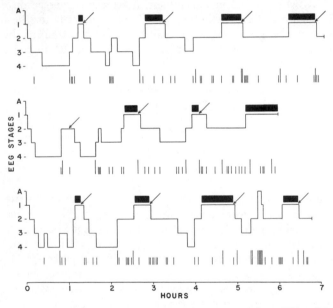

FIGURE 2. Plots of EEG stages during three nights. The *thick bars* above the EEG lines indicate periods during which rapid eye movements were seen. The *arrows* indicate the end of one EEG cycle and the beginning of the next. The vertical lines below each plot stand for body movements. The longer lines indicate large movement, changes in position of the whole body; the shorter lines represent smaller movements. (Reprinted by permission from Dement, W. C., and Kleitman, N. Cyclic variations in EEG during sleep and their relation to eye movements, body motility, and dreaming. Electroenceph. Clin. Neurophysiol., 9: 673, 1957.)

The NREM sleep EEG is not usually subdivided in other animals, with the exception of primates. For example, in the cat the NREM sleep EEG is characterized by a combination of slow waves and spindles with little variability. It is of more than passing interest that an NREM sleep EEG is frequently seen in the cat when behavioral sleep, in the sense of recumbency, is not actually present. In most such cases the animal is obviously not wide awake. However, some animals can apparently sleep in a sitting or standing position quite readily. These observations support findings in which a dissociation between EEG patterns and behavior has been demonstrated pharmacologically and surgically, with frank sleep or waking patterns accompanying their behavioral opposites.

SKELETAL MUSCULAR ACTIVITY

Sleep has always been considered a time of muscular relaxation in the service of rest and restoration, and in almost all cases a recumbent position is assumed. In humans, a deliberate reduction of muscular activity always precedes sleep.

In NREM sleep there is immobility, and muscular tension in the usual sense is not present. However, if electromyographic (EMG) recordings are taken, one finds that EMG potentials continue to be present in a tonic fashion during NREM sleep. In addition, a number of spinal reflex responses may be readily elicited, particularly the tendon reflexes. And special conditions invariably associated with sleep are contractions, or at least resistance to forcing from inside, of anal and vesicular sphincters.

A great deal of body movement is initiated during NREM sleep, but it is a moot question as to whether or not sleep is actually present in the usual sense during the movement. EEG tracings at these moments generally show changes suggesting transient wakefulness, but the subject is not necessarily responsive, nor is he likely to recall having moved. A recent study of sleepwalkers has shown that, even during actual locomotion, the brain waves do not show fully awake patterns. Thus, the sleepwalker is actually asleep, even though walking. All of this points to a diminution of motor activity during NREM sleep but no active and potent inhibition of motor functions.

OCULOMOTOR ACTIVITY

NREM sleep has its own characteristic eyeball activity—a slow, pendulous, side-to-side movement. One of the most precise indicators of some fairly abrupt transition from wakefulness to sleep, in humans at least, is the appearance of this slow oscillation of the eyes. These slow movements may occur even before there is evidence of a brain wave change. Their appearance is paralleled by a psychological alteration: The predominant mental content changes from the conceptual mode to the perceptual mode. In other words, the appearance of these eye movements correlates with the occurrence of hypnagogic imagery.

Respiratory Activity

A respiratory change is often considered one of the cardinal signs of sleep. Snoring, in particular, makes the presence of sleep almost certain unless it is being simulated. However, some investigators have found no difference in respiratory rates during NREM sleep and during quiet wakefulness. Nonetheless, in contrast to the vast repertoire of responses of the respiratory apparatus during wakefulness, NREM sleep is characterized by a relatively slow, regular respiratory cycle.

Of greater significance is an increase in alveolar CO_2 during sleep. This increase suggests a decrease in excitability of the respiratory center. Ventilatory response to CO_2 is found to be decreased during NREM sleep, with the decrement being proportional to the depth of sleep as measured by the EEG. The change in ventilatory response with the onset of sleep or arousal is so abrupt that a neural mechanism is strongly suggested.

Cardiovascular Activity

As might be expected, heart rate is slowed during NREM sleep, although there is considerable variation from subject to subject, and blood pressure generally falls during the night. Peripheral vasodilation is closely associated with the onset of sleep. In cats, however, direct measurement of blood pressure by arterial cannulation has shown that almost no change occurs in the transition from wakefulness to NREM sleep. Using the nitrous oxide technique, one can demonstrate a statistically significant increase in cerebral blood flow; this is of theoretical importance in eliminating cerebral anemia from consideration as a cause of sleep. Cerebral oxygen uptake during NREM sleep does not appear to be changed. However, a recent investigation has shown that there is a drop in the whole organism's oxygen consumption that tends to parallel the EEG stages.

Other Bodily Activities

Falling body temperature, increasing basal skin resistance, and decreasing urinary output serve to distinguish NREM sleep from wakefulness. There is little evidence to support the presence of a characteristic change in the activity of the gastrointestinal tract. Spontaneous changes in basal skin potential occur much more frequently during NREM sleep stage 4 than at any other time. The basis for this autonomic hyperactivity, which is analagous to the very alert waking state, is unclear.

NREM Sleep Versus Wakefulness

A large share of the studies of the physiological concomitants of sleep have been done on humans because their sleep is regular and predictable. However, one difficulty in attempting to assign particular significance to any physiological alteration is that many changes thought to be characteristic of sleep can be brought about merely by assuming a recumbent position.

Certainly an important feature of NREM sleep is its overall low level of activity. Since most of our older notions about sleep as a whole are based almost exclusively on the physiology of the NREM phase, its low level of activity is responsible for the idea that the essential difference between wakefulness and sleep *is* the level of activity. This is unquestionably true when comparing NREM sleep to wakefulness as a whole, but it fails to take into account the tremendous repertoire of the waking state.

The main reason we think of sleep as a slowing down, a resting or idling state, is that we generally compare it to the active waking state. The fact is that most of the changes thought to be characteristic of falling asleep are actually a result of recumbency and relaxation and can be easily achieved while still awake. If a subject lies down in a quiet room and closes his eyes and relaxes both physically and mentally, nearly every physiological measurement will show a decline in activity. The cardiac and respiratory rates will slow down, blood pressure will fall, body temperature will drop, metabolic activity will decrease. If recumbency and relaxation are maintained long enough, there may be no further change in any of these measurements when sleep finally intervenes. Accordingly, the essential difference between wakefulness and NREM sleep may not lie in the absolute level of activity in these various functions.

Interaction with the environment. The difference between wakefulness and NREM sleep may lie in the less easily quantifiable change in attentiveness and responsiveness to the outside world. Levels of activity in the waking state are usually higher than in NREM sleep because the former state is ordinarily a time of interacting with the environment. When we *voluntarily* suspend this interaction with the environment, we may achieve a low level of activity, but we are still awake. When the suspension is *involuntary*, we are asleep.

The onset of sleep is associated with a marked and abrupt change in sensorimotor function or sensory responsiveness. This change seems to be fairly accurately paralleled by EEG changes and the appearance of slow eye movements. A dramatic illustration of this parallelism has been observed in subjects whose eyes were taped open. The subjects were able to fall asleep under these conditions. While awake, they were stimulated repeatedly with a bright light, which they easily apprehended. However, at the instant the slow eye movement appeared, even before EEG changes were apparent, the bright flash of light was not consciously experienced or later recalled by the subjects. In another experiment, subjects whose eyes were taped open were stimulated intensively in all modalities and were still able to fall asleep.

Diurnal rhythm. Newborn babies show no consistent relationship of body temperature to time of day. However, within six to ten weeks, there is a distinct diurnal variation, with lower body temperatures occurring at night. This cycle continues, for all practical purposes, throughout life. Its development and maintenance stem from being born into and living in a family and community run according to alterations of day and night. Nearly every visceral function, including temperature, gets pulled into the cycle.

During complete sleep deprivation in adults the twenty-four-hour rhythms or circadian (around twenty-four hours) rhythms continue to occur. In studies at Walter Reed Hospital, body temperatures were recorded during sleep deprivation lasting four days. A diurnal variation was found that was nearly identical with that seen during a baseline period. The same sort of variation during prolonged wakefulness occurs in adrenal steroid excretion, urinary output, etc. Changes ascribed to sleep, particularly in human subjects, may be attributed to the diurnal rhythm of many bodily functions.

Summary. If one were to characterize the basic nature of NREM sleep, the definition would have to be in terms of some sort of change in the pattern of organization of cerebral activity in which there is a profound effect on sensorimotor interaction with the environment. Absolute changes in level of activity are in large part artifactual.

REM SLEEP

The first hint of the dual nature of sleep came with the observation by Aserinsky and Kleitman, reported in 1953, that during certain periods of sleep the eyes of human subjects moved rapidly. Further studies of eye movements in conjunction with other variables established that these periods were so radically different from the remainder of sleep that the unitary concept of sleep simply would not suffice.

ELECTRICAL ACTIVITY OF THE BRAIN

Rapid eye movements during sleep take place within discrete intervals that are characterized by a particular EEG pattern similar to that of stage 1 (see Figure 1), a low-voltage, relatively fast, mixed-frequency pattern. Initially, this REM sleep pattern seemed to be identical with the NREM stage 1 pattern, which suggested that the eye movement periods represented the lightest phase of cyclic variation in depth of sleep. However, the pattern associated with REM periods actually includes saw-tooth waves that are unique to these periods (see Figure 3).

REM sleep exists throughout the family of mammals. In subhuman species, with the possible exception of the chimpanzee, the EEG during REM sleep is indistinguishable from that seen during wakefulness. Subcortical structures show unique patterns, with particular emphasis being placed on hippocampal theta rhythms seen in the cat, rat, rabbit, and (to some extent) the monkey, but not the human. This pattern is generally associated with a high degree of arousal when seen during wakefulness.

In addition, spikelike discharges appear in the pons and visual system

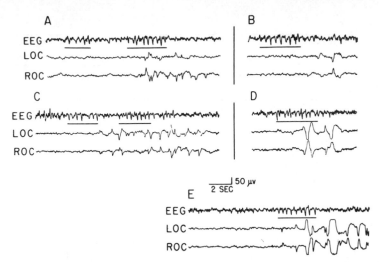

FIGURE 3. REM sleep EEG patterns. These sample tracings show the saw-tooth waves that precede bursts of rapid eye movement. EEG is monopolar from the central electrode; LOC, left outer canthus to ears; ROC, right outer canthus to ears. (From Dement, W. C. Eye movements in sleep. In *The Oculomotor System*, M. Bender, editor. Hoeber Medical Division, Harper & Row, New York, 1964.)

during REM sleep. These discharges are unique to the REM period and are simultaneous with or actually trigger the rapid eye movements.

OCULOMOTOR ACTIVITY

Eye movements, which are one of the most striking characteristics of the REM state, are bilaterally synchronous in the human and move with a velocity that approaches or equals that exhibited during fixation shifts in the waking state. There is no particular pattern to the movement (see Figure 4), but a complex combination of all sizes and directions of arc are seen. The resemblance to purposeful waking movements is quite striking. During these movements, subjects sleeping with the eyelids taped open look uncannily awake. In the monkey, eyelid relaxation in REM sleep permits direct observation of the eyeballs; the pupils are constricted during REM sleep, and there is a certain amount of slow eye movement.

CARDIOVASCULAR ACTIVITY

In human subjects the heart rate shows a small degree of acceleration and increased variability during REM sleep as compared to adjacent periods of NREM sleep. Blood pressure rises, and finger pulse volume, which is a measure of peripheral vasoconstriction, is usually decreased.

In the cat the heart rate is more likely to be decreased during REM sleep, and blood pressure shows a consistent drop. Cerebrocortical blood flow is markedly increased in the cat, and plethysmographic techniques

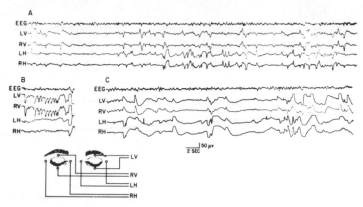

FIGURE 4. Sample tracings of rapid eye movements showing that they are binocularly synchronous. The concomitant EEG is low-voltage, non-spindling. The four eye movement pens give the left and right vertical and horizontal derivations as shown in the diagram. (Reprinted by permission from Dement, W. C. Eye movements during sleep. In *The Oculomotor System*, M. Bender, editor. Hoeber Medical Division, Harper & Row, New York, 1964.)

indicate an increase in cerebral pulse volume. There is also a rise in cerebral spinal fluid pressure, which suggests an increase in cerebral blood flow.

RESPIRATORY ACTIVITY

Respiration is dramatically changed during REM sleep, with an overall acceleration and a striking increase in variability. The major volumetric change appears to be episodic shallowing, and these periods are usually associated with bursts of eye movement and a decrease in oxygen saturation of the blood. Recent studies have shown that there is an increase in oxygen utilization during REM sleep in the human.

GASTROINTESTINAL ACTIVITY

An old study by Lockhardt described the inhibition of gastric motility during periods of sleep in the dog that were characterized by twitching limb movements. Although REM sleep was unknown at the time, these twitching movements were almost certainly those that characterize this state. Studies of gastric acid secretion have shown a slight elevation in REM sleep and a dramatic elevation during REM sleep in peptic ulcer patients.

GENITOURINARY ACTIVITY

There appears to be a decrease in urinary output during REM sleep. Of great interest are recent studies indicating that the REM period is characterized by penile erection. This has been seen in newborn infants as well as adult males. It has also been seen in cats and monkeys.

INTEGUMENTARY ACTIVITY

Spontaneous changes in skin resistance are decreased during REM sleep, and there is no consistent change in basal skin resistance.

NEUROPHYSIOLOGY

Microelectrode studies on unrestrained and unanesthetized animals reveal that REM sleep is almost invariably accompanied by a marked increase in spontaneous neuronal discharge. This increase has been seen in the visual cortex, mesencephalic reticular formation, pontine reticular formation, vestibular nuclei, lateral geniculate nuclei, and sensorimotor cortex. The discharge tends to be more paroxysmal than patterned. In addition, recent findings have shown an increase in pyramidal tract discharge.

Measurements of brain temperature indicate a substantial rise during REM sleep. There is also a marked negative shift of the transcortical DC potential. Evoked potential measurements suggest that the REM state is akin to the waking state in the handling of sensory input. There is also contraction of the middle ear muscles. When the middle ear muscles are cut, inhibition of auditory evoked potential disappears.

MUSCULAR ACTIVITY

One of the more dramatic aspects of REM sleep is the presence of peripheral twitching movements of limbs, facial muscles, etc. In dogs, particularly pets, these twitches account for the frequently described running movements that owners have inferred to be associated with dreams of chasing rabbits. However, the twitches are entirely phasic in nature, with virtually no tonic component.

An important feature of REM sleep is the presence of a tonic inhibition of motor output. Jouvet, the first to study muscular activity during REM sleep, observed the disappearance of EMG potentials (see Figure 5) and the complete abolition of decerebellate rigidity, which were present during NREM sleep. Reflex discharges are also completely suppressed. The organism during REM sleep is completely flaccid. The only muscles that maintain tonicity appear to be certain special groups, such as the extraocular muscles, middle ear muscles, and anal and vesicular sphincters.

REM SLEEP VERSUS WAKEFULNESS

As the descriptive work proceeds, it is likely that any variable studied will show some kind of unique or dramatic change in association with the REM state. A question suggests itself at this point: How can we call the REM period a state of sleep or even one kind of sleep? REM sleep is very different from the ordinary conception of sleep as a state of rest, and it is very different from NREM sleep, a state of regular, low-level activity. The

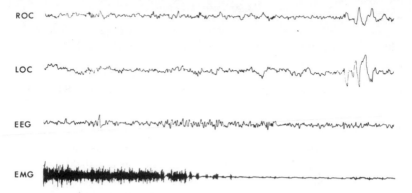

FIGURE 5. The onset of REM sleep. Electrode placements: *ROC*, right outer canthus referred to ears; *LOC*, left outer canthus referred to ears; *EEG*, left parietal electrode referred to left occipital electrode; *EMG*, bipolar electrodes placed on anterior neck muscles. Note that the tonic EMG potentials that were present all during NREM sleep disappear rather abruptly. A few seconds later, the first rapid eye movement potentials appear (at the *right of the figure* in ROC and LOC). Although it is not obvious in this brief segment of record, the EEG has changed to stage 1. (From Dement, W. C. An essay on dreams. In *New Directions in Psychology*, vol. 2. Holt, Rinehart and Winston, New York, 1965.)

real question, however, is: What holds the organism to its sleeping position in the face of all the central nervous activity? The probable answer is that REM sleep, in contrast to wakefulness, is a time during which a tonic inhibitory influence is brought to bear upon motor outflow. This has the effect of either attenuating or blocking the complex motor output that is elaborated at higher levels.

Temporal relationship of REM Sleep and NREM Sleep

Just as all mammals that have been studied show the occurrence of two kinds of sleep, they also show a characteristic cyclic alternation between the two during any lengthy period of total sleep. In the human, REM sleep interrupts NREM sleep on the average of once every 90 minutes, lasts approximately 20 minutes, and accounts for 20 to 25 per cent of the total sleep time in young adults. In the cat, REM periods last about 7 minutes and NREM periods last about 10 to 20 minutes. In the rat, REM periods last about 1 to 2 minutes and NREM periods last about 7 to 8 minutes.

Figure 2 shows the typical sleep cycle for the adult human. NREM sleep is predominantly stage 4 in the early periods of the night, and the REM periods tend to get longer as the night wears on. This particular characteristic is more typical of humans than of other species.

The periods devoted to REM sleep and to NREM sleep vary according to age. In the immediate neonatal period in humans, REM sleep accounts for 50 per cent or more of the total time spent in sleep. Since the infant sleeps more than an adult, he experiences about four to eight times as much REM sleep as the adult. An even greater percentage of REM sleep occurs in the premature infant. This suggests that, at some point in its intrauterine existence, the human organism has nothing but REM sleep. This point of view receives support from observations on newborn kittens, in which REM sleep appears to occupy 100 per cent of the sleeping time.

In all normal adult organisms, NREM sleep generally occurs first and is then interrupted by REM sleep. Only in special circumstances do mammalian organisms go directly from wakefulness into the REM state.

DREAMING

REM sleep has also been called "dreaming sleep," for it appears to be associated with dreaming activity in a very intimate fashion. Human subjects, when awakened during REM sleep, report complex dream experiences in a high percentage of cases. In addition, the length of the REM sleep period corresponds to the length of the recalled dream. The patterns of the rapid eye movements themselves are intimately related to the visual imagery in a way that suggests the dreamer is, in fact, watching his dream. (Figure 6 shows an example of the correspondence between dream content and eye movements.) Supporting this notion are the facts that the eye movements *do* resemble purposeful waking movements and that the neurophysiological background of the REM state *is* compatible with a

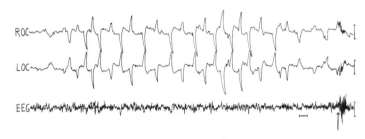

FIGURE 6. Example of rapid eye movement-dream imagery correspondence. After an amazingly regular sequence of twenty-six eye movements alternating leftward-rightward, the subject was awakened (*arrow*). In his dream narrative, he reported that, just prior to being aroused, he was standing at the side of a ping pong table, watching a game between two friends and looking back and forth to follow the ball. He stated that a fairly lengthy volley had just taken place. (*ROC*, right outer canthus monopolar electrode; *LOC*, left outer canthus monopolar electrode; *EEG*, monopolar parieto-occipital electrode. Calibrations, 1 second and 50 microvolts.) (Courtesy of William C. Dement.)

waking level of function.

However, the so-called scanning hypothesis of rapid eye movements has been called into question by a number of findings. Among these are the occurrence of rapid eye movements in newborn infants, decorticated animals, and subjects who have been blind from birth. Also, the close relationship of eye movements to the pontine spike discharges, although it has not been shown in humans, suggests a different kind of mechanism. Eye movements may occur as part of a nonspecific neural activation in young organisms that is later integrated into the total psychophysiological experience. In cats, as opposed to primates, the eye movements do not appear to resemble scanning movements; rather, they resemble nystagmoid jerks.

The problem of whether or not dreaming is exclusively confined to REM sleep seemed unimportant in the original series of studies because dream recall from awakenings during NREM sleep was at such a low level. However, more recent studies have suggested that something akin to dreaming does occur in NREM sleep, particularly at the onset of sleep, and that mental activity does take place during NREM sleep. The problem of the definition of a dream is basic to this difficulty. In general, the experiences during REM sleep appear to be more vivid, complex, emotional, and bizarre than those during NREM sleep. Recall of dreams from REM sleep seems less dependent on variables that seem to influence the incidence of recall from NREM sleep.

REM period awakenings to gather dream content from laboratory subjects have afforded considerable insight into the psychological aspects of sleep. The richness and variety of dream experience is quite impressive when the opportunity of recall is optimal. In addition, it has been shown that dream content can be influenced by external stimuli, presleep experiences, certain chemical agents, and hypnosis.

Summary

It has been suggested that during the REM state the brain is doing everything it would be doing if the same experience were occurring in the waking state, except that it is receiving no sensory input. In addition to an elaboration of motor output to the extraocular muscles, there are middle ear muscle contractions of a dramatic degree. And there is very likely an organized motor output to the skeletal muscles. The only thing lacking in this quasi-awake dream state is the sensory input. The endogenous elaboration of this sensory input is one of the mysteries of dream formation.

MECHANISMS OF SLEEP

NREM Sleep Mechanism Theories

In the past, sleep was thought of as a period of minimal functioning of the organism that ostensibly fulfilled a need for rest and restoration. The main problem was how this low level of function was achieved. This question now applies to NREM sleep only.

Reduction of afferent impulses. One of the most popular early theories attributed sleep to an active inhibition of nervous activity, mainly at the cortical level. However, Kleitman emphasized that sleep could also be thought of as a passive state, requiring no special mechanisms for its onset, and that the real problem was to explain the initiation and maintenance of wakefulness. He marshalled a great deal of evidence to support the hypothesis that the nervous system is maintained in a state of waking activity by the constant bombardment of afferent impulses and that the immediate cause of sleep is the reduction of afferent inflow below some critical level necessary for the waking state.

A classical experiment supporting this hypothesis was done by Bremer, who showed that transection of the brain stem at the midcollicular level, thereby depriving the forebrain of all but optic and olfactory input, immediately resulted in an uninterrupted condition of sleep, as judged by the cortical EEG and myosis of the pupils.

Normal humans prepare for sleep by imitating the effect of brain stem transection. By retiring to a quiet room, switching off the lights and radio, removing constricting clothing, lying down, and closing their eyes, they bring about a drastic reduction in afferent stimulation. In the absence of an afferent bombardment, the activity of the nervous system passively falls below some critical level, and sleep ensues.

Reduction of reticular impulses. A new twist was given to the above notion with the experiments of Moruzzi and Magoun and subsequently many others, which showed that high-frequency stimulation of the brain stem reticular formation caused EEG activation and behavioral arousal. It was also found that large lesions within the brain stem reticular formation resulted in a comatose state associated with EEG slowing that resembled changes seen during sleep. The new formulation was that the maintenance of a waking state could be attributed to a tonic barrage of ascending reticular impulses, and the steady flow of sensory messages coursing along the classical pathways appeared to be without importance for the physiology of wakefulness. The reticular activating system was conceived of as a crucial structure, interposed between the forebrain and the sensory input, that seemed to be capable of modulating or amplifying the influence of the latter. The reticular formation, particularly its mesencephalic portion, was found to receive collateral fibers from all the afferent pathways, together with centrifugal fibers from a variety of important forebrain structures. By adding its own intrinsic activity to this multiple innervation, the reticular formation could, it seemed, control changes in waking or sleeping behavior to some extent independent of the immediate environmental input.

Nonetheless, the essential factor producing sleep remained a passive one, except that, instead of occurring as a consequence of a reduction in direct afferent stimulation, it was the reduced number of impulses relayed by the reticular formation that allowed the activity of forebrain structures to fall below the waking level. In effect, the brain stem reticular formation became the wakefulness center.

However, many facts militate against this relatively simple hypothesis. For example, it has been shown that two-stage lesioning of the reticular formation that ultimately produces a total destruction ordinarily large enough to induce perpetual coma is virtually without effect when enough recovery time is allowed between the two lesions. It has also been shown that high-level brain stem transection, which effectively isolates the forebrain, is nonetheless eventually followed by the return of waking patterns in the EEG if the preparation is maintained in good condition. In addition, high-frequency stimulation of many areas of the brain, including the cerebral cortex and the amygdala, has been shown to elicit arousal, although this arousal is presumed to be by centrifugal pathways to the reticular formation. And although the reticular activating system hypothesis explains the *how* of sleep, it does not explain the *why* of sleep. It is presumed that activity in the reticular formation falls partly because of neuronal fatigue. Yet this does not explain how sleep may be postponed so easily nor why it is frequently maintained so long after fatigue would be presumably reversed.

Microelectric recordings of individual neurons in the brain stem also fail to support this hypothesis. However, this evidence cannot be considered conclusive because of the small number of neurons that can be sampled. It is nonetheless true that there is apparently no decrease in rate of discharge of reticular neurons in NREM sleep versus quiet wakefulness. Prior to this, it was found that the transition from wakefulness to sleep was not necessarily accompanied by a reduction of spontaneous discharge in neuron populations in the cerebral cortex.

Neuroanatomical mechanism. A variety of studies have demonstrated that low-frequency stimulation of many brain areas will precipitate the onset of EEG slowing and behavioral sleep. This is supported by evidence from our personal experience of the soporific effect of monotony. These considerations suggest the possibility of an active mechanism involved at least in the onset of sleep.

The concept of an active mechanism is not new. An early study by Nauta in the rat suggested some sort of sleep center, since destructive lesions in the anterior hypothalamus seemed to result in insomnia. The work of Hess and his colleagues having to do with thalamic stimulation at low frequencies also suggested the presence of a diencephalic sleep center.

In recent years the notion of active processes initiating sleep has been given great impetus by the work of Moruzzi and his colleagues. One of their first experiments involved the so-called midpontine pretrigeminal preparation. It was found that, immediately after a transection in this area, a larger portion of the total recording time was occupied by waking patterns in the cortical EEG. This suggested that the transection had eliminated the influence of some sleep-inducing mechanism located behind the lesion. Subsequent experiments showed that—after the basal artery had been clamped at the midpontine level, which shifted the rostral pontine region from the vertebral to the carotid blood supply—intracarotid injections of Thiopental sodium led to EEG synchronization, whereas intravertebral injections had exactly the opposite effects. This suggested that the more caudal regions of the brain stem exercised synchronizing effects on the EEG. There is a good deal of evidence that low rates of stimulation in the brain stem reticular formation and specific areas elicit EEG synchronization.

In contrast to the notion of synchronizing and sleep-inducing structures in the brain stem is the work of Jouvet on decorticate cats, from which he hypothesized that NREM sleep is actively induced by the action of the cerebral cortex. His major point is that the neodecorticate cat has almost no NREM sleep but that REM sleep is virtually unimpaired. In addition, it is claimed that EEG synchronization cannot be elicited in subcortical areas by slow stimulation or barbiturates in the absence of the neocortex.

Endogenous poisoning. Although it seems that the precipitation of NREM sleep can be explained by a neural mechanism, a glance should be taken at other theories. The oldest notion with regard to sleep has to do with the idea that sleep is a result of an endogenous poisoning: Certain toxins accumulate during the waking state and are eliminated during sleep. As metabolic activity eliminates the toxins, sleep ends, and wakefulness ensues. As Kleitman has pointed out, the major objection to this is that, during complete sleep deprivation, subjects almost invariably feel better and more alert the morning after a night without sleep than they did in the middle of the night.

There is no question that a variety of drugs and humoral agents can cause sleep, but there is no good evidence that sleep is associated with or dependent on some humoral or neurochemical agent. In recent years, only the work of Monnier and Hösli supports such a mechanism.

Summary. It seems likely that the processes involved in the development of NREM sleep are complex and interrelated and probably both passive and active. The major problems lie in the establishing of a hierarchy among the various possibilities and in separating out those effects that bear upon EEG activity alone (synchronization and desynchronization) and those that subserve behavioral wakefulness and waking performance.

REM SLEEP MECHANISMS

Neuroanatomical mechanism. Although REM sleep has been known a much shorter period of time, more definitive progress has been made in clarifying its underlying nueroanatomical substrate. In contrast to the NREM phase, REM sleep seems to depend on the integrity of a single organ located in the pontine reticular formation. There is apparently a mechanism for initiating REM sleep in this area, since lesions here seem to abolish it totally. Massive destruction of tissue elsewhere does not have this effect. It has also been shown that the motor-inhibitory process associated with REM sleep is located in this area.

Cats who had bilateral destruction of the nucleus locus coeruleus still seemed to enter the REM state. However, although certain EEG concomitants were identical with those seen in normal REM sleep, *behavioral wakefulness was retained*. This result suggests that the activity of the central nervous system during REM sleep involves elaboration of motor output, which is ordinarily prevented from reaching the periphery by a specific inhibitory mechanism. After destruction of the nucleus locus coeruleus, no such inhibition is present, and fully organized behavior patterns appear. However, the cats were totally oblivious to the environment during these "behaving" REM phases.

Biochemical mechanism. Once a REM period has occurred, another cannot be initiated or will not occur for some finite period of time. Stimulation of the brain stem in the region of the nucleus pontis caudalis may precipitate a REM period, but, once it has run its course, stimulation of this region is totally ineffective for about fifteen minutes. This suggests the necessity of some sort of metabolic or biochemical build-up.

Other evidence suggesting a biochemical mechanism is the effect of drugs. Ordinarily, REM sleep is relatively constant from day to day, in contrast to NREM sleep, which seems to have the capacity to expand and contract temporally almost without limit. Certain compounds, however, augment the amount of REM sleep, notably indole derivatives, including tryptophan, 5-hydroxytryptophan, and lysergic acid diethylamide. Monoamine compounds or compounds that effect monoamine metabolism selectively block rapid-eye-movement sleep. Among these are Dexedrine, Parnate, and reserpine.

Finally, there is the curious effect of short-chain fatty acids, first noted by Jouvet, who studied γ-hydroxybutyrate, and more recently reported by Matsumora and his colleagues, who studied a number of other such acids. Whether or not short-chain fatty acids actually precipitate REM sleep is not certain, however, since they may simply have elicited favorable conditions for the REM-inducing mechanism.

Temperature factors. REM sleep appears to be absent in the presence of fever, and it persists or is augmented when body temperature is lowered to about 30° centigrade.

FUNCTION OF SLEEP

Although experimental research on sleep is extensive, and much is known, very little can yet be said about the function of sleep, either NREM or REM. Indeed, it is not certain that sleep is entirely necessary, even though we seem obliged to spend a good bit of time engaged in it.

EFFECTS OF SLEEP DEPRIVATION

The effects of total sleep deprivation have not been conclusive, and, as is now apparent, such studies confound the results of depriving the organism of two separate things. Since NREM sleep generally occupies the greater portion of total sleep time, the results of total sleep deprivation may reflect mainly NREM sleep deprivation.

The major effects of total sleep deprivation are an impairment of performance and the development of a tendency toward somnolence and drowsiness, of which the impaired performance may be merely a behavioral concomitant. No organic changes have been conclusively shown to be caused specifically by sleep deprivation. A major problem is keeping the organism awake long enough to demonstrate changes, if they occur, in the presence of greatly decreased motivation to stay awake plus the tendency toward somnolence. Recently a 17-year-old boy managed to stay awake for eleven consecutive days. This represented a considerable loss of NREM sleep, 65 to 75 hours. When he was finally allowed to sleep, very little extra sleep occurred prior to his return to full alertness and normal performance.

The nature of NREM sleep is more consistent with notions of a state that subserves the function of rest and restoration than is the nature of REM sleep. However, crucial experiments that would demonstrate such a function are virtually impossible. There is no practical way to separate a specific effect of loss of rest from loss of sleep per se. Furthermore, the results of sleep deprivation experiments must always have the objection that one not only takes away sleep but adds an additional amount of activity, since wakefulness cannot be maintained in the absence of activity. Nonetheless, it appears that the total amount of NREM sleep can be greatly decreased without harm to the organism. The question remains as to whether or not all NREM sleep could be permanently dispensed with.

EFFECTS OF REM SLEEP DEPRIVATION

The function of REM sleep is possibly even less clear than that of its companion. Certainly, its physiological properties do not lend themselves to facile inferences. The high level of activity does not suggest a restorative or resting function. However, REM sleep does have the property of behaving homeostatically and pre-emptively in the face of prior selective deprivation. A number of studies have shown that a certain amount of REM sleep must occur each day. If it does not occur, a deprivation effect occurs: REM sleep is made up by increasing its proportion during recovery if total sleep is held at the baseline level.

The effects of prolonged selective REM sleep deprivation are somewhat surprising and seem to involve the development of neural hyperexcitability, as indicated by experiments showing enhanced auditory recovery cycle and decreased electroconvulsive seizure threshold. Nonetheless, adult animals that have been deprived of REM sleep for long periods of time do not seem drastically impaired. There has been speculation that the major function of REM sleep may be developmental, since much larger percentages are seen during the sleep of neonates and prematures. It has been suggested that REM sleep is a state that allows the developing nervous system to maintain high levels of activity and to execute or try out behavior patterns before they actually must be used in coping with the environment.

CLINICAL IMPLICATIONS

Sleep Pathologies

There is no question that a disturbance of the mind can manifest itself in the sleeping state as well as during wakefulness. In fact, the sleeping state is often the more sensitive barometer of psychic turbulence.

Insomnia. One of the most common of all human ailments is insomnia, which is usually viewed as a symptom and assumed to be the result of some underlying anxiety, worry, conflict, or other emotional upset deriving chiefly from events in the life of the patient. There is little to do about *mild insomnia* beyond reassuring the patient, since there is no evidence that a small degree of sleep loss is harmful in any way. Naturally, it is difficult to evaluate the degree of insomnia without objective studies of sleep. The patient's description may not be an accurate portrayal. There is evidence suggesting that people who claim to be awake most of the night actually do sleep, as shown by sleep patterns in the EEG. But even when confronted with the EEG proof of sleep, they deny having slept. NREM mentation appears to be particularly intense in these subjects. Since an awareness of thinking is not compatible with their notions about the state of sleep, these people simply assume that they were awake. Another study has shown that body temperature and heart rate are chronically higher in subjects who sleep restlessly.

Severe insomnia may be viewed as a symptom of a very severe underlying disturbance. In addition, it may play a causal role either directly or as a precipitating stress.

Activity during sleep. Studies have been done on subjects who walk or talk in their sleep, and neither group has shown any special predilection to behave this way during REM sleep. In fact, sleepwalking tends to be initiated more frequently out of NREM stage 4 sleep early in the night, as does *pavor nocturnus.* Bed-wetting in both children and adults does not appear to occur during REM sleep. In the younger group, it usually occurs during stage 4; in the older ages, it occurs in the waking state or the drowsy state. Of sleep pathologies definitely associated with REM sleep, only bruxism and rhythmic head-banging have been identified.

Nightmares. These, of course, occur during REM sleep. It is quite likely that frightening dreams may precipitate a certain degree of insomnia by arousing the subject repeatedly, as may happen in the case of traumatic neurosis. One study has shown that the incidence of nightmares can be influenced by a large intake of an amino acid, tryptophan.

Idiopathic narcolepsy. This should probably be accorded the status of *the* pathology of sleep. It is an illness characterized by overwhelming sleep attacks, together with one or more of the following auxiliary symptoms: cataplexy, episodes of muscular weakness, usually induced by laughter or anger; sleep paralysis, attacks of inability to move, developing in the transition between arousal and sleep; and hypnagogic hallucinations, vivid visual and auditory sensations occurring at the onset of sleep.

Studies utilizing new techniques have shown that the sleep attacks of patients with narcolepsy and cataplexy are actually episodes of REM sleep. Because of the clear involvement of the REM sleep mechanism, cataplexy and sleep paralysis are viewed as the dissociated occurrence of the motor inhibitory component of REM sleep, and hypnagogic hallucinations appear to be nothing more than the vivid dreams associated with REM sleep. The essential identifying pathology in these patients is the occurrence of REM sleep at the *onset of sleep,* which never occurs in normal subjects. In a fair number of instances, cataplectic attacks have led to the development of a full-blown REM episode.

OTHER CONDITIONS

Although not actually disorders of sleep, there are a few other illnesses in which sleep may play a role. For example, there are marked differences in epileptic seizure discharge in the various stages of sleep. Observations on the lowering of convulsive threshold associated with REM sleep deprivation suggest a causal relationship between seizures and sleep disturbances. REM deprivation in epileptic subjects may also increase seizure discharge in the EEG.

Gastric secretion during sleep in ulcer patients is markedly elevated during REM sleep and may account for the overall elevated nocturnal secretion, which is thought to be one of the causal factors in the formation of peptic ulcer.

The cardiovascular changes during REM sleep as well as the respiratory changes may be implicated in nocturnal disturbances in patients with hypertension, emphysema, and congestive heart failure.

DIAGNOSTIC VALUE OF DISTURBED SLEEP

Although it is a common observation that severe sleep disturbances accompany severe emotional disorders, there have been few studies in which precise correlations have been made between sleep disturbances and other measures of clinical change. One problem is that casual estimates of sleep behavior by hospital personnel are often very misleading. For example, catatonic patients may lie in bed all night with a degree of immobility that suggests deep sleep while actually not sleeping at all.

The few studies that have been done suggest that sleep disturbance has a very high correlation with clinical change. In one study, catatonic schizophrenics showed no tendency to sleep, even after being kept awake for an entire night. And in occasional cases where an acute psychosis has developed during prolonged sleep deprivation, the usual tendency to sleep has been drastically reduced.

PSYCHOSIS OF SLEEP DEPRIVATION

Even though total sleep deprivation must have at least two separate aspects, it is possible that it is the combination of both that is psychotogenic. Recent studies of a subject who remained awake for 264 hours without showing the development of any significant psychopathology indicate, however, that psychosis is not an inevitable outcome of prolonged wakefulness. And, since fifteen and sixteen days of selective REM deprivation in human subjects did not precipitate a full-blown psychosis in another study, it is unlikely that reported psychotogenic effects of total sleep deprivation for periods of less than ten days were due solely to REM deprivation. It seems likely that there were predisposing factors in those cases where full-blown psychosis appeared. Along this line, chronic schizophrenics deprived of all sleep for 100 hours showed a reemergence of the acute psychotic picture in every instance.

STUDIES OF REM SLEEP IN MENTAL ILLNESS

Early REM deprivation studies suggested that the procedure might have an adverse effect, which led to the speculation that some abnormality of REM sleep might be associated with mental illness. In an early study, REM sleep was found to be present in a group of chronic schizophrenics, although there was no systematic attempt at quantification. More recent studies have not demonstrated dramatic quantitative differences between schizophrenics and normals. However, a significant reduction of REM time was noted in patients termed "actively ill."

Fisher and Dement studied five borderline schizophrenic patients and found a mean nightly REM time that was significantly higher than the mean for a comparable group of normals.

The finding of a high nightly REM time was confirmed in another study on a group of chronic schizophrenics in remission. Other abnormalities in this group of patients were failure to inhibit muscle potentials and an abnormal abundance of eye movements in some cases. Studies of severely depressed patients have not produced consistent results.

POSSIBLE ROLE OF REM DEPRIVATION IN THE DEVELOPMENT OF ACUTE PSYCHOSIS

An all-night sleep recording will not necessarily reveal the presence of a state of REM sleep deprivation. The REM-NREM ratio obtained from an all-night recording is probably the net result of many factors, the degree of REM deprivation being only one. In view of this and because of the apparent ubiquity of severe sleep disturbance in the period just prior to the full-blown emergence of an acute psychosis, a possible mechanism by which interference with REM sleep may play a role has been proposed. In this formulation, it is assumed that a predisposed individual sooner or later encounters in his life experience a situation that is extremely stressful. The resultant anxiety leads to some degree of insomnia, with a disproportionate reduction in REM sleep. This situation could continue for a long time. As REM deprivation mounts, neurochemical changes in the brain increase what might be called drive pressure. In the average individual this change might be without serious consequence, but in the schizophrenic it could be overwhelming and devastating. His weak defenses cannot cope with the greater impulsivity, the greater appetites, the hyperexcitability, etc. A vicious circle can be visualized: Anxiety is heightened, which, in turn, interferes even more with REM sleep. Studies in normal subjects have shown that the effect of partial REM deprivation is cumulative for at least twenty days.

Finally, the individual reaches the point of acute psychotic disruption, generally characterized by markedly disorganized behavior, uncontrolled agitation and excitement, etc. In addition to this general effect, it is also possible that the neurochemical change induced by REM sleep deprivation may engender the formation of abnormal, possibly psychotomimetic, substances. The occurrence of abnormal compounds in the urine of schizophrenic patients and the fact that indole amines provide the nucleus for the most potent psychotomimetic compounds and also increase the amount of REM sleep support this possibility.

If this formulation is valid, it follows that the most effective way of reversing the acute psychotic state would be for REM sleep to occur. There is some evidence that phenothiazines permit the occurrence of REM sleep in acutely ill patients. Also, there is the possibility that electroconvulsive therapy causes changes in the brain that are analogous to those that occur during REM sleep.

Sleep Therapy

Studies of a variety of sleep therapies have failed to show consistently favorable results in the treatment of mental disorders with this method. However, it is invariably the case that patients receiving sleep therapy are never monitored in a way that would permit one to conclude that REM sleep has or has not occurred. In recent years sleep therapy has been used sparingly, usually as an auxiliary procedure. It is obvious that the whole subject must be re-evaluated in the light of recent findings pertaining to REM sleep. In view of the difficulty of precipitating REM sleep pharmacologically, it is not likely that REM sleep therapy will receive an immediate clinical trial.

REFERENCES

Dement, W. The effect of dream deprivation. Science, 131: 1705, 1960.

Dement, W. Eye movements during sleep. In *The Oculomotor System*, M. Bender, editor, p. 366. Hoeber Medical Division, Harper & Row, New York, 1964.

Dement, W. An essay on dreams: the role of physiology in understanding their nature. In *New Directions in Psychology*, vol. 2, p. 137. Holt, Rinehart and Winston, New York, 1965.

Dement, W. Recent studies on the biological role of rapid eye movement sleep. Amer. J. Psychiat., 122: 404, 1965.

Dement, W. Psychophysiology of sleep and dreams. In *American Handbook of Psychiatry*, S. Arieti, editor, vol. 3, p. 290. Basic Books, New York, 1966.

Dement, W., Rechtschaffen, A., and Gulevich, G. The nature of the narcoleptic sleep attack. Neurology, 16: 18, 1966.

Fisher, C. Psychoanalytic implications of recent research on sleep and dreaming. I. Empirical findings. J. Amer. Psychoanal. Asso., 13: 197, 1965.

Fisher, C. Psychoanalytic implications of recent research on sleep and dreaming. II. Implications for psychoanalytic theory. J. Amer. Psychoanal. Asso., 13: 271, 1965.

Kety, S., editor. Sleep and altered states of consciousness. Res. Publ. Asso. Res. Nerv. Ment. Dis., 45: 1966.

Kleitman, N. *Sleep and Wakefulness*, ed. 2. University of Chicago Press, Chicago, 1963.

Mandell, A., and Mandell, M., Biochemical aspects of rapid eye movement sleep. Amer. J. Psychiat., 122: 391, 1965.

Moruzzi, G. Active processes in the brain stem during sleep. Harvey Lect., 58: 233, 1963.

Oswald, I. *Sleeping and Waking*. Elsevier, Amsterdam, 1962.

Rechtschaffen, A., Verdone, P., and Wheaton, J. Reports of mental activity during sleep. Canad. Psychiat. Asso. J., 8: 409, 1963.

Roffwarg, H., Dement, W., Muzio, J., and Fisher, C. Dream imagery: relationship to rapid eye movements of sleep. Arch. Gen. Psychiat., 7: 235, 1962.

Roffwarg, H., Muzio, J., and Dement, W. The ontogenetic development of the sleep-dream cycle in the human. Science, 152: 604, 1966.

Snyder, F. Progress in the new biology of dreaming. Amer. J. Psychiat., 122: 377, 1965.

Williams, H., Lubin, A., and Goodnow, J. Impaired performance with acute sleep loss. Psychol. Monogr., 73: 1, 1959.

CHAPTER 6

The Neuron

ROBERT W. DOTY, Ph.D.

GENERAL STRUCTURE, COMPOSITION, AND METABOLISM

STRUCTURE

A neuron is a cell of most peculiar shape (see Figures 1 and 2). This can easily be emphasized by enlarging a Betz cell or spinal motoneuron 40,000-fold—that is, from its actual diameter as a barely visible 50-μ speck to an irregularly shaped balloon the size of a tall man. On this enlarged scale such a neuron sends a sinuous pipe, the axon, 0.4 m. in diameter, for up to 40 km., from cortex into lumbar cord or from cord to foot or hand. Axons 4 km. long are common on this scale, crossing the corpus callosum or projecting to or from thalamus and cortex. A large field of repeatedly branching dendrites may extend up to 40 m. or more. Since on this scale the nerve impulse moves down such an axon at a speed of 7,000,000 km. an hour, the fiction had best be dispensed with to return to real axons, which conduct at sufficiently dramatic rates from 3.6 to 360 km. an hour (1 to 120 m. a second).

The neuron's bizarre shape is dictated by two of its major functions. First, neurons provide surfaces for integrating information from diverse sources. As many as 10,000 synaptic endings may play on one neuron, and 80 per cent of this receptive area may be provided by its dendrites. Second, the ultimate effect of this synaptic input is to generate temporally encoded digital events (impulses), which are transferred down the often prodigious lengths of the axon to form a portion of the input to still another neuron or to an effector organ.

The shape of individual neurons is revealed clearly only by the Golgi stain, which in a manner wholly mysterious deposits silver throughout the

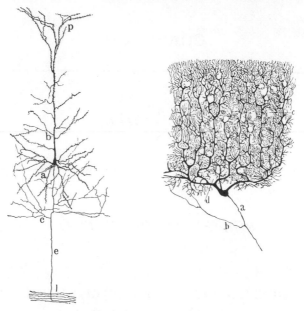

FIGURE 1. Cells stained by Golgi method. *Left*, pyramidal cell from neocortex of a mouse, similar in configuration to Betz cells of man; *a*, basilar dendrites; *b*, apical dendrite and branches; *c*, recurrent collaterals of the axon; *e*, descending axon; *l*, white matter. *Right*, Purkinje cell from human cerebellum. Profusely branched dendritic surface accommodates up to 100,000 synapses. In all vertebrates the dendritic arborization of these cells is fan-shaped, being spread extensively in the anterior-posterior plane, as viewed here from the side, and very narrow in the right-left plane. *a*, axon; *b*, axon collateral; *c*, *d*, space in which stellate cells are accommodated. (From Ramon Cajal, S. *Histologie du Système Nerveux de l'Homme et des Vertébrés*, vol. 1. Translated by L. Azoulay. Consejo Superior de Investigaciones Cientificas, Madrid, 1952.)

entire extent of occasional cells (see Figures 1 and 2). Although all neurons have the same general features of soma (= perikaryon = cell body), axon, and dendrites, there are about sixty distinguishable types of neurons in mammals. Since both man and mouse have the same sixty types of neurons, a profound principle is immediately clear: The human intellect must arise from and be explicable in terms of mechanisms of neural operation common to all mammals. Wherever this principle has been tested— in the electrophysiology of the human brain, in the functional correlates of interference with comparable neural structures in man and animals, in neuroanatomy and neurochemistry—the results have been decisively consistent with this thesis of commonality among mammalian nervous systems.

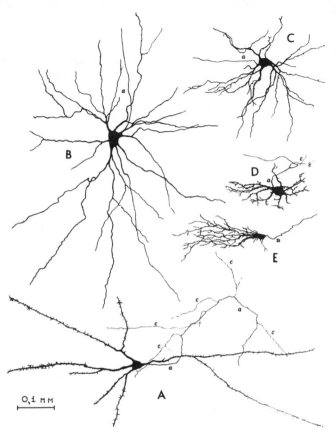

FIGURE 2. Types of neuron in brain stem and spinal cord of dog as seen with Golgi stain. A, reticular type of neuron; B, motoneuron from nucleus of seventh nerve; C,D,E, sensory neurons from cuneate nucleus, descending trigeminal tract and main sensory trigeminal nucleus, respectively. *a*, axons. (From Leontovich, T. A., and Zhukova, G. P. The specificity of the neuronal structure and topography of the reticular formation in the brain and spinal cord of carnivora. J. Comp. Neurol., *121*: 347, 1963.)

Since the general functions of neurons are reflected in their shape, it is also to be expected that more subtle specializations can be discerned in the varying morphologies of the sixty types of neurons. For the brain stem and spinal cord, neurons fall into three distinct morphological categories, which in turn correspond to three functional groupings (see Figure 2). Neurons receiving afferent fibers from peripheral sources characteristically have short but profusely branched dendrites densely covered with spines (see Figure 2, *C, D,* and *E*). Brain stem neurons of this type are thus categorized as sensory. Electron microscopy reveals these spines to be complex structures associated with synaptic endings (see Figure 3). Motoneurons have few or no spines on their dendrites but otherwise have a large dendritic field often similar to that of sensory neurons (see Figure 2*B*). The third category consists of reticular neurons, which are distinguished by few, poorly ramified dendrites having large but rather sparse spines (see Figure 2*A*). The axons of reticular neurons usually branch in a complex fashion, sending collaterals up and down the brain stem. The reticular neurons constitute the elements of the medullary and mesencephalic reticular formations, where anatomical and electrophysiological studies indicate that single cells receive afferents from many sources. Neurons of the reticular type also make up the substantia gelatinosa of Rolando, the central gray, substantia nigra, zona incerta, hypothalamus, globus pallidus, and many other nuclear groups; in addition, they are found scattered in specific sensory and other nuclei. Since units are encountered electrophysiologically in all these structures that respond nonspecifically—that is, to stimuli applied to two or more widely different loci—and since in sensory nuclei these nonspecific units are continuously active but those responding specifically to a single afferent source are silent until stimulated, it is possible that the reticular type of neuron will be found to have these distinctive physiological features wherever it is located.

A more certain relation between morphology and physiological characteristics is established for the basket cell system surrounding the Purkinje cells of the cerebellum or pyramidal cells of the hippocampus. In each case this dense system is the source of a deep and protracted inhibition of the Purkinje or pyramidal cells. Other opportunities abound in the visual system for identifying unique types of cells with specific physiological functions, and indeed ultimately it will no doubt be possible to infer from structure alone most of the analytical properties of a given set of neurons.

COMPOSITION

One is accustomed to thinking of the human brain with its 10 billion richly interconnected neurons (actually, there are 10 billion granule cells in the cerebellum alone) as the most complex object in the known universe. If it is possible to enhance the awesomeness of this fact, it is because each of these 10 billion units itself approaches a similar complexity in its construction. The cell body of a moderately large neuron contains 6 billion molecules of protein (assuming molecular weight = 277,000), 10 billion lipid molecules (molecular weight = 1,000), perhaps 600 billion molecules of ribose nucleic acid (RNA), and 21×10^{12} potassium ions. Such a neuron is aflood with hundreds of species of complex molecules still unidentified. Beyond the overwhelming impression of mere numbers is the

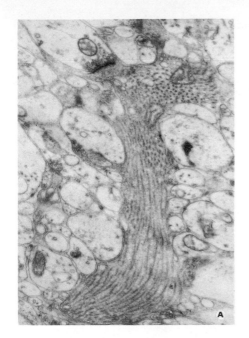

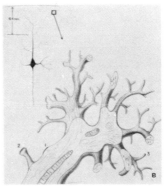

FIGURE 3. Dendritic tubules and spines in neocortex of adult cat. A, electron micrograph of section through a large dendrite showing prominent 230-Å diameter tubules cut at various angles. Two dendritic spines can be seen in the *upper portion* with typical synaptic ending containing synaptic vesicles apparent on the *left*. B, diagram of dendrite terminating in uppermost cortical neuropil (*upper left*). Diagram shows tubules extending into finest terminals, portion of elongated mitochondrion and two typical mitochondria, two multivesicular bodies, and thickening of postsynaptic membrane on dendritic trunk (*1*); spine (*2*); and terminal process (*3*). (From Pappas, G. D., and Purpura, D. P. Fine structure of dendrites in the superficial neocortical neuropil. Exp. Neurol., *4*: 507, 1961.)

intricacy of the molecular framework. The RNA Nissl substance (see Figure 5) constitutes about 9 per cent of the dry weight of the cell and is organized in parallel threads, suggestive of a crystalline structure, running in a continuous network of membrane-bound cavities throughout the cytoplasm but not penetrating axon or dendrites. This is the endoplasmic reticulum that after rupture of the neuron can be isolated as microsomes, irregularly shaped vesicles 300 to 600 Å in diameter bounded by a single 80-Å membrane, which in turn account for almost all the neural synthesis of proteins. A second reticulum, agranular but with 100-Å membranes and 200-Å lumen, also permeates the cytoplasm and seems to correspond to the Golgi apparatus of other cells. A system of tubules is characteristic of dendrites (see Figure 3) and other filaments, and tubules are found in the axon (see Figure 4). The prominent nucleus, packed with deoxyribonucleic acid (DNA), is surrounded by a double membrane, and free

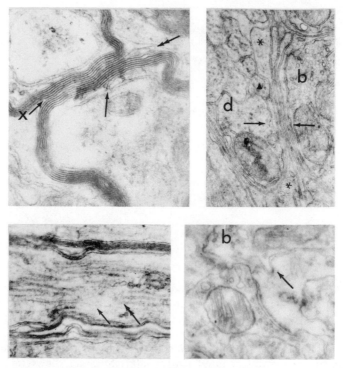

FIGURE 4. Neurotubules and filaments in myelinated axon in inferior olive of adult cat. *Arrow* points to filament, *double arrow* to tubule. Tubules measure 200 to 250 A in diameter. The *dark multiple lines at top and bottom* are the layers of myelin. (From Walberg, F. An electron microscopic study of the inferior olive of the cat. J. Comp. Neurol., *120:* 1, 1963.)

within it is suspended a spherical mass of several thousand RNA particles, the nucleolus (see Figure 5). A small nucleolar satellite of DNA, 0.5 μ^3, is prominent only in cells of females and bears one of the X chromosomes (see Figure 5). The satellite is present in neurons of males, but it is much smaller and is seldom observed except in neurons that have been intensely stimulated. Scattered in the cytoplasm are numerous structures of unknown function, such as multivesicular inclusion bodies, mostly in dendrites (see Figure 3B), and granular inclusion bodies.

The mitochondrion (see Figure 3) is another type of complex structure within the cytoplasm, and its intricately enfolded surfaces provide the complete metabolic machinery for obtaining usable energy from the oxidation of glucose. The intense metabolic activity of neurons is reflected in the great numbers of mitochondria found in them. From presently available measurements it seems that neurons have a greater percentage of their mass devoted to mitochondria than any other cell in the body, half again as much as liver cells, the nearest contenders. Mitochondria make up about 66 per cent of the dry weight of the neuron and average roughly

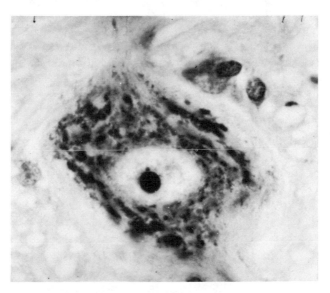

FIGURE 5. Nucleolar satellite containing one of the X chromosomes as seen in motoneuron of the cat. Satellite is prominent in neurons of females only and is visible here as small dark spots just *above* the dark round nucleolus within the nucleus of this cell. The Nissl material containing high concentrations of RNA is seen scattered profusely within the cytoplasm. (From Barr, M. L., Bertram, L. F., and Lindsay, H. A. The morphology of the nerve cell nucleus, according to sex. Anat. Rec., *107*: 283, 1950.)

1,500 a cell. Maintenance of a stable intracellular environment despite an enormous surface area for exchange with extracellular fluids places an extraordinary metabolic demand on neurons. An indication of this is seen in the fact that—as neurons mature after birth, adding greatly to their surface area by growth of dendrites—64 per cent of the new protein formed goes into mitochondria.

METABOLISM

From measurements on Betz cells isolated from the precruciate cortex of cats, it can be estimated that each mitochondrion can process about ten atoms of oxygen each microsecond. Almost all of this oxygen goes to burn glucose. Accounting in man for about 2 per cent of the body weight, the brain takes about one-fourth of the total blood flow and removes proportionately more oxygen from the blood than any other organ in a resting state. Venous blood from the brain is only about 62 per cent saturated with oxygen, and there is a continuous anaerobic metabolism, producing lactic acid even during normal circulation. Within twenty-two minutes after subcutaneous injection of ^{14}C-glucose into cats, the cerebral cortex contains almost double the specific ^{14}C activity of the heart. A large proportion of the glucose has already passed into the glycolytic and tricarboxylic acid metabolic pathways, and, in striking contrast to other tissues, more than 70 per cent of the glucose has been converted into amino acids (see Table I). The amino acid metabolic system of the brain is highly

TABLE I

Distribution of ^{14}C 22 Minutes after Subcutaneous Injection[a]

	Specific Activity	Percentage as Glucose	Percentage as Lactic, Pyruvic, and Tricarboxylic Acid Cycle Intermediates	Percentage Amino Acids	Percentage of Aspartate and Glutamate in Amino Acid Content
	c.p.m./gm. fresh tissue				
Blood	14,490	90	5	3	11
Liver	11,560	79	12	8	39
Heart	7,320	34	19	46	76
Frontal cortex	14,280	3	24	71	80
Parietal cortex	13,470	3	20	74	79
Temporal cortex	11,640	8	20	70	77
Corpus callosum	10,930	7	32	56	72
Spinal cord	5,720	6	45	48	63
Muscle	3,060	66	18	12	39

[a] From Gaitonde, M. K., Marchi, S. A., and Richter, D. The utilization of glucose in the brain and other organs of the cat. Proc. Roy. Soc. London., Ser. B, 160: 124, 1964.

developed and unique in its capacity to produce γ-aminobutyric acid. It is significant that about 80 per cent of the amino acids produced are glutamic and aspartic acids, both of which appear to be involved in some aspect of synaptic excitation of neurons.

NEURONS VERSUS GLIA

All estimates agree that glial cells are several times more numerous in the brain than are neurons. Efforts to understand cerebral function must thus face this fact and cope with the frequent suggestions that glial rather than neural activity underlies or is importantly related to mental phenomena or memory. All evidence so far strongly suggests that the glia perform mere ancillary service to supply the highly specialized environment required for neural function and that the latter is the *sine qua non* of mental life. Only neurons have the form and facility for transmitting information from and to the external world with millisecond timing and thus unquestionably serve as the afferent and efferent portals to the mind. Only neurons have the interconnectivity and demonstrable capability for rapid computation of integrated outputs derived from multiple and hence distant sources— that is, from other brain loci. Consciousness is so fragile a phenomenon that ten seconds without oxygen erases it, and only neurons have the intense metabolism expected to be associated with this phenomenon. RNA is associated with the manufacture of protein in accordance with phylogenetic engrams, the genetic code, and is thus at least an a priori candidate for a role in ontogenetic engrams; and only neurons have the extraordinary RNA metabolism likely to be associated with such function. Neurons thus meet all the major known requirements for correlation with mental processes, and glia do not. Assumptions, then, that important aspects of mental function are held in glia at least one step removed from neurons are, to say the least, gratuitous.

There are three types of glia: astroglia, microglia, and oligodendroglia. The astroglia weave a continuous sheet of cytoplasm into all interstices about the neurons and interpose themselves between the neurons and blood vessels. They thus appear to serve as regulators of the ionic environment of the neurons, and their rather vacant-appearing cytoplasm is consistent with this concept. The microglia are of mesodermal origin; they arise embryologically from nonneural tissue. Since they appear in great numbers at points of infection or degeneration, it is felt that their function may be primarily phagocytic. The oligodendroglia are more interesting. They are similar to the Schwann cells, which form tubes around peripheral nerve fibers and which secrete the fatty insulating substance myelin. Certain oligodendroglia probably perform similar functions in the central nervous system. Others undergo changes in metabolism consequent to changes in the neurons with which they are associated, and neurons of Clarke's column (nucleus dorsalis of the spinal cord) have proportionately more oligodendroglia around them the longer their axon. The oligodendroglia may serve as a metabolic reserve system for the neurons. From measures of glia in tissue culture, tumors, and fiber tracts, such as corpus callosum, their metabolism seems to be only 0.1 to 0.25 that of neurons, with the oligodendroglia having the highest rate. Thus, despite their large numbers, glia probably account for only a small proportion, 5 to 15 per cent, of the total metabolism of the brain.

Astroglia and oligodendroglia undergo periodic, sometimes rhythmical contraction in tissue culture. Such contractions, commonly lasting about 2 minutes and requiring 7 to 13 minutes for relaxation, can be triggered by electrical stimuli. The contraction is in this case preceded by an electrical response lasting 4 to 6 seconds. Neither the electrical response nor contraction is all-or-none in nature. Since similar electrical responses can be obtained in the intact brain, there is some possibility the contractile phenomena may also be characteristic of glia under normal circumstances as well as in tissue culture.

NEURONS AS SECRETORY CELLS AND THE RELATION OF THEIR SECRETION TO THEIR FUNCTION

In their possession of a prominent nucleolus, endoplasmic reticulum, and high levels of RNA, neurons closely resemble other cells capable of intense secretory activity, such as those of the pancreas or salivary glands. Secretory activity is clearly evident in many neurons of the hypothalamus that manufacture hormones subsequently transferred to the hypophysis. However, all neurons at their termination seem to produce particles extruded onto other cells. These particles are the synaptic vesicles (see Figure 3), which analyses show to be associated with synaptic transmitters, such as acetylcholine and noradrenaline. There is every reason to believe that synaptic transmission is effected by the sudden release of groups of these particles from the presynaptic terminals and that a sporadic, low-level release of individual vesicles is occurring at all times. It is the thesis of this chapter that, in addition to or in association with the transmitter substances, other chemical agents pass continually between neurons and are necessary to establish and maintain neural interconnections. In this view, the secretory activity of neurons is related directly to their function, both in supplying the abrupt transients for synaptic transmission and in determining which neuron will accept or supply synapses from or to which others.

Since the microscopic structure of the nervous system can so far be viewed only in fixed preparations, the impression is easily gained that its organization is static. Living mammalian neurons in tissue culture, however, are in continual motion, sending out and retracting pseudopodia, forming synapses that remain for days or months but move about over a limited range on the surface of the contacted neurons. There is organized cytoplasmic streaming, and particles can be seen passing in persistent directions either up or down the axon. Material is transferred from nucleus or nucleolus to cytoplasm, particularly when the neuron is stimulated. The neurons produce slow, pumping movements, taking six to eight hours in a cycle of contraction and expansion and seeming to effect thereby an extrusion of cytoplasm down the axon. The presence of surprisingly normal electron microscopic, histological, and electrophysiological characteristics in such explanted neurons strongly suggests that similar motility may be a common feature of neurons in their normal environment.

That axons in the mammalian central nervous system are capable of changing their connections is shown in the following experiments.

In the first stage several dorsal roots on one side are cut both rostral and caudal to a single surviving dorsal root. During the course of several months, the terminals of the cut roots die and disappear, leaving a clear field to the single surviving dorsal root. That this root sends new terminal fibers into the fields formerly innervated by its neighbors is now shown by cutting it and comparing the zone of degeneration of this root on the deafferented side with that of the corresponding root on the other, intact side. It is found that the degeneration on the deafferented side extends in the dorsal and ventral horns several segments beyond that on the intact side. A similar extension of the normal innervation zone of dorsal root fibers follows partial deafferentation by extirpation of neocortex or section of a pyramidal tract. Physiological changes accompanying these deafferentations are concordant with the histological results and offer some basis for explaining certain pathological responses after such lesions in man.

Aside from the physiological demonstration that these enlarged central innervation zones can produce functioning synapses, little is known about the pattern, type, or stability of these new connections. In peripheral autonomic ganglia the situation is more favorable for analysis. Experiments show not only the probing of fibers to form new connections as vacancies occur in the synaptic surface of neighboring cells but a subtle coding that selects the connections that will be most enduring (see Figure 6). The cervical sympathetic ganglion receives its preganglionic fibers by the thoracic ventral roots T_1 through T_7 from neurons in the anterolateral cell column of these segments. The cervical sympathetic ganglion cells give rise to postganglionic fibers that, among other things, innervate the circular muscles of the iris and the smooth muscle of arterioles in the ear, producing pupillary dilation and a fall in skin temperature of the ear

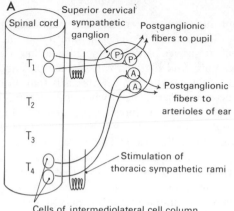

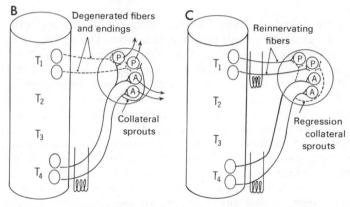

FIGURE 6. A, Stimulation of root at T_1 produces pupillary dilatation, and stimulation at T_4 produces decreased ear temperature. B, After degeneration of T_1 fibers, T_4 fibers have grown onto cells with synaptic vacancies, and stimulation at T_4 now produces pupillary dilatation as well as decrease of ear temperature. C, In-growing T_1 fibers select type of neurons they formerly innervated and displace T_4 fibers from them, thus restoring normal specificity of functional connections. (Adapted from Guth, L., and Bernstein, J. J. Selectivity in the re-establishment of synapses in the superior cervical sympathetic ganglion of the cat. Exp. Neurol., 4: 59, 1961.)

as a consequence of arteriolar constriction. In the cat, stimulation of the T_1 root normally produces pupillary dilation without affecting ear temperature, but that at T_4 does the reverse; the fibers from these two roots go to different populations of ganglion cells. If the T_1 (and T_2-T_3) fibers are crushed, the fibers from T_4 expand their innervation zone so that, one month after the crushing, stimulation of the

T_4 root produces pupillary dilation as well as decrease of ear temperature. Yet after six months, when the T_1 fibers have grown back into the ganglion, the normal situation is found to be restored. These facts provide strong prima facie evidence that the fibers normally innervating ganglion cells going to the ear send out collateral sprouts to form functional connections with those supplying the iris and that these strange connections recede after reestablishment of contact of these ganglion cells by the fibers formerly innervating them. It also demonstrates considerable precision in the ultimate organization of cellular interconnections, despite the potentiality for more diffuse yet functional synaptic relations.

A third example of changing neural connection is found in the visual cortex of kittens. When examined in the first weeks of life, prior to any visual experience of the animal, about 80 per cent of the cells in area striata can be influenced by stimuli to either eye; this situation is normally maintained throughout life. However, if the animal is prevented from using one eye for several months by suturing the eyelids together, or even if it is merely prevented from using the two eyes concurrently because of a divergence of 20° in the optical axes produced by section of a medial rectus muscle, only 5 to 20 per cent of the cells have significant binocular input. This recession of previously effective synapses in the absence of concurrent action suggests that at least in this stage of life there is some competition for synaptic space upon particular neurons and that the normal pattern of innervation represents a dynamic balance rather than a fixed arrangement.

These abnormalities of the kitten visual system become permanent as measured both electrophysiologically and behaviorally. A kitten raised without vision in either eye has difficulty learning to see but is ultimately able to do so. In the case of monocular deprivation, however, the normal eye becomes so dominant that the animal apparently can never learn to use the deprived eye. A similar permanence is achieved if vision is normal throughout the first year of life, for it appears that these abnormalities of binocular vision cannot be produced if the procedures are carried out on adult cats.

EFFECTS OF POSTSYNAPTIC STRUCTURES

Despite the presence of a critical period in the last instance, it is clearly possible from all the foregoing to hypothesize that certain neurons in the central nervous system are continually sending out collateral, probing fibers that may establish temporary liaison with a variety of other neurons but that can maintain enduring connections only where the chemistries or activities of the two cells mesh appropriately.

In many cases it can be inferred that fibers secrete some material essential to the nutrition of the neurons they innervate, since the neurons degenerate or even die after denervation.

Of course, it is possible that the denervation produces degeneration from lack of stimulation rather than from lack of a secreted neural substance. That this is not entirely the case is shown again by relations in the visual system. Within a year after section of the optic tract or loss of an eye in primates, neurons of the lateral geniculate nucleus have degenerated to the point where they have lost up to 80 per cent of their normal volume. Yet in man mere lack of activity in lateral geniculate neurons of many months standing, as evidenced by blindness and caused by pressure on the optic chiasm from a pituitary adenoma, does not produce serious degeneration, since vision returns within hours after relief of thé pressure. Similarly, in the adult cat maintenance in total darkness for seventeen months does not produce a decrease in efficacy of the postsynaptic response of the large cell system of the lateral geniculate nucleus. This lack of effect may arise because darkness is a stimulus to certain elements of the visual system, but when the dark activity is presumably removed by destruction of the photoreceptors, leaving retinal ganglion cells intact, the effect is not degeneration but increased functional capacity of the system, as tested by the postsynaptic response to electrical stimulation of the optic tract.

The trophic effect of neurons on peripheral structures is even more striking. Sensory neurons induce the formation of taste buds in the tongue, and motoneurons induce motor end plates on muscle fibers. In the nictitating membrane of the cat, normally innervated by adrenergic postganglionic fibers from the cervical sympathetic ganglion, the hypoglossal nerve is able to form functional endings that are cholinergic in nature. For skeletal muscle the presence or absence of innervation effects changes in metabolism and functional characteristics throughout the entire muscle fiber. For instance, in the normally innervated fibre, microjets of acetylcholine solutions, directed at the surface of the fiber elicit electrical responses only in the region of the end plate, but in denervated fibers their entire surface becomes sensitive to such application. Within a few days after reinnervation the sensitivity recedes, to be limited again to the end plate region. De-efferented muscle fibers also consistently show fibrillation—arrhythmic, brief contractions at 1 to 30 a second.

The duration of contraction in response to an electrical stimulus is slowed in de-efferented muscle, particularly in those muscles normally participating in rapid, phasic movements as contrasted to the protracted (tonic) contractions necessary for maintenance of posture. This phenomenon has been particularly well-studied in the hind leg of the cat, where it is found that the slow, postural muscles are innervated by a population of motoneurons whose electrophysiological characteristics are distinctly different from those innervating the fast, phasic muscles. Motoneurons to slow muscles tend to fire at low frequencies, such as 10 a second, but in long-sustained periods of activity, whereas those to fast muscles more commonly fire in briefer bursts at higher frequencies, such as 30 a second. In a single twitch the slow muscles normally take 60 to 80 milliseconds to reach their peak of contraction, whereas a time of 25 milliseconds is typical of a fast muscle. Within a few weeks after denervation, these figures change to 75 to 100 and 45 milliseconds, respectively. Within a few days after reinnervation, these values approach the normal range. More interesting still, if the innervation to a fast muscle is directed onto a slow muscle, contraction of the slow muscle becomes much faster, falling to about 40 milliseconds, and the reverse occurs with fast muscles innervated by nerves normally supplying slow muscles (see Figure 7). Some complex interactions with the amount of neuromuscular activity are not considered here, but these experiments, together with the facts cited above, demonstrate that neurons exert a powerful influence on the complex morphology, chemistry, and functional characteristics of the cells on which they terminate.

There is every reason to believe that these effects are produced by substances secreted at the neural terminals. Furthermore, there is strong suggestive evidence that essential ingredients of this postulated secretion are manufactured in the cell body and pass continually down the axon. When an axon is severed, that portion lacking connections with the cell body disintegrates. Within 19 hours there is a detectable change in the appearance of the neural filaments, and by 1 week many fibers are only vacant tubes of myelin. The Schwann cells phagocytize the axoplasm and myelin. Conduction of nerve impulses survives for up to 3 days in the severed axon, but its failure is hastened by frequent stimulation. The fact that the axon has been severed is also somehow communicated back to the cell body, for within a matter of hours it begins to undergo drastic changes in metabolism and structure. Cell volume doubles within 5 days, apparently mostly from intake of water, and then begins a prolonged increase in number and size of mitochondria and in proteins and RNA associated with the outgrowth of a new length of axon. The new axon is regenerated at a rate of about 4 mm. a day. To produce this rate of growth, the neuron must manufacture several times its own volume of cytoplasm each day and must do so to form ultimately a total of 50 to 1,000 times the volume of its soma, depending on the length of the axon (0.1 to 1 m.). Motoneurons that are prevented from establishing peripheral connections frequently die after a few months, probably from exhaustion.

Were this rate of growth a feature of normal neurons, axonal proc-

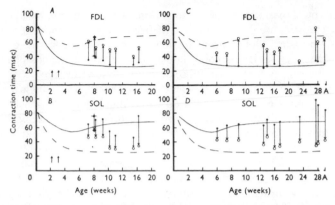

FIGURE 7. Effects of innervating soleus (SOL), a slow muscle, with nerve fibers normally going to flexor digitorum longus (FDL), a fast muscle; and vice versa. Cross-union of nerves performed on kittens 16 to 22 days old (*arrows*) and contraction time (in milliseconds) of muscles tested at various times thereafter. The *continuous lines* plot the normal development of contraction time for the muscle being studied, whereas the *broken lines* plot this function for the muscle whose nerves now supply the studied muscle. In A and B the *solid points* are values for muscles (in contralateral limb) reinnervated by their own nerves, whereas in C and D the *solid points* are for undisturbed, normal muscles of the animal used. *Open circles* in all cases indicate values for muscles receiving alien innervation, and it is obvious that these values consistently approach those expected on the basis of their innervation rather than their anatomical type. (From Buller, A. J., Eccles, J. C., and Eccles, R. M. Interactions between motoneurones and muscles in respect of the characteristic speeds of their responses. J. Physiol., 150: 417, 1960.)

esses could move about within the central nervous system from one cell to another—that is, grow 60 μ, the diameter of a large neuron, within 20 minutes. Evidence for the continued outgrowth of central axons is presently lacking. It is, however, firmly established that phosphoproteins move down the axons of normal motoneurons from the cell body toward the periphery at about the same 4 mm. a day seen above in the case of regeneration. The mass of material manufactured and moved is probably not nearly so great in normal neurons as in neurons regenerating axons, but it is clear that it occurs. Smaller molecules can move even more rapidly, apparently through rather than with the axoplasm, since phospholipids can be observed to move out of hypoglossal motoneurons along the hypoglossal nerve at 70 mm. a day.

Retrograde effects. The nature of the signal received by the cell body from the axon is unknown, and there are many unexplained

factors in the phenomenon of changing cell metabolism consequent
to loss of fiber terminations. For instance, such changes occur in
dorsal root ganglion cells only when the peripherally projecting fibers
are cut and not when the equally long centrally projecting dorsal root
fibers are cut. Cells in the thalamus degenerate within a week or two
after extirpation of the neocortical area to which they project. In the
rapidity with which degeneration ensues, these thalamic changes are
much different from those in spinal cord motoneurons after nerve
section. Yet for some thalamic cells, such as those in the medial geniculate body of the cat, full degeneration is procured only by very
widespread cortical removals, and loss of limited regions within this
field produces little or no apparent change. This may be explained by
supposing that the axons of these cells branch extensively and that
degeneration follows only upon removal of a certain number of these
branches. The delicate trophic balance between neurons is further
illustrated in cases where the degeneration proceeds transsynaptically
even in a retrograde direction. For instance, in both man and macaque, loss of striate cortex produces degeneration in the lateral geniculate nucleus, and after several years the geniculate cells gradually
die and disappear. The loss of the cells on which they formerly terminated also causes the retinal ganglion cells to die, even though
many of them have collateral terminations in the midbrain. A similar
retrograde transsynaptic degeneration is seen in the medial mammillary nucleus after extirpation of the cingulate cortex in rabbits. Cells
of the medial mammillary nucleus terminate in the anterior thalamic
nuclei. When the cells of the anterior thalamus degenerate after loss
of their cortical terminations, the terminations from the medial
mammillary nucleus must also be disturbed, and degeneration is then
seen in the latter nucleus as early as 2 weeks after the cortical loss.

It is, of course, possible or even likely that certain retrograde
changes or the maintenance of a normal metabolic state require
some material that passes along the axon toward the cell body. That
particles could move in axons seemed to be demonstrated for neurotropic viruses as well as by the observations in tissue culture. The
viruses of herpes, rabies, and poliomyelitis move exclusively along peripheral nerves to gain access to the central nervous system. They
progress at about the same rate of 2 to 4 mm. a day seen for substances moving centrifugally in the axon. The movement of these
viruses, however, may be in perineural spaces rather than within
axons so that, until the location of the viruses can be demonstrated
with the electron microscope, this evidence for the centripetal movement of particulate matter within axons is not decisive.

A retrograde influence of muscle fibers on the neurons innervating
them seems necessary to explain the coordinated movements seen in
supernumerary limbs grafted on salamanders. The muscles in the
grafted limbs are found to contract concurrently with their homo-

logues in the intact, normal limbs. There is no learning involved in
these movements, and prima facie it appears as though the neurons
that terminate on the grafted muscles accept only those central synapses that are cognate to the type of muscle innervated. An alternative explanation is that the motoneurons send out collaterals to contact various muscles and that from the many connections so formed
only those appropriate to each motoneuron survive, much as in the
case with sympathetic preganglionic fibers in Figure 6. Such an explanation seems to suffice for some cases but perhaps not for all. Such
selectivity in motoneuronal termination is not the case in the mammalian neuromuscular system, although nerve fibers do form more
effective connections with the type of muscle previously innervated
than they do with strange muscles. On the other hand, when nerves
in the hind limbs of kittens are directed into strange muscles, there is
good evidence that a small but significant change occurs in the central connections influencing these redirected motoneurons.

SELECTIVITY OF CONNECTIONS. Although the case
for centripetal influences of terminus back upon cell body thus remains somewhat confusing, it can be conclusively demonstrated that
central fibers display an extraordinary degree of specificity in their site
of termination. This can best be illustrated by examples from the
visual system, although equally specific effects are obtained with vestibular or cutaneous systems. If the optic nerve is cut in fish or amphibia, the retinal ganglion cells are able to send fibers through the
scar tissue along the former course of the optic tract to re-establish
connections in the optic tectum. The fibers penetrate the scar in an
apparent tangle of confusion (see Figure 8) but then sort themselves
out according to retinal locus and follow highly specific courses
through the optic tract, ultimately terminating again on essentially
the same cells as they did initially. There is some possibility that the
final site of termination may be refined by processes analogous to
those in sympathetic ganglia (see Figure 6), but both behavioral and
electrophysiological evidence is consistent in revealing the reestablishment of the former order. Again, learning plays no part, since, in
a frog with eyes rotated so that its world and behavior is upside down
and reversed, fibers growing in from the reversed eyes after section of
the optic nerves reestablish the old connections as well as the maladaptive behavior in response to the reversed visual world. Mammalian
optic nerve fibers cannot regrow in this manner, but their initial organization as to locus and type of ending are at least equally precise.
Fibers from the retinal ganglion cells in the monkey sort themselves
out at the chiasm into crossing and noncrossing groups and then
arrange themselves within the tract according to ultimate destination
in the lateral geniculate nucleus. The precision of termination carries
through several stages of the system since cells found in area striata

FIGURE 8. Photomicrograph of optic fibers transversing the area of scar tissue of cut optic nerve in a newt. A restoration of the original position of the fibers in the nerve and ultimately in optic areas of the brain is effected. (From Sperry, R. W. Mechanism of neural maturation. In *Handbook of Experimental Psychology*, S. S. Stevens, editor, p. 247. Wiley, New York, 1951.)

with a particular type of response to various colors of light have this same type of response to stimulation of either eye.

MATURATIONAL EFFECTS ON NEURON MODIFIABILITY

In dealing with these concepts, one must take care to distinguish the effects obtained in the adult, stabilized system versus those obtained in embryonic or juvenile stages.

For instance, if the eyes are rotated in amphibia sufficiently early in life, the optic nerve fibers are able to induce central changes sufficiently extensive that inverted vision and behavior do not result. In newts it is even possible in embryonic stages to remove the eyes from a species with poor vision and replace them with the larger eyes of a species having better vision. The larger eyes induce a larger optic tectum in their hosts.

As maturation proceeds, the nervous system is progressively less capable of rearrangement, and most connections ultimately seem to become immutable, all as in the situation with the kitten visual system cited above.

The stubborn fixity of these inherent, all-pervasive connections cannot be overemphasized. A monkey with the flexor and extensor muscles of its arm reversed must undergo months of careful training before it is able to make even a simple, limited movement in the sense opposite to its inherent central neural arrangement—that is, to contract its reverse-inserted extensor muscles to produce a flexion of the arm to obtain a banana. Human patients with similar reversals have similar problems, and those with innervated skin reversed from upper to lower lips or bottom to top of finger, although able to report the proper orientation of an object touching them at these points, still continue to experience the touch as though it came at the original location of the skin. The probably small percentage of connections within the human nervous system that are modifiable can thus with effort and training be used with some success to override the effects of those that are not. The degree of modifiability, however, remains severely limited, and even modified behavior requires for its expression a vast substrate of inherent connections. The gist of these pages has been that both the mutable and immutable connections are likely to arise from and be maintained by the secretory interchange between neurons.

REFERENCES

Clemente, C. D. Regeneration in the vertebrate central nervous system. Int. Rev. Neurobiol., 6: 257, 1964.

Elliot, K. A. C., Page, I. H., and Quastel, J. H. *Neurochemistry.* Charles C Thomas, Springfield, Ill., 1962.

Geiger, R. The behavior of adult mammalian brain cells in culture. Int. Rev. Neurobiol., 5: 1, 1963.

Kety, S. S., and Elkes, J., editors, *Regional Neurochemistry.* Pergamon Press, New York, 1961.

McIlwain, H. *Biochemistry and the Central Nervous System,* ed. 2. Little, Brown, Boston, 1959.

Sperry, R. W. Mechanisms of neural maturation. In *Handbook of Experimental Psychology,* S. S. Stevens, editor, p. 236. Wiley, New York, 1951.

Waelsch, H., editor. *Ultrastructure and Cellular Chemistry of Neural Tissue.* Hoeber Medical Division, Harper & Row, New York, 1957.

Windle, W. F., editor. *Biology of Neuroglia.* Charles C Thomas, Springfield, Ill., 1958.

CHAPTER 7

The Nerve Impulse
and Synaptic Transmission

ROBERT W. DOTY, Ph.D.

RESTING POTENTIAL

THE INTERIOR of most cells is electrically negative with respect to the outside. Nerve and muscle cells are unique in using this difference in electrical potential as a source of energy for rapid communication from one part of the cell to the other. A simplified but adequate explanation of the origin and polarity of this electrochemical potential, the resting potential of the cell, can be given wholly in terms of potassium ion concentrations. There is a high concentration of K^+ within the cell as compared with the outside, and these ions are relatively free to move through the cell membrane. The mobility of K^+ being much greater than that of the large organic anions within the cell, the tendency for outward diffusion of the positive charge (K^+) leaves the interior of the cell negative. However, if the interior of the cell is sufficiently negative, then the positive charges are electrostatically attracted and held. An equilibrium is thus set up where the difference in chemical concentration of K^+ inside and outside the cell is exactly balanced by the negative electrical potential holding K^+ within the cell. This potential is known as the equilibrium potential, and it can be mathematically defined in terms of concentrations and mobilities for any ionic species.

If the concentration of external K^+ is increased, the resting potential diminishes according to such mathematical prediction. By this and other means, it is shown that the resting potential arises almost entirely from the difference in potassium ion concentration inside and outside the cell.

Mechanisms of K+-Na+ gradient. This concentration difference is maintained by two mechanisms. Both mechanisms must operate in the face of the fact that sodium ions are present in high concentration outside the cell and are to some extent free to enter it. The first mechanism is simply the selective adsorption of K+ rather than Na+ by large, fixed anions. Thus, a muscle fiber deprived of all energy sources by anoxia, metabolic poisons, and activity to the point of exhaustion and in a solution at 0° C., can still adsorb K+ and extrude Na+ against their concentration gradients. This probably arises because the hydration diameter of K+ is slightly smaller than that of Na+, thus allowing a closer approach between positive and negative charges and hence, on a statistical basis, holding K+ more strongly than Na+. It is presumably this same principle of selective binding that allows potassium to be held in the soil while sodium is leached out and runs off to salt the sea. In addition to this, potassium is also accumulated inside the cell by metabolic processes. This second mechanism is known as the sodium pump, which contributes a metabolically dependent fraction of the resting potential by actively extruding Na+ from the cell in exchange for K+. Despite two decades of intensive research, the manner in which this metabolic pump operates to extrude Na+ is still obscure.

EXCITATION

Application of electric currents through axons or other excitable tissues produces both passive and active changes. The passive changes are spoken of as "electrotonic," and their magnitude is directly proportional to the current applied (see Figure 1). An electrotonic potential diminishes exponentially with distance from its point of origin. In its spread along an axon or dendrite, such an electrotonic potential is altered and slightly delayed by the electrical characteristics of these structures—that is, by their electrical resistance and parallel capacitance along an extended surface resembling a cable.

Mechanisms of excitation. Anodal current applied externally to axons merely adds to their resting potential, thus producing a hyperpolarization. This is only a passive effect without active response from the axon. The axon membrane shows some electrical rectification, since externally applied cathodal currents pass more readily than do anodal currents. Cathodal current diminishes the resting potential; it acts to depolarize the axon, and the response of the axon is to add to this depolarizing effect, producing a local response that augments the depolarizing action and prolongs it. As more depolarizing (cathodal) current is applied, the local response becomes progressively larger (see Figure 1) until at a critical level (the threshold) an explo-

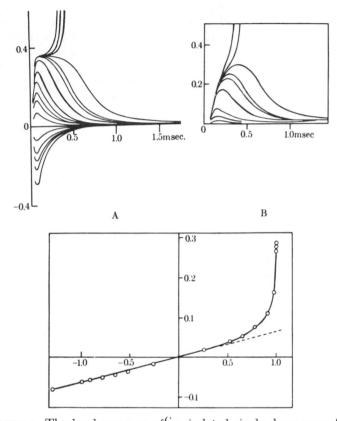

FIGURE 1. The local response of an isolated single, large axon from a crab. A, the responses recorded at the site of electrical stimulation. Anodal stimuli (downward deflections) produce only electrotonic potentials directly proportional to stimulus intensity. Cathodal stimuli (upward deflections) also produce electrotonic potentials; but with stimulus intensities half or more that required for elicitation of a propagated spike potential (*uppermost lines*), the response is more than a mirror image of the anodal response. This additional potential, the local response generated by the axon, is shown in B, where the electrotonic component, as determined by comparable anodal responses, has been subtracted from the records in A. These relations are plotted in C for values taken 0.29 millisecond after application of the stimulus. *Abscissa* here is the strength of stimulus as a fraction of threshold showing departure from a purely electrotonic, linear function at values about half-threshold. *Ordinate* in each case is the potential as a fraction of the spike potential. (From Hodgkin, A. L. The subthreshold potentials in a crustacean nerve fiber. Proc. Roy. Soc. London, Ser. B, **126**: 87, 1938.)

sive all-or-none change occurs that generates the nerve impulse. It is interesting that the threshold is attained by reducing the resting potential; if the resting potential should be already lower than this critical threshold level of depolarization, the axon or cell is inexcitable. Hyperpolarization never produces excitation but, instead, makes excitation more difficult the further the membrane potential is increased away from the threshold level of depolarization.

In round numbers the resting potential of a normal axon or nerve cell is about -70 mv. With depolarization to a level of about -65 to -55 mv., the membrane potential within about 0.2 millisecond reaches $+30$ mv. and then almost as abruptly begins to return to the resting level. This action is the spike potential associated with the nerve impulse. By changing the internal and/or external concentration of Na^+, one can show that the maximum of the spike potential is the equilibrium potential for Na^+ and that, during the rising phase of the spike potential, most of the transmembrane current is carried by Na^+. The spike potential thus arises from a sudden, transient change in membrane permeability to sodium ions. During the course of the spike, the permeability to potassium ions also increases. The time course of this change is many times slower than that for sodium ions, and the repolarization is not accomplished so rapidly as depolarization. These changes in permeability can be thought of actually as changes in conductivity that, in a manner similar to the variable resistors in an equivalent circuit, control the power drawn from the ionic concentration differences (batteries). Because of the very brief time course of the conductivity change, very little ionic movement actually occurs, most of it going simply to discharge or charge the membrane capacitance. Since these changes in sodium and potassium permeability are to a considerable degree concurrent, the ionic exchange attributable to this capacitance is three to four times that which would be expected were the changes consecutive.

The measured influx is about three sodium ions/100 $Å^2$ of membrane surface. This influx is almost negligible in the relatively large internal volume of an axon, so that thousands of impulses are required before internal ionic concentrations change significantly. With structures of smaller diameter, however, such as terminal dendrites where the surface to volume ratio may be one thousand times greater than in axons, ionic concentrations are much more readily altered by activity.

Actually, the situation is somewhat more complicated than just described, since it sometimes takes several hundred milliseconds before the resting state is fully restored. The spike potential is commonly followed first by a negative after-potential (as recorded externally and referring to a state of transmembrane depolarization) that is relatively brief and during which a neuron may be hyperexcitable since it would take less current to reach the threshold. An after-hyperpolarization or positive after-potential than ensues that is much longer than the negative after-potential and during which the excitability of the neuron is reduced. The positive after-potential seems to be the result of an increased permeability to potassium ions and varies greatly from one type of cell or axon to another.

Excitation increases the metabolism of axons, perhaps partly in relation to the restoration of ionic balances. In any case it has been repeatedly shown that the metabolism associated with activity is qualitatively different from that at rest.

The manner in which the sodium permeability is abruptly and briefly altered remains unknown. The controlling systems seem to depend on phospholipids rather than protein in the membrane. Treatment of axons with phospholipase quickly destroys their excitability, whereas the structural protein can be dissolved to the point where the nerve is a mere pulp without seriously affecting its ability to generate spike potentials. Calcium ions also play a very important role in regulating membrane permeability to sodium ions and hence control the triggering mechanism for the spike potential. The axoplasm per se plays no essential role in these events. In large axons it can be replaced with various solutions of electrolytes without altering the phenomena of excitation and conduction.

Excitation is normally initiated in axons by currents in the cell body or, in the case of afferent fibers, by currents set up in receptor structures. The latter are spoken of as "generator potentials" and are D.C. potentials, usually proportional to the logarithm of the stimulus energy. The effect of a steady, depolarizing potential is qualitatively similar in afferent endings and cell bodies (see Figure 2), but quantitative differences are great, depending on the characteristics of accommodation and recovery in various instances. The general effect, however, is to produce a continuing series of impulses at frequencies proportional to the intensity of the depolarizing current.

CONDUCTION

A transmembrane current of 6×10^{-10} amp. is sufficient to excite an axon. During the spike potential the axon generates a current of about 30×10^{-10} amp. Thus, there is about a five-fold gain between the stimulating and action currents. The action current passes through adjacent regions of the axon and is sufficiently strong to excite them, and in this manner it produces a self-propagating spike potential. Thus, the nerve impulse is conducted successively from each point of excitation by means of eddy currents. The velocity of its propagation depends on how quickly the eddy currents can produce a threshold change in consecutive regions along the axon. If the external resistance is made high—as, for instance,

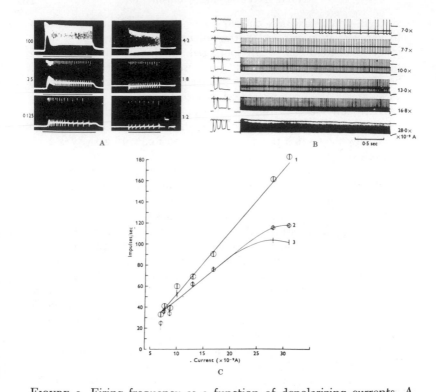

FIGURE 2. Firing frequency as a function of depolarizing currents. A, from eccentric cell in the eye of the horseshoe crab. At *left* is response to light of relative intensities, 100, 2.5, and 0.125 (flash indicated by *black line beneath records*). On *right* are similar frequencies of discharge in the same cell elicited by intracellular depolarizing currents of 4.2, 1.8, and 1.2 × 10⁻⁹ amp. *Black line,* 1 second; calibrating pulse, 20 mv. B, response of rat motoneuron to intracellular depolarizing currents. Rhythmic discharge occurs at 7.7 × 10⁻⁹ amp. or above, but 7.0 × 10⁻⁹ amp. merely increases rate of sporadic discharge. Records on *left* with 1,000 a second sine wave show responses at onset of current. C, relation of impulse frequency to depolarizing current for records in B; 1, at 0.33 second after onset; 2, at 1.3 seconds; 3, at 2.6 seconds. For *curves 2 and 3* the slope constant is 4.1 impulses a second per μamp., and for the visual cell of the crab in A, 4.4 impulses a second per μamp. Such precise correlation is instructive but fortuitous, since the cell in A is at room temperature and that in B is at 37° C. (Part A is from Fuortes, M. G. F. Initiation of impulses in visual cells of *Limulus. J. Physiol.,* 148: 14, 1959. Parts B and C are from Granit, R., Kernell, D., and Shortress, G. K. Quantitative aspects of repetitive firing of mammalian motoneurones, caused by injected currents. *J. Physiol.,* 168: 911, 1963.)

by immersing a single axon in oil—the resulting restriction of current flow slows the conduction velocity, since the threshold depolarization is reached at each new point somewhat later in the course of the action potential at the antecedent point. If, on the other hand, a shunt is provided so that the neurally generated currents can flow through a metallic conductor to a point far down the axon, the excitation jumps immediately to that distant point and thus lessens the conduction time. Both of these maneuvers, incidentally, prove the fact that the eddy currents are responsible for the propagation of the nerve impulse.

A jumping or saltation actually occurs in vertebrate nerves, but from a channeling rather than a shunting of the currents. The fatty insulating material myelin present throughout the 0.4 to 1.5 mm. between nodes of Ranvier, prevents the eddy currents from entering the axon except at the nodes. Such saltation helps to increase the conduction velocity of nerve fibers, but its major advantage is probably one of conserving metabolic energy. It is obviously more efficient to limit the ionic exchange and re-sultant metabolic demands of excitation to a small area, probably about 1 per cent, of the axon rather than to involve the entire axonal surface in the process.

> In intact peripheral nerves the internodal distance is proportional to the diameter of the fiber. However, when a nerve is cut and the fibers regenerate, the internodal distances are about the same for all types of fiber, yet the conduction velocity differences are still main-tained. Thus, conduction velocity is a function of fiber diameter rather than internodal distance. The importance of the fiber diameter in conduction velocity arises from the fact that the longitudinal re-sistance of the fiber is a function of its diameter. The lower the longi-tudinal resistance, the more rapidly the eddy currents depolarize a node to the threshold level, and thus the more rapidly the impulse can be propagated. This emphasizes the fact that the eddy currents must flow *through* the axon to cause its excitation, and from this it is easy to understand how the arrangement of myelin and the random alignment of nodes between fibers renders the influence of one fiber on another virtually nil in vertebrate nerves.

MYONEURAL JUNCTION

The myoneural junction provides a conveniently accessible site for study-ing the transmission of excitation from one cell to another. The junction or end plate is a complicated structure characterized by repeated folds in the muscle membrane (see Figure 3). Arrival of the nerve impulse at the axon terminal induces a 30- to 40-mv. depolarization in the muscle fiber, which normally has a resting potential of about −90 mv. This depolari-zation is the end plate potential (EPP). It is several times the magnitude

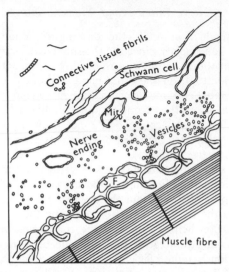

FIGURE 3. Myoneural junction in sartorius muscle of frog. Note complex folding of muscle membrane subjacent to the nerve ending, and presence of great numbers of particles, the synaptic vesicles, in the latter. (From Birks, R., Huxley, H. E., and Katz, B. The fine structure of the neuromuscular junction of the frog. *J. Physiol.*, *150*: 134, 1960.)

necessary to achieve the critical level of depolarization at which excitation becomes self-sustaining to propagate over the membrane of the muscle fiber thus triggering the mechanical contraction of the fiber.

CHEMICAL INITIATION OF THE END PLATE POTENTIAL

It might be supposed that the EPP arises merely from the electrical excitation received from the axon terminal. It has, however, been conclusively shown that this is not the case but, rather, that the EPP arises under the influence of chemical transmitters released from the axon terminal. Indeed, many lines of evidence point to the probability that the end plate region and other subsynaptic surfaces are electrically inexcitable, that the membrane in these regions lacks the characteristics necessary for the abrupt change in sodium ion conductance needed to support a spike potential. Instead, subsynaptic membranes change their permeability only under chemical influences. A few types of invertebrate and vertebrate synapses are known in which electrical transmission does occur from one cell to another, but these instances are relatively rare.

The most critical evidence favoring chemical transmission at the myoneural junction is as follows:

The EPP endures for several milliseconds longer than the muscle spike potential, and its time course is unaffected by the discharge of an artificially induced spike potential propagating into the end plate region. Such independence of the EPP from extraneous electrical influences suggests that it is chemically rather than electrically controlled. In frog muscle at 20° C. there is a delay of 0.5 millisecond, sometimes even ranging out to as much as 4 milliseconds, between the time of arrival of the excitation at the axon terminal and the beginning of the EPP. This delay would be wholly inexplicable were the EPP electrically evoked, whereas it is not at all unexpected if the potential is dependent on the mobilization, release, and diffusion of a chemical transmitter across the myoneural junction. More direct proof comes from the identification of acetylcholine as the chemical transmitting agent. Acetylcholine is released at the myoneural junction during excitation by the motor axon, and EPPs can be produced by brief jets of acetylcholine solutions directed at the end plate region.

Records from the end plate region always show even at rest a random, low-voltage activity. In mammalian muscle at 37° C. these sporadic potentials are about 0.4 mv. and occur at an average frequency of about 1.4 a second. The amplitude of these miniature end plate potentials (MEPPs) shows a slight variation from one to another, depending probably on the origin of the potential in respect to the recording electrode, but analysis shows them to be all essentially identical; they are quantal in nature. They disappear upon degeneration of the nerve fiber, and, although they subsequently return at a very low frequency when the Schwann cell has phagocytized the axon terminal and replaced it at the end plate, no one questions the neural origin of the MEPPs. Since the normal axon terminal contains great numbers of uniform structures, the synaptic vesicles (see Figure 3), it seems very likely that these morphological quanta are related to those observed physiologically. The vesicles would thus contain acetylcholine, and the sporadic, random escape of vesicles from the synaptic terminal would produce the MEPPs. Although vesicles from the myoneural junction have not yet been analyzed to determine whether they contain acetylcholine or not, vesicles of similar appearance isolated from the central nervous system definitely do. The myoneural junction of the frog (see Figure 3) contains about 10^6 vesicles, and it can be estimated that concurrent release of roughly 200 of them would be required to produce the full EPP in normal circumstances. The estimates are still somewhat rough, but it seems likely that there are about 2,000 molecules of acetylcholine in each vesicle.

The amplitude of the EPP is proportional to the amplitude of the presynaptic spike potential. If the latter is diminished by artificial depolarization of the presynaptic terminals—as, for instance, by increasing external K^+—the EPP is diminished, whereas, when a larger presynaptic spike is obtained by electrically hyperpolarizing the presynaptic membrane, the EPP is greatly increased. Since the manipulation of the presynaptic potential does not alter the amplitude of the MEPPs, it must be presumed that the increased EPP arises from a greater number of quanta released. The effects of hyperpolarization versus depolarization are asymmetrical. The effect of the former continues to increase gradually during many seconds of polarization, in one instance augmenting the EPP ten-fold after polarization for 74 seconds. Upon cessation of hyperpolarizing current, EPPs remained enhanced for some 40 seconds. Depolarizing currents, on the other hand, produce their relatively small effects immediately and have little or no after-effect. The size of the EPP is also linearly related to the logarithm of the calcium ion concentration.

MORPHOLOGY OF CENTRAL SYNAPSES

Axon terminations on cell bodies and dendrites are packed with vesicles highly similar in appearance to those found in the myoneural junction (see Figures 3 and 4). The postsynaptic membrane commonly shows a slight thickening but none of the complex folding seen at the myoneural junction.

Specialized forms of central synapses. There are, however, highly specialized forms of central synapses—as, for instance, those of the mossy fiber endings on the dendrites of hippocampal pyramidal cells (see Figure 4) in which an unmyelinated axon 0.3 μ in diameter gives rise to a presynaptic bag 4 μ in diameter. The postsynaptic membrane of the dendrite (see Figure 4) enmeshes itself within the presynaptic terminal, thus creating on the dendritic surface an outcropping known as the dendritic spine, which is prominent in Golgi preparations (see Figures 1, 2, and 3 in Chapter 6). In the neocortex these axodendritic synapses and the dendritic spines are not so highly developed as in the hippocampus, but they still form a synapse, known as the type I synapse, which is distinctly different from the type II synapse on cell bodies. In the type I synapse, which has an average length of 0.46 μ (visual cortex of the rat), there is thickening of both the presynaptic and postsynaptic membranes throughout 90 to 100 per cent of the length of their apposition. The gap between the membranes of about 300 Å contains a faint web of material. Within the dendrite there is often a spine apparatus, which consists of several saclike, membrane-bounded spaces with dark bands between. In the type II or axosomatic synapse there is thickening for only 30 to 40 per cent of the length of the apposed membranes, they are only 200 Å apart, and an intermediate band is essentially absent. In addition to these types, axoaxonic endings are common in which an axon terminal is itself contacted by another terminal. The axoax-

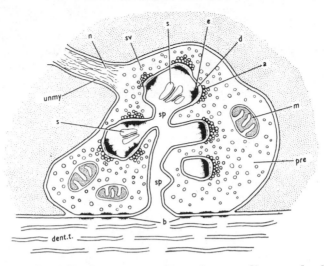

FIGURE 4. Specialized synaptic ending of mossy fiber on dendrite of pyramidal cell in the hippocampus. The mossy fibers arise from granule cells in the nearby dentate gyrus. *a*, area of thickening on a small dendritic spine (*sp*) greater than for presynaptic membrane; *b*, thickening of postsynaptic membrane on the dendritic shaft (*den*) about equal to that of presynaptic membrane; *d*, electron dense material in widened gap of *a* type thickening; *dent. t.*, dendritic tubules (see Figure 3 in Chapter 6); *e*, dense material in dendritic spine adjacent to *a* type thickening; *m*, mitochondria; *n*, neurofilaments; *pre*, presynaptic bag; *s*, spine apparatus; *sp*, dendritic spine; *sv*, synaptic vesicles; *unmy*, unmyelinated axon of granule cell. *Stippling* indicates glial and other elements. (From Hamlyn, L. H. The fine structure of the mossy fibre endings in the hippocampus of the rabbit. *J. Anat.*, 96: 112, 1962.)

onic contacts are all of type II. It is of considerable interest that the same axon terminal can form a type II ending on another axon and continue on to form a type I contact with a dendrite in the immediate vicinity.

Some Anatomical Details of the Spinal Cord

In the human spinal cord there are about 800,000 afferent fibers and only 200,000 efferent fibers on óne side. This preponderance of afferent over efferent fibers is typical of the mammalian spinal cord. The great importance of afferent inflow to the coordination of movement is seen in the fact that total deafferentation of a monkey's arm produces a condition of paralysis, despite intactness of pyramidal and extrapyramidal systems. With training the animal can learn to use this arm to a limited extent, but the deficiency remains profound.

Probably the main reason for the great dependence of movement on the afferent system is the presence of the powerful proprioceptive system coming from the muscle spindles. These spindle afferents in turn are driven by a special set of motoneurons, called gamma motoneurons or fusimotor neurons, which cause contraction of special muscle fibers in which the spindle receptors are embedded. By means of this fusimotor system, the central nervous system initiates afferent discharge that sums with that set up by the already-present state of stretch of the muscle and feeds this combined information back into the spinal cord to control the alpha motoneurons that produce ordinary muscular movements. Many of the afferent fibers from the muscle spindles are among the largest and fastest nerve fibers known. The intricacies of the gamma feedback loop, the fusimotor-spindle-alpha motoneuron system, are beyond the scope of this text. It should be realized, however, that a single spindle afferent fiber forms at least four major types of connection in the spinal cord. (1) It ends directly on motoneurons that are synergistic in their action to the muscle in which the afferent fiber originates and on motoneurons innervating surrounding portions of the originating muscle. These monosynaptic connections are excitatory. (2) It forms connections with interneurons, which in turn play directly on motoneurons supplying muscles antagonistic to that from which the spindle afferent originates. Such connections inhibit the action of the motoneurons supplying antagonistic muscles. (3) It forms powerful monosynaptic, excitatory connections within nucleus dorsalis (Clarke's column) on the cells that project into the dorsal spinocerebellar tract. (4) It excites an interneuronal system that by multisynaptic relays comes to play on other afferent fibers near their synaptic terminations and reduces their action by means of presynaptic inhibition (see below).

A motoneuron, of course, sends its axon into the ventral root; but it also sends collateral fibers into a small group of cells at the ventrocentral margin of the spinal cord gray known as Renshaw cells. The system of Renshaw cells produces inhibition on motoneurons synergistic to those that supply them with collaterals. In other words, when a motoneuron discharges, it inhibits its neighbor through the Renshaw system. There is also a weak effect of inhibiting the inhibition—that is, disinhibition of antagonistic motoneuronal pools.

In addition to these afferent and collateral systems, there are many others driven by afferents from the joints, tendons, and skin, from contralateral as well as ipsilateral sources, together with a great variety of influences playing into the spinal cord from higher centers. Most of the current knowledge involves large-cell, large-fiber systems that are comparatively easy to analyze. Unfortunately, these are numerically the least important systems, since there are three to four times as many unmyelinated fibers 0.3 to 1.3 μ in diameter as there are larger myelinated fibers up to 12 to 20 μ in diameter.

ELECTRICAL EVENTS IN MOTONEURONS

Motoneurons can be impaled by microcapillary electrodes having a tip diameter of 1 to 2 μ. The entrance of the capillary tip into a neuron is signalled by an abrupt change in recorded potential from zero to about -70 mv. as the tip is advanced a few microns. Motoneurons can be unequivocally identified as such by their being excited antidromically by stimulation of a ventral root. Similarly, in preparations with severed dorsal roots, the motoneuron can be further specified exactly as to which muscle it innervates simply by finding which muscle nerve excites it antidromically. The Renshaw cells, which are also activated by antidromic stimulation of motor axons, cannot be confused with motoneurons, since their response is not of an antidromic type.

A double-barrelled microelectrode is often employed so that the membrane potential can be set electrically by a voltage clamp or the internal ionic environment altered by electrophoretic injections with one barrel, while the second barrel of the electrode is used to record the reaction of the impaled cell. When by such means a motoneuron is hyperpolarized, it becomes less likely that it will be invaded by antidromic impulses. This manipulation reveals three all-or-none stages in the antidromic invasion of the neuron (see Figure 5). The interpretation of these stages is as follows: (1) With intense hyperpolarization only a small potential, the M spike, is recorded in the soma. The M spike represents the distant impulse subsiding at the first myelinated segment as it fails to propagate into the hyperpolarized region. (2) With less severe hyperpolarization the antidromic invasion proceeds somewhat farther, presumably into the initial segment of the axon, where it produces the IS spike which, however, is still remote from the recording electrode. (3) Usually at normal levels of membrane potential, the cell body and probably the dendrites are invaded, giving rise to the SD spike, which is the fully developed, all-or-none spike of the motoneuron per se. With orthodromic excitation or with excitation from intracellularly applied currents, the motoneuron discharge is always initiated by a potential exactly like that of the antidromically analyzed IS spike. Hence, it seems certain that excitation originates in the initial segment rather than in the soma or dendrites (see Figure 5). Thus, the initial segment of the axon is critical in the excitatory processes of the neuron, since it has the lowest threshold and its discharge propagates a spike both down the axon and up over the soma and into the dendrites.

The SD spike is commonly followed by delayed depolarization and/or by hyperpolarizing and finally by depolarizing after-potentials (see Figure 6). The dendrites presumably make important contributions to these potentials, since they are not seen after an IS spike. The delayed depolarization usually is of the order of 3 to 7 mv. on

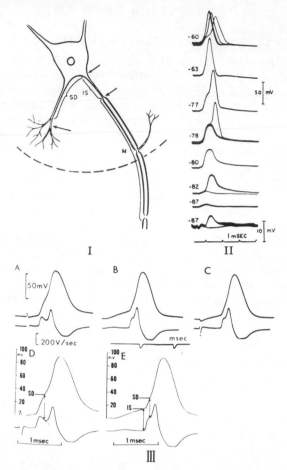

FIGURE 5. Components of potentials generated in motoneurons. *I*, segments of motoneuron; *II*, the responses obtained by antidromic stimulation when membrane potential, −80 mv. at rest in this cell, is set at different levels by intracellularly applied currents (see the text). In *III* a motoneuron with −70 mv. resting potential is stimulated antidromically (A, D), by a monosynaptic EPSP (B, E) and by a depolarizing intracellular pulse (C). The *lower trace of each pair* is an electrical differentiation showing the rate of change of potential in the *upper traces*, making more clear the fact that similar components are present in each case. In D and E the *perpendicular lines* indicate the start of the IS and SD components and the *horizontal lines* indicate their respective thresholds. (From Eccles, J. C. *The Physiology of Nerve Cells.* Johns Hopkins Press, Baltimore, 1957; and from Eccles, J. C. The excitatory responses of spinal neurones. In *Progress in Brain Research*, J. C. Eccles and J. P. Schadé, editors, vol. 12, p. 1. Elsevier, Amsterdam, 1964.)

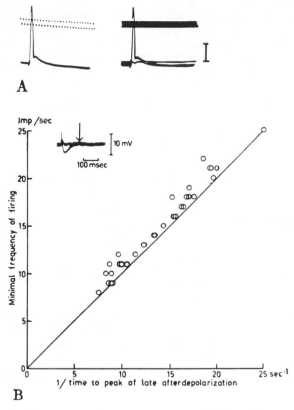

FIGURE 6. After-potentials in motoneurons. A, from L₄ segment in rat showing delayed depolarization (hump after spike) and beginning after-hyperpolarization after orthodromically elicited spike. Record to *right* shows repeated traces with near-threshold stimuli in which spike sometimes did not develop, thus providing baseline of resting potential from which to judge the magnitude of the after-hyperpolarization. Calibration 20 mv. and 1,000 Hz. B, relation between minimal frequency of steady repetitive firing of cat motoneurons and reciprocal of the time to peak of after-depolarization (*arrow on inset*). *Inset*, at slow sweep speed, shows antidromic response of neuron with deep after-hyperpolarization and late after-depolarization, barely visible at this gain. (*Part A* is from Granit, R., Kernell, D., and Smith, R. S. Delayed depolarization and repetitive response to intracellular stimulation of mammalian motoneurones. J. Physiol., 168: 890, 1963. *Part B* is from Kernell, D. The limits of firing frequency in cat lumbosacral motoneurones possessing different time courses of after-hyperpolarization. Acta Physiol. Scand., 65: 87, 1965.)

the falling phase of the SD spike and lasts 3 to 6 milliseconds (see Figure 6A). The after-hyperpolarization is much more protracted, attaining about 5 mv. at 10 milliseconds and then, for motoneurons innervating fast-contracting muscles, endures for about 70 to 80 milliseconds; for motoneurons innervating slowly contracting muscles, it may last 150 milliseconds. This after-hyperpolarization is independent of that produced by the Renshaw system, which has similar effects lasting about 50 milliseconds, and arises from a slight change in membrane permeability permitting a greater outward flux of potassium ions.

By stimulating the neurons directly with depolarizing currents supplied through an internal microelectrode, one may reveal a number of interesting and important features. First, the form of response of the neuron is essentially identical to that which occurs to natural, orthodromic excitation (see Figure 5, *Part III*). At a certain level of depolarizing current, the neuron begins to discharge repetitively and regularly so long as the current is maintained (see Figure 2B and C). Below this current level it merely discharges sporadically. The frequency of discharge is highest immediately after onset of a continuous current, falls slightly during an adaptation period of 0.1 to 1.0 second, and is then maintained steadily for long periods. Within the physiological range of discharge from a minimum steady rate of about 15 a second to a maximum steady rate of 50 a second, the relation of the frequency to the intensity of the depolarizing current is essentially linear (see Figure 2C). There is, however, a ten-fold range in the slope of this frequency-intensity relationship; some neurons have an output 10 times greater than others for the same input. This means that the effectiveness of a given excitatory background on a given neuron depends on the neuron's size, geometry, locus of synapses, and other factors. The neuron's characteristics in this regard can be predicted from its after-potentials (see Figure 6B). The minimal frequency of steady repetitive firing is related to the peak of the later after-depolarization and matches the frequency at which the innervated muscle is known to begin mechanical summation of contractions. The maximum steady frequency, on the other hand, is closely related to the duration of after-hyperpolarization and in turn matches the maximum useful frequency for obtaining tetanic fusion in the innervated muscle. Thus, the temporal characteristics of neurons fit them precisely into various physiological roles, and it seems safe to assume that similar principles hold for many other neuronal systems of the brain. For instance, it is found that interneurons in the spinal cord fire much more rapidly for a slight change of intracellular depolarizing current than do motoneurons. Interneurons should thus be well-suited for amplifying incoming signals, and with their higher output frequencies they provide the natural depolarizing pressure required for sustained activity in the motoneurons.

EXCITATORY POSTSYNAPTIC POTENTIAL

A single orthodromic synchronous volley entering the dorsal roots after stimulation of an appropriate muscle nerve produces a brief depolarizing action in an impaled motoneuron. This depolarization is the excitatory postsynaptic potential (EPSP) arising from activity of afferent fibers with direct, monosynaptic connections to motoneurons.

The amplitude of the EPSP depends on how many afferent fibers are synchronously discharged, and hence the EPSP can be graded by changes in stimulus intensity. Up to the point of exciting all fibers, the number of fibers excited in a nerve depends on the intensity of an electrical stimulus. The EPSP rises to a maximum within about 1.0 millisecond and then decays with a time constant of about 5 milliseconds (see Figure 7). This rather long course of action probably results from residual transmitter action. Since a significant fraction of the depolarization continues even out to 12 milliseconds, a second EPSP induced within this time can sum with the first. The neuron discharges by initiating an IS spike when depolarization from the EPSPs reaches 5 to 18 mv.

Because spontaneous neural discharge is omnipresent in the central nervous system, it is very difficult to determine whether random miniature EPSPs, analogous to the MEPPs at the myoneural junction, occur in the absence of presynaptic spikes. However, when all conduction is blocked in the isolated spinal cord of the frog by treating it with solutions with a high magnesium content, a background of EPSPs, many with identical amplitude, can still be recorded.

This suggests that the quantal release of transmitter occurs spontaneously at central synapses as well as at the myoneural junction, as it also does in autonomic ganglia.

INHIBITORY POSTSYNAPTIC POTENTIAL

Brief hyperpolarizing potentials are produced in an impaled motoneuron by stimulation of nerves from muscles with action antagonistic to that innervated by the impaled neuron. Since hyperpolarization carries the membrane potential away from the threshold level, it has the effect of inhibiting the activity of the neuron. Hence, these potentials are termed inhibitory postsynaptic potentials (IPSPs).

The IPSPs are essentially a mirror image of the EPSPs (see Figure 7), although their time course is slightly shorter. The amplitude of the IPSP also depends on the number of fibers active in the synchronous afferent volley.

It can be inferred that the same fiber can generate EPSPs in one set of motoneurons and IPSPs in other motoneurons. These direct inhibitory connections, however, have a slight but significantly longer latency than the excitatory. Measuring from the time when the affer-

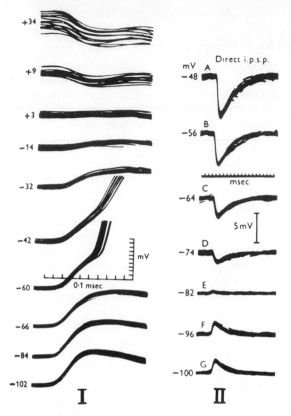

FIGURE 7. Excitatory (*I*) and inhibitory (*II*) postsynaptic potentials of cat motoneurons as modified by setting of the membrane potential at different levels. Upward deflection indicates depolarization. Membrane potential is controlled through one of the two electrodes impaling the cell, and its level is indicated at the *left of each set* of about 20 superimposed responses. *I*, biceps-semitendinosus motoneuron with resting potential of −66 mv. Equilibrium potential for EPSP is ∼ +3 mv., and when membrane potential is greater than this value (for example, +9 and +34 mv.), it also moves toward +3 mv. during the EPSP process. In *II*, a biceps-semitendinosus motoneuron with a resting potential of −74 mv. is subjected to inhibitory volleys from quadriceps afferent fibers. The equilibrium potential for the IPSP is apparently about −80 mv., and the potential moves toward this value whether depolarized (−64, −56, and −48 mv.) or hyperpolarized (−82, −96, and −100 mv.) (see the text). (*Part I* is from Coombs, J. S., Eccles, J. C., and Fatt, P. Excitatory synaptic action in motoneurones. J. Physiol., *130:* 374, 1955. *Part II* is from Coombs, J. S., Eccles, J. C., and Fatt, P. The specific ionic conductances and the ionic movements across the motoneuronal membrane that produce the inhibitory post-synaptic potential. J. Physiol., *130:* 326, 1955.)

ent volley enters the spinal cord over the dorsal roots until action is produced in an impaled motoneuron, it takes about 1.0 millisecond longer to evoke an IPSP than it does to evoke an EPSP. This 1.0-millisecond delay is prima facie evidence for the existence of an inter-neuron in the inhibitory pathway. The following evidence is suffi-ciently convincing to validate the existence of such an inhibitory in-terneuron. It might first be supposed that the inhibitory nerve branches were smaller than the excitatory ones as they approached their termination in the cord or that it took a longer time to mobilize and release the inhibitory as opposed to the excitatory transmitter, thus accounting for the extra delay for the IPSP. This is not the case, however, since on stimulation within the ventral horn, where the pre-synaptic fibers producing EPSPs and IPSPs can be directly stimu-lated, the latencies for the two processes are identical. The delay at the synaptic terminal is about 0.3 millisecond in each case. IPSPs can be produced by concurrent stimulation of two separate afferent sources where neither alone has any affect. Thus, there must exist remote from the motoneuron a common site, an interneuron, where such summation occurs. Finally, interneurons in the intermediate nucleus of the cord have been found that fire in appropriate relation to the timing of the IPSPs. Stimulation in this nucleus can produce IPSPs.

Ionic Basis of EPSPs and IPSPs

One of the most ingenious triumphs of neurophysiology has been the identification of the ionic events underlying the generation of EPSPs and IPSPs. This was accomplished by determining the equilibrium potentials for the IPSP and EPSP processes and then altering the intracellular concentration of various ions to determine which ionic species contributed to these equilibrium potentials. The procedure is illustrated in Figures 7 and 8. The motoneuron is impaled with a double-barrelled microelectrode. Through one barrel of the electrode the membrane potential is clamped at any desired voltage level, and with the other barrel the response of the neuron to excitatory and inhibitory volleys is then recorded. In Figure 7 I, at −60 mv. the excitatory volley produces an EPSP sufficient to attain the threshold and discharge a spike potential. This still occurs when the membrane potential is artificially set at −42 mv., but at this level the processes are slowed by the lack of adequate driving voltage. At −32 mv. the EPSP is considerably reduced, and the neuron probably could not discharge, since it is being held depolarized beyond the threshold level. The equilibrium potential is seen to be about +3 mv. where no current flows during the EPSP, since the electrical potential bal-ances the ionic concentration differences that underlie the generation of the EPSP. When the membrane potential is set at still more posi-

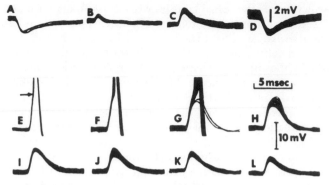

FIGURE 8. Intracellular recording, through a double-barrelled micro-electrode filled with 3 M KCl, of IPSPs generated in a cat biceps-semitendinosus motoneuron by quadriceps afferent volleys. A, shortly after penetration of the cell; B and C, reversal of IPSP by diffusion of Cl^- from electrode; D, restoration of hyperpolarizing effect of IPSP when membrane potential set at −41 mv. Cl^- was then deliberately injected into the cell for one minute, thus changing the equilibrium potential for Cl^- to a level less than the threshold of the cell. Hence, the membrane potential moves toward this level during the IPSP and, crossing the threshold, discharges the cell (E, F, G). Diffusion gradually reduces the intracellular concentration of Cl^- (G to K), until the previous level (C) is reached (L) (see the text). (From Eccles, J. C. *The Physiology of Nerve Cells*, p. 107. Johns Hopkins Press, Baltimore, 1957.)

tive voltages, the current actually moves in the opposite direction, toward the equilibrium potential, during the impingement of the excitatory volley. A similar analysis is shown in Figure 7 II for an inhibitory volley producing IPSPs that, at the resting level of −74 mv., produced hyperpolarizing IPSPs. The equilibrium potential is found to be approximately 80 mv.; when the membrane potential is moved beyond this equilibrium to −96 or −100 mv., the potential change during the inhibitory action is reversed, since it still moves toward the equilibrium potential.

The equilibrium potential for the SD spike is approximately +40 mv., which is the same as that found for the spike process of peripheral nerve. This and other evidence indicate that the process generating the SD spike changes the membrane conductance only for sodium ions. The equilibrium potential of −10 to ±0 mv. for the EPSP is the same as for the EPP, and both appear to be generated by simultaneous changes in membrane permeability to all the major electrolytes, Na^+, K^+, Cl^-.

The equilibrium potential of −80 mv. for the IPSP process can be shown to arise from a change in membrane permeability to ions with a hydrated diameter similar to that of K^+ or Cl^-. The case for the participation of Cl^- is illustrated in Figure 8. The motoneuron was in this case penetrated with an electrode containing KCl. Immediately after penetration, an inhibitory volley produced the usual IPSP, as shown in Figure 8A. Within a short time (see Figure 8B and C), however, the gradual diffusion of Cl^- from the electrode was sufficient to produce a significant change in the intracellular concentration of Cl^-. As this occurred, the equilibrium potential of the IPSP changed, ultimately becoming less than the resting potential (−59 mv.). Thus, during the inhibitory volley, the membrane potential moved toward a new equilibrium potential for the IPSP—that is, in a depolarizing direction. When the membrane potential was artificially set at −41 mv. (see Figure 8D), the inhibitory volley again produced a hyperpolarizing response as the potential still moved in the direction of the new equilibrium potential of the IPSP. Chloride ions were then deliberately injected into the cell for one minute by passing a current of 3.2×10^{-8} amp., electrode-negative. After such a loading of the neuron with Cl^-, inhibitory volleys produce depolarizing potentials sufficient to attain threshold and produce an SD spike (see Figure 8E, F, and G). During the course of about one minute (see Figure 8E to L), the excess chloride leaves the cell, and the previous situation is restored (compare L with C in Figure 8). Such an effect would result if the membrane became highly permeable to Cl^- during the IPSP. With a high intracellular concentration of Cl^- the equilibrium potential for Cl^- would be considerably less than the membrane resting potential, and hence, as the IPSP changed the permeability for Cl^-, this equilibrium potential would predominate.

Anions fall into two groups: those that can and those that cannot mimic these effects of Cl^-. The distinguishing characteristic for effectiveness versus ineffectiveness in this regard seems to be purely a function of the hydrated diameter of the ion. Only the smaller anions —such as Cl^-, Br^-, NO_2^-—are effective. Since K^+ and Cl^- are the only ions within this range of diameters normally present in the cell in significant amounts, it must be assumed that these are the only ions that participate in the IPSP process. Proof of the participation of K^+ in the IPSP is difficult, since the intracellular concentration of K^+ is so high that it cannot easily be changed significantly. However, all evidence currently available points strongly toward the normal equilibrium potential for the IPSP being the balance between the equilibrium potentials of Cl^- (approximately −70 mv.) and K^+ (−90 mv.) to give the observed value of −80 mv. for the IPSP.

PRESYNAPTIC INHIBITION

Both EPSPs and IPSPs are postsynaptic events; that is, they occur in the cell on which the afferent terminals impinge. The inhibitory action arises because the IPSPs sum with and thus reduce the magnitude of EPSPs. In presynaptic inhibition, which is probably a more common arrangement than postsynaptic inhibition, the magnitude of the EPSPs is also reduced, but no IPSPs ever appear in response to the inhibitory volley alone. It must thus be inferred that the inhibitory volley somehow acts directly on the afferent fibers or the presynaptic terminals to reduce their capacity to generate EPSPs. The axoaxonic endings mentioned above are presumably the anatomical substrate for this presynaptic effect.

It had long been known electrophysiologically that certain inhibitory effects are accompanied by positive potentials at the surface of the spinal cord and in the dorsal roots. These potentials have a latency of about 5 milliseconds after the entry of an inhibitory volley into the cord, reach their maximum at about 20 milliseconds, and usually take more than 200 milliseconds to subside. The temporal course of these potentials has now been found to coincide precisely with that of presynaptic inhibition. The relatively long latency arises apparently from multisynaptic relays in interneurons of the dorsal horn, whose action is necessary for presynaptic inhibition. During the course of presynaptic inhibition, the threshold for the stimulation of the inhibited afferent fibers is diminished, thus suggesting that they are partially depolarized. Direct proof of this state of depolarization has been obtained by intracellular recording from primary afferent fibers. Presynaptic inhibition is thus produced by a multineuronal circuit that partially depolarizes afferent terminals, thereby diminishing their action potentials and the consequent release of synaptic transmitter.

The pharmacology of presynaptic inhibition is distinctly different from that of postsynaptic inhibition. Whereas IPSPs in motoneurons are diminished or abolished by injections of strychnine, this drug has no effect on presynaptic inhibition. Picrotoxin, on the other hand, abolishes presynaptic inhibition without affecting postsynaptic inhibition. Strangely, barbiturates enhance presynaptic inhibition.

By using the criteria of latency and time course, depolarization of afferent terminals, and pharmacological analysis, one may demonstrate the existence of presynaptic inhibition at many places in the central nervous system. In the spinal cord, presynaptic inhibition is produced predominantly by cutaneous fibers, by fibers from spindles in flexor muscles, and by fibers from the corticospinal tract. These effects are exerted on afferent input to motoneurons and to ascending sensory pathways. Similar effects are obtained at the main sensory nucleus of the trigeminal nerve. Figure 9 summarizes electron microscopic findings consonant with physiological experiments showing that the pyramidal tract can control synaptic transmis-

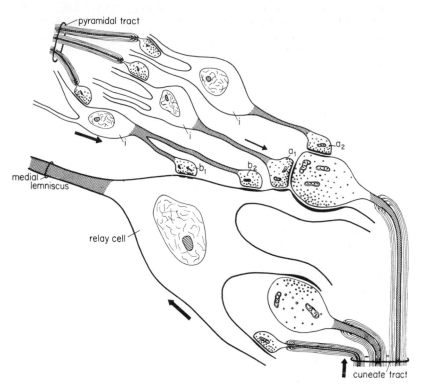

FIGURE 9. Diagram of certain connections in the cuneate nucleus based on electron microscopic findings correlated with degeneration experiments and electrophysiological findings. Myelinated somesthetic afferent fibers (cuneate tract) ascending in the dorsal columns of the spinal cord terminate on relay cell, which projects into ventrobasal thalamus through the medial lemniscus. The relay cells and terminals of the cuneate tract are both controlled by the pyramidal tract through interneurons. Pyramidal tract fibers diagrammed here originate in pericruciate cortex of cat or pre- and postcentral gyri in macaques. The axoaxonic synapses, a_1 and a_2 presumably mediate the presynaptic inhibition observed to follow pyramidal tract or cortical stimulation, and b_1 and b_2 produce IPSPs or EPSPs in the relay cell. Possible connections for pre- and postsynaptic inhibition from collaterals from cuneate tract or relay cells are not shown, although physiological evidence suggests their existence in some parts of the nucleus. (From Walberg, F. Axoaxonic contacts in the cuneate nucleus, probable basis for presynaptic depolarization. Exp. Neurol., 13: 218, 1965.)

sion in the dorsal column nuclei by means of presynaptic inhibition. Note that some terminals form synaptic relation both with the dendrites and with the large presynaptic terminals, which, as degeneration experiments show, originate from the cuneate tract. Similar anatomical arrangements have been observed in the lateral geniculate nucleus of cats and monkeys, and electrophysiological experiments demonstrate that the cerebral cortex and mesencephalic reticular formation control synaptic transmission through this nucleus partly by means of presynaptic inhibition.

OTHER SYNAPSES AND PHENOMENA

The anatomical arrangement of recurrent collaterals from the motor axons projecting onto Renshaw interneurons at the base of the ventral horn has been described above. On stimulation of the ventral roots, these interneurons discharge at extremely high rates, up to 1,500 a second in the initial burst, for as long as 50 milliseconds. The time course of their discharge is correlated with IPSPs and inhibition of motoneurons. A similar arrangement, where axon collaterals play on interneurons that in turn send inhibition back on neighbors of the cell originally excited, has been found physiologically for the cells giving rise to the pyramidal tract (Betz cells), in the cuneate nucleus and ventrobasal complex of the thalamus, in the pyramidal cell system of the hippocampus, and in the olfactory bulb.

FUNCTIONS

An obvious function for such an inhibitory system is the confinement of excitation to a discrete neural pathway. Once excitation is sufficient on a given set of neurons, their discharge suppresses, by means of this surround inhibition, any marginal tendency for neighboring cells to discharge, thus focusing and sharpening the center of activity. When such inhibitory feedback is widespread within an active system, it is also likely to engender rhythmic. activity by locking inhibitory periods in phase for a large group of cells and thus synchronizing the probabilities of their discharge.

Specific neurons that serve as inhibitory interneurons have been identified in the hippocampus and cerebellum. In both these structures a very dense network of synapses envelops the soma of the hippocampal pyramidal cells or the cerebellar Purkinje cells. These axosomatic endings originate from basket cells. The evidence that these basket cells give rise to inhibition is as follows: When intracellular records demonstrate prolonged and powerful IPSPs, extracellular records show that the focus of the inhibitory action is at the cell body and not in the dendrites. Such records are meaningful in the cerebellum and hippocampus because in these structures cell bodies are aligned in precise laminae. Since the axosomatic endings and only these endings are powerfully activated during IPSPs and since these endings arise predominantly from the basket cells, the latter must be inhibitory interneurons. On the rising phase of these IPSPs, a ripple of high-frequency activity can sometimes be observed that corresponds well with the frequency of cell discharge concurrently occurring in regions where the basket cell bodies are known to be located.

For the hippocampus it can be shown that the basket cells are activated by antidromic stimulation of hippocampal pyramidal cell axons. The cerebellar basket cell system, on the other hand, is probably not activated by axons of the Purkinje cells, since the latter are inhibitory in their effect.

It bears emphasis that axon collaterals from hippocampal pyramidal cells, Betz cells, or motoneurons are not likely to be the only input to the basket cells, Renshaw cells, or other interneurons responsible for recurrent inhibition. In other words, these inhibitory systems can probably be activated from several sources.

Synaptic Transmitters

Acetylcholine. Sine acetylcholine is released by motor axons at their presynaptic terminals on muscle fibers, it is reasonable to suppose that the axon collaterals of these same neurons release acetylcholine on Renshaw cells. The correctness of this expectation has been repeatedly confirmed in pharmacological experiments on spinal cord systems. One of the more striking is the demonstration that Renshaw cells are readily excited by the electrophoretic application of minute quantities of acetylcholine in their immediate vicinity by means of microelectrodes, whereas similar applications to other interneurons or to motoneurons is essentially without effect.

Similar electrophoretic application elsewhere in the brain demonstrates that about 10 to 25 per cent of the isolated neurons can be excited by acetylcholine, and roughly 5 per cent are inhibited by it. These effects have been particularly well studied in the neocortex. In the visual cortex of the cat, cells responding at "on" "off" or at both "on" and "off" of light are affected or not affected by electrophoretic application of acetylcholine in the same proportion as other cortical neurons—that is, about 20 per cent excited, 5 per cent inhibited. On the other hand, over 90 per cent of the Betz cells in the precruciate motor cortex of the cat are excited by acetylcholine, whereas in the postcruciate area only 64 per cent of the pyramidal tract cells are cholinoceptive, and only about 20 per cent of the nonpyramidal tract cells in these areas can be activated by acetylcholine. Throughout the cortex the cholinoceptive cells do seem to lie in the deeper cortical layers, suggesting that they may be pyramidal cells in most instances.

The onset of the effect of acetylcholine is characteristically slower for cortical neurons than for Renshaw cells, and the effect outlasts the cessation of application by many seconds. Furthermore, the response of Renshaw cells to acetylcholine is nicotinic, since it is blocked by curariform agents; whereas at the cortex, responses, particularly inhibitory responses, tend to be muscarinic in that they can be blocked by application of atropine or hyoscine but not by curariform agents. Cells in the mesencephalon and diencephalon seem to give both muscarinic and nicotinic responses. Although neurons of the lateral geniculate nucleus and the ventrobasal complex are cholinoceptive, neither atropine nor curariform drugs block their response to stimulation of optic tract or medial lemniscus. This suggests that the cholinergic input to these nuclei arises from the centrencephalic system rather than from the specific optic or somesthetic afferents.

Stimulation of the mesencephalic reticular formation can activate cholinoceptive units in neocortex, but the latency is rather long. Some such units have transcallosal afferents or afferents from nonspecific thalamic nuclei, but most are activated best by stimulation of specific thalamic nuclei, although again the latencies are usually long. Thus, it is still not possible to specify precisely the organization of corticipetal cholinergic systems. Electron microscopic evidence indicates that cholinesterase is located exclusively in the type I axodendritic synapses, but, of course, no claim can be made that all such synapses are cholinergic. Differential staining techniques also indicate that neocortical pyramidal cells, the caudate nucleus, putamen, and septal nuclei have high concentrations of acetylcholinesterase.

Two other lines of evidence suggest that the foregoing experimental findings are actually related to functional cholinergic systems in the brain. First, acetylcholine is continuously released from the surface of the cerebral cortex and from the caudate nucleus. This release is increased severalfold by direct electrical stimulation of these structures or, in the case of the somatosensory cortex, by stimulation of peripheral nerves but not by transcallosal stimulation. Second, acetylcholine is found in large amounts only in that fraction of brain homogenates that contains the synaptic vesicles.

It can thus be concluded with considerable confidence that acetylcholine functions as a transmitter at many synapses in the brain. However, there are still many difficulties involved in appraising these facts. For instance, acetylcholine excites some neurons and inhibits others. This perhaps should not be surprising, since it produces hyperpolarizing potentials in the heart and in certain central synapses of snails and sea slugs but elicits depolarizing potentials at other central synapses in sea slugs, at vertebrate myoneural junctions, etc. The nature of the action of the transmitter may thus be determined by the subsynaptic membrane. There are several instances of neurons being excited or inhibited by more than one type of transmitter. For instance, although the nicotinic type of response is characteristic of Renshaw cells, there is some evidence that they possess still another type of acetylcholine receptor. Furthermore, when cholinergic transmission is blocked at Renshaw cells, they continue to respond vigorously to electrophoretic application of glutamic acid. Similarly, cells in the pons and medulla respond to electrophoretic application of acetylcholine, norepinephrine, and 5-hydroxytryptamine, giving various combinations of excitation and inhibition to these substances specific to any one cell. Finally, there is the complication (see Figure 10) that two types of synaptic vesicles can be found in the same synaptic ending.

Amino acids. Much evidence is accumulating to indicate that γ-aminobutyric acid (GABA) is an inhibitory transmitter in the mammalian central nervous system. The evidence begins with the discovery that a factor, now identified as GABA, isolated from mammalian

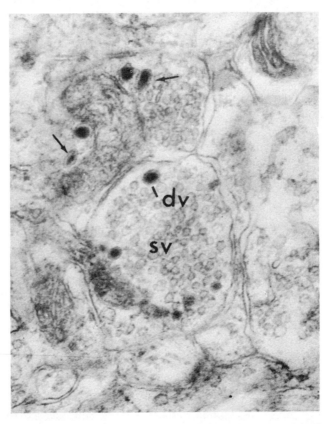

FIGURE 10. Two types of vesicles in single synaptic terminals in the anterior hypothalamus of the rat. *sv*, the common type of vesicle, with an average diameter of 400 to 500 Å, constituting about 80 per cent of the vesicles found in these hypothalamic terminals; *dv*, dense vesicle, identical in appearance with vesicles in proved adrenergic terminals. The dense vesicles have a mean diameter of about 1,300 Å and account for about 20 per cent of the vesicles present. Similar terminals with two types of vesicles have also been found in the thalamus. (From Pellegrino de Iraldi, A., Farini Duggan, H., and de Robeitis, E. Adrenergic synaptic vesicles in the anterior hypothalamus of the rat. Anat. Rec., *145*: 521, 1963.)

brain can cause inhibition of the stretch receptor neuron in the crayfish. The inhibitory axon that normally inhibits this cell in the crayfish contains very high concentrations of GABA, whereas adjacent axons that have an excitatory effect do not. The relevance of these facts to the mammalian central nervous system is that glutamic acid metabolism is uniquely important in brain as compared to other tissues (see Table I in Chapter 6), and that brain but no other mammalian organ contains GABA in large amounts. GABA is found in highest concentration in the fractions of homogenized brain that contain the synaptic vesicles. It is released continuously from the surface of the neocortex in the resting state. During the slow-wave phase of sleep, this release increases threefold and is abolished during states of arousal maintained by occasional stimulation of the mesencephalic reticular system.

The Purkinje cells of the cerebellum produce IPSPs in the cells of Deiter's nucleus. Similar hyperpolarization is produced in Deiter's cells by electrophoretic application of GABA, and the Purkinje cells contain unusually high concentrations of GABA. Thus, several lines of evidence suggest a role for GABA as inhibitory transmitter.

However, its electrophoretic application to most cells in the mammalian central nervous system, although inhibiting their discharge, does not produce in them the hyperpolarization that would be expected were GABA the transmitter producing IPSPs. Instead, the effect of GABA is more one of stabilizing the membrane potential so that both EPSPs and IPSPs are diminished. This is suggestively similar to the effect on presynaptic terminals required to produce presynaptic inhibition. It is thus of interest that picrotoxin, which blocks presynaptic inhibition in the mammalian central nervous system, prevents the action of GABA in invertebrate systems. The case with Purkinje cells, however, is contrary to this supposition that GABA may be particularly related to presynaptic inhibition.

Many other neutral amino acids have effects similar to those of GABA, but acidic amino acids are uniformly excitatory. Certain amino acids can thus be grouped in pairs. Glutamic, aspartic, and cysteic acids have powerful excitatory effects on all neurons to which they are electrophoretically applied, whereas their decarboxylated congeners—the neutral amino acids β-alanine, GABA, and taurine, respectively—depress the activity of all neurons. The uniformity of these effects on all varieties of neurons and the failure of these compounds to imitate the actions of EPSPs and IPSPs make it difficult to conceive of these substances as being involved in the more usual forms of synaptic transmission.

Norepinephrine and serotonin. There is strong suggestive evidence that norepinephrine and possibly 5-hydroxytryptamine (serotonin) are active as synaptic transmitters in the central nervous system. These monoamines and their metabolites are of extraordinary interest because they are influenced by psychotropic drugs and appear to be abnormal in psychotic individuals. Norepinephrine (noradrenaline) is the transmitter at peripheral junctions of the sympathetic nervous system. Its immediate precursor is dopamine, which is ultimately derived from the amino acid phenylalanine. The amino acid tryptophan, with its indole ring, yields 5-hydroxytryptamine through 5-hydroxytryptophan as an intermediate. Of the monoamines, only the catecholamines norepinephrine and dopamine and the indoleamine 5-hydroxytryptamine occur in the brain in significant amounts.

When frozen tissues are dehydrated and then subjected to formaldehyde vapor at 80° C., a highly specific reaction occurs that converts monoamines into fluorescent compounds. With the use of this technique of fluorescence microscopy with careful controls, it is now possible to trace various monoamine systems in the brain with great accuracy. Such data confirm previous chemical analyses showing high concentrations of norepinephrine in the hypothalamus and of dopamine in the caudate nucleus and putamen. Monoamines are essentially absent in neocortex and cerebellum. Terminals containing norepinephrine or 5-hydroxytryptamine are found in the intermediolateral cell column of the spinal cord and also on motoneurons and in the substantia gelatinosa of Rolando in the dorsal horn. Cells containing monoamines occur in the raphe and ventrolateral nuclei of the reticular formation of the medulla, and intense stimulation for one to two hours at these loci halves the norepinephrine content of the spinal cord and diminishes the monoamine fluorescent reaction in the dorsal and ventral horns. Other monoamine-containing cells are found in the ventral tegmental area, substantia nigra, and mesencephalic reticular formation. By means of lesions it can be demonstrated that these neurons control the monoamine content of the forebrain, probably as contained in their axons and presynaptic terminals. Cutting the median forebrain bundle, subthalamic area, and cerebral peduncle produces a 75 per cent decrease in norepinephrine and 5-hydroxytryptamine levels and total loss of dopamine in the forebrain ipsilateral to the lesion. By fluorescence microscopy, terminals containing dopamine are normally found in caudate and accumbens nuclei, the putamen, and the olfactory tubercle; norepinephrine in cingulate gyrus, pyriform cortex, amygdala, septum, hippocampus, preoptic area, and hypothalamus; and 5-hydroxytryptamine in the globus pallidus, septal area, amygdala, and hypothalamus. Almost all these terminals depend on the mesencephalic systems.

Electrophoretic application of these compounds through multibarrelled microelectrodes depresses the activity of cells in the neocortex and lateral geniculate nucleus. Since monoamines are not prominent at these loci, although they are found at a few bipolar-ganglion cell junctions in the retina, the significance of this is problematical. In the medulla, pons, and mesencephalon about half the neurons are inhibited, but 40 per cent are excited by 5-hydroxytryptamine; with norepinephrine about 20 per cent are inhibited and 30 per cent excited. The time course of these effects, however, is rather slow.

Since cell bodies, axons, and terminals all show fluorescence, the monoamines are probably manufactured in the cell body and passed down the axon. When the sciatic nerve is compressed, an accumulation of fluorescing material, probably norepinephrine, begins within twelve hours in the central portion of the compressed axons. It is not known whether, in addition to receiving norepinephrine through the axoplasm, the presynaptic terminals are themselves capable of synthesizing it. They do, however, absorb norepinephrine when it is present in their environment. This characteristic is of value in further identifying adrenergic terminals by their absorption of tritiated norepinephrine. In adrenergic terminals of the peripheral nervous system and in association with tritiated norepinephrine, large synaptic vesicles are consistently found with dense osmiophilic cores (see Figure 10). As with acetylcholine and GABA, the monoamines and their relevant enzymes are found predominantly in those fractions of homogenized brain that contain synaptic vesicles.

Conclusions

In summary, acetylcholine, GABA, norepinephrine, and 5-hydroxytryptamine are all likely to be central synaptic transmitters. The analysis is complicated by the probability that the type of response that each produces may be determined predominantly by the nature of the postsynaptic membrane. There may also be many transmitter substances still undiscovered, since those at hand are not very successful in imitating the phenomena of central synaptic excitation and inhibition.

Postsynaptic inhibition in the spinal cord may differ from that in the brain stem and cortex, since in the cord IPSPs endure only about 12 milliseconds and are blocked by strychnine, whereas above the obex 200-millisecond IPSPs are the rule, and strychnine has no effect on them. The morphology of synapses and synaptic vesicles has to date posed far more difficult problems than it has solved. First among these is the occurrence of two types of vesicles in one synapse (see Figure 10). This might be merely an outcome of the specificity of subsynaptic membranes—that is, the presynaptic terminal serves a cafeteria selection of transmitters, and the subsynaptic membrane takes its choice—but the significance is likely to be more subtle and reflect a greater efficiency than this. It seems likely, however, that the smaller vesicles with osmophobic cores may contain any of several transmitters. Thus, there is no apparent difference in vesicles at axo-somatic endings that electrophysiological evidence indicates are inhibitory from those in the presumably excitatory endings on the dendrites. Nor does the difference in type I versus type II endings specify excitation versus inhibition, since inhibitory action also seems to impinge on dendrites, whereas type II synapses do not. Finally, there are instances where vesicles occur on each side of what seem to be junctions between dendrites.

Enduring Consequences of Synaptic Action

Rapid, repetitive activation of synapses produces changes in their effectiveness both during the course of activation and for a considerable period thereafter. For continuous stimulation of afferents from muscle spindles, EPSPs evoked in motoneurons remain relatively constant until stimuli occur at 0.5 a second. The amplitude of the EPSPs then falls with increasing frequency until at 10 a second it is only about 85 per cent of control levels. With further increase of frequency, however, the amplitude recovers until at about 50 a second it is restored to control levels and then falls off again to reach 90 per cent at 100 a second. The size of the EPSP probably reflects the amount of transmitter released. These synapses thus operate with greater efficiency at 50 a second than at 20 a second, but optimally and minimally effective frequencies vary with different synaptic systems. The total amount of transmitter released per unit of time will, of course, be much greater at 100 than at 50 a second, even though the amplitude of each EPSP is smaller, and indeed the maximum rate of release is reached only at 300 a second.

Some synaptic systems become and remain inoperative during rapid stimulation, a phenomenon known as Vedensky inhibition. Such suspension of function could arise in several different ways: (1) by refractoriness in presynaptic terminals rendering them inexcitable; (2) by depletion of immediately available transmitter; (3) by a saturation of the postsynaptic membrane with the transmitter, thus desensitizing the EPSP or IPSP mechanism; or (4) by keeping the postsynaptic cell continuously depolarized beyond its threshold level, thus inactivating it.

With onset of a burst of stimuli, there is a brief period of depression and adjustment before the EPSPs attain a stable level. Presumably a mobilization of transmitter from presynaptic sources is required to accommodate the greatly augmented rate of its release. Once such mobilization is achieved, it remains accessible for several minutes after a few seconds of high-frequency stimulation. In systems where MEPPs are observed, their rate increases greatly during this postactivation period. The amplitude of EPSP to single stimuli actually increases only 1.5 to 2 times after intense activity—for example, tetanization at 200 per second for 15 seconds—but this moderate increase often is enough to discharge 4 to 10 times as many cells in a motoneuronal pool as did the same stimulus prior to tetanization. Naturally, if the stimulus initially discharges all the cells, it can do no more, and, therefore, no potentiation of reflex discharge can be obtained, even by doubling the amplitude of EPSPs. The magnitude of possible potentiation is thus a function of the number of cells subliminally excited by the original stimulus; it is dependent on the existence of a subliminal fringe.

In work with monosynaptic reflexes in the spinal cord, it can be shown that the locus of the augmented responsiveness is in the presynaptic terminals subjected to the tetanization. During the period of potentiation, the excitability of the tetanized afferent fibers is unchanged, as is the antidromic response of the motoneurons or their responsiveness concurrently tested by nontetanized synaptic systems. The effect is thus limited to the activated synapses. The presynaptic terminals of the potentiated system are hyperpolarized, a common finding in fibers of small diameter after intense activity. As discussed above for the myoneural junction, such hyperpolarization could account for an increase in the release of transmitter for each impulse that succeeds in invading the terminal. Attractive as such an explanation of postactivation potentiation may be, it probably is not altogether true, since a three- to eight-fold postactivation increase in EPSPs is obtained in the ciliary ganglion of the chick, but both direct and indirect measurements show no change in amplitude of presynaptic spikes.

The existence of synaptic changes that endure for minutes rather than milliseconds is of obvious interest in behavioral contexts. The interest is further enhanced by certain cases in which these effects last for hours. If a dorsal root is severed distal to the ganglion, the central projections survive but are wholly inactive because of lack of peripheral stimulation. After a few weeks the reflexes evoked by electrical stimulation of such unused dorsal roots are greatly diminished in comparison to similarly evoked reflexes on the intact side. Tetanization of the unused paths, however, restores their efficacy to near-normal levels, and the restoration survives for several hours. Potentiation and depression of synaptic transmission in the lateral geniculate nucleus of cats under barbiturate anesthesia can also endure for hours, depending on conditions of stimulation.

If synaptic systems A and B are both able to discharge the same interneuron and if the interneuron follows high-frequency stimuli, then potentiation established by activity in system A and the interneuron is also accessible by system B. Examples of such transferable potentiation have been studied in the mammalian spinal cord. At first glance, this seems relevant to phenomena of learning. More careful consideration, however, reveals in this paradigm the present shortcomings of synaptology in explaining learning or, perhaps more important, reveals a peculiarity of the temporal organization of learning. After activity in A, the effectiveness of B and of A is changed for a relatively long time. In other words, antecedent action in one system produces a protracted change in the consequences of subsequent action in another system. This makes neurophysiological sense but is exactly the opposite of what happens in learning. In learning, the consequences change not for the subsequent stimulus but for the antecedent. This temporal paradox is easiest to illustrate with conditioned reflexes, although it applies to many other situations. In behavioral conditioning the antecedent stimulus, A, is the conditional stimulus, and the subsequent stimulus, B, is the unconditional stimulus. During the course of conditioning, a change occurs so that the consequences of A are altered, whereas the response to the subsequent stimulus, B, remains relatively constant. Until very recently there was no known neurophysiological parallel to such restrospective alterations.

They have now, however, been observed in certain small cells in the abdominal ganglion of the sea slug, *Aplysia depilans*. In about 15 per cent of these cells the following phenomenon could be observed. Repeated stimulation of a powerful afferent system that evokes large EPSPs and discharges the cell has no effect on the EPSPs subsequently evoked by stimulation of a different, less effective afferent system. Thus, the postactivation paradigm above is not fulfilled. If, however, the stimuli are paired, so that the less effective stimulus is repeatedly given 0.3 to 0.5 second prior to the highly effective stimulus, the EPSP evoked by the first stimulus gradually increases, often to the point where it too can discharge the cell. Although the increase in effectiveness of the antecedent stimulus gradually subsides after pairing ceases, some augmentation endures for 4 to 20 minutes.

The experiment with *A. depilans* thus duplicates exactly the temporal paradox of learning. Further, it provides the basis for a general hypothesis concerning synaptic alterations underlying conditioned reflexes. It is proposed that for a brief period after its excitation and only at such times a synaptic terminal is permeable to material from neighboring terminals, from other axons ending on it, or from the subsynaptic membrane. If, during this period of heightened permeability, discharge also occurs in a more effective synaptic system, material (synaptic vesicles) from the second system are incorporated into the first and alter its characteristics. There are many ramifications to such a proposal, but only two need be mentioned here. First, such alteration of synaptic effectiveness depends not only on timing and relative potency of the synaptic actions but on the contiguity of the synapses. In *A. depilans* relatively few cells seem to have the appropriate arrangements for this effect. It is thus possible that certain cell types are specialized to support this phenomenon. Second, if such enhancement is effected by chemical exchange, the role of the synaptic vesicle is extended in scope. It becomes then not merely a packet of transmitter but a set of instructions for contiguous cells, available only in the circumstance of precisely time-locked action.

Such speculations obviously are far afield from the sea slug, but they perhaps illustrate why an understanding of synapses may yet be important for students of behavior—if only to deal with such speculations.

REFERENCES

Bullock, T. H. Comparative neurology of excitability and conduction. In *Structure and Function in the Nervous System of Invertebrates*, T. H. Bullock and G. A. Horridge, vol. 1, p. 123. W. H. Freeman, San Francisco, 1965.

Bullock, T. H. Comparative neurology of transmission. In *Structure and Functions of the Nervous System of Invertebrates*, T. H. Bullock and G. A. Horridge, vol. 1, p. 179. W. H. Freeman, San Francisco, 1965.

Eccles, J. C. *The Physiology of Nerve Cells*. Johns Hopkins Press, Baltimore, 1957.

Eccles, J. C. *The Physiology of Synapses*. Academic Press, New York, 1964.

McLennan, H. *Synaptic Transmission*. W. B. Saunders, Philadelphia, 1963.

Pharmacology of the central nervous system. Brit. Med. Bull., 21: 1, 1965.

deRobertis, E. *Histophysiology of Synapses and Neurosecretion*. Pergamon Press, New York, 1964.

CHAPTER 8

Electrical Activity of the Brain

ROBERT W. DOTY, Ph.D.

DENDRITES

THE CEREBRAL CORTEX and other masses of uniformly oriented neurons cannot be understood until it is known how dendrites function in neural processes. One of the first questions to be asked is whether the alignment and packing of dendrites (see Figure 1) serves to promote some interchange of information among them or whether this arrangement is but a convenience of developmental organization, lacking major functional import. The dendrites make up 30 per cent or more of the cortical volume but 90 per cent of the surface area of cortical neurons. About 2,000 to 4,000 other neural cell bodies, to say nothing of other dendrites, lie within the dendritic field of each stellate cell or among the basal dendrites of each pyramidal cell. The opportunities for intercommunication are, thus, enormous for each cell, and it is difficult to conceive how any precision of integration could be obtained were each cortical neuron diffusely influenced by the activity of its neighbors. Indeed, such little knowledge as is available points to the likelihood that cortical neurons perform their integrative functions despite rather than by means of electrochemical gradients produced by their orientation en masse (see below and Figure 2 II). The chemical step in synaptic transmission, the intricate morphology of synapses, and the synaptic spine apparatus all seem admirably adapted for assuring highly specific influences between cells and for excluding interference from possibly irrelevant action merely by reason of cellular adjacency.

MODALITY-SPECIFIC CELL COLUMNS

Under light barbiturate anesthesia the cells in somesthetic and visual cortical areas of cats and somesthetic areas in macaques (see Figure 3) are

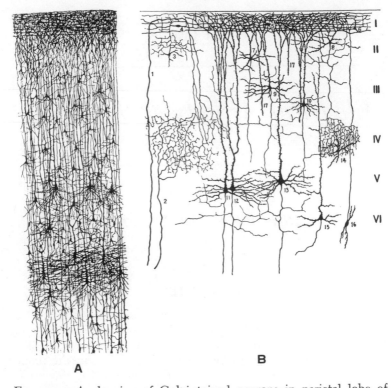

A   **B**

FIGURE 1. A, drawing of Golgi-stained neurons in parietal lobe of a one-month-old human infant; B, composite picture made of camera lucida drawings from Golgi and Golgi-Cox preparations of brains of mouse and rat, showing general arrangement of various neurons in cerebral cortex. *1*, recurrent afferent fiber from thalamus, which ascends to molecular layer, runs for a short distance horizontally and then descends and terminates in fourth layer with repeated branchings; *2*, special afferent from thalamus terminating in fourth layer with profuse arborizations; *3*, short axon cell in second layer; *4*, *5*, and *6*, three Cajal cells with their horizontal fibers in molecular layer; *9* and *10*, medium pyramidal cells in third layer; *11*, *12* and *13*, large pyramidal cells in fifth layer; *14*, typical Golgi type II or stellate cell in fourth layer; *15*, medium-sized pyramidal cell in sixth layer, with apical dendrites that usually do not reach molecular layer; *16*, Martinotti cell; *17*, shaft and apical dendrites of pyramidal cells the cell body and axon of which were left undrawn. Customary designation of cortical layers shown by *Roman numerals at right*. (*Part A* is from Ramon y Cajal, S. *Histologie du Système Nerveux de l'Homme et des Vertébrés*, vol. 2, p. 638. Consejo Superior de Investigaciones Cientificas, Madrid, 1955. *Part B* is from Chang, H-T. Dendritic potential of cortical neurons produced by direct electrical stimulation of the cerebral cortex. J. Neurophysiol., *14*: 1, 1951.)

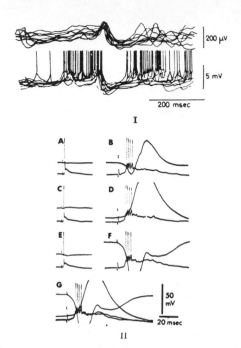

FIGURE 2. Correlation (*I*) and lack of correlation (*II*) between electrical activity recorded from the surface of the cerebral cortex and activity of immediately subjacent neurons. *Upper channel* is EEG of pericruciate cortex in the cat, negative deflection upward; *lower channel*, intracellular record from Betz cell. *I*, Superposition of nine traces phased at peak of a spontaneously recurring negative wave reveals that the cell invariably discharges during an EPSP occurring during the rising negativity and then undergoes a hyperpolarization for about 100 milliseconds during the surface-positive phase of the wave. *II*, A, C, and E, intracellular response to antidromic stimulation of medullary pyramid showing shock artifact and spike and delayed depolarization that remains unchanged during surface polarization. *B*, fully developed augmenting response from stimulation of ventrolateral nucleus. A prolonged EPSP begins about six milliseconds after the stimulus, and three spikes are discharged during the surface positivity. In *C* and *D*, anodal, in *E* and *F*, cathodal polarizing currents, 50 μamp. per mm.² are applied to the cortex just above the impaled Betz cell. The polarity of the augmenting response is dramatically reversed by the polarization, but the Betz cell's response is unaltered, as shown in *G* by superposition of traces taken under the two conditions. (*Part I* is from Creutzfeldt, O. D., Watanabe, S., and Lux, H. D. Relations between EEG phenomena and potentials of single cortical cells. II. Spontaneous and convulsoid activity. EEG Clin. Neurophysiol., 20: 19, 1966. *Part II* is from Purpura, D. P., and McMurty, J. G. Intracellular activities and evoked potential changes during polarization of motor cortex. J. Neurophysiol., 28: 166, 1965.)

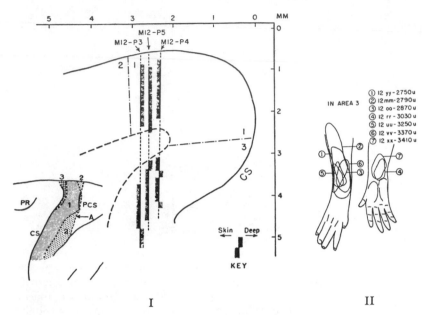

I   II

FIGURE 3. Modality-specific columns of cells in somatosensory cortex of postcentral gyrus of lightly anesthetized macaque. *Inset in Part I* indicates (A) level of penetration of microelectrode in relation to cytoarchitectonic pattern (Brodmann areas 1, 2, and 3; CS, central sulcus, PCS, postcentral sulcus). Three penetrations are reconstructed at *upper right*, showing passage of electrode first through area 1, then into area 3. *Grayed portion of track*, multiunit recording; *dark bars*, single units. Excitation by light touch of the skin represented to *left of line of penetration*, to *right* for excitation by rotation of joints or pressure on fascia or periosteum. When penetration is perpendicular to surface, only one of these forms of excitation is effective along the entire track, but when the penetration passes tangentially through the cortex (as in area 3), the effective modality often changes with progression of the electrode. *Part II* shows receptive fields determined for seven of the twenty-three units encountered at the indicated depths along the right-hand track in *Part I*. Note that fields have similar location along any particular portion of the penetration. (From Powell, T. P. S., and Mountcastle, V. B. Some aspects of the functional organization of the cortex of the postcentral gyrus of the monkey: a correlation of findings obtained in a single unit analysis with cytoarchitecture. Bull. Johns Hopkins Hosp., *105*: 133, 1959.)

found to be organized into modality-specific columns. This is evidenced by the fact that a microelectrode passing through the cortex perpendicular to its surface encounters cells of similar function throughout the entire course of the track. Similar observations have been made for auditory cortical projection areas and the motor cortex of the cat. The modalities in these columns are not the usual ones of touch, temperature, or color but, rather, are related to location of the receptors and/or a particular pattern of stimulation—such as, in the case of the visual system, direction of movement. The diameter of such a column is difficult to estimate but probably does not average much more than 500 μ.

The strong organization of vertically directed systems is readily apparent in the histological structure throughout the cortex (see Figure 1). The columnar arrangement probably forms a basic unit of cortical function. Dividing the cortex vertically into a grid of small islands effects no great change in its ability to integrate complex behavior. Nor does circumsecting a cortical region in which electrical stimulation serves as a signal for performing a learned act alter the performance, whereas limiting the spread of excitation to transcortical pathways at first abolishes the response. These meager behavioral data are at least concordant with the concept that cortical function has a strong vertical organization that is effective despite limitation of tangential, intracortical elaboration. It is thus possible at this stage to picture the cortex as a mosaic of functionally specific columns. The great interdigitation of dendrites between neighboring columns (see Figure 1A) would defeat the specificity of such an arrangement were there to be significant cross-talk between these intertwined elements.

Recent electron microscopic observations in the olfactory bulb and retina have suggested the existence of reciprocal dendrodendritic synapses—that is, contacts between apparent dendrites in which synaptic vesicles are seen on both sides. Specific dendrodendritic interactions might thus occur. However, the contacts so far have not been seen in other areas, and the two locations where they have been found are noted for amacrine cells, which, in the classical description, lack axons. The reciprocal dendrodendritic synapse may reflect merely a peculiarity of this type of neuron.

Properties of dendrites. The problem remains as to the role of dendrites. The high internal resistance of terminal dendrites, arising from their small diameter, presents a serious impediment for the spread of electrotonic potentials or the propagation of action potentials. Yet without propagation it is apparent that the great numbers of synapses on distal dendrites (see Figure 1) must lack significant influence on the electrical behavior of the neuron and its generation of spike discharges. Much still remains to be learned about the operation of this seemingly paradoxical arrangement, but data from the hippocampus and dorsal horn of the spinal cord suggest an explanation along the following lines. Postsynaptic potentials in the dendrites, when sufficiently numerous or when occurring in proximal portions, exert an electrotonic influence on the soma and the trigger zone in the initial segment of the axon, thus influencing the threshold for all-or-none discharge. Since the spike potential usually does not propagate very far into the dendrites, this electrotonic influence survives essentially unaltered by soma-axon behavior. Under certain conditions of spatial or temporal synchronization of afferent bombardment, the dendrites may become sufficiently depolarized to conduct an action potential, at about 200 to 400 μ a millisecond, toward the soma and thus provide an additional trigger zone in the proximal dendrites for eliciting spike potentials in the soma and axon. A proximo-distal gradient in synaptic effectiveness seems an inevitable consequence of dendritic structure and performance. Influenced by subtle intracellular chemical changes associated with correlated discharge, as discussed at the end of the preceding chapter, synaptic endings might gradually migrate from distal dendrites to a proximal and more effective position for controlling the behavior of the cell on which they terminate and thus provide a basis for some of the phenomena of learning. Such migration, of course, is pure speculation, but it is of considerable interest that the various synaptic systems terminating on the dendrites of hippocampal pyramidal cells do so in an orderly fashion so that each system has a strong predilection for ending at a particular proximo-distal level along the dendritic system.

EVOKED POTENTIALS

LOCATION OF ACTIVITY

Within the 2-mm. thickness of the neocortex, about 50,000 neurons would lie directly under an electrode having a 1-mm.^{2} contact with the surface. Roughly 75,000 fibers would be leaving and 25,000 entering the cortex in the subtended area. The great majority of fibers are about 1 μ in diameter and roughly 80 per cent are less than 2 μ. The discrepancy between number of cortical cells and efferent fibers indicates both the possibility of branching and the inadequacy of available data.

The surface electrode records the action of subjacent and neighboring elements in proportion to their degree of synchronous phasing and in inverse proportion to their distance from the electrode. A 100-μv. potential may thus represent very strong synchronous action at a considerable distance from the electrode or a rather weak action in its immediate vicinity. The true nature of a response cannot be determined with a single, stationary electrode. The same is true for the polarity of the response. A depolarizing action, excitatory postsynaptic potentials (EPSPs) appears negative to an electrode at the site of action. However, since the depolarization is occurring in a conducting medium, currents flow from the surround, which acts as a source for the current flowing to the negative or sink area. Thus, an electrode remote from the site of the depolarizing action records positively. The reverse holds true for hyperpolarizing, inhibitory postsynaptic potential (IPSP), activity. It follows that an electrode may become positive because of remote EPSPs or spike activity or because of IPSPs in its immediate vicinity. Analysis of cortical potentials requires tracking the electrode through the cortical mass to determine the origin (by amplitude) and true polarity of the responses obtained. Since the cells of any one type are not precisely aligned in depth and several types, which may have widely differing characteristics, may be concurrently active in any particular layer, interpretation of intracortical electrical events is difficult; but there are certain consistent features about which some certainty exists.

RESPONSE TO THALAMIC AFFERENTS

When an electrical stimulus is applied to a thalamic relay nucleus, such as the lateral or medial geniculate nuclei or the ventrobasal complex, a highly synchronous volley ascends the afferent fibers to the corresponding cortical projection areas. There the afferent terminals effect predominantly excitatory connections with the stellate cells centered around layer IV. These in turn immediately relay the excitation into a second set of cells and probably then to a third set, each relay ascending closer toward the surface. All these events are registered as positive deflections at the surface, lasting roughly one millisecond each, corresponding to spike potentials. A much slower negative-positive sequence, undoubtedly the result of postsynaptic potentials, then ensues.

This sequence is characteristic of sensory cortex activated by highly synchronous volleys from specific afferents. Much different sequences are seen in other cortical areas or with other types of stimuli. With natural stimuli having abrupt onset—flashes, clicks, or tapping the skin—positive-negative sequences reminiscent of these electrically evoked responses can be obtained in the appropriate sensory areas (see Figure 4 I). Abruptness of onset is necessary to synchronize the action so that it may be detected as different from the background, spontaneous activity. Since the response is relatively constant in amplitude and latency and the background action usually random with respect to it, repetition of the stimulus and summing of the activity in the immediate poststimulus period enhances the response and cancels the background. By this technique of averaging, it is even possible to record such evoked potentials through the human scalp 2 cm. or so from the brain. The intervening tissue seriously distorts and

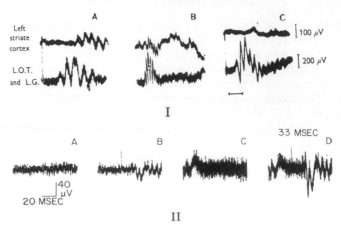

FIGURE 4. Photically evoked potentials and their alterations under various conditions in the primate visual system. *I* and *II*, response in squirrel monkeys to brilliant, 10-microsecond strobotron flash. *I A* and *B*, alert monkey with chronically implanted electrodes, oscillations at 160 a second in tract, 200 a second appearing about 15 milliseconds later in area striata. *I C*, same animal under Nembutal anesthesia, which almost abolishes cortical response while leaving substantial oscillatory activity in the optic tract. Time calibrations: *A*, 10 milliseconds; *B*, 40 milliseconds; *C*, 20 milliseconds. *II*, another monkey under Dial anesthesia. *II A*, background activity in optic radiation; *B*, response to flash delivered at moment of artifact; *C*, slight evoked potential and greatly augmented background activity after single pulse applied to mesencephalic reticular formation at beginning of trace; *D*, response to flash delivered 33 milliseconds after pulse applied to reticular system—that is, about 50 milliseconds prior to appearance of photically elicited response in the central nervous system. Note great augmentation of response when preceded by mesencephalic stimulation. (*Part I* is from Doty, R. W., and Kimura, D. S. Oscillatory potentials in the visual system of cats and monkeys. J. Physiol., 168: 205, 1963. *Part II*, Doty, unpublished.)

diminishes the potentials, and scalp electrodes inevitably record from a very large area in comparison with those in direct contact with the brain. The response recorded depends on the complex spatial relations between the electrodes and the responding area, and it may also be that individual brains, even in animals, have highly individual types of response, could the technical problems only be resolved to reveal it. In any event, under standardized conditions the evoked response in man is exceedingly stable and can be as characteristic of the individual as his fingerprints (see Figure 5).

Direct cortical response. Electrical stimulation of the cortex

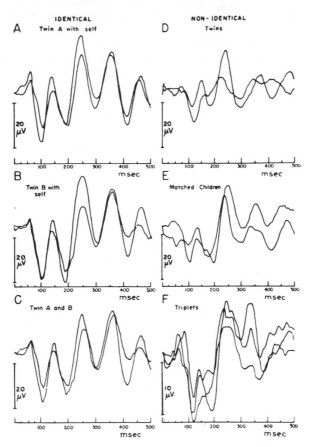

FIGURE 5. High degree of reproducibility and genetic determination of wave forms of potentials evoked in human occipital lobes by flashes of light under carefully standardized conditions. Averages of responses to 100 flashes delivered 1 every 3 seconds. A and B, records from identical twins taken 6 months apart and superimposed for comparison; C, one record from each twin; D, records from nonidentical twins; E, two unrelated children of same age as the twins and triplets; F, triplets. Correlation coefficients for curves from identical twins (A, B, C) were 0.90; for D, 0.53; for E, 0.64. (From Dustman, R. E., and Beck, E. C. The visually evoked potential in twins. EEG Clin. Neurophysiol., 19: 570, 1965.)

evokes a direct cortical response (DCR) that reveals a number of important properties of cortical organization. A weak stimulus applied to the surface evokes a simple, almost monophasic surface-negative wave, lasting 10 to 20 milliseconds and propagating for

about 5 mm. from the point of stimulation at a velocity of 0.7 to
2 m. a second. Stimulating with a penetrating electrode, one no longer
obtains this simple surface-negative response after penetrating more
than 0.1 mm. into the cortex. Its lateral propagation is abolished by
cuts limited to the molecular layer (see Figure 1B, layer I), but propagation is undisturbed if all the remaining cortex is cut through save
the molecular layer. It thus appears that this must be the response of
the apical dendrites and horizontal cells of Cajal. The latter are re-
puted to be rare in adult cortex, but the conduction velocity of the
surface-negative DCR is faster than that found in the dendrites of
hippocampal pyramidal cells, the distances of propagation are greater
than the lateral extent of all but a very few apical dendrites, and the
duration of the response indicates that it is postsynaptic. It is perhaps
significant that there is no sign of IPSPs in this response of the molecular layer, again suggesting the association of hyperpolarizing responses with the soma rather than dendrites.

With stronger stimulation a further negative component is added
that appears 5 mm. from the point of stimulation, diminishes with
further distance, but then is reinforced—that is, becomes larger again
at a 10-mm. distance. This additional negative response is undoubtedly synaptically propagated, apparently through U fibers just beneath the cortex, but its conduction time is only slightly longer than
that for the primary negative wave and hence must be propagated in
faster fibers.

Intracortical stimulation at various depths evokes more complex
types of response. In sensory but not other types of cortex, stimulation at or below layer IV evokes the same type of response as does
stimulation of the thalmic relay nucleus.

Surface stimulation at an intensity double that for the threshold of
the primary negative wave and eliciting about 20 per cent of the maximal response of the latter also produces a surface-positive wave if
applied to unanesthetized cortex. The strength required is approximately the same as that for eliciting discharge in Betz cells. This
positivity can propagate without attenuation through many millime-
ters of cortex at a velocity of 0.1 to 0.2 m. a second. The positive
response has a duration of more than a second and is characterized by
an overlying ripple of very fast activity, indicating that it arises from
a burst discharge of neurons deep within the cortex, where concurrently intense negativity and spike discharges can be recorded. Most
interestingly, this burst discharge continues to recur aperiodically for
up to an hour after 5 to 10 stimuli and requires no extracortical
interchange, since it proceeds best in neuronally isolated slabs of cortex.

Antidromic effects. With antidromic stimulataion of the pyramidal tract, it can be shown that Betz cells give off recurrent collater-

als intracortically, producing an inhibitory effect for 100 to 200 milliseconds. Such analysis is not possible for other cortical areas, since purely antidromic responses cannot be obtained. However, it is likely that recurrent inhibition plays an important role in cortical function, just as it does in the spinal cord and elsewhere.

Cells sending axons to pyramidal tract. The opportunity to analyze the behavior of a specifiable type of cortical neuron, as offered by the pyramidal tract systems (see Figure 2 *II*), provides much fascinating information. The pyramidal tract (PT) cells can be influenced and discharged by a great variety of inputs. Some of them respond to flashes and clicks as well as to somatosensory stimuli to either side of the body. The PT cells have a wider and much more flexible responsiveness than do other, non-PT neurons encountered in the same microelectrode penetration. The recurrent inhibition, set up by antidromic stimulation of the pyramidal tract, is particularly effective in curtailing their response to marginally excitatory stimuli. The contrast with responses of non-PT cells in the somatosensory cortical projection area immediately posterior to the motor area is striking. Cells of the latter type respond only to a single modality of stimulation applied to a restricted, relatively fixed area of the body, topographically related to areas giving responses in neighboring cells (see Figure 3). Non-PT cells in the somesthetic area do not respond to proprioceptive stimuli, such as, from muscle spindles, whereas such stimulation is effective on PT cells. In summary, the cells of the cortical somatosensory system respond predictably from anatomically fixed paths, whereas the response of PT cells is labile and available over functionally fluctuating pathways.

The latter arrangement has obvious importance. When a monkey is trained to make a highly specific movement upon command, such as to a flash, it is found in the precentral gyrus that the PT cells controlling the learned movement begin to fire within 70 milliseconds after the onset of the response that the flash evokes in area striata. The pathways involved in exciting PT cells optionally by flashes are still unknown, but the techniques do seem to be available for determining the location and nature of the events occurring in this critical 70 millisecond period of voluntary decision. Much of it may be by corticocortical connections, since recent findings in cats show that responses to flashes can be obtained in several cortical areas, including precruciate motor areas and the orbital gyrus, even though the entire diencephalon has been removed with the exception of the lateral geniculate nucleus.

DIRECT CURRENT POTENTIALS AND POLARIZATION

Characteristics

A nonpolarizable electrode placed on neocortex records a positive D.C. potential, usually of several millivolts, in reference to other points, such as the lateral ventricle, sciatic nerve, or frontal sinus.

Typical values are: 0.5 to 5 mv. for unanesthetized rabbits; 1 mv. for neonate rats, increasing with age to as much as 20 mv. in adults; 0.3 to 7 mv. in man. So long as conditions remain constant and there is no stimulation or change in alertness of the individual, the potential remains steady.

The sources of this potential are undoubtedly various. Of greatest interest is the probable contribution of gradients in potential between neuron soma and dendrites. The staggering of cell bodies in neocortex makes it impossible to obtain meaningful measurement there, but analysis of the uniformly oriented hippocampal pyramidal cells shows the soma to be negative with respect both to apical dendrites and to basilar dendrites plus axon. Some of the surface positivity of neocortex undoubtedly arises because of the polarization of apical dendrites with respect to soma. Measurements of intracortical potential gradients are at least consistent with this idea, as are the rapid changes produced by sensory or centrencephalic stimulation. A slight decrease in the D.C. potential of the cortical visual area may be the first detectable response to stimulation of the optic tract too weak to elicit the usual evoked potential sequence. With more intense sensory stimulation, a negative shift of a few hundred microvolts lasting several hundred milliseconds and followed by an equivalent enhancement of positivity is the unfailing accompaniment of evoked potentials, although not commonly recorded because of technical difficulties. These short-latency, brief shifts in D.C. potential can be assigned with certainty to neural action in the vicinity of the cortical electrode. The source of more-protracted changes is not so clear. For instance, in passing from stages of sleep with high-voltage, slow electroencephalogram (EEG) to either wakefulness or paradoxical sleep, a 50 to 500 μv. negative shift occurs in the D.C. potential and is accompanied by an increase in brain temperature of up to 0.6° C. The opposite changes occur when the EEG passes from low-voltage, fast activity to high-voltage, slow activity. However, since the D.C. potential of the entire brain, white matter as well as cortex, changes to about the same degree, it probably originates in metabolic effects or alterations of the blood-brain barrier.

Voluntary movement in man is preceded for about 1 second by a gradually increasing negative shift of the cortical D.C. potential. This contingent negative variation or *Bereitschaft* (readiness) potential occurs over wide areas of the scalp, although it is most fully developed over the precentral area contralateral to the moved limb. It appears in preparation for a movement, even though the movement may then be withheld, and in this respect it is the response to a contingency. Within 30 to 90 milliseconds after the beginning of muscle contraction a complex, surface-positive evoked potential begins, representing the afferent discharge initiated by the movement itself. The latter but not the former occurs almost equally well if the limb is moved passively in the same manner by external manipulation. An apparently similar negative shift accompanies movement in rats and is of the same genre as the negative shifts occurring with arousal reactions in the EEG. A six-to-nine-a-second rhythm in midline thalamic structures and dorsal hippocampus also precedes the initiation of movement by rats. The possible relation of these subcortical events to human volition remains unstudied.

Infraslow oscillations. Semirhythmic, infraslow oscillations in the D.C. potential, 0.3 to 1.5 mv., 0.5 to 8 a minute, have been recorded from neocortex and hypothalamus in rabbits. Such oscillations are absent from thalamus, periaqueductal gray, and the mesencephalic reticular formation and seem to be relatively independent of influence from these systems, since mesencephalic stimulation, for instance, which produces an arousal reaction in the EEG, does not alter the infraslow oscillations. On the other hand, repeated stimulation of the ventromedial nucleus of the hypothalamus or other stressful procedures favor their development. The rhythm is not necessarily the same in various areas of the cortex, but cortical excitability is to some degree modulated by these oscillations. Their source seems to be in metabolic and hormonal factors, but their significance remains to be evaluated.

Spreading depression. Another form of D.C. shift is definitely pathological. This is the phenomenon of spreading depression, which is a complex of electrical, metabolic, and circulatory changes elicited most readily by strong electrical or mechanical stimulation or certain agents such as KCl, applied to neocortex. It can also be elicited in other regions of the brain but is most readily obtainable from cortex that has been maltreated by cooling or drying. It is probably the immediate cause in man of the phenomenon of scintillating scotoma. On application of the abnormally strong stimulus, a wave of depression of all background and evoked electrical activity begins and spreads from the initiating area in all directions with a velocity of about 5×10^{-5} m. a second, 2 to 3 mm. a minute. With this very slow progression of the wave, the depression endures from 2 to 6 minutes at a given point, and recovery requires 10 to 15 minutes. The advancing wave is heralded by an intense surface negativity of 3 to 15 mv. that persists throughout the depression and is accompanied by a fall of pO_2, cortical volume, and a visible vasoconstriction. The wave can propagate through any cortical layer save the first and is resistant to deep anesthesia. The apparent cause of this remarkable phenomenon is a convulsive outburst of activity so intense that the stimulated neurons lose sufficient K^+ to change the ionic environment of their neighbors, thereby depolarizing them and causing their intense discharge, etc. The evidence in support of this explanation, besides its inherent plausibility, is the recording of a prolonged burst of single-cell activity at the advancing edge of the wave, the leakage of K^+ accompanying the phenomenon, its ready production by KCl, and the migration of Cl^- into the apical dendrites, probably in association with Na^+, during spreading depression.

Failure to recognize this phenomenon in certain earlier electrophysiological experiments led to some serious misconceptions. Among these was the scheme of suppressor strips, still having its 20-year run in certain texts. In this case unrecognized spreading depression was elicited by electrical or chemical stimulation just rostral to the motor area in the macaque's precentral gyrus. After a matter of minutes, movement elicited by stimulation of the motor cortex was abolished for 10 minutes or so, but reflexly elicited movement was unaffected. The idea was subsequently developed that a special strip, area 4-S, functioned to suppress hyperkinetic tendencies, and the concept was furthered by the discovery of monosynaptic connections between this area and brain stem regions known to inhibit reflex action. The diagrams then showed 4-S as suppressing hyperreflexia through the brain stem, neglecting the latency of minutes required for operation of this supposedly monosynaptic connection and its initially observed lack of effect on reflex action. Such nonsense illustrates the dangers of schematizing confirmatory evidence only while neglecting contradictory or puzzling data

Applied gradients. Efforts to assay the significance of the electrically polarized condition of the cortex have involved altering the transcortical potential artificially. Rather low-intensity currents have pronounced effects on the polarity of evoked potentials but not necessarily on the response of many of the subjacent neurons (see Figure 2 *II*). Surface anodal polarization has the effect of increasing the negative component of evoked potentials and diminishing the positive component. This may be explained by assuming that the current hyperpolarizes apical dendrites and to some extent concurrently depolarizes the deeper-lying cell bodies. EPSPs near the surface would thus be large because of the augmented membrane potential and produce a greater negativity as recorded at the surface, and their depolarizing action in the deeper layers, which produces surface positivity, would be concurrently diminished; correspondingly, IPSPs in the depths, which produce surface negativity, would be augmented, etc. The converse argument holds for the augmentation of positive components by surface cathodal polarization.

With stronger currents the excitability of PT cells can be altered, surface anodal polarization producing depolarization and excitation. The effects on non-PT cells are more variable, some responding to much lower currents than do PT cells, some being hyperpolarized by surface anodal polarization, and 40 per cent remaining uninfluenced.

It is difficult to say whether the normally existing D.C. potential gradient across the cortex has significant influence on the function of the cortical elements. It is likely, however, that the potential is only a reflection of the functional conditions of the subjacent cortical cells rather than a mechanism for their control or integration, the same considerations applying here as in the discussion above concerning the role of dendrites. In some instances local changes of metabolism or perhaps intercellular relations can apparently be altered by very minimal and discrete polarization (see Figure 6). Such effects endure for extraordinary periods of time and are of great potential interest in their possible relations to mnemonic processes. The phenomenon remains unexplained, however, and so far no known natural occurrences of this sort have been encountered.

SPONTANEOUS ACTIVITY

Correlation with Spike Discharge and Behavior

Except under conditions of the very deepest narcosis or asphyxia, continued electrical oscillations can be recorded from all cellular regions of the nervous system. The amplitude and frequency of these oscillations vary greatly, depending on the functional state and region of the brain. Each region has a characteristic pattern, so that, for instance, the cerebral cortex can be divided into sectors having a particular variety of background rhythm and wave form, and the sectors correspond closely with cytoarchitecturally differentiable areas.

As a general rule, low-voltage, fast (LVF) patterns correspond with a state of alertness and increased neural activity, and high-voltage, slow (HVS) patterns are correlated with relaxation or reduced awareness and, in some respects, with a diminished level of neural activity. It is difficult, however, to press such general formulations, since important and often puzzling exceptions are common. Among the most interesting is that— during the rapid eye movement, LVF stage of sleep—the electrical patterns of spontaneous activity in the neocortex are essentially indistinguishable from those of a fully alert individual, even though, in cats at least, the state of sleep is demonstrably deeper than during stages with HVS activity. The converse of this paradox is seen with human patients having general-

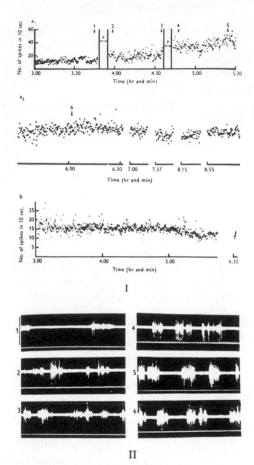

FIGURE 6. *I*, enduring effect of local polarization through a micropipette on background activity of single neurons. Recorded 0.5 mm. beneath surface of somatosensory cortical representation of forepaw in rat under urethane anesthesia. At X and again at Y, 0.25-μamp. anodal current was passed for 10 minutes. Elevation in number of spikes per 10-second period was maintained for several hours (a_1 and a_2 continuous). *b*, another preparation, in which no polarizing current was passed and activity remained constant for several hours, even as judged on an expanded ordinate scale. *II*, actual records (1-second samples) taken from experiment in a_1 and a_2 at times indicated by *numbers*. Note that both the bursts per second and the number of spikes per burst increase. Vertical calibration, 0.5 mv. (From Bindmann, L. J., Lippold, O. C. J., and Redfearn, J. W. T. The action of brief polarizing currents on the cerebral cortex of the rat (1) during current flow and (2) in the production of long-lasting after-effects. J. Physiol., *172*: 369, 1964.)

ized background EEG patterns of 3 a second for many years without apparent impairment of alertness or mental functioning. Such dissociations between the expected EEG pattern and behavior can be produced by lesions in cats. For instance, after loss of the posterior hypothalamus, a fully developed alerting reaction in the EEG (transformation from HVS to LVF patterns) can still be produced by electrical stimulation of the mesencephalic reticular formation, but, despite this, the animal shows no behavioral alteration in its comatose state. Conversely, with small lesions in the mesencephalic reticular system, attentive behavior may be recovered despite the persistence of HVS patterns. Absence of behavioral correlates is also common for evoked potentials. Thus, the exceedingly high amplitude, slow potentials of the recruiting response (see Figure 7) produce no subjective changes in man or any prima facie disturbance in a monkey's performance of simple, learned acts, the control of which is importantly influenced by the cortical areas engaged in the recruiting response. A similar case arises in cats that are wholly unable to detect stimulation limited to the largest afferents from muscle spindles, even though the stimuli evoke prominent potentials in sensorimotor cortex. It is apparent, then, that in certain instances the gross electrical activity of the brain is an astonishingly poor indicator of its functional state or capacity.

The explanation is to be sought in the relation between the oscillations recordable from the surface and the spike discharge of neurons within the cortex (see Figure 2). It is only the all-or-none discharge of the neuron, propagated down the axon, that is the sine qua non of neural integration or that can be expressed in behavior. Because of their brevity and usual lack of synchrony the spike discharges produce only the most minimal or no detectable change in the surface record. The latter must thus originate primarily from longer-duration action, mostly in dendrites, which all evidence equates with postsynaptic potentials. The correlation between the EEG or evoked potentials and the functional output of the cortex depends on the degree to which EPSPs and IPSPs, variously synchronized among the multitudes of cortical neurons, reflect significant control of the spike discharges relevant to the system being studied (see Figure 2). That the significant neural action may be impossible to infer from the surface record is readily illustrated with findings on the behavior of PT neurons in macaques during sleep with HVS patterns, sleep with LVF activity, and wakefulness. The EEGs in the latter two conditions are scarcely distinguishable, and the overall frequencies of discharge in PT neurons are roughly similar, about 12 a second, compared to 6 a second for HVS sleep. The pattern of discharge for wakefulness, however, is entirely different from that in LVF sleep. In the latter, interspike intervals of less than 10 milliseconds are 3 times more frequent than in the former, and the discharge is clustered into bursts, in striking

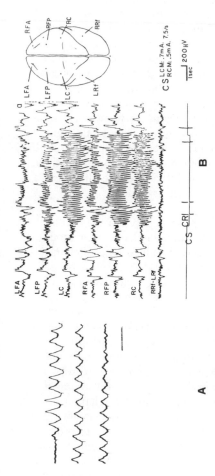

FIGURE 7. Recruiting responses and their lack of behavioral effect. A, recruiting response recorded from subdural electrode over inferior premotor area in alert human patient during stimulation in the region of nucleus centrum medianum at 8 a second. Note typical quick increment in the response and slow decrement with continuing stimulation. Other subjective or objective changes were not apparent. Calibration: 100 a second, 100 μv. B, squirrel monkey making learned movement of lever pressing (deflections labeled CR *in bottom line*) to avoid shock, the imminence of which is signalled by intense, bilateral stimulation of nucleus centrum medianum. Movement is made with right hand, for which the cortical representation lies close to electrode LC (*inset*) in the center of area with high-amplitude recruiting response. Note symmetry and lack of it between the two hemispheres for various loci, indicating that, although recruiting is a diffuse response, it is by no means global. Large, slow deflections occurring simultaneously are artifacts caused by animal's movements. Monkey could also respond when stimulation was one-third the intensity shown, and recruiting responses were not produced. (*Part A* is from Housepian, E. M., and Purpura, D. P. Electrophysiological studies of subcortical-cortical relations in man. EEG Clin. Neurophysiol., 15: 20, 1963. *Part B* is from Pecci-Saavedra, J., Doty, R. W., and Hunt, H. B. Conditioned reflexes elicited in squirrel monkeys by stimuli producing recruiting responses. EEG Clin. Neurophysiol., 19: 492, 1965.)

contrast with the smoother temporal distribution during wakefulness. Non-PT cells, encountered adjacent to the PT cells, have still different characteristics in their pattern of discharge in the three conditions.

ORIGIN

Intracellular records from neocortical neurons display constant fluctuations ranging up to several millivolts and having all the characteristics of postsynaptic potentials. Analysis of their frequencies shows them to be identical with those of the EEG. Recorded extracellularly with two microelectrodes 30 to 50 μ apart, the fluctuations are seen to be very local events, as expected of postsynaptic potentials (PSPs). The amplitude of these fluctuations seen in extracellular records or intracellularly in glia is only about one-tenth that recorded intracellularly in neurons, and the recorded activity must, therefore, be generated in the neurons. The correlation between the EEG recorded from the cortical surface and the intracellularly recorded PSPs is understandably very poor. If each of the 50,000 neurons beneath the recording electrode had only 100 synapses that fired only once a second, 5,000,000 PSPs a second would be generated.

Since, at rest or during HVS sleep, rhythms of moderately high-amplitude rhythmic potentials can be recorded from the surface, considerable synchrony in the PSPs must be inferred on such occasions. The mechanisms that control the degree of synchrony are not entirely clear. As discussed in Chapter 7 and illustrated in Figure 8, recurrent inhibition has an important role in this connection. The protracted and widely ramified inhibition from the recurrent collateral system serves to modulate the activity of a large number of neurons and bring their excitability cycles into step. If these neurons are subjected to excitation just as the IPSP is subsiding, they all fire in phase and further ramify the recurrent inhibition. Thus, stimuli in the range of 6 to 10 a second, having intervals that correspond to the duration of the IPSPs, are uniquely effective in synchronizing cellular discharge and EEG rhythms at this frequency.

Since the first few such stimuli bring more and more neurons into the system of synchronized discharge, the responses increase in amplitude and are called recruiting responses for the case of surface-negative waves produced by stimulation of the thalamic components of the centrencephalic system (see Figure 8 *I* and Figure 7), and augmenting responses for the surface-positive waves produced by stimulation of the thalamic relay nuclei (see Figure 8, *II*). The recruiting responses are of particular interest because of their similarity to the spindling activity that occurs during sleep or light barbiturate anesthesia. Higher-frequency stimulation within the pertinent nucleus or imposed on it from artificial or natural engagement of systems afferent to it tends to disrupt the synchrony and return the cortex

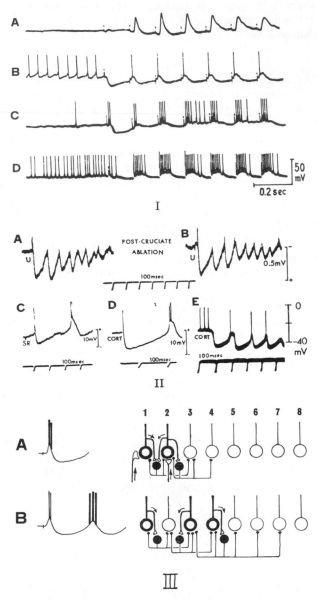

FIGURE 8. Role of IPSPs in generation of rhythmic activity. *IA*, surface- negative recruiting responses (see Figure 7) recorded from motor cortex in cat during stimulation of nucleus centrum medianum at 7 a second; *B* to *D*, intracellular records from various thalamic cells recorded in this same animal during such stimulation. *B*, ventral anterior thalamus;

to LVF activity. Although the cortex probably has recurrent inhibitory processes that participate in the development of its various rhythms, the control of these patterns appears to be exerted predominantly by, and certainly requires the presence of, subcortical systems.

Hippocampal theta rhythm. The theta rhythm of the hippocampus is somewhat instructive in the understanding of certain aspects in the generation of EEG activity. This sinusoidal, high-amplitude pattern, 4 to 7 a second, is particularly well developed in rabbits and also occurs in cats but is essentially absent in primates. The same stimuli that produce LVF activity in the neocortex concurrently induce the theta rhythm in the hippocampus. In other words, stimulation of the mesencephalic reticular formation is highly effective in producing theta activity, and to some degree the frequency of the theta rhythm is proportional to the intensity of the reticular stimulation. With very intense stimulation, however, a second, faster rhythm, 20 to 40 a second, is superimposed on the theta rhythm. The brain stem origins of these two patterns appear to be separable to some degree, so that stimulation of the central gray, medial hypo-

---

C, ventrolateral; D, intralaminar region. It is apparent that the stimulus evokes a moderate, early EPSP in all these cells, followed by a pronounced IPSP that limits further excitation until its termination, thus locking all the affected cells in phase. IIA and B, rhythmic response of nucleus ventralis posterolateralis (VPL) (somatosensory relay nucleus) to single shock applied to ulnar nerve in cat under Nembutal anesthesia. Removal of all responding somatosensory cortex leaves thalamic response unchanged (B), thus demonstrating its thalamic origin. The cuneate nucleus sends only a single volley up the medial lemniscus under these conditions. IIC and D, prolonged IPSP and subsequent depolarizing overshoot or EPSP leading to second discharge of cell in VPL after a single shock to radial nerve (C) or to somatosensory cortex (D). IIE, same in another cat, on slower time scale, showing IPSPs and rhythmic thalamic action after single cortical stimulus. Thus, antidromic stimulation, seen intracellularly in D, generates rhythmic effects, suggesting the schema in III. In A, afferent volley dicharges *cells 1* and *2,* with recurrent collaterals that excite inhibitory interneurons *(solid black);* electrical record of this stage is shown at *left.* In B, *cells 3* and *4,* recovering from inhibition also discharge, in addition to repeat discharge by *1,* further elaborating the process and yielding further portion of electrical record at *left.* (*Part I* is from Purpura, D. P., and Shofer, R. J. Intracellular recording from thalamic neurons during reticulocortical activation. J. Neurophysiol., 26: 494, 1963. *Part II* and *Part III* are from Andersen, P. Rhythmic 10/sec activity in the thalamus. In *The Thalamus,* D. P. Purpura, and M. D. Yahr, editors, p. 143. Columbia University Press, New York, 1966.)

thalamus, or preoptic area induces theta activity, whereas the hippocampal fast activity arises from stimulation of the lateral hypothalamus or medial septal area. The phase relations (see below) of the fast versus theta activity appear to be the same across the layer of pyramidal cell bodies, but the two follow different pathways. Lesions of the medial septal area (see Figure 4 in Chapter 9) irreversibly abolish all theta activity without affecting the fast patterns. Lesions of the entorhinal area, on the other hand, have no effect on the theta rhythm, but observations are apparently lacking for their effect on the faster rhythms.

The importance of the medial septal area in the generation of theta activity is seen in two other facts. First, stimulation here with high frequencies abolishes the theta rhythm, but frequencies of 4 to 30 a second evoke potentials in the hippocampus somewhat resembling the theta rhythm that they disrupt. Second, large cells in the medial septal area and nucleus of the diagonal band of Broca (see Figure 7 in Chapter 9) discharge bursts precisely correlated with the theta waves. The origin of the burst activity in these cells is unknown, but it seems certain to provide the essential component for generating the theta rhythm in the hippocampus, being projected through the fornix onto the dendrites of the pyramidal cells.

The theta activity arises as an oscillating dipole across the somata of the hippocampal pyramidal cells. One pole arises from EPSPs in the apical dendritic layers (see Figure 3 in Chapter 9), but the origin of the activity in the axonal-basilar dendritic layers is not clear. A null point exists and apparently lies at the level of the cell bodies, thus indicating that the somata probably do not participate actively in generation of the rhythm. The existence of the null point proves that the oscillation and phase shift does not involve propagation of activity up or down the dendrites. The null point at the level of the somata is puzzling, however, as most hippocampal pyramidal cells fire in bursts phase-locked with the theta rhythm. Since their discharge produces recurrent inhibition, positivity should appear in the region of the cell bodies. Obviously, the evidence is insufficient to demonstrate precisely how the theta rhythm is produced, but it is certain that it requires afferent input from the medial septal area and that it involves nonpropagating PSPs in dendrites.

The hippocampal pyramidal cells are peculiar among central neurons in having a very prominent depolarizing after-potential with no hyperpolarizing after-potential. This may arise because of the tight glial investiture of these cells, which leaves such a small extracellular space that the K^+ leakage during a spike potential could significantly change its extracellular concentration, thus producing depolarization. In any event, with this depolarizing after-potential the hippocampal pyramidal cells tend to fire in bursts of two or three spikes and are particularly prone to abnormal, seizure discharge, a fact not without clinical significance. The possible relation between this predilection toward burst discharge and the existence of the theta rhythm remains to be investigated.

One last problem is the phase in the theta rhythm between one part of the hippocampus and another. The lag is systematic, suggesting a propagation through the hippocampus at a rate of 0.03 to 0.04 m. a second. This is much too slow to be explained in terms of conduction velocities in afferents from the septum, and there is no evidence to support other possible explanations. In cats the wave is usually initiated from the dorsal hippocampus and progresses toward the entorhinal area (see Figure 4 in Chapter 9), but, during the period of a learned-approach decision, the direction of this propagation is reversed.

CONTROL OF NEOCORTICAL ACTIVITY: THE CENTRENCEPHALIC SYSTEM

ISOLATED CORTEX

Just as generation of the theta rhythm of the hippocampus depends on afferents from the septum, all normal EEG rhythms of neocortex require afferent support from subcortical areas. To what degree the normal patterns are merely imposed on the cortical system and to what degree they arise from cortical modulations of afferent input is by no means clear. It is thus of interest to know what capabilities are possessed by the cortex alone.

As mentioned above, the propagation of direct cortical responses or spreading depression is essentially the same in undercut as in intact cortex. Photically evoked potentials also can propagate at 1 to 2 m. a second throughout a slab of visual cortex isolated for about 10 mm. by destruction of the white matter except at one end. Since such propagation can occur into partially isolated cortex, total isolation is required to study cortical capabilities per se. Even total isolation has varying effects, depending on the size of the isolated slab, whether U fibers remain, and the degree to which success is achieved in preserving the vascular supply, which enters only through the pia mater. Obviously, the cortical denervation is much more severe when the U fibers are cut, and in such instances as many as one-third of the cortical neurons degenerate. This type of preparation has not been adequately examined for spontaneous activity over long periods without interference from anesthesia and circulatory disturbances. In slabs 10 × 5 mm. or larger in which U fibers are preserved, there is only a minor loss of cells, and considerable electrical activity returns. The rhythm is never normal, but many components of normal activity occur briefly. The records are characterized by sporadic activity, bursts of slow waves or spikes alternating with periods of silence.

In human patients such sporadic activity remained relatively constant at 15 to 30 bursts a minute for at least fifteen months from the moment of isolation of large areas of frontal cortex. Isolated cortex can produce the major forms of pathological electrical activity, such as three-a-second spike-and-wave patterns, seizure discharge, and after-discharges. Indeed, a supersensitivity of denervation occurs within two weeks, so that seizure discharge is much easier to induce with electrical or chemical stimulation in chronically isolated than in intact cortex.

CENTRENCEPHALIC SYSTEM

Normally, the most important contribution to the character of the background activity of the EEG arises in the centrencephalic system. This system is more a functional concept than an anatomical entity. It was originally conceived primarily as a diencephalic system regulating and accounting for the bilateral symmetry in the electrical activity of corresponding cortical areas of the two hemispheres and effecting the general coordination of background activity of the cortex. Since these regulatory mechanisms also involve medullary, pontine, and mesencephalic levels, the term "centrencephalic" has been enlarged to include these components. The functions of such a system obviously are not to regulate electrical patterns per se but to support some aspect of the total neural process. These functions are still being defined, but they are related to the control and processing of sensorial input; to attention, awareness, sleep; and perhaps to the transmutation of neural activity into the unity of consciousness. The centrencephalic system can thus be loosely defined as a functionally related system of neurons, for the most part found near the midline and coursing from obex to septum, controlling sensorial input and thereby controlling attention, alertness, and their electrophysiological manifestations. How exact the correspondence may be between the centrencephalic system and neurons of the reticular type (see Figure 2 in Chapter 6) remains to be investigated.

MESENCEPHALIC RETICULAR FORMATION: ISOLATED FOREBRAIN

In many respects the hub of this system is the mesencephalic reticular formation, since it is here that lesions or stimulation produce the most global effects. Cells here are commonly activated from a variety of sources, and their background rhythm is steady, in contrast to cells in thalamic relay nuclei, with background that consists usually of grouped discharges. Electrical stimulation of relatively high frequency but low intensity produces in resting animals both behavioral arousal and a transition from HVS to LVF patterns in all cortical areas. It is presumed that a natural stimulus that produces such alerting does so largely through collateral systems that account for the multimodal excitability of the reticular neurons. However, the cerebral cortex also possesses the capability of influencing this arousal system, and it is not at all unlikely that a part of the arousal process normally involves a loop through cortex and then to the mesencephalon to effect a widespread reaction. In man the telencephalon may actually have primacy in the phenomenon of consciousness. In hemispherectomized patients, intracarotid injection of Amytal on the side of the remaining hemisphere produces an immediate loss of consciousness, and angiography indicates that the Amytal should not reach the mesencephalon in significant quantities. Moreover, injection of Amytal into the vertebral circulation in other patients produces vertigo; oculomotor, facial, and lingual paralysis; and loss of pupillary light reflex; but it has no influence on consciousness. This is definitely paradoxical, since midbrain lesions produce coma in man as well as in animals. It probably means that the mesencephalic reticular system is not so sensitive to barbiturates as is believed and that it simply remains unaffected by the brief exposure to intravertebral Amytal, as is also the case with the auditory, respiratory, and cardiovascular systems.

Bulbar and pontine system also exert important influences, predominantly inhibitory, on the mesencephalic component. If the medullary influence, probably arising near portions of nucleus solitarius, is removed by a section at the caudal border of the pons, stimulation of the mesencephalic reticular system yields a more protracted arousal than previously. Cats with brain stem transected at midpontine levels maintain an almost constant LVF activity in neocortex for days. The latter result is somewhat unexpected, since the caudal pons seems to be the site controlling the appearance of LVF activity during the rapid eye movement phase of sleep, but evidently a tonically active system promoting HVS activity must also lie caudal to the midpontine transection. The LVF activity of the midpontine preparation is associated with seeming alertness rather than deep sleep, since a midpontine cat tracks objects visually and can learn and perform conditioned reflexes, such as pupillary dilatation to photic stimulation, using electrical stimulation of the posterior hypothalamus as unconditional stimulus.

Medial lesions of the rostral pons or mesencephalic reticular formation produce coma and continuous HVS activity, neither of which within the first few postoperative days can be interrupted. This certainly dramatizes the cardinal importance of this area of the brain and the diffuse paths traversing it. The meaningful operation of the nervous system is brought to a halt, despite the fact that all the major afferent and efferent systems are intact and sensory stimuli readily evoke potentials in neocortex. The condition is not permanent, however, and, within a few weeks after such a bilateral lesion, a cat can again acquire simple conditioned reflexes and display many aspects of normal behavior. Even with total transection and elimination of any connection between fore- and midbrain, normal LVF activity gradually returns in the isolated forebrain. Such recovered preparations have LVF activity for hours at a time and periodic episodes of HVS activity lasting about one hour, showing no correlation either with electrical activity of the brain stem or, usually, with the behavior controlled by the brain stem. In some instances of intense arousal by painful stimuli, sneezing, or defecation, however, the forebrain HVS patterns are interrupted, suggesting a humoral effect. Apparently, no such interruptions occur during episodes in brain stem activity, which are normally associated with the rapid eye movement phase of sleep. HVS episodes in the forebrain can be interrupted by olfactory stimuli but not by visual stimuli, suggesting that the mesencephalic reticular system may be essential for arousal by the visual system. Otherwise, the electrical activity of the forebrain remains the same after coagulation of both optic disks and aspiration of the olfactory bulbs. The sustained LVF activity in the isolated forebrain requires the presence of the diencephalon.

The gradual assumption by the diencephalon of the ability to engender LVF activity in neocortex proceeds unilaterally, as can be shown by serial hemisections (see Figure 9). The nature of this compensatory reaction is unknown. It seems that, normally, arousal to electrical stimulation of the thalamus proceeds by posteriorly projecting paths through the posterior commissure and pretectal area, for, with acutely produced lesions, the arousal reaction does not survive isolated transection of this path posterior to the point of thalamic stimulation.

DIFFUSE THALAMOCORTICAL PROJECTION SYSTEM

The thalamic component of the centrencephalic system inevitably emerges as existing primarily to originate sleep spindles and recruit responses in neocortex, since it is the intensive study of these phenomena that has generated most of the knowledge about it. Unfortunately, even this knowledge is frustratingly inadequate, since the anatomical paths by which centrencephalic influences reach the cortex from either thalamus or midbrain cannot yet be specified precisely.

Study of these systems began with the finding that, in cats under very deep barbiturate anesthesia, stimulation of the sciatic nerve produced, in addition to the primary response of 8- to 10-millisecond latency localized in contralateral somatosensory cortical areas, a secondary response with a latency of 30 to 80 milliseconds engaging the entire cortex bilaterally. A hemisection of the brain stem at the intercollicular level ipsilateral to the primary response abolished the latter but did not change the distribution of the secondary response. The

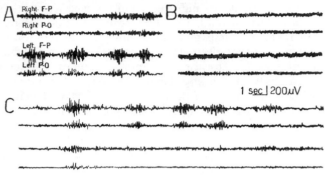

FIGURE 9. Unilateral reorganization of tonic, background EEG activity after hemisection of the mesencephalon. *A*, The left mesencephalon was transected under ether anesthesia a few hours earlier, and bursts of high-voltage, slow EEG activity predominate in records from the left hemisphere. At such times intense noise can produce arousal reactions (not shown) in the affected hemisphere, but they are much shorter in duration than in the intact hemisphere. *B*, Seven days later, symmetry was restored in the EEG, and low-voltage, fast activity persisted equally in both hemispheres. The right mesencephalon was then transected (producing a cerveau isolé), and it was found (*C*) that the low-voltage, fast pattern of the previously transected side was maintained by some reorganization intrinsic to that hemisphere rather than from augmented control by the originally intact hemisphere, since the low-voltage, fast pattern was now maintained on the left in the face of high-voltage, slow patterns on the right. Electrode loci: *F*, frontal; *P*, parietal; *O*, occipital. (From Cordeau, J. P., and Mancia, M. Effect of unilateral chronic lesions of the midbrain on the electrocortical activity of the cat. Arch. Ital. Biol., 96: 374, 1958.)

secondary response in such an instance must represent a double crossing, once below the level of the hemisection and again above it from the intact to the deafferented hemisphere, and is obviously distinct from direct sensory pathways. This second crossing was demonstrated to be by way of the corpus callosum. On the other hand, electrical stimulation of medial thalamic structures can produce recruiting responses with a rather wide bilateral distribution. That the bilaterality does not arise simply from physical spread of stimulating current across the midline is shown by the fact that latencies of the contralateral recruiting responses are about double those of the ipsilateral response, such as 40 versus 20 milliseconds. Such findings gave rise to the concept of a diffuse thalamocortical projection system, but its very diffuseness, together with its lability, makes it very difficult to study. Several points bear emphasis. First, this system exerts its influence on the cortex independently of the thalamic relay nuclei of the specific sensory systems. Its diffuseness and nonspecificity are apparent only in certain circumstances. The location of thalamic regions from which recruiting responses can be obtained are very restricted, since movement of an electrode by 0.5 mm. makes the difference between presence and absence of recruiting responses. Furthermore, slight movements of the stimulating electrode often make great changes in the distribution of the response (see Figure 7B). In more lateral thalamic areas from which recruiting responses can be induced, the responses are almost entirely unilateral.

Bilateral symmetry: corpus callosum. Although the thalamic component of the centrencephalic system can operate to achieve a bilateral symmetry in neocortical electrical patterns, there are indications that its contributions in this regard are not particularly strong. Besides the absence of thalamic transfer of the secondary response, of compensation to chronic hemisection, and of recruiting responses from lateral loci, section of the corpus callosum and anterior commissure greatly reduces the degree of bilateral symmetry in the EEG. Thus, these latter structures also function in correlating the electrical activity of the two hemispheres. Since the corpus callosum in man has about 200 million fibers, roughly 2 per cent of the cortical neurons send fibers through it. The density of this projection varies greatly from one cortical area to another. The primary visual projection area, for instance, has no direct interhemispheric connections and, in primates at least, can communicate with its corresponding contralateral half to achieve unity in an otherwise split visual field only by callosal connections passing between prestriate areas. Similarly, in cats it has been demonstrated that transfer of somatosensory information from one hemisphere to another proceeds only through specialized cortical areas. In at least some instances the same cortical points that intercommunicate by the corpus callosum also do so by a much slower pathway traversing the mesencephalic reticular system. Thus, an electrical pulse applied to such a cortical point elicits an initial response, which is a mixture of orthodromic and antidromic effects, beginning in the homotopic cortical area within one to two milliseconds; and a second more widely distributed potential, the interhemispheric delayed response (IDR), with a latency of 40 to 65 milliseconds. The IDR is very labile, is sensitive to anesthesia, and can also be produced by midbrain stimuli. It is unaffected by sectioning the corpus callosum, psalterium, anterior and posterior commissures, and the entire diencephalon. Some degree of bilateral symmetry in cortical activity can still be observed in such split-brain preparations.

In summary, it can be concluded that the symmetry in the electrical activity of the two hemispheres is maintained by three systems: the commissural, the medial thalamic, and the mesencephalic reticular, the contributions of which undoubtedly fluctuate according to a variety of circumstances.

CORTICAL INFLUENCE ON THE CENTRENCEPHALIC SYSTEM

The neocortex exerts continuous control over the thalamic and mesencephalic systems. For instance, extirpation of neocortex greatly augments the background activity in nucleus centrum medianum and doubles the amplitude of responses seen there to somatic stimulation. Similarly, decortication enhances and widens the distribution of photic responses seen in the thalamus outside the lateral geniculate body. It has also been reported that the brain stem structures no longer display HVS background activity after total decortication.

Stimuli applied to certain restricted areas of neocortex in macaques —excluding area striata, middle temporal gyrus, and frontal pole— evoke potentials and alter conduction in the mesencephalic reticular formation. The presence of potentials in the mesencephalic reticular formation after somatosensory stimuli seems to be specifically under control of the second somatosensory area (SII), since local cooling here abolishes the response in the mesencephalon while leaving that at primary somatosensory cortex (SI) unaffected. Cooling of SI has no effect until the responses in SII are reduced.

CONTROL OF SENSORY SYSTEMS

By recording from a single fiber in the human radial nerve, one can show that a brief, 5° displacement of a hair on the hand produces a single-nerve impulse; yet such displacement can be detected subjectively. It is obvious, however, that not all such displacements yield a subjective reaction, and, indeed, the nervous system must be bombarded with tens of thousands of impulses each second that remain without effect unless attention is focused on them. Within the past decade or so, it has become possible to specify a number of mechanisms available to the nervous system to perform this selective focusing.

The first of these is the control exerted at the peripheral end organ or the early synaptic stations in the central nervous system. The gamma-efferent system provides a striking example, since in this instance the nervous system can actually initiate its own input over the muscle spindle afferents in the absence of any peripherally imposed change. This is a bad example, however, for subjective sensation per se, since neither cat nor man can perceive stimulation limited to these afferents. For perceptually effective somatic afferents the control is exerted at the first synaptic relay in the dorsal horn of the spinal cord, in the trigeminal complex, or in nucleus gracilis of cuneatus (see Figure 9 in Chapter 7). Presynaptic inhibition of discharge to afferent input can be obtained in all these regions through the pyramidal tract after stimulation of sensorimotor cortex. Stimulation in the medullary or mesencephalic reticular systems can also depress transmission of somatosensory information at these first central stations. These centrencephalic connections may be responsible for the ability of clicks or flashes to affect the excitability of cells in the chief sensory trigeminal nucleus.

Activity in the olfactory bulb is controlled by systems in the prepiriform cortex, olfactory tubercle, and the other olfactory bulb, which sends fibers through the anterior commissure. Stimulation of these centrifugal fibers depresses background and evoked activity in the bulb, and isolation of the bulb enhances its background and responsivity.

Centrifugal fibers arising in the superior olive form the olivocochlear bundle, three-fourths of which decussate near the floor of the fourth ventricle. It passes into the cochlea to form large endings on the hair cells, where they contact the afferent fibers. The olivocochlear bundle constitutes about 1 to 2 per cent of the fibers of the auditory nerve. A similar system, probably arising in the lateral vestibular nucleus and not decussating, passes into the labyrinths, where the efferent fibers seem to contact the afferent fibers. Stimulation of the olivocochlear bundle depresses the cochlear microphonic and thus reduces auditory input. The response in the cochlear nuclei is in turn affected by a system running from the ventral temporal cortex through the medial aspect of the medial geniculate nucleus, the ventral part of the inferior colliculus, and along the medial edge of the nucleus of the lateral lemniscus.

The retina is also supplied with efferent fibers that end in the layer of bipolar cells and can alter or initiate responses in retinal ganglion cells. The function and even the origin of these fibers are unknown, although stimulation in the mesencephalic reticular system can evoke the efferent effects. In the pigeon the retinal efferent fibers arise from the isthmo-optic nucleus in the caudal midbrain. They constitute about 1 per cent of the optic tract and seem to form axosomatic endings on amacrine cells.

A most important point of control in the visual system is the lateral geniculate nucleus. In primates the mesencephalic reticular system has such powerful influence here that it sometimes appears almost literally to turn the visual system on or off (see Figure 4, II)— "gating," as it is called in engineering parlance. Such control, in fact, may be the raison d'être for thalamic relay nuclei, for there is nothing to be gained from a 1:1 relay, and the pyramidal system demonstrates that interruption of long central pathways is at least not a necessity. Be that as it may, a single pulse applied to the mesencephalic reticular formation in monkeys produces presynaptic inhibition lasting about 30 milliseconds for both parvo- and magno-cellular elements, followed by facilitation for 100 milliseconds or more. Such stimulation also has the behavioral effect of improving the performance of monkeys in perceiving tachistoscopically presented stimuli. Lesions in this mesencephalic area have such catastrophic effects that it is difficult to study the resultant visual deficiencies, but there are a number of indications that they are severe. The multimodal inputs of the mesencephalic reticular system allow influences to be brought to bear on the visual system from many other sources and no doubt account for such findings as those in the cat in which, under conditions of heightened excitability, potentials can be evoked in the lateral geniculate nucleus and its neurons discharged by touching the paws.

It might be suspected that one of the major purposes of this midbrain control of the visual system is to supply a blanking of vision while the eyes are in motion or to adjust the visual input relevant to the position of the eyes. If so, these effects do not seem to be supplied by collaterals of oculomotor neurons, since their stimulation is without effect; but they may, instead, be supplied by the systems that control eye position. During the rapid eye movement stage of sleep, presynaptic inhibition is applied to the lateral geniculate nucleus at the same time that the eyes are moved, and there is a close correlation between spikes appearing in the pontine nuclei, lateral geniculate nucleus, and visual cortex. Thus, centrencephalic control of the visual system can originate even at pontine levels, a fact possibly to be anticipated from the connections between the vestibular and oculomotor systems. In cats the vestibular effects are well developed, since all neurons that can be isolated by microelectrodes in the visual cortex can be influenced or discharged by moderate vestibular stimulation. The latencies for the effect range from 25 to 200 milliseconds, compared with 8 to 20 milliseconds for responses in the vestibular projection area for these same stimuli. The effects at visual cortex may pass through the diffuse corticothalamic projection system, since the vestibular stimuli do not affect neurons in the lateral geniculate nucleus. Stimulation of this thalamic system itself can discharge or inhibit 70 per cent of neurons isolated in the contralateral visual cortex of cats, mostly after latencies exceeding 25 milliseconds. During the various stages of sleep and wakefulness, the excitability of the lateral geniculate nucleus and visual cortex in cats can vary independently, even in opposite directions. The visual cortical system is by no means passive in this regard, since it in turn influences the excitability of neurons in the lateral geniculate nucleus and, probably by the superior colliculus, the mesencephalic reticular system as well. Corre-

sponding experiments have not yet been done in primates, but preliminary information suggests that centrencephalic control is exerted
predominantly on the lateral geniculate nucleus, with only minimal
influence on striate cortex.

The auditory system has been little-studied in this regard, but
arousal greatly increases potentials recorded in the auditory cortex
after electrical stimulation of the medial geniculate nucleus. For the
somatosensory system there appears to be much less direct convergence of centrencephalic influences onto cortical neurons responding
to somatic stimuli than is the corresponding case for neurons in the
visual cortex responding to photic and thalamic stimuli. The same is
true in comparing somatosensory areas with motor or association cortex; cortical neurons driven by stimulation of the ventrobasal complex are not usually discharged by stimulation of the diffuse thalamic
projection system, even though their response to the former may be
altered—usually increased—by the latter. This relative ineffectiveness
of centrencephalic control probably accounts for the stability of response in the non-PT cells of the cortical somatosensory system, as
described above. The association areas, on the other hand, have a
high degree of multimodal convergence and receive a powerful centrencephalic input. The middle suprasylvian gyrus of the cat is the
best-studied in this respect. Of the neurons isolated here, 80 per cent
respond to flashes, 50 per cent to clicks, 30 per cent to electrical
stimulation of the paw, 50 per cent to stimulation of the lateral posterior nucleus (the thalamic projection nucleus for this area), 50 per
cent to stimulation of nucleus centrum medianum, and 85 per cent
directly to transcallosal stimulation; 40 per cent participate in the
interhemispheric delayed response. Obviously, each neuron tends to
respond with EPSPs or IPSPs to input from many sources. In another series of experiments, comparison could be made directly for
the convergence of influences from the midline thalamus and specific
thalamic projection nuclei. Convergence was found for 75 per cent of
the neurons isolated in the suprasylvian association cortex, 41 per
cent in the motor cortex, and only 8 per cent in the somatosensory
cortex.

It seems reasonable to suppose that neurons receiving multimodal input
are uniquely important in forming learned associations between stimuli.
The prominence of multimodal representation in the centrencephalic system and this system's exceptionally powerful influence on the multimodal
systems of the neocortex seem likely to have some intimate relation to
mnemonic processes.

REFERENCES

Beritof, J. S. *Neural Mechanisms of Higher Vertebrate Behavior*. Little, Brown, Boston, 1965.

Buser, P., and Bignall, K. E. Non-primary sensory projections on the neocortex. Int. Rev. Neurobiol., in press.

Jasper, H. H., Proctor, L. D., Knighton, R. S., Noshay, W. C., and Costello, R. T., editors. *Reticular Formation of the Brain*. Little, Brown, Boston, 1958.

Ochs, S. *Elements of Neurophysiology*. Wiley, New York, 1965.

Purpura, D. P., and Yahr, M. D., editors. *The Thalamus*. Columbia University Press, New York, 1966.

Sholl, D. A. *The Organization of the Cerebral Cortex*. Wiley, New York, 1956.

Stumpf, C. Drug action on the electrical activity of the hippocampus. Int. Rev. Neurobiol., 8: 77, 1965.

CHAPTER 9

Limbic System

ROBERT W. DOTY, Ph.D.

INTRODUCTION

MOST OF THE GREAT SYSTEMS of the neocortex are concerned with the external world, its spatial properties and directionality. In striking contrast, the limbic system is concerned with the self. It controls exchange between the body and the external world and, through its command over the autonomic and endocrine systems, regulates the internal world. To these functions of preserving the individual, nature has cunningly linked the functions of preserving the species. In achieving these ends, the limbic system serves as a repository for phyletically significant, instinctual behaviors. From its organization come such species-specific activities as feeding, drinking, defense-flight reactions, aggression, sexual and probably maternal responses, grooming, and temperature regulation. The stimuli associated with these behaviors are motivational in that the organism seeks or avoids them, and there is every reason to believe that it is the limbic system that assigns that motivational value to particular stimuli.

The effects of stimulating or ablating most neocortical areas are motivationally insignificant. Stimulation of the limbic system, on the other hand, often produces motivational effects (either avoidance or approach) of overpowering intensity, and lesions in the limbic system commonly effect a profound derangement of basic behavior. These principles can be illustrated with laboratory experiments, although they sometimes appear with almost equal clarity in clinical cases. The elementary personality of cats is unchanged by removal of all neocortex. So long as the subcortical limbic system, including the hippocampus and basal ganglia, remains intact, decorticate cats that preoperatively showed aggressive resistance to handling of any kind continue to do so, whereas gentle animals still purr and stretch when petted after decortication. Gentle cats can be made permanently ferocious by lesions in the ventromedial nuclei of the hypothalamus; conversely, savageness disappears from intractable cats after bilateral amygdalectomy, unless they are strongly provoked by painful stimuli. Amygdalectomy has similar effects in such feral animals as the lynx, gray rat, and macaque; and after lesions in the homologue of the amygdaloid system of mammals, mallard ducks, normally extremely fearful, can be captured by hand.

With section of the optic chiasm and corpus callosum in macaques, unilateral excision of the tip of the temporal lobe, including the amygdala, produces a fascinating situation. When the animal views the world with both eyes or with the eye connected to the hemisphere in which the amygdala is present, it displays the macaque's usual fearful-aggressive behavior toward man. However, when it sees only through the eye ipsilateral to the amygdalectomy, the monkey is without fear. It accepts man's presence calmly, and only when handled does it show savage behavior. The monkey's attitude toward the external world is thus dependent on the state of the limbic system in the brain with which he views it.

Such facts obviously have direct relevance to psychiatry and, indeed, to medicine in general. In man it can be verified that strong emotion accompanies the manifestations of activity in the limbic system, and disturbance of emotional balance is a frequent correlate of pathology in this system. In turn, the play of emotions or, what is probably the other side of the same coin, certain activity within the limbic system can alter the entire body economy. Psychosomatic medicine originates in this fact. The limibc system regulates digestion, renal activity, sexual cycles, basal metabolism, and the pressure, distribution, and composition of the blood. It thus provides —or is the channel by which the mental self interacts with—the body self; and its derangement may be expressed in body or mind or both. A patient with abnormal functioning of the central visual system may fail to see certain colors or in certain directions or may see nonexistent obejcts; with disease affecting the motor system, he may be paralyzed or experience convulsions or incessant, purposeless movement; but one afflicted with pathology within the limbic system may suffer rage, unbridled fear, or some equally overwhelming, ineffable, and mysteriously distorted appraisal of the world and its relation to himself. In the latter circumstance he is psychotic. The pathological neural substrates of psychosis cannot yet be identified, but the evidence grows consistently stronger that they are to be sought primarily in the limbic system. Only twenty-five years ago a prominent text in neuroanatomy could with some truth comfort the medical student, perplexed by the intricacies of the hippocampus or amygdala, by noting that study of the limbic system had but limited application to the practice of medicine. With the appearance of neuroendocrinology, such assurance has quietly subsided; in its place may well be substituted the prediction that the psychiatrist of the future will be a neurologist specializing in disorders of the limbic system.

ANATOMY

Limbic Cortex

The term "limbic" is taken from *limbus* (border) and signifies the structures bordering the medial aspect of the hemisphere. These include temporal-insular, orbitofrontal, cingulate, and retrosplenial cortex (see Figure 1). This limbic neocortex, plus the hippocampal gyrus, forms the hub of

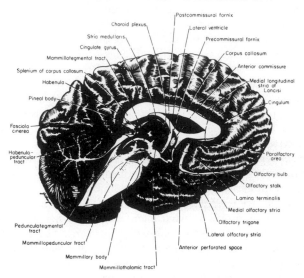

FIGURE 1. Medial view of hemisphere diagrammatically dissected to illustrate certain structures of the limbic system. *Parolfactory area* is roughly equivalent to the septal area. The *fasciola cinerea* is a small extension of the hippocampal system. (Reprinted with permission of The Macmillan Company from Crosby, E. C., Humphrey, T., and Lauer, E. W. *Correlative Anatomy of the Nervous System*, p. 316. © The Macmillan Company, New York, 1962.)

the system through and with which many other components of the system are connected.

The limbic cortex can be divided into four systems on the basis of thalamic projection nuclei and the afferent connections of these nuclei. (1) The hippocampal gyrus is allocortex rather than neocortex and has no known direct thalamic connection. It serves as the primary afferent channel into the hippocampus. (2) The orbitofrontal cortex is innervated by the magnocellular division of nucleus medialis dorsalis. The latter receives afferents from the piriform cortex, which is a major relay station of the olfactory tract. Thus, the orbitofrontal cortex has a rather direct relation to olfactory input. The magnocellular component of nucleus medialis dorsalis in primates also receives fibers from the fornix system. (3) Insular cortex receives fibers from nucleus ventralis anterior, which in turn is innervated predominantly from the globus pallidus. (4) The cingulate gyrus receives fibers from the anterior thalamic nuclei. This is the most extensive of the limbic cortical systems, and the various anterior thalamic nuclei project to the entire expanse of the cingulate gyrus. The anterior thalamic nuclei are richly innervated by the mammillothalamic tract from the medial mammillary nucleus.

The posterior portion of the cingulate gyrus receives afferents from nucleus lateralis dorsalis, a nucleus that also has a rather heavy innervation from the fornix system. Thalamic input to the retrosplenial area in primates is not well known. This area adjoins directly on the primary visual cortex (area striata), so it is perhaps not surprising that it receives afferent fibers from striate cortex and that neurons in the retrosplenial area can be discharged by photic stimuli. Other portions of the limbic cortex also receive fibers from and send them into supralimbic cortex. The cingulate cortices of the two hemispheres are interconnected by the corpus callosum; the insular-temporal cortices are interconnected by the anterior commissure (see Figure 2). Temporal cortex also projects on the amygdala and, by fibers joining the fornix after penetrating the corpus callosum, probably on the lateral septal nucleus. Efferent connections from the limbic cortex to the corresponding thalamic projection nuclei have been described, as have connections to the basal ganglia.

Although not part of the limbic system in the sense of location, in terms of connectivity much of the rostrodorsal convexity of the frontal lobe must be included. This is the cortex receiving projections from the extensive parvocellular portions of nucleus medialis dorsalis. The parvocellular components have two major inputs: (1) large fibers that ascend from the ventromedial midbrain and ventral tegmental area of Tsai, passing along the anterior border of the habenulo-penduncular tract; (2) large fibers arising in the medial septal nucleus of the diagonal band of Broca. Thus, the primary input to the prefrontal cortex by the nucleus medialis dorsalis arises from areas that are part of the limbic system. These areas of the prefrontal cortex also join the limbic system in sending efferent fibers into putamen, claustrum, head of the caudate nucleus, the cingulum, and the periaqueductal gray.

A large band of fibers completely encircles the limbic cortex and serves as its major efferent and association pathway. Ventrally this fiber system is the uncinate fasciculus, forming a two-way connection between orbitofrontal and insular-temporal cortex. The predominant system, however, is the cingulum, which runs a looping course above

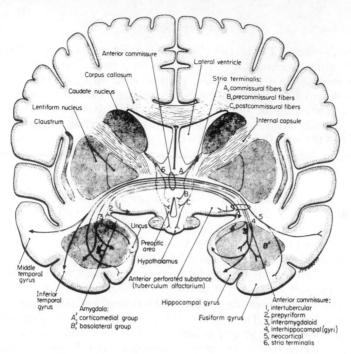

FIGURE 2. Diagram of human brain showing components of the anterior commissure and stria terminalis. (Reprinted with permission of The Macmillan Company from Crosby, E. C., Humphrey, T., and Lauer, E. W. *Correlative Anatomy of the Nervous System*, p. 401. © The Macmillan Company, New York, 1962.)

the corpus callosum medially within the white matter of the cingulate gyrus (see Figure 1). It arises diffusely in the prefrontal cortex, exclusive of the orbital area, and, although fibers course in both directions within it, the greatest projection is from the rostral to caudal portions. Axons of pyramidal cells from cingulate cortex frequently branch, sending one collateral rostrally into septum or striatum and the other caudally. Great numbers of the fibers from the cingulum reach the entorhinal and subicular areas, which in turn project into the hippocampus.

Hippocampal system. The focal point of the hippocampal system is a curving strip of precisely aligned pyramidal cells with dense apical dendrites projecting within the central core of the cornu Ammonis (see Figure 3). Differences in size and other characteristics have prompted the division of the pyramidal cells into four fields designated, CA_1, CA_2, etc. The cells in CA_3 and CA_4 are the largest and send branches, the Schaffer collaterals, from their axons to end principally on the apical dendrites of CA_1 and CA_2 pyramids (see Figure 3). Other collaterals are given off by the pyramidal cells to end on

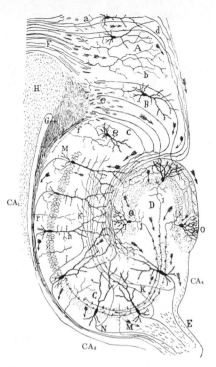

FIGURE 3. Schematic drawing of the structure and connections of cornu
Ammonis. A, entorhinal area; B, subiculum; C, cornu Ammonis; D, dentate gyrus; E, fimbria; F, cingulum; G, hippocampal commissure; H, corpus callosum; J, alveus; CA_1, CA_3, CA_4, sectors of cornu Ammonis; b,
termination of cingulum in entorhinal area; c, perforant fibers of temporoammonic tract; h, apical dendrites of pyramidal cells; M, basal dendrites
of pyramidal cells; N, axons of pyramidal cells (note recurrent collaterals
in CA_1, perhaps contacting basket cells, which are not shown); K, Schaffer
collaterals; O, granule cells; J, mossy fibers; a, b, d, fibers from cingulum;
g, cell of subiculum. (From Ramon y Cajal, S. *Histologie du Système
Neurveux de l'Homme et des Vertébrés*. Consejo Superior de Investigaciones Cient., Madrid, 1955.)

basket cells, which produce recurrent inhibition of neighboring pyramidal cells, as discussed in Chapter 7.

   There are three major efferent paths from cornu Ammonis: (1) a
diffuse and poorly understood pathway into adjacent neocortex, (2)
the hippocampal commissure or psalterium that connects the two
hippocampi, and (3) the fornix. The efferent hippocampal component of the fornix is formed by axons that gather on the hippocampal
surface to form the alveus and then pass laterally and rostrally in the
fimbria. The fimbrial fibers, augmented by contributions from the

hippocampal gyrus, consolidate medially to form the fornix, which then descends into the septal area. The alveus, fimbria, and fornix are all in direct contact with cerebrospinal fluid, since these structures form the ventromedial wall of the lateral ventricle. The projection into the septal area splits around the anterior commissure, forming the precommissural fornix, which terminates in the septal and preoptic areas, and the postcommissural fornix, which continues back through the hypothalamus to reach the mammillary bodies.

In man 2,700,000 fibers constitute the main body of the fornix, and 900,000 fibers go into the hypothalamic portion. The corresponding figures for macaques are 500,000 and 100,000. The fornix thus shows an over-all fivefold increase in man and a ninefold increase in its projection to the hypothalamus and medial mammillary nucleus. That these figures indicate an increase in the relative importance of the hippocampal system in man can be seen in other comparisons. The optic nerve, for instance, has about 1 million fibers in both man and macaque; despite the much greater body and brain size in man, there is only about a twofold increase (to about 1 million fibers) of the pyramidal tract in man versus macaque. The size of the neurons in man is smaller, yet the volume of the medial mammillary nucleus is about six times greater than in macaques, and it constitutes about 6 per cent of the total hypothalamic volume in man versus 3.5 per cent in macaques, further indicating the increased importance of the fornix-mammillary system in man.

There are, however, several complications in evaluating the relations in the fornix system. The postcommissural fornix gives off fibers into the hypothalamus, and it also receives hypothalamic fibers. In the rabbit the postcommissural fornix starts out with about 200,000 fibers, but only half reach the mammillary body; in the cat, with 160,000 fibers, 100,000 also reach the mammillary body. Midway in the hypothalamic portion of the fornix in the cat there are considerably fewer than 100,000 fibers, so either fibers branch as they approach the mammillary nuclei or new fibers join the fornix from the hypothalamus. In all species examined so far (rat, rabbit, cat, macaque), fornix fibers also pass beyond the mammillary body into the central gray. The pyramidal cells in CA_1 give rise to fibers that project principally to the anterior thalamic nuclei and to the mammillary body; those in CA_3 and CA_4 project mostly into the precommissural fornix and distribute to the medial and lateral septal nuclei, nucleus of the diagonal band and nucleus accumbens. However, not all of the fornix arises in the hippocampus. In man and other species, large bundles of fibers from area striata and the cingulate area pass directly through the corpus callosum and form the dorsal fornix. The destination of these fibers in the dorsal fornix is not well-known, but they appear to terminate mostly in the hippocampus and septal area.

Fibers (the white stria of Lancisi) from the induseum griseum, an embryological remnant of hippocampal tissue lying on the dorsal surface of the corpus callosum, also cut through the corpus callosum to join the dorsal fornix. In the rat and guinea pig, some of the dorsal fornix projects directly to the superior central tegmental nucleus of Bekterev in the caudal mesencephalon.

In addition to these neocortical efferent fibers, the fornix contains a large contingent of afferent fibers arising principally from the medial septal nucleus and nucleus of the diagnonal band of Broca. It is possible that some of the proportional increase found in the human fornix system involves these afferent or neocortical efferent components in addition to the probable increase in efferents from cornu Ammonis. The relative increase in the medial mammillary nucleus, however, is definitive. In both the cat and the rabbit, there is an approximately one-to-one relation between the number of premammillary fornix fibers, number of cells in the medial mammillary nucleus, and number of fibers in the mammillothalamic tract. Many of the efferent fibers from the medial mammillary nucleus branch and project posteriorly into the deep tegmental nucleus of Gudden as well as into the mammillothalamic tract. The deep tegmental nucleus in turn projects on the medial mammillary nucleus. The great majority of the fibers in the mammillothalamic tract are less than 1.5μ. They form a dense plexus in the anterior thalamic nuclei, developing knot-like excrescences along their terminal filaments that are highly similar to the mossy fiber endings in the cerebellum.

The anterior thalamic nuclei, as mentioned above, project into the cingulate cortex. The latter projects into the hippocampal gyrus by way of the cingulum, and the path then returns on the cornu Ammonis, completing a potential loop of activity, the Papez circuit: cornu Ammonis-fornix-mammillary body-anterior thalamic nuclei-cingulate gyrus-cingulum-entorhinal area-cornu Ammonis (see Figure 4). Of course, several of the links in this circuit might be inhibitory rather than excitatory, so this arrangement is unlikely to be one for producing self-sustaining or avalanching activity. Furthermore, the topographic projections of the pathways are sufficiently complex that the resulting elaboration of impulses through the system would far exceed anything understandable in terms of a simple re-entrant circuit.

The afferent pathways into cornu Ammonis are complex and still not fully defined. The afferents of the fornix terminate on the basilar dendrites and proximal portions of the apical dendrites of pyramidal cells in CA_3 and CA_4 and on granule cells in the dentate gyrus. The major afferent pathway arises in the entorhinal cortex (area 28), an area particularly well developed in man and higher primates. The principal afferent path into the entorhinal cortex, in turn, comes

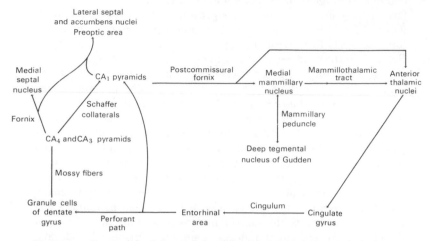

FIGURE 4. Summary of major connections of the hippocampal system.

from the cingulum. A second well-established system comes into the entorhinal area more diffusely from the olfactory tubercle and peri-amygdaloid cortex (uncus). This system undoubtedly serves as a relay for olfactory input but also conveys influences arising from many other sources. The inputs to cornu Ammonis thus filter through a continuous sheet of cortex, the cytoarchitecture of which varies considerably as it approaches the hippocampal fissure and the dentate gyrus. Following this cortex from its rostral environs, all medial to the rhinal fissure and looping up the surface of the hippo-campal gyrus, one can identify olfactory tubercle (anterior perforated space in man), prepiriform cortex, periamygdaloid cortex (piriform cortex, uncus in primates), entorhinal cortex, parasubiculum, pre-subiculum, subiculum, and prosubiculum. An interesting feature in several of these areas is the gathering of similar-sized cells into clus-ters or islands. Most highly developed are the islands of Calleja in the olfactory tubercle (see Figure 5). The giant cells in the islands of Calleja in man resemble motoneurons in appearance, but other larger islands are formed by granule cells only 5 μ in diameter. The afferent fibers to the islands of granule cells come from the direction of the caudate nucleus and form an extremely dense plexus within the island. Smaller clusterings of large or small cells are found in periamygdaloid and entorhinal cortex and in the subiculum. The periamygdaloid cortex of man also contains many cells with spectacu-larly developed basal dendrites. All these cortical areas have a pattern of organization that differs distinctly from that of the neocortex and

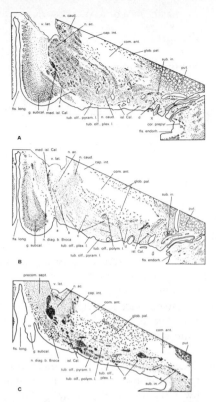

FIGURE 5. Transverse sections through rostral (A), middle (B), and posterior (C) levels of human olfactory tubercle, illustrating various cellular groupings. *a*, ventral extension from medial island of Calleja toward neocortex; *b*, further extension of the medial island of Calleja suggesting a boundary of the caudate nucleus; *c*, neurons intercalated between the olfactory tubercle and the caudate nucleus; *cap. int.*, internal capsule; *com. ant.*, anterior commissure; *cor. prepyr.*, prepiriform cortex; *d*, large neurons of olfactory tubercle; *fis. endorh.*, entorhinal fissure; *fis. long.*, longitudinal fissure, midline; *g. subcal.*, subcallosal gyrus or medial septal nucleus; *glob. pal.*, globus pallidus; *isl. Cal.*, island of Calleja; *med. isl. Cal.*, medial island of Calleja; *n. ac.*, nucleus accumbens; *n. caud.*, caudate nucleus; *n. diag. b. Broca*, nucleus of the diagonal band of Broca; *precon. sept.*, lateral septal nucleus or parolfactory area; *put.*, putamen; *sub. in.*, substantia innominata of Reichert; X, indication of folding in cortical layer of olfactory tubercle; *tub. olf. plex. l.*, plexiform layer; *tub. olf. polym. l.*, polymorphous layer; *tub. olf. pyram. l.*, pyramidal cell layer; *v. lat.*, lateral ventricle. (From Crosby, E. C., and Humphrey, T. Studies of the vertebrate telencephalon. II. The nuclear pattern of the anterior olfactory nucleus, tuberculum olfactorium and the amygdaloid complex in adult man. J. Comp. Neurol., 74: 309, 1941.)

are classified as "allocortex."

The entorhinal area gives rise to groups of fibers that cut directly through the subiculum to end in complex ramifications among the dendrites of the granule cells of the dentate gyrus (see Figure 3). This perforant or temporoammonic path also sends fibers among the apical dendrites of CA_1 and CA_2 pyramidal cells (see Figure 3). The granule cells of the dentate gyrus send out very fine axons, which, however, have large bulbous endings (see Figure 5 in Chapter 7). These enclose the dendritic spines of the apical dendrites of CA_4 and CA_3 neurons. With the Golgi stain these bulbous endings give the axons a characteristic appearance, so they are called "mossy fibers" (see Figure 3). The mossy fiber endings and/or the dendritic spines are peculiar in containing relatively large amounts of zinc.

AMYGDALOID SYSTEM

The amygdala is a group of a dozen or more nuclei covered by the peri-amygdaloid cortex of the uncus and forming part of the hippocampal gyrus (see Figure 2). The nuclei can be divided into two groups: the corticomedial, which can be traced phylogenetically back to cyclostomes; and a basolateral group that first appears in reptiles and in man forms the major component of the system.

Like those for the hippocampus, the connections of the amygdala follow two principal pathways: a diffuse one, which constitutes the predominant pathway in man; and a compact fiber bundle, the stria terminalis (see Figures 1 and 2), which, like the fornix, follows a long, looping path into the septal-preoptic region and contains both afferent and efferent fibers. The description of these pathways is still garbled by the inability to separate the contribution of the periamyg-daloid cortex from that of the amygdala per se.

The stria terminalis arises mostly from the caudal portion of the corticomedial complex. It passes first caudally and then follows the upward and rostrally curving course of the tail of the caudate nucleus. As it plunges toward the anterior commissure, it divides into several components (see Figure 2), a small part going rostral to the commissure, some fibers crossing through the commissure, but most descending into the medial preoptic area and anterior hypothalamus. In man and other mammals the stria terminalis is accompanied throughout its course by a bed nucleus, forming a strip of neurons that are clustered like the islands of Calleja. Similar islands occur in the central nucleus of the amygdala, where the stria forms, and in nucleus accumbens and the substantia innominata of Reichert (see Figure 5), not far from where it ends. At commissural levels the bed nucleus of stria terminalis enlarges considerably and becomes continuous with the bed nucleus of the anterior commissure and of the medial forebrain bundle (see Figure 2); it has been described as a continuation of the anteromedial nucleus of the thalamus. It seems likely that the cells of the bed nucleus give rise to afferent fibers that course through stria terminalis into the amygdala. At commissural levels the cells in the bed nucleus of stria terminalis are innervated by many fibers that appear to be of thalamic origin. Some of these fibers continue on into the stria.

In man the stria terminalis is relatively small, and most fibers leaving and entering the amygdala course ventromedially through a sublenticular path. This bundle of fibers is about the size of the anterior commissure, although not nearly so compact. Within the amygdala it arises principally from the basolateral complex as the longitudinal association bundle of Johnston. It passes into the lateral preoptic area and lateral hypothalamus. Rostrally, this ventral amygdalofugal pathway forms the diagonal band of Broca, conveying fibers to the olfactory tubercle, substantia innominata, and medial septal nucleus.

The periamygdaloid cortex projects strongly into the amygdala, in part relaying olfactory input. The cortical nucleus of the amygdala receives fibers from the lateral olfactory tract and thus forms part of the same system as the periamygdaloid cortex. Afferents to the amygdala from other sources are ill-defined. Two-way connections between the amygdala and insular-temporal cortex, however, have often been described.

The many nuclear groups seen in the amygdala with Nissl stains do not differ from one another in any obvious way in Golgi preparations, and nuclear boundaries are then obscured. Cells in the corticomedial group do seem to have fewer dendrites than do cells in the basolateral group. The system of axon collaterals in the amygdala is very profuse, indicating the occurrence of extensive intranuclear elaboration of amygdaloid activity.

HABENULAR-INTERPEDUNCULAR SYSTEM

This system seems to be relatively undeveloped in man and has not been thoroughly studied in any species. The habenulae are nuclear masses of the epithalamus divisible even in cyclostomes into two distinctly different nuclei. An early problem in cerebral dominance is presented in these structures, since for petromyzonts the right habenula is always larger than the left, but the reverse is true for sharks; and among teleostean species either right or left dominance or a symmetrical arrangement can be found.

In mammals the medial habenular nucleus consists of small, palestaining cells, 10 to 15 μ in diameter, of the sensory type with short dendrites that, together with afferent fibers from the stria medullaris (see Figure 1), form complex glomerular structures. The axons of these small cells pass directly into the medial aspect of the habenu-

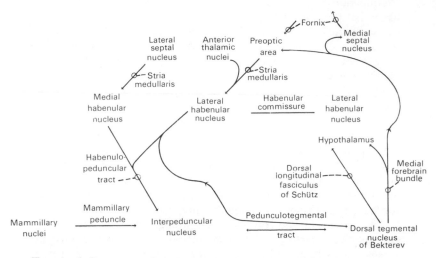

FIGURE 6. Summary of major connections of the habenular-interpeduncular system.

lopeduncular tract without branching. Cells of the lateral habenular nucleus, on the other hand, are of the typical reticular type, 20 to 26 μ in diameter. Fibers from the stria medullaris ramify profusely within the lateral nucleus. This diffuseness of effect is enhanced by numerous intranuclear collateral fibers given off by axons of the cells of this nucleus as they pass toward the habenulopeduncular tract. The lateral habenular nuclei are also interconnected with each other by the habenular commissure.

Fibers from the posterior septal area pass to the medial habenular nucleus, and the lateral habenular nucleus receives a powerful input from the preoptic area and the anterior nuclei of the thalamus (see Figure 6). These inputs course in the stria medullaris. Many other sources for the stria medullaris have been claimed, but the foregoing probably constitute the major direct pathways. Electrophysiologically the fornix can be shown to project by way of the stria medullaris into the habenula and interpeduncular nucleus, but a synapse apparently occurs prior to the stria medullaris portion of this projection.

The interpeduncular nucleus contains cells of several types. The afferent fibers from the habenulopeduncular tract (see Figure 1) lose their myelin upon entering the nucleus, and the bare axon then follows a peculiar figure-eight course, crossing the midline and then returning to give off collaterals and break up into terminal arborizations. Afferents are also derived from the mammillary nuclei (see

Figures 1 and 6). Efferents project diffusely into the posterior tegmental area, particularly to the dorsal tegmental nucleus of Bekterev. These efferents join fibers of similar destination from the lateral habenular nuclei, which course down the hebenulopeduncular tract but bypass the interpeduncular nucleus. A few fibers from the substantia innominata of Reichert in the preoptic area even follow the peculiar course through stria medullaris, habenulopeduncular tract, peduncular-tegmental tract to reach locus coeruleus.

The tegmental areas project back on the interpeduncular nucleus and to some degree even to the lateral habenular nucleus. They also project into the hypothalamus through the dorsal longitudinal fasciculus of Schütz and along the medial forebrain bundle system into the preoptic area, medial septal nucleus, and nucleus of the diagonal band of Broca. The latter two groups project into the hippocampus through the fornix (see Figures 4 and 7).

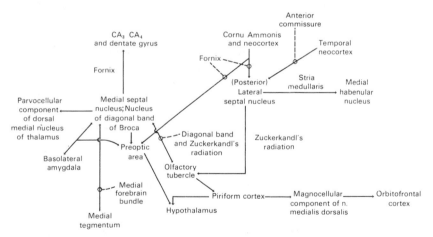

FIGURE 7. Summary of major connections of the septal area.

BASAL FOREBRAIN: RHINENCEPHALON

The entrance zone of the olfactory tracts on the rostrobasal surface of the brain is marked by extreme anatomical complexity. The system associated with the olfactory input is termed the "rhinencephalon," and, except for omission of neocortical components, the term is essentially synonymous with limbic system. The realization that most rhinencephalic or limbic structures, with the possible exception of the dentate gyrus and the corticomedial components of the amygdala, are equally well developed in birds or cetaceans that lack olfactory input has prompted a reappraisal of the role of the limbic system in olfaction. Nevertheless, it is clear phylogenetically that the limbic system has developed in association with the olfactory system. Furthermore, it is easy to understand how emotional reactivity and species-specific, stereotyped behaviors have been organized primarily under olfactory control. Every night for at least 100 million years the early vertebrates appraised their future solely with the olfactory sense as they swam forward in the dark and silent seas to eat or be eaten. The same nocturnal appraisal, with all its associated reactions for mammalian prey and predator alike, continues to provide a prime link to survival. Sexual contact and behavior have similarly come to be dominated by olfactory cues, and a well-supported perfume industry bears familiar testimony to the lingering relevance of olfaction in the sexual activity of man.

The primary olfactory input is processed first within the intricate systems of the olfactory bulb, where a reduction of about 300:1 occurs between the number of incoming and outgoing fibers. Axons of the large mitral cells of the bulb pass centrally in the olfactory tract. They are joined by axons of cells from the anterior olfactory nucleus that are scattered within the tract. As the olfactory tract spreads into the brain, so does the anterior olfactory nucleus, merging posteriorly with the prepiriform cortex and laterally into neocortex. The olfactory tract divides into lateral and medial components. The former spreads diffusely into prepiriform and piriform cortex, in the corticomedial nuclei of the amygdala, and, to some degree, into the lateral boundary of the anterior perforated substance. The smaller, medial olfactory tract of fine fibers, arising largely from tufted rather than mitral cells of the olfactory bulb, passes mostly across the anterior limb of the anterior commissure to the contralateral olfactory bulb. It probably also sends fibers into the medial septal nucleus, nucleus of the diagonal band, and the medial portion of the anterior perforated substance.

The latter area (see Figures 1 and 5) is marked by a dense infiltration of small blood vessels and by the islands of Calleja. Its major afferent supply comes not from the olfactory tracts but from the septal area by way of the diagonal band. Its efferents form one of the major components of the median forebrain bundle and also project into the piriform and entorhinal cortex, medial septal nucleus, and olfactory bulb.

At its caudal border the anterior perforated substance joins part of the olfactory radiations of Zuckerkandl, which in turn merge with the diagonal band of Broca. The nucleus of the diagonal band is continuous with the medial septal nucleus and laterally with the globus pallidus, all being characterized by rather large cells of the reticular type. Further relation of the limbic system with a basal ganglia is found in this region with the continuation of the caudate nucleus as nucleus accumbens septi (see Figure 5), and with the large cells of the substantia innominata of Reichert, which are the rostral elements in a system known as the nucleus basalis of Meynert. The latter is associated with the globus pallidus and is particularly well-developed in primates, forming clusters of cells between the optic tract and anterior commissure and the medioventral border of globus pallidus. The nucleus basalis degenerates after lesions of the temporal lobe.

As seen in several instances above and in phylogenetic development, the basal ganglia have an intimate relation with the limbic system. Furthermore, much stereotyped behavior depends on the basal ganglia for its organization, and stimulation of the basal ganglia not uncommonly produces motivating effects. Thus, there is some inclination to look on the basal ganglia as important ancillary structures of the limbic system. However, since the basal ganglia are also intimately related with the neocortex, their equal association with the limbic system cannot be unduly emphasized.

The lateral septal nucleus is distinguished from the medial in having neurons of the sensory rather than the reticular type. Its afferents come predominantly from the fornix, and it is probable, because of its cell type, that it rather than the medial septal nucleus gives rise to the fibers that project to the sensory-type cells of the medial habenular nucleus (see Figure 7). Stimulation of the septal area also evokes potentials in the dorsomedial nucleus of the thalamus.

The septal nuclei, nucleus of the diagonal band, the anterior perforated substance, and substantia innominata posteriorly shade over into the preoptic area, which in turn becomes the anterior hypothalamus (see Figure 2). The preoptic area consists mostly of cells with short axons; receives input from the fornix, septum, and amygdala; and is traversed by and contributes to the medial forebrain bundle and fiber systems passing from piriform cortex to the dorsal medial nucleus of the thalamus. It also sends many fibers to the lateral habenular nucleus.

In summary (see Figure 7), the basal forebrain is a point of focus and/or transit for about eight systems: (1) olfactory input to piriform cortex; (2) connections to and from the hippocampal system and the septal and preoptic areas; (3) connections to and from the amygdala and the preoptic-septal region; (4) connections to and from the tegmentum and septal area; (5) afferents to the habenular-interpeduncular system; (6) relations to the temporal lobes through the anterior commissure and the nucleus basalis; (7) afferents from piriform cortex to the magnocellular component of nucleus medialis dorsalis and the projection of the latter on orbitofrontal cortex; and (8) efferents into the hypothalamus through the median forebrain bundle. In addition, recent electrophysiological evidence indicates that this basal forebrain region distributes centrencephalic influences onto the dorsal convexity of the frontal lobe.

NEUROENDOCRINOLOGY AND THE HYPOTHALAMUS

The connections to and from the hypothalamus place it definitively within the limbic system, and the physiological and behavioral correlates of its activity affirm this classification. In Golgi stain the cells of the hypothalamus are all of the reticular type, and, in the lateral hypothalamus particularly, the reticular organization is also apparent in the arrangement of fibers and cells. Of course, there are many varieties of reticular neurons, and in man Nissl stains demonstrate about nine principal cell types in the seventeen nuclei into which the hypothalamus can be divided. For the present discussion, however, only the anterior, lateral, and ventromedial hypothalamic areas need be considered, plus the nuclei specifically giving rise to neurosecretory tracts.

The ventromedial nucleus seems to be organized to serve as a distribution center. Fibers from this nucleus first ramify extensively within it, then pass to all parts of the hypothalamus, especially to anterior and lateral areas, some attaining the lateral area of the other side through Meynert's commissure associated with the optic chiasm. The afferents to the ventromedial nucleus are mostly of small caliber and branch profusely, thus producing a diffuse and random-appearing network. The terminals are small but filled with the usual type of synaptic vesicles. The afferent and efferent exchange of the lateral hypothalamus is with distant areas, outside the lateral hypothalamus. It probably receives more nonhypothalamic afferents than any of the other hypothalamic areas. Collaterals of efferent fibers from the lateral hypothalamus do not ramify within this area but, instead, project into the medial nuclei.

The most powerful afferent system playing on the hypothalamus arises in the rostral mesencephalon—that is, in the reticular formation and central gray. There are essentially no direct connections of neocortex with the hypothalamus, but, since the dorsal prefrontal cortex projects into the foregoing mesencephalic areas, a potentially strong link exists. The amygdala and, especially, the septal-preoptic area also contribute numerous afferents to the hypothalamus.

Descending efferents from the hypothalamus pass through the dorsal longitudinal fasciculus of Schütz, but they are rather meager from the medial nuclear groups. This suggests that most of the longer efferents arise in the lateral hypothalamus, although this possibility is difficult to study independently of the medial forebrain bundle. It does indicate that the dorsal longitudinal fasciculus is predominantly afferent to the hypothalamus. None of the hypothalamic efferents reach the spinal cord, and most terminate in the midbrain rather than the medulla. The rostromedial groups project anterodorsally and contribute fibers to the stria medullaris and possibly the stria terminalis.

Two efferent paths supply neurosecretory material to the hypophysis. The first is the well-known hypothalamohypophyseal tract, in man about 100,000 fibers, arising from large cells in the supraoptic and paraventricular nuclei and terminating on blood vessels (see Figure 8) in the neurohypophysis (posterior lobe of the pituitary gland). The supraoptic and paraventricular nuclei have a particularly rich blood supply. Within the cell bodies and all along the nerve fibers, aggregations of specially staining material are readily discernible. The fibers often have a beaded appearance from the presence of organized masses (Herring bodies) of this material ranging in size up to that of the cell body itself. For many years it was thought that the pituicytes within the neurohypophysis stored the hormonal material. Electron microscopic evidence (see Figure 8), however, indicates that the 750- to 2,000-Å neurosecretory granules of the nerve endings only rarely get into the pituicytes, seemingly by phagocytosis. The pituicytes are similar in appearance to fibrous astrocytes. In the newborn monkey they form a glialike barrier that disappears from around the blood vessels as the animal matures. Their role, if any, in the hormonal activity of the posterior lobe is thus unknown. Perhaps equally puzzling in the neurosecretory process is the presence of typical synaptic vesicles along with the secretory granules and small Herring bodies in the endings that the hypothalamohypophyseal tract forms on the capillary network within the posterior lobe (see Figure 8). In macaques the hormonal release appears to be accomplished primarily by the passage of intact small Herring bodies into the vascular system. Nerve endings are also sometimes pinched off and pass into the blood stream. In addition, the secretory granules of the nerve endings are depleted individually of their osmiophilic core, as in the opposum (see Figure 8), and/or release the entire neurosecretory granule.

The other secretory efferent path is the tuberoinfundibular tract. This is a fine-fibered system arising from small cells of the periventricular, tuberal, and possibly other nuclei. The beads of secretory material found in these fibers have entirely different staining characteristics from those in the hypothalamohypophyseal tract. The fibers terminate on capillaries and as palisades overlying the Mantelplexus, a dense capillary plexus on the surface of the pars tuberalis.

The neurosecretory material could be carried thence to the adenohypophysis by way of the portal circulation. However, beyond the fact that the hypothalamus definitely controls the adenohypophysis and that the portal

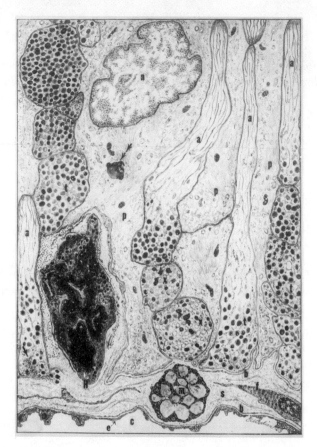

FIGURE 8. Diagram of the electron microscopic features, at about
9000 ×, of the neurohypophysis of the opossum. *c*, lumen of blood
vessel; *e*, endothelial lining of capillary with numerous pores; *s*, septal
zone, which consists of collagen bounded by basement membranes (*b*).
The septal zone separates the axon terminals (*t*) from the blood vessel
wall and contains mast cells (*m*) and fibroblasts (*f*). Synaptic vesicles
(*arrow*) are clustered almost exclusively at tips of terminals abutting on
the septal zone. The axons themselves (*a*) are generally free of neurosecretory granules (*the dark, small spherules with light ring about them*).
In some axon terminals (X) many of the granules have lost their osmiophilic core. The small Herring body (H) also contains neurosecretory
granules. The pituicytes (*p*) are relatively clear, with a light nucleus (*n*)
and occasional dense inclusions (*double arrow*). The arrangement in macaques is basically similar to this except for the presence of greater numbers of small Herring bodies and a reduced pituicyte system. (From Bo-
dian, D. Cytological aspects of neurosecretion in opossum neurohypophysis.
Bull. Johns Hopkins Hosp., *113*: 57, 1963.)

circulation moves from the tuberal region to the pars distalis (anterior lobe), morphological knowledge concerning the transport, storage, and release of the hormonal materials is almost nonexistent.

NEUROHYPOPHYSEAL SYSTEM

Two types of response are produced by neurohypophyseal hormones: (1) alteration of the permeability of certain membranes to water and (2) contraction of smooth muscle. Two different hormones are secreted, but each can, to some degree, produce both types of responses. The hormones are peptides that are species-specific and display a fascinating phyletic constancy (see Figure 9). Oxytocin is present from amphibia on through

Oxytocin (amphibians, reptiles, birds, mammals)

$$\overline{Cys\text{-}Tyr\text{-}Ile\text{-}Glu(NH_2)\text{-}Asp(NH_2)\text{-}Cys}\text{-}Pro\text{-}\mathbf{Leu}\text{-}Gly(NH_2)$$

Arginine vasotocin (amphibia, reptiles, birds)

$$\overline{Cys\text{-}Tyr\text{-}Ile\text{-}Glu(NH_2)\text{-}Asp(NH_2)\text{-}Cys}\text{-}Pro\text{-}\mathbf{Arg}\text{-}Gly(NH_2)$$

Arginine vasopressin (echidna, oppossum, man, monkey, dog, rat, horse, cow, sheep, camel, peccary)

$$\overline{Cys\text{-}Tyr\text{-}\mathbf{Phe}\text{-}Glu(NH_2)\text{-}Asp(NH_2)\text{-}Cys}\text{-}Pro\text{-}\mathbf{Arg}\text{-}Gly(NH_2)$$

Lysine vasopressin (pig, hippopotamus)

$$\overline{Cys\text{-}Tyr\text{-}\mathbf{Phe}\text{-}Glu(NH_2)\text{-}Asp(NH_2)\text{-}Cys}\text{-}Pro\text{-}\mathbf{Lys}\text{-}Gly(NH_2)$$

FIGURE 9. Chemical structure of neurohypophyseal hormones in various species.

mammals. In the latter it is particularly effective in producing uterine contractions and milk ejection. Arginine vasopressin is found in monotremes, marsupials, and most mammals. It causes contraction of arteriolar smooth muscle and thus increases blood pressure. Its major role, however, is the control of the osmolality of the blood by its action on water reabsorption in the distal tubules of the kidney. In this latter role it is called the antidiuretic hormone (ADH). Its absence after hypothalamic lesions has long been recognized as the cause of diabetes insipidus.

Conditions that change the osmolality of the blood quickly affect the release of ADH and alter the amount of neurosecretory material that can be demonstrated in the hypothalamohypophyseal system.

Thus, drinking hypertonic solutions or injecting them intravenously causes a great outpouring of ADH to conserve water, and the neurosecretory material then becomes sparse. On the other hand, overloading the organism with water induces a spectacular increase in the amount of neurosecretory material. The stainable material seen with the light microscope is not the hormone per se but is likely to be a lipoprotein to which the hormone is attached. The role of this protein material or even whether the hormone is indeed attached to it in the nerve fibers remains uncertain.

ADH secretion is also altered by many seemingly nonspecific factors, such as pain, cold, and electrical stimulation of certain limbic areas. The neural control is thus rather complex, and the question arises whether or not it is integrated primarily within the supraoptic nuclei and whether secretory cells have the electrophysiological behavior of other neurons. The latter question received an unequivocal answer in the goldfish, where intracellular recordings can be made from secretory neurons in the preoptic nucleus, which in reptiles, birds, and mammals differentiates into the supraoptic and paraventricular nuclei. Spike potentials, excitatory and inhibitory postsynaptic potentials, etc., are all comparable to those of any large neuron. Antidromic stimulation of the preopticohypophyseal tract induces inhibitory postsynaptic potentials of such short latency as to suggest that recurrent collaterals of the secretory neurons have direct intranuclear inhibitory connections. Extracellular records from neurons in the mammalian supraoptic nucleus also demonstrate spike potentials, and their background frequency is determined by the osmolality of the blood. Since a hypothalamic island containing the supraoptic nuclei and intact hypophyseal system isolated from the rest of the brain can still respond to changes in blood electrolytes, it seems very likely that the secretory neurons are themselves the osmoreceptors. Their possession of normal electrophysiological activity also suggests that these neurons may integrate activity impinging on them from several other neural sources and that it is neural discharge that liberates the hormone from the nerve endings. Support for the latter concept comes from the fact that neurohypophyseal hormonal stores, though temporarily ample, cannot be released by hypertonic injections after section of the hypothalamohypophyseal tract.

ADENOHYPOPHYSEAL SYSTEM

Six hormones are known to be secreted by the anterior lobe of the pituitary gland. These hormones are peptide or protein in nature and have varying degrees of specificity. They control the action of other endocrine glands. Adrenocorticotropic hormone (ACTH) is the only one so far identified chemically. It is a straight peptide of thirty-nine amino acids having a molecular weight of about 4,500. The secretions of the adrenal cortex—which regulate salt and sugar metabolism, leukocyte behavior, and general body responses to inflammation and stress—are controlled almost completely by ACTH. The other hormones are: follicle-stimulating hormone (FSH) and luteinizing hormone (LH), necessary for maintenance of functioning gonads in either sex and paramount in the regulation of the female sexual cycle; prolactin, which produces secretion from the mammary glands and also has a luteotropic hormone (LTH) effect; thyroid-stimulating hormone (TSH), controlling general metabolic rate and thus a wide variety of body functions and neural maturation; somatotropic hormone (STH), which also regulates body metabolism in a general and poorly understood manner and controls growth, particularly by its influence on bone epiphyses.

There are only two cells types, the acidophils and basophils, in the adenohypophysis that are likely to be the source of these six hormones. Which hormone comes from which cell is by no means certain. Furthermore, hormonal production is almost wholly dependent on the hypothalamus. The one exception to this is prolactin, the production of which is inhibited by the hypothalamus; after hypothalamic lesions, transplantation of the gland beyond reach of the portal circulation, or explantation of the gland to artificial media, prolactin production is augmented, but the other hormones essentially disappear. Adding hypothalamic but not other neural tissue to a culture of the adenohypophysis supports the production of ACTH. Similarly, if adenohypophyseal tissue is implanted into the hypothalamic area from which the tuberoinfundibular tract arises, normal basophils and sexual cycles in hypophysectomized female rats can be maintained; but, if the tissue is implanted elsewhere in the brain, the basophils atrophy, and the females remain anestrus. The survival of acidophils in such transplants depends solely on whether the thyroid gland is maintained in a good trophic condition.

The evidence thus points strongly to the likelihood that the tuberoinfundibular tract releases substances into the portal circulation that are necessary for the manufacture and release of the adenohypophyseal hormones. Whether these substances, which seem to be peptides, are incorporated into the hormones themselves or merely exert a control over the secretory cells remains unknown, and they are presently spoken of only as releasing factors.

In a number of instances, release of adenohypophyseal hormones has been obtained by electrical stimulation of the hypothalamus or other areas of the limbic system, whereas stimulation of the adenohypophysis itself is ineffective. More important, of course, is the fact that a great variety of natural stimuli processed by the nervous system are capable of profoundly influencing hormonally controlled processes. Most familiar perhaps is the production of menstrual irregularities in women by emotional disturbances. The influence may be more subtle, as in the frequent failure of pregnancy to develop in mice under conditions of crowding or when exposed to the odor of male mice of another strain. In many species the sexual cycle is under control of photoperiodicity. Ovulation occurs in some species, such as the cat and the rabbit, only after vaginal stimulation, and such stimulation can be demonstrated to produce bizarre electrical patterns in the lateral hypothalamus. Pain or other stress causes great augmentation of ACTH release. The neural mediation of these effects was dramatically demonstrated in a dog maintained for months with its brain stem transected at the collicular level. ACTH was not released in this animal after a laparotomy, which is usually a powerful stimulus, whereas it was augmented when the animal was restrained in a strange environment —thus demonstrating some degree of awareness in the isolated forebrain.

The neurons from which the tuberoinfundibular tract originates also seem to be sensitive to the titer of hormones secreted by the target organs of the adenohypophysis. This chemoreceptor function of the hypothalamic neurons thus provides for feedback regulation of the hormonal system. A high hormone titer causes the hypothalamic neurons to diminish production or release of the appropriate releasing factor and thus lowers stimulation of the target organ by the adenohypophysis. If the receptive mechanism of the hypothalamus is deceived by the implantation of a pellet of hormone—such as estradiol, testosterone, or hydrocortisone —in the appropriate nucleus, the curtailment of releasing factor and consequent failure of adenohypophyseal support of the target organ are so severe as to be equal to hypophysectomy in their effects.

OTHER POSSIBLE NEUROHORMONAL SYSTEMS

After thyroidectomy, cells in the medial habenular nucleus undergo a 10 to 20 per cent decrease in size. Habenular lesions, on the other hand, produce a slight obesity, detectable changes in the histology of the adenohypophysis and thyroid, and an impaired ability to increase thyroid activity on exposure to cold. This somewhat ter uous connection of the habenula with the thyroid gland can be associated with an equally suggestive but tenuous relation to temperature regulation. The major source of habenular afferents is the preoptic area, which is directly and exquisitely sensitive to temperature changes. Local heating of the preoptic area inhibits shivering and produces panting without reference to general body temperature. The effect can be imitated by electrical stimulation either in the preoptic area, in the habenula, or in the interpeduncular nucleus. Section of the stria medullaris, however, does not abolish panting to raised body temperature, whereas preoptic lesions do; but it does forestall the pronounced emotional panting seen in rabbits under restraint.

A role for the habenula in temperature regulation may have arisen phylogenetically from its association with the pineal organ. The latter has two distinct components—one for photoreception, the other for secretion.

In fish, amphibia, and reptiles, both elements are present. In some, the pineal eye is very well developed, with a clear cornea, typical rods and cones, and ganglion cells from which spike potentials can be recorded in response to light. Behaviorally, the pineal eye seems to effect changes in pigment distribution and temperature regulation (basking in the sun) and have some influence over thyroid function. In primitive vertebrates the glandular portion of the pineal organ appears to be even more important than the hypophysis, and it is only this glandular element that survives in mammals. The pineal gland receives a rather rich innervation from fibers arising in the superior cervical ganglion. They end on pineal parenchymal cells in terminals packed with the norepinephrine type of synaptic vesicles.

The nature of the undoubted secretion of the mammalian pineal organ remains elusive, as does its relation with the subcommissural organ with which it is connected by a portal circulation reminiscent of that between the hypothalamus and hypophysis. The circulation passes from the subcommissural organ to the pineal body, but the analogy cannot be pressed far, since the subcommissural organ is composed of secretory cells closely similar to those in the pineal body. The subcommissural organ lies just beneath the habenular commissure and covers the surface of the posterior commissure and the oral-dorsal surface of the aqueduct. It is richly vascular, with rosettes of secretory cells surrounded by capillaries. In addition to secretion into the blood stream, it also gives rise to a strange secretion into the cerebrospinal fluid. This is Reisner's fiber, a continuous strand of protein, 5 to 25 μ in diameter in man, which passes through the aqueduct into the fourth ventricle and often down the central canal of the spinal cord. In lower forms it reaches the end of the central canal, and the secretion leaves through a network of periependymal lymphatic vessels. The subcommissural organ is particularly well developed in young individuals and regresses considerably in most adults. The organ is apparently concerned with water and electrolyte metabolism and is related to the aldosterone secretion of the adrenal cortex. In this connection it is of interest that adrenalectomy also produces an increase in size of cells in the medial habenular nucleus.

The subfornical organ, lying against the fornix at the rostral end of the third ventricle and adjoining the origin of the choroid plexus, is a nodule of tissue highly similar to that of the pineal-subcommissural system. Its function is completely unknown save for its serving as a receptor site for the production of hyperglycemia after the intraventricular injection of morphine.

BEHAVIORAL ASPECTS

Electrical stimulation of the limbic system in anesthetized animals readily reveals its links with the autonomic and endocrine systems. Cardiovascular and/or respiratory responses are common, as are changes in muscular tone; and a wide variety of other effects are obtained, among them ovulation, gastric or bladder motility, penile erection, chewing, licking, swallowing, salivation, piloerection, vocalization of attack, and changes in blood sugar or renal function. Lesions in the limbic system similarly affect various aspects of these functions. It is, however, in the behavior of waking, active animals that the most significant effects are obtained. Interest in the behavioral manifestations of limbic system disturbances received a great impetus in 1937 with the discovery, made on a monkey prophetically named Aurora, of the constellation of effects now known as the Klüver-Bucy syndrome after bilateral removal of the tips of the temporal lobes. The four major effects are: (1) tameness and lack of fear; for example, the wild animal no longer flees from man or snakes; (2) hypersexuality; (3) persistent oral exploration (obejcts repeatedly mouthed and grasped with lips in preference to hands; dietary changes also notable); and (4) visual agnosia (objects compulsively explored again and again; difficult visual discriminations require very extensive training, even though learned preoperatively). It is conceivable that this peculiar visual deficit accounts in some measure for symptom (1) above.

The lesion producing this syndrome includes all of the uncus and amygdala and most of the hippocampus. If the lesion is limited to the neocortex, there is a permanent deficit in visual abilities (and the optic radiation is intact) and temporary tameness and oral exploratory behavior.

Fear-Aggression

Electrical stimulation throughout an extensive subcortical area in freely moving cats produces growling, spitting, pupillary dilatation, piloerection, and arching of the back. Whether the animal flees or attacks under these circumstances is determined as much by its opportunities as by the location and intensity of the stimulation. Frequently, it endeavors to escape from the locale where it found itself at onset of the stimulation, but if escape is blocked or if there is a suitable object—such as a rat, another cat, a stuffed animal, or an experimenter's hand in the immediate vicinity—a directed attack is made on this object. Cats so stimulated learn to seek objects to attack, as though in such circumstances the performance of the attack was rewarding.

Stimulation in the amygdala, afferent fibers in stria terminalis, preoptic area, much of the dorsomedial hypothalamus, and, especially, the central gray produces these effects. Lesions in the hypothalamus do not interfere with the effects obtained by stimulation of the central gray, whereas destruction of the central gray temporarily abolishes such responses to stimulation at other loci and subsequently predisposes the animal to flight rather than attack. Stimulation at slightly more lateral loci in the hypothalamus can produce attack that has more the aspects of hunting-predatory behavior, without such severe spitting, crying, and piloerection. Elements of this hunting behavior can be released by large lesions involving the central gray and dorsal tegmentum. Cats with these lesions may spend their entire waking life slinking up on nonexistent prey, carrying objects in their mouths as though they were prey, or fishing and pawing into holes, corners, or water. In other words, they constantly display portions of predatory behavior completely out of context.

Some rats immediately kill and eat mice placed in their cage, but other rats never harm the mice. This is a genetically determined trait. However, nonkillers can be converted into savage killers by bilateral removal of the olfactory bulb, prepiriform cortex, or section of the lateral olfactory tract. It might be inferred from this that killers merely have a deficiency in their olfactory system. This is disproved, however, by the fact that killers start to attack a young rat the size of a mouse but abruptly stop when they smell it. Rats without olfactory bulbs and with their eyes closed, whiskers cut, and ears filled with wax, although handicapped in sensing the presence of a mouse, still kill immediately on contacting a mouse or, in this instance, a small rat. The killing is separable from eating, since animals that are aphagic and adipsic after lesions of the lateral hypothalamus still kill mice, even though they don't eat them. Bilateral destruction of the central (not lateral or basal) nucleus of the amygdala or complete interruption of the diffuse subpallidal amygdalohypothalamic path permanently abolishes the killing behavior. Section of stria terminalis has no effect. It is thus possible to specify with considerable precision the anatomical substrate organizing this aggressive behavior.

FEEDING

Electrical stimulation of the lateral hypothalamus just within the debouchment of ansa lenticularis causes fully satiated animals to eat avidly. Bilateral lesions in this area produce aphagia and adipsia. With long and careful nursing, some degree of natural feeding can be restored, but usually only for the most palatable foods, and adipsia is likely to be permanent. The deficit is one of appetite rather than ability to feed. Adipsia, together with impairment of temperature regulation but without aphagia, is produced by preoptic lesions. Lesions in the ventromedial nucleus of the hypothalamus, on the other hand, produce animals that are savage and obese. Their obesity, however, is maintained only with palatable food, and they will starve more readily than normal animals if forced to feed exclusively on unpalatable material, such as food with quinine in it.

It can be hypothesized as a first approximation that the lateral hypothalamic area is concerned with appetitive food intake and that the ventromedial nucleus acts as a satiety center, inhibiting the lateral-lying feeding center. The concept gains some support from the rather strange fact that adrenergic agents placed in the lateral hypothalamus induce feeding behavior, whereas cholinergic agents at the same locus or in many other loci in the limbic system induce drinking of water. A number of facts, however, point to the possibility that the globus pallidus may participate in the organization of feeding behavior. The sites of electrical stimulation in the lateral hypothalamus from which feeding can be induced lie directly in the path of pallidofugal fibers, and stimulation along their course in the ventral tegmental area of Tsai and beneath the central gray is also able to elicit immediate feeding in satiated animals. Cholinergic drugs in the globus pallidus also elicit feeding, and lesions there produce aphagia. Finally, cats with cortex and basal ganglia removed do not feed spontaneously, even though the lateral hypothalamus has not been directly affected, whereas essentially normal feeding behavior is present in decorticate cats with most of the basal ganglia intact.

SEX

Since sexual activity in most laboratory animals except primates is under rather close hormonal control, efforts to elicit sexual behavior by electrical stimulation of the brain have not been numerous. Such stimulation in squirrel monkeys has revealed several areas in the limbic system from which penile or clitoral erection can be induced. In this species, however, penile erection serves as a display in social interchange within the colony, so the sexual significance of the systems studied is contaminated by other complex behaviors.

The hypersexuality of the Klüver-Bucy syndrome has been well studied in cats, and the relevant locus has been found to lie in the piriform cortex. Male cats with lesions in this area attempt copulation almost continuously in any territory and with any object they can grasp. Without testosterone such behavior gradually subsides. The complex sexual pattern of calling, treading, and rolling seen in the female cat is also entirely under control of the estrogen titer of the blood. It can, however, be elicited in full by implantation of a small pellet of stilbestrol in the posterior hypothalamus, which does nothing to the peripheral genital system.

The situation has been observed in an even more fascinating manner in rats. Implantation of testosterone in the medial preoptic area of either male or female rats can occasionally elicit strong maternal behavior of nest-building and retrieval of pups. The demonstration that males possess the neural organization necessary for maternal behavior is of considerable import. On the other hand, when the testosterone is placed in the lateral preoptic area, male sexual behavior of mounting and thrusting is sometimes displayed by female rats.

Rats seem to be born with a sexually undifferentiated nervous system of the female pattern, which then normally becomes either fixed by the presence of estrogens or changed into the male pattern by testosterone. The permanence of the fixation of these behavior patterns by the early hormonal environment is remarkable. A single injection of testosterone in a four-day-old female produces an adult that has no cycles. The trouble is in the brain, not the ovary or adenohypophysis, for either of the latter appropriately transplanted into an ovariectomized or hypophysectomized female, previously normal, can then support normal sexual function when controlled by a sexually competent hypothalamus. So far, such effects have not been obtained in rabbits, a species that, unlike the rat, is normally acyclic.

SELF-STIMULATION

By training an animal to press a lever to obtain food and then arranging things so that each lever press also delivers stimuli to particular loci in the brain, one can determine whether the animal seeks, avoids, or is indifferent to stimulation in various neural systems. From such studies it is immediately apparent that the overwhelming majority of points where stimulation is either sought or avoided lie within the limbic system. This is perhaps not surprising in view of the goal-directed activities organized by the limbic system, but it does stand in striking contrast to the fact that, except for occasional and short-lived curiosity, animals are almost wholly indifferent to neocortical or cerebellar stimuli, even those producing violent movements.

The motivational effects produced by central stimulation are often stronger than those produced by natural stimuli. For instance, rats given an opportunity to choose between stimulating the medial forebrain bundle in their lateral hypothalamus and eating will, even though starving, choose the hypothalamic stimulus. This becomes somewhat paradoxical when a point is selected in the lateral hypothalamus where stimulation induces the animal to eat. It might be supposed that the rat applies stimuli that make it hungry rather than eating the food to satisfy that hunger. However, the tests have not been that definitive, since the stimulation that demonstrates that the rat will eat when stimulated endures for several seconds, whereas the stimulation that the animal chooses to apply to its brain lasts only 0.5 second. The choice of central stimulation over food nevertheless remains mysterious. Since the limbic system is particularly susceptible to seizure activity and since seizures have an amnestic effect, it is possible that the self-stimulation arises from a confusional state; for example, the animal initiates a lever press, but the resulting stimulation erases the record or feedback from the action, and the animal is left where it was—about to press the lever, etc. This supposition gains support from the fact that much higher currents are required at many loci for the initiation and maintenance of self-stimulation than for the animal to perceive and use stimulation of the same neural point as a signal. In addition, self-stimulation often produces bizarre electrical activity in the limbic system.

Although confusional states and seizure activity may be associated with self-stimulation in a number of instances, it is unlikely that self-stimulation at most loci arises from such factors. Throughout the medial forebrain bundle system, which yields the highest rates of self-stimulation, the currents required for the effect are very low. It can also be shown that the animals are in contact with and perceiving events in their environment at all times during most self-stimulation. And administration of anticonvulsant drugs has the paradoxical effect of increasing self-stimulation to some extent by curtailing seizures that were an interfering side effect.

Exploratory experiments indicate various interactions between androgen level or hunger, avidity for self-stimulation, and location of stimulating electrodes. A further complication is found with variation of the duration of the burst of stimuli resulting from each lever press. The effects of train-duration are particularly dramatic for stimulation of the posterior hypothalamus in cats. For a 0.5-second train the animal presses every 2 to 3 seconds for 10 to 20 minutes at a time, each press giving pupillary dilation, a slight dart forward, and piloerection. The animal appears frightened but presses avidly. If, however, the stimulus lasts for 1.0 rather than 0.5 second for each press, the stimulation becomes strongly aversive.

Experiments so far suggest that from any particular locus the excitation can be elaborated over several different pathways. Ventral tegmental lesions, however, may abolish self-stimulation in septal loci. This is of considerable interest, since stimulation of these tegmental sites is extremely aversive. It is possible that one of the effects of self-stimulation is to dampen the activity of aversive systems. This rather hazy concept does receive some support from work with human subjects. A few patients have apparently found that stimulation in septal areas relieves anger and frustration. There seems little question but that such stimulation might have important therapeutic value were only enough of its neurophysiology understood. On the other hand, the conscious concomitants of self-stimulation in man are often so vague or bizarre as to discourage much hope of being able to comprehend the psychological effects on man or animals in any simple terms. Some of the effects are frankly sexual, but a cool taste, a high feeling, and a feeling of being about to remember something interesting are the best verbal reports of these effects that some self-stimulating patients can give. Points presumed to be in the central gray or hippocampus yield reports of melancholy, terror, or "sick all over." Such adverse effects sometimes survive for considerable periods but can be promptly relieved by stimulation at loci that yield self-stimulation. Such drastic changes of mood affirm the import of activity of the limbic system. Reliably specific therapeutic control of these powerful effects by means of localized stimulation requires a great extension of present knowledge and techniques, but few areas of research hold greater promise than this for relief of human suffering.

MEMORY

The temporal lobe has some special relation to memory processes, particularly those concerned with the recording of recent events. Just which temporal lobe structures are associated with these phenomena is still uncertain, but most evidence points to the hippocampus. If more than the uncus and amygdala are included, bilateral loss of the inferior temporal area in man makes the learning or long-term retention of new information almost impossible. Basic intelligence and skills and memories acquired earlier are essentially unimpaired in such individuals, yet they ask the same question again and again, remembering neither the answer nor the fact that they have previously asked the question. Old friends and names are recognized, but new ones are not. Such patients find their way about formerly familiar neighborhoods but are unable to acquire such orientation in new situations. They can describe in detail plays in baseball games attended in the remote past before their injury but can recall virtually nothing of a game witnessed just a few minutes prior to questioning.

Electrical stimulation within the depths of the temporal lobe in epileptic patients can produce an amnesia for recent events without apparent disturbance of recall of events long past. The more prolonged the stimulation, the longer the duration of amnesia, and the farther back in time the patient's memory may be disrupted. Thus, in one patient stimulation for 2 seconds disturbed recall of a five-digit number given just before the stimulation, with recovery occurring within 1 to 2 minutes. Stimulation for 5 seconds produced amnesia for events of the current day, such as what had been eaten for breakfast, and recovery required 5 to 10 minutes. With stimulation for 10 seconds, the patient usually could no longer remember coming to the hospital 3 weeks earlier, why he was there, who the doctor was, etc.; yet he could describe boyhood friends and experiences. Such a state required 1 to 2 hours to clear. On the other hand, stimulation of the more dorsal portions of the surface of the temporal lobe in other epileptic patients is able to evoke a vivid reliving of past events. Such experiences are sometimes reproducible upon repeated stimulation and often involve auditory, visual, and emotional components in a fully integrated hallucination of a previous experience.

Lack of understanding of the nature of the deficit apparent in short-term memory, produced in man by temporal lobe lesions, together with the great complexity of these effects, makes it difficult to devise tests for demonstrating comparable defects in animals. Macaques with temporal lobe lesions and displaying the typical Klüver-Bucy syndrome are best characterized as having an inability to learn complex auditory and visual discriminations rather than as lacking short-term memory. Some of the deficiencies in human patients can be similarly described as a deficit in learning rather than retention per se.

Cats are unable to perform a simple leg-flexion-conditioned reflex during the course of bilateral seizures in the hippocampal complex. Yet if all the animal's training, the pairing of conditional and unconditional stimuli, is given only during the presence of these seizures, it can be shown that learning still occurs. After such training, flexion-conditioned reflexes are given immediately to the conditional stimulus if it is presented while the cat is in the normal state, without seizure activity in the limbic system. Thus, abnormalities of hippocampal activity appear to interfere with performance but not with learning. A similar conclusion can perhaps be drawn from studies in which the electrical activity of the hippocampus of cats was monitored during the learning and performance of a visual discrimination. When correct discrimination was made, it was accompanied by a highly regularized theta rhythm at six a second. Subthalamic lesions produced a temporary disturbance in this rhythm, and, as long as it was disturbed, the animals failed to discriminate properly, although the learned motor act of selection and approach was performed normally. Thus, in this instance, a less overwhelming interference with hippocampal activity is manifested in a more subtle loss in performance.

It is apparent from the foregoing and from many facts not discussed here that—in addition to its role in instinctual behavior, motivation, and the control of autonomic-endocrine effects—the limbic system has an important, although ill-defined, role in learned behavior and memory.

CLINICAL IMPLICATIONS

It can readily be appreciated that abnormalities in the function of the limbic system can produce gastric ulcers, pulmonary edema, or menstrual irregularities. Not so easily perceived, perhaps, is the concept that pathological activity in the limbic system is capable of producing psychosis and may be responsible for many, if not all, psychotic states. The major evidence for this comes from two sources, psychomotor epilepsy and the psychotropic drugs.

The features of temporal lobe epilepsy are extremely varied. The uncinate fit is usually ushered in by an aura of unpleasant odor, epigastric sensation, and a feeling of fear, strangeness, or familiarity (*déjà vu*). The fit may involve only a transient clouding of consciousness and a series of automatic movements, such as chewing, although in many instances a full convulsive seizure also develops. Of interest to psychiatry is the fact that this psychomotor epilepsy displays other forms that range from episodic assaultive rage to frank schizophrenia. In developing the thesis that psychopathology may be predominantly associated with disturbances in the limbic system, one meets a number of difficulties. First is the indisputable fact that a few patients with psychomotor epilepsy, electroencephalographic spiking in the temporal area, or demonstrated small lesions in cornu Ammonis retain a normal personality. However, such findings can plausibly be attributed to unilateral or small lesions or to locations or processes that differ from those producing personality disturbances. The more striking fact is that from 50 to 90 per cent of patients with psychomotor epilepsy or temporal lobe spiking manifest psychopathology that may be identical with that seen in the psychoses not accompanied by demonstrable brain lesions. The psychiatric problem is associated with the temporal lobe rather than with epilepsy per se, since most authorities agree that focal epilepsy in other areas seldom produces personality changes.

Since the disturbance in personality is more or less permanent, it cannot be attributed wholly to the temporal lobe episodic seizure. It must be presumed, instead, that epileptogenic foci in the temporal lobe produce a continuing abnormal neuronal discharge, just as occurs from such foci in dorsal neocortex, and that this background abnormality results in the alteration of personality. On the other hand, it can also be recognized that in some instances psychomotor seizures may last for minutes or even hours and that patients at such times can still perform complex acts, such as driving a car, for which they are subsequently wholly amnesic.

Patients with psychomotor epilepsy are not uncommonly diagnosed as having schizophrenia. The question arises, of course, as to whether they have one disease or two; schizophrenics may have psychomotor epilepsy in addition to schizophrenia. A distinction is made on the fact that such patients with psychomotor epilepsy obviously have a motor component in their seizures and also have more frequent and prolonged remissions than do schizophrenics. However, since patients with the diagnosis "psychomotor epilepsy" can be every bit as paranoid and psychologically disturbed as those whose diagnosis is "schizophrenia," the most parsimonious approach would be to consider these but slightly different manifestations of a basically similar pathology. Procedures that control the epilepsy usually do not relieve the psychosis; instead, they often have the paradoxical effect of exacerbating it. (But convulsions are used as therapy for psychoses.) On the other hand, a few dramatic instances are also known in which unilateral temporal lobectomy has relieved profound psychoses that were associated with electrical and histological abnormalities of cornu Ammonis. Thus, as a general rule, procedures that affect the epilepsy also influence the psychosis in a manner at least compatible with the hypothesis that there is a single cause for the two conditions.

The other side of this coin is that electrical abnormalities would undoubtedly be a much more common finding in psychotic patients were they all studied with intracerebral electrodes. High-voltage, convulsive spikes generated by applying strychnine to the mesial temporal cortex in man simply give no indication of their existence when records are taken only from the scalp.

Similarly, in Figure 10 no indication of the underlying pathology can be seen in records from the scalp until the patient is in a definite psychomotor seizure (see Figure 10D). This patient displayed basic schizoid trends with paranoid symptoms and suffered from *grand mal* as well as psychomotor epilepsy. He had episodes of psychotic paranoid behavior lasting from a few hours to several days. When the patient was symptom-free (see Figure 10A), the electrical activity was nearly normal. During the recording shown in Figure 10B, the patient was irritable and agitated and had a low threshold for rage. During the recording shown in Figure 10C, he was psychotic, compulsively chanting psalms, detached from his environment, and hallucinating. The stages of pathological behavior are cor-

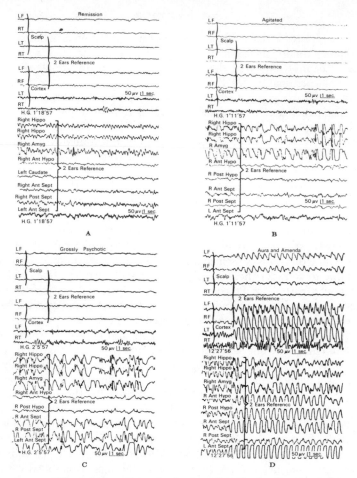

FIGURE 10. Electrical activity in brain of patient whose psychomotor epilepsy was accompanied by periodic psychosis. Records from scalp (*F*, frontal; *T*, temporal), implanted electrodes over cortex, and various leads aimed at hippocampus, amygdala, septum, anterior and posterior hypothalamus, and caudate nucleus. In *A*, January 10, 1957, patient was symptom-free, and records showed essentially normal activity. In *B*, January 11, 1957, patient was irritable and agitated; records from scalp and neocortex were still normal, but convulsive activity was apparent in right hippocampus and amygdala. In *C*, February 5, 1957, patient was hallucinating and reciting psalms; neocortex was still normal, limbic system was in turmoil. In *D*, December 27, 1956, psychomotor seizure, neocortex was involved; patient complained of bad taste and nausea and was subsequently amnesic (see the text). (From Heath, R. G. Correlation of electrical recordings from cortical and subcortical regions of the brain with abnormal behavior in human subjects. Confin. Neurol., *18:* 305, 1958.)

related closely with the degree of electrical abnormality in limbic structures.

There is, of course, no reason to expect, even given the peculiar predilection of the limbic system for seizure discharge, that all the pathological processes producing psychoses should be so reflected in neuronal abnormalities recordable with gross electrodes. Nevertheless, the evidence is increasingly clear that in a very high proportion of psychotics such records can be obtained *intracerebrally* and that the focus of such electrical abnormality is in the limbic system.

The psychotropic drugs, which have been so successful in the treatment of mental illness, have profound effects on the metabolism of the monoamines. In turn, monoamines are found in important concentrations in or above the mesencephalon only in the basal ganglia and limbic system. In addition to being useful in the treatment of psychoses, alterations of monoamine metabolism can also produce psychotic symptoms. Thus, for example, prolonged treatment of hypertension by administration of reserpine not uncommonly results in serious psychotic reactions in previously well-adjusted individuals. These patients experience depression; depersonalization; disturbances of perception, such as distortions of size or distance; attacks of terror without reference to external events; etc. These effects can persist for several months after cessation of the reserpine treatment.

In summary, all knowledge gained from stimulating or ablating the limbic system in animals or man is consistent in revealing its power to overwhelm behavior with pathological emotion. Corollary evidence is now forthcoming that both the pathology and the therapy of psychotic conditions may be centered on the limbic system.

REFERENCES

Field, J., Magoun, H. W., and Hall, V. E., editors. *Handbook of Physiology: Neurophysiology*, vol. 2. American Physiological Society, Washington, 1960.

Fulton, J. F. *Functional Localization and Relation to Frontal Lobotomy*. Oxford University Press, New York, 1949.

Nalbandov, A. V., editor. *Advances in Neuroendocrinology*. University of Illinois Press, Urbana, 1963.

Passouant, P., editor. *Physiologie de l'Hippocampe*. Centre Nationale de la Recherche Scientifique, Paris, 1962.

Ramon y Cajal, S. *Studies on the Cerebral Cortex (Limbic Structures)*. Lloyd-Luke, London, 1955.

Solomon, H. C., Cobb, S., and Penfield, W., editors. The brain and human behavior. Res. Publ. Ass. Res. Nerv. Ment. Dis., 34: 1958.

Szentágothai, J., Flerkó, B., Mess, B., and Halász, B. *Hypothalamic Control of the Anterior Pituitary*. Akademiai Kiado, Budapest, 1962.

Valverde, F. *Studies on the Piriform Lobe.* Harvard University Press, Cambridge, 1965.

Wolstenholme, G. E. W., and O'Connor, C. M., editors. *Ciba Foundations Symposium on the Neurological Basis of Behaviour.* Little, Brown, Boston, 1958.

CHAPTER 10

Cerebral Cortex

CHARLES J. SMITH, Ph.D.

RECOVERY OF FUNCTION AFTER CEREBRAL LESIONS

ASSESSMENT OF RESIDUAL FUNCTIONS after a cerebral lesion is one of the techniques that has been used in order to investigate the functions of the cerebral cortex. Analysis of the functions of the brain would be simpler if removal of an area were followed by a stable loss of a given set of functions. Such is not the case, however, as has been shown repeatedly in both clinical and experimental studies. A loss that may be severe shortly after operation dissipates to a greater or lesser degree over time. This waning of the syndrome after a cerebral lesion has given rise to various propositions about the mechanisms involved. According to the theory of *diaschisis*, there is, after a discrete lesion of the brain, a loss of facilitative effects that arose from the destroyed areas and acted on various intact areas, leaving them in a depressed condition. Recovery from this shocklike state was believed to occur spontaneously over an unspecified time. In attributing function to the area lost by the lesion, one could use only the residual impairment. According to another theory, that of functional substitution or vicarious functioning, other neural centers take over the function of the lost area and substitute for it functionally. Such surrogate areas may include the corresponding area in the opposite hemisphere in the case of unilateral lesions. This theory gains support from the fact that, after a monkey recovers use of the contralateral hand after a unilateral lesion of the motor area, a second lesion, in the opposite motor area, produces a reappearance of paresis. It has been shown that, after limited removal of the primary motor cortex, a monkey is unable for a time to perform delicate, skilled acts with the contralateral hand. There is considerable recovery from this deficit. If the cortex adjacent to the original lesion is then stimulated electrically, hand responses that could not be elicited by electrical stimulation during the first operation are seen. Ablation of this adjacent zone produces a reappearance of paresis and a second and more enduring loss of skilled movements. Bilateral ablations of motor cortex have yielded comparable conclusions. Removal of both right and left primary motor cortex (area 4) in monkeys permits more recovery from motor symptoms than does removal of areas 4 and 6 on the two sides. Many of these principles apply to at least some of the complex behavior found in man, particularly language. There is considerable recovery of verbal function after destruction of frontal cortical speech areas if the remaining cortex on the dominant side of the brain has not been damaged.

When the cortex adjacent to a region ablated in infancy is stimulated, the range of movements elicited is considerably wider than in unoperated control subjects. This has led some to postulate the growth of new pathways, a notion that flies in the face of most data on regeneration in the central nervous system but that probably should not be dismissed out of hand. A more conservative point of view is that after lesions there are brought into activity pathways that had already existed but that were not active to any significant degree. The activity of these pathways may have been suppressed by the centers removed. This century-old idea has been made somewhat more palatable by recent neurophysiological demonstrations of inhibition of cells in the sensory cortex surrounding an area of high activity and of greatly increased evoked potentials in some subcortical centers after inactivation of the cortex.

The assessment of recovery of function after cerebral lesions must take account of whether there is substitution of another function similar in purpose to the one lost or restitution of the original function. The dysphasic patient who manages to construct grammatical sentences, despite a marked vocabulary loss, by use of periphasis is substituting, just as is the monkey who solves a puzzle by a different sequence of movements than he did prior to operation. On the other hand, the patient who regains his skill in typewriting after a cerebral lesion—using the same habit skills he used before, such as finger positions—may be said to have a restitution of function. Such a patient would resemble the rat that, after complete bilateral ablation of the visual cortex, can relearn a black-white discrimination at the same rate as it did prior to operation. It is, of course, not always easy or even possible to distinguish the processes of restitution and substitution in any given case or experiment.

Although the theory of diaschisis maintained that recovery after lesions was spontaneous, there is considerable evidence that many functions do not recover spontaneously and that training can restore them or speed up their reacquisition significantly. The generality of effect of the training appears to be a function both of the type of skill and of the locus of the brain damage. It has been found, for example, that practice after operation is indispensable for reinstatement of the monkey's ability to solve correctly a patterned string problem after occipital lobectomy on one side. There is no spontaneous cortical reorganization of this task, nor is there wide generalization of the effects of practice. Practice on one pattern does not necessarily transfer to another string problem. After the cortical projection area for central vision is removed in the monkey, there is a transient inaccuracy of reaching for objects. If an operated monkey is kept in darkness for 10 days, he misreaches in just the same way as a monkey does immediately after operation, although nonoperated monkeys kept in darkness for the same period are unimpaired in this reaction. Here again, spontaneous reorganization is, at the least, unlikely, and visual experience is necessary for recovery.

Experience can influence the outcome of cerebral lesions in another way. It is frequently found that bilateral removal of homologous areas on the two sides of the brain is followed by a smaller decrement in performance when the operation is performed in two stages than when the operation is carried out all at once. The degree of sparing by the two-stage operation is a function of the stimulation provided the animal in the interval between the two operations. On visual tasks there is considerable recovery of a brightness discrimination when the subjects are kept in illuminated cages between stages, and there is complete recovery if the habit is practiced shortly after the first operation. But maintaining the animal in darkness in the interval between operations produces a deficit in visual discrimination performance of the same order as a bilateral, one-stage operation. The slow formation of a pseudofovea in cases of human occipital damage implicates a prolonged period of learning by the patient. In both man and monkey, recovery after occipital injury at maturity seems more a matter of substituting the remaining intact portions of the visual field than one of restitution of function within scotomata.

Recovery from motor lesions is hastened by requiring the animal to use the affected limb, and recovery in cases without formal training may be due in considerable part to the animal's use of the member in negotiating his environment. Recovery from lesions of the motor cortex seems to be somewhat more general than in the case of occipital lesions. The same is true for the temporal neocortex. Bilateral ablations in the temporal area cause loss of visual discrimination habits. If the animals are retrained on visual problems different from the ones they learned prior to operation, retesting on the original problems shows recovery of most of them. Controls show that there is no spontaneous recovery over this period and that visual discrimination habits are not lost if no operation intervenes. Practice on discriminations involving touch have no effect on visual discrimination performance, indicating that the recovery of the habits is not a highly generalized improvement in learning ability after the brain operations.

Effects of Lesions as a Function of Age

The brain of the infant organism differs from that of the adult by having a greater plasticity, as may be seen by the smaller effects of lesions on discriminative and motor performance. Unilateral removal of the primary motor area, the entire frontal lobe, or an entire hemisphere in a baby monkey has much less effect on the motor system than does an equivalent lesion in the mature animal. Bilateral ablation of motor and premotor cortex in the adult monkey has profound effects on volitional movements and produces marked spasticity. The same lesion carried out on the infant has less dramatic effects, and even these dissipate to some extent, leaving as a residual a spasticity that increases with age to about 1½ years. The findings in experiments on sensory discrimination show even less permanent effect of cortical lesions when they are carried out soon after birth. Kittens operated on for removal of the somatosensory cortex showed, as adults, practically no deficit on discrimination of roughness, whereas the same ablation, carried out on adult cats, produced severe impairment of the discrimination. The only residual deficit seen in the case of infant operations was a small increase in the difference threshold. Removal of the primary visual cortex in the kitten a few days after birth does not abolish visual pattern discriminations in the adult survivor, even though complete degeneration of the lateral geniculate nucleus establishes that all the striate area has been removed. Visual function is not entirely normal in such animals, as may be shown by a battery of tests, but the retention of a significant degree of pattern vision is in striking contrast to the complete loss in adult animals suffering extirpation of the entire visual cortex. Optic potentials can be elicited in remaining cortex in such preparations operated on in infancy, and the areas from which potentials can be recorded are implicated in the visual functions that persist, as extension of the lesion to these areas results in extremely poor visual performance on all tasks at maturity. A similar finding in the motor system is relevant to this point. Ablation of the frontal association fields in the monkey, after bilateral removal of the motor and premotor cortex in infancy, adds to the paresis and spasticity. There is no parallel increment in the motor deficit when the association fields are removed after the motor and premotor areas are taken out in the adult animal. Such observations are consistent with the concept of vicarious function, at least as it may be applied to lesions that occur early in life.

Although not much information is available on the more highly integrated types of behavior, especially in phylogenetically more advanced forms, it has been shown that the delayed response (the classical test for which consists of placing a food reward under one of two covers in view of the subject, then interposing a screen for the delay period, and, finally, allowing a choice between the two food wells), when tested for at four months, the time of its first appearance in the normal monkey, is unaffected by lesions of the frontal cortex made during the first week of life. This response, when tested for in the usual manner, is abolished by lesions made in mature animals. These operated infants, although at first somewhat slower to learn delays as long as 40 seconds, actually surpassed unoperated control animals during the course of an extended series of tests. The often-profound effects of cerebral disease in children on integrative behavior later in life have suggested that certain types of cerebral insult should work greater effects on young organisms than on adult ones. Until the specific anatomical differences between the kinds of damage done characteristically by disease in childhood and at maturity are known, experimental approaches to the problem will be impeded.

CEREBRAL LOCALIZATION

Experimental work and some clinical observations are drawn on to indicate in general terms the functions of various regions of the cerebral hemispheres. The problem of localization of brain function has a long history, and many of the questions raised a century and a half ago remain as pertinent and unsolved as they were at their inception. What is localized? Given localization of something, how do the various regions of the cortical mantle work together in an integrated fashion? In the recent past there was a period when localization of anything but the most elementary sensory and motor functions was doubted by many, as a result of overextension of the principles of mass action and equipotentiality. Equipotentiality refers to the ability of any intact part of a cortical system to execute the functions of other parts of that system. This may or may not involve a reduction in over-all efficiency to the system. Equipotentiality is subject in turn to the principle of mass action, which holds that the general efficiency of a complex behavioral function may be reduced in proportion to the extent of destruction of tissue within a system of relatively unspecialized parts. The finding that for the maze habit in the rat the system of relatively unspecialized parts make up the entire cerebral cortex led many writers of the 1930's and 1940's to suppose that the brain was equipotential for all higher functions and that the law of mass action had quite obliterated functional localization of anything more than muscle twitches or dermatomes.

Although the perplexities of higher brain functions are still with us, we are fortunate in that at the present time localization of function has come into somewhat clearer perspective. The evidence to be summarized below indicates that some functions, especially those most closely related to sensory discrimination and motor control, are rather discretely localized; other traits, such as certain verbal and perceptual mechanisms, tend to be focalized within rather broad regions of the brain. And, in its broadest sense, the organism's over-all capacity to deal effectively with its environment is probably diminished by any damage to the brain, although some parts may play a proportionately larger role than others. A discrete lesion of the cerebral hemispheres, therefore, has a rather specific effect, a somewhat more generalized effect on some capacity or group of related capacities, and a global effect on integrated behavior.

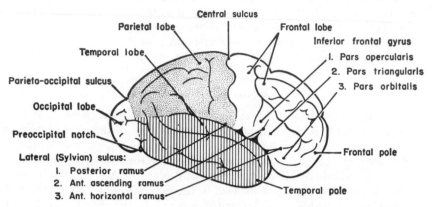

FIGURE 1. Lateral surface of the right cerebral hemisphere, showing lobes of the brain. (From Truex, R. C., and Carpenter, M. B. *Strong and Elwyn's Human Neuroanatomy*, p. 52. Williams & Wilkins, Baltimore, 1964.)

The most powerful tool available at the present time for analysis of the question of localization of function is double dissociation. By this is meant that lesion A depresses performance I but not performance II and that lesion B depresses performance II but not I, lesions A and B being of approximately equal size. When this condition is met, and it is more often than not in contemporary studies, functions can be ascribed with some confidence to various regions of the brain. Defining a region is not in itself an easy matter. Although size is a readily manipulatable variable, location presents a finite but vast number of possibilities, defying the attachment of a single value to locus, as one can with size. In the past the principal guideline for locating a lesion to be made experimentally was the cytoarchitectonic maps of a past generation of neuroanatomists. There has been a tendency more recently to shift from cellular organization of the cortex as a criterion to criteria based on connections. According to this principle, one removes an area, all parts of which have similar connections, whether to some extracortical region or within the cortex itself. These areas may be defined neuroanatomically or by such electrophysiological means as evoked potentials or strychnine neuronography.

FRONTAL LOBE

Although many frontal removals have been done in man for therapeutic purposes, the data available from this source have not revealed a great deal about normal frontal lobe function because most patients were unable to cooperate fully in procedures to assess their status prior to disease. We have many reports on tests applied before operation but few on tests applied before the onset of the disease that prompted the use of brain surgery. Such data are available in very limited numbers, and they indicate a small but significant loss on formal intelligence tests when premorbid scores—that is, scores obtained before signs of psychosis had appeared—are (1) compared with postoperative scores obtained after the patient appears to have recovered from his psychosis and (2) evaluated against control patients who recovered without surgical intervention. Despite the inherent superiority of man as a source for data, we must continue to make recourse to animal experimentation to analyze the functions of the frontal areas.

The idea of the frontal lobes as the seat of higher integrative functions has now been abandoned. Ablation studies on mammals high and low on the phylogenetic scale have revealed that, although performance decrements can be shown on certain types of tasks, there is no generalized deterioration. Conditioning experiments show that unconditioned responses elicited by noxious stimuli become more vigorous and that positive conditioned responses, in which the animal carries out some active behavior in order to avoid the unconditioned stimulus, are either unaffected or increased after removal of frontal neocortex anterior to the motor zone. Animals are not impaired on visual discrimination learning, nor do they lose a discrimination habit learned prior to operation. The kinds of losses that do occur after prefrontal ablations center around inhibition of responses and the delayed response. A number of experiments have shown that frontal damage can produce failure to withhold responses when this is demanded for correct solution of the problem. Thus, inhibitory conditioned responses in dogs are disinhibited by ablation of the frontal pole, monkeys are less effective in withholding responses on negative trials, and cats show deficits in passive avoidance conditioning, which requires them to avoid approaching an electrified food dish. In all of these cases, the focus within the frontal lobe appears to be the orbital area, as restricted lesions avoiding this zone fail to produce any marked interference with response inhibition.

The delayed response, on the other hand, is selectively impaired by dorsolateral frontal lesions. Recent work has shown that various modifications of the classical method of testing for delayed response enable a monkey with dorsolateral frontal lesions to solve the problem with a high degree of success. These modifications include a go-no-go situation (single food well in which the experimenter either places or does not place bait on a given trial; on negative trials the animal must withhold or inhibit its response), gradual introduction of delay, increasing the degree of hunger motivation, and making the correct response dependent on the subject's predelay choice rather than the experimenter's. It has been suggested that these variations of the delayed response experiment show that the crucial element in frontal deficit in monkeys is not delay but one involving attentional factors operating during the predelay period. This finding in the monkey is consistent with the failure to find any deficit of immediate memory in human patients with frontal lobe damage.

Another loss characteristic of the frontal operate is difficulty in overcoming initial preferences in choice situations. Errors made by a frontal lobe monkey in discrimination performance consist not of failure to stick with the correct object when he hits it by chance on the first trial but in failing to switch promptly to the other choice when he selects the incorrect object on the first trial. A similar deficit is found in patients with dorsolateral frontal lesions on card-sorting tasks. The situation differs somewhat in that the patient is required to sort cards according to some category that he must determine by being told whether he is right or wrong. After 10 successive correct sorts, the category is changed by the tester. The frontal patients were unable successfully to shift their sorting sets and consequently committed perseverative errors. The average I.Q. of these patients was normal, and many could verbalize what was required in the situation, but they persisted in their perseverative and incorrect choices.

PARIETAL LOBE

The parietal region of the brain has attracted less experimental work than the frontal and temporal lobes, despite the implication of this region in a number of complex functions in man. Consistent with the presence of the primary somatosensory area in the parietal lobe, tactile discrimination performance by monkeys and apes is impaired by lesions in this region. There are, however, functions beyond these simple somatosensory discriminative ones that may be demonstrated by the placement of lesions. Monkeys with unilateral lesions of the posterior parietal lobe failed to reach food by an approach on the side opposite the lesion when a roundabout route was required. When visual cues were excluded, the inability to reach the bait on the side opposite the lesion was relatively less. This finding suggests that the posterior parietal lobe may be concerned with the coordination of visual cues with purposeful movements, a hypothesis consistent with anatomical data indicating that fibers from the occipital lobe end here and that the posterior parietal area projects in turn to both the somatosensory and motor areas. The hypothesis of visually related functions in the parietal lobe receives further support from the finding that extensive learning experience with tactile stimuli fails to facilitate performance on a visual learning set series in monkeys with posterior parietal lesions. Even more straightforward visual spatial discriminations are impaired to some extent by bilateral posterior parietal ablations. Careful observations on patients with long-standing parietal injuries has shown, in addition to the expected tactile sensory losses, an impairment in the ability in patients with left parietal injury to indicate successively a series of points on the body surface and in external space. Lesions of either side located predominantly in the parietal zone produce an impairment in the ability of patients to follow a map, using either tactile or visual cues. This deficit is independent of sensory defect or of losses in general intelligence, although the degree of impairment is correlated statistically with somatosensory defect. There is extensive evidence that, whereas injury in man's right somatosensory region produces difficulties related only to the left hand, left somatosensory lesions tend to produce bilateral impairment. Injuries to the left hemisphere are more likely to be associated with dysphasia and with a greater intellectual loss than right hemisphere injuries.

TEMPORAL LOBE

Experimental lesions in primates have demonstrated conclusively that a major focus for visual integration exists in the temporal lobe. Tests for discrimination of patterns show a persistent loss after bilateral removals of the inferior convexity of the temporal lobes, a loss not found after lesions of the dorsolateral temporal neocortex or other associative areas of the cortex or after removal of temporal pole, hippocampus, or amygdala. Long-term studies of operated monkeys indicate that this loss is persistent and probably permanent. The degree of loss is correlated with the difficulty of the problem, the greater impairments being most clearly demonstrated by difficult discriminations. When animals are trained successively on a large number of pattern discrimination problems, establishing a learning set, and are then subjected to bilateral inferotemporal removals, the learning set is lost and cannot be regained with extensive retraining. Object discriminations are less affected by temporal lesions, although some impairment is seen. This deficit does not seem to be one of attentiveness, as monkeys with temporal ablations continue to discriminate, even when the stimuli are exposed for as short a time as 10 milliseconds. The probable route for arrival of visual information to the temporal lobe is through the primary visual cortex of the same side of the brain. Interruption of visual afferents to the striate cortex by cutting of the optic tract, followed by ablation of temporal cortex on the opposite side, produces a marked impairment in visual discrimination. Such an impairment does not occur when the optic tract and temporal lobe are interfered with on the same side of the brain. Lesions of possible subcortical routes to the temporal lobe, such as superior colliculus or pulvinar, fail to duplicate the temporal lobe discriminative loss, giving additional support to a neocortical relay from the visual cortex.

Temporal removals in man indicate a laterality difference of function as strong as, or possibly stronger than, that found in the parietal region. Although the over-all I.Q. seems to be little affected by unilateral temporal lobe operations, there are difficulties in verbal recall, especially of rapidly presented material, when the lesion occurs on the left side. Right-sided temporal operations, on the other hand, are associated with inefficiency of comprehension of pictorial material. Memory defects, when seen in association with temporal lobe damage in man, seem to be referable strictly to rhinencephalic structures. Ideomotor and ideational apraxia are predominantly, perhaps exclusively, associated with left or bilateral damage to the temporal zone. Tachistoscopic recognition is also affected differentially. Recognition of letters is poorer in the visual half-field opposite the side of the lesion, but, since in normal subjects such recognition is not as good in the left field as in the right, one may conclude that right-sided lesions impair both half-fields, whereas lesions on the left side give a deficit only in the right visual field. Thus, the right temporal neocortex participates to some degree in visual functions through the entire visual field. So far, there is no indication of similar right-left differences in experimental animals.

OCCIPITAL LOBE

Research on the occipital lobe in man and animal has focused on visual field defects after lesions. A few observations suggest strongly that more than field defects are involved, but, unfortunately, they have not yet inspired well-controlled studies to clarify the nature of the mechanisms that may be involved. It was noted long ago that ablations of the rat's visual cortex produce losses on maze performance that cannot be duplicated by peripheral blinding, and more recent work on peripherally blinded monkeys indicates that they, too, are impaired in finding their way about after extensive lesions of the primary visual cortex. Lesions in man, which may extend beyond the confines of the striate area, have been associated with deterioration of subtests of intelligence tests, particularly digit span and arithmetic problems. Studies such as these indicate that the striate cortex has nonvisual functions, just as nonvisual cortex—the temporal lobe, for example—has visual functions. Visual field defects are particularly difficult to map in experimental animals, so one may expect that studies on patients after occipital injury will be the more fruitful avenue of approach.

REFERENCES

Beach, F. A., Hebb, D. O., Morgan, C. T., and Nissen, H. W., editors. *The Neuropsychology of Lashley*. McGraw-Hill, New York, 1960.

Piercy, M. The effects of cerebral lesions on intellectual function: a review of current research trends. Brit. J. Psychiat., 110: 310, 1964.

Solomon, H. C., Cobb, S., and Penfield, W., editors. The brain and human behavior. Res. Publ. Ass. Res. Nerv. Ment. Dis., 36: 1958.

CHAPTER 11

Neurophysiological Correlates of Learning and Memory

E. ROY JOHN, Ph.D.

INTRODUCTION

THE PURPOSE of this chapter is to acquaint the reader with the broad outlines of present knowledge and current research related to problems of information storage and retrieval in the brain. Although space does not permit a more detailed presentation, the current understanding is inadequate for a definitive exposition.

Two types of processes can be distinguished in the functions of the nervous system—innate and acquired. Innate processes display essentially similar characteristics in all individuals of the same species, follow the same maturational course, and are probably mediated by approximately identical mechanisms from individual to individual. Innate processes subserve the essential functions necessary to maintain the health and integrity of the organism, fulfilling requirements common to all members of a species. Acquired processes vary greatly among individuals of the same species, do not follow the same maturational course, and may be mediated in radically different ways by various individuals. Acquired processes permit the individual to adapt to and benefit by his unique personal life experiences. The nervous system is thus endowed with plasticity of response, enabling the organism to establish adaptive behaviors. Behavior can be altered by changes in the novelty of stimuli, by the results of environmental events or particular responses, and by associations based on the similarity, dissimilarity, or contiguity between exteroceptive or interoceptive stimuli. These and other changes in behavior resulting from the accumulation of experience are classified as *learning*.

Learning or defects in learning can result in maladaptive as well as adaptive behaviors. Many psychiatric disorders may be the result of inappropriate learning, undesirable experience, or malfunction of the neural mechanisms of information coding, storage, and retrieval. Other disorders that seem related to malfunction or imbalance of neural systems concerned with arousal, attention, or motivation may be amenable to procedures that use systematic experience to improve function or restore balance. Much of psychiatric treatment can be viewed as the attempt to establish conditions conducive to learning adaptive behaviors or unlearning maladaptive behaviors, whether achieved by electroconvulsive therapy, medication, or psychotherapy.

THEORIES OF LEARNING AND MEMORY

Since learning requires the modification of future behavior as a result of past experience, two distinct processes must be explained: (1) the neural mechanisms involved in storage of a representation of an experience and (2) the neural mechanisms that are intermediaries in the retrieval of such stored information and its interaction with present experience. The first function might be called "read in" or memory, and the second "read out" or remembering.

CLASSICAL CONDITIONED REFLEX

Early attempts to analyze the nature of these processes were strongly influenced by anatomical considerations. The laboratory study of the physiology of learning consisted largely of investigations of conditioned reflex mechanisms. The classical conditioned reflex arises from the association of two stimuli and can be thought of as stimulus substitution.

A conditioned stimulus that excites sensory receptors is systematically paired with an unconditioned stimulus that activates muscular or glandular effectors. After a series of paired presentations, occurrence of the conditioned stimulus alone is capable of eliciting a conditioned response closely resembling the effect of the unconditioned stimulus. The conditioned stimulus was presumed to activate neurons in brain regions of the corresponding receptor system and the unconditioned stimulus to activate neurons localized in regions that mediated the appropriate response functions. Paired presentation of conditioned stimulus and unconditioned stimulus was assumed to result in the formation of a connection between these two neural regions. This connection consisted of a pathway of neurons whose synaptic relationships were altered during conditioning, either by facilitation of existing synapses or by the growth of new synaptic processes. The memory was localized in the interconnections of the neurons constituting this pathway. Remembering consisted of the selective conduction of nerve impulses arising from the conditioned stimulus along this new pathway to the regions previously excited by the unconditioned stimulus, thus eliciting performance of the conditioned response. Similar explanations were proposed to account for other forms of learning, such as instrumental conditioned responses or maze habits, analyzed in comparable stimulus-response terms.

Attributing changes in behavioral response, after experience, to the establishment of new neural routes traversed by nerve impulses initiated by stimuli led to a search for the anatomical locus of the site of closure and for the connection between the input and output pathways, which was the memory or engram. The fundamental tool in this search for a connection was the correlation of deficits in the acquisition or performance of learned responses with lesions or ablations localized in various brain regions.

LASHLEY'S GENERAL THEORIES

Although lesion studies revealed that particular brain regions were involved in the mediation of learned responses, it was not possible to demonstrate that memories were localized in specific areas or pathways. Deficits in performance after brain damage could usually be rectified by further training of lesser degree than that required for the initial establishment of the behavior. Interference with the set to perform, with motivation, with attention, or with level of arousal seemed to constitute the basis for such deficits, rather than obliteration of the memory trace.

Summarizing a vast amount of lesion data, Lashley proposed two related general theories: (1) the law of mass action, which proposed that defects after brain ablations correspond in severity to the amount of tissue destroyed rather than to the location of that tissue, and (2) the law of equipotentiality, which held that, although a given region may normally be responsible for mediation of a given function, other regions are often capable of taking over the same role.

MEMORY STORAGE AND RETRIEVAL

Implicit in Lashley's formulations was the conception of memory as a process diffused throughout an extensive anatomical domain. Further experiments revealed that the effects of localized lesions varied as a function of time after acquisition of the new behavior. These experiments suggested that different brain areas became involved at *different stages* in the elaboration of a memory. In particular, the hippocampus seemed to be involved in the process by which recent events were transferred to permanent storage.

It has long been known that the ability to remember lists of memorized material varies as a function of the amount and kind of activity interpolated between initial learning and subsequent testing. Systematic study of sufferers of traumatic head injury revealed that a large proportion of such persons could not recall events immediately preceding the injury. Evidence of this sort suggested that, immediately after an experience, the neural representation of that event was in a labile phase and was susceptible to disruption; after this period, the memory was somehow stabilized in long-term storage. With the introduction of electroconvulsive shock therapy, studies revealed that the disruptive effects of such treatment on recent memories diminished systematically as a function of the time between experience and shock.

Numerous studies have indicated that interference with on-going brain activity for a period of time after an event prevents registration of that event in memory. Among the agents capable of such action are electroconvulsive therapy, anesthetics, convulsions induced by various chemical agents, and insulin hypoglycemia. This evidence had led to the concept of a consolidation phase, during which the neural representation of an experience gradually shifts from a labile to a stable mediating process. Recent studies have shown that systemic injection of analeptic drugs immediately after an experience can extend the period of labile representation, can bring about more rapid acquisition of learned responses, and can accelerate the rate of consolidation.

It is generally believed that the representation of an experience during the labile phase is mediated by continued reverberatory activity in neural networks. The mechanism responsible for long-term storage is the subject of intensive current research.

CHEMICAL STUDIES

The remarkable persistence of memory in spite of the relatively rapid turnover of chemical compounds in the brain directed the attention of numerous investigators to those chemical systems capable of specifying templates for the continued synthesis of particular molecules, ribonucleic acid (RNA) in particular. A mass of evidence accumulated in recent years suggests that ribonucleic acid and protein synthesis are somehow involved in long-term information storage in the brain. It has been shown that (1) RNA turnover in nerves increases upon stimulation, (2) RNA turnover is increased in neural tissue that undergoes learninglike experiences, (3) interference with RNA synthesis impedes learning, and (4) facilitation of RNA synthesis or increased availability of RNA results in more rapid learning.

Although such evidence suggests that RNA is involved in memory storage, the demonstration that the blockade of protein synthesis by intracerebral puromycin injection may erase previously established learned responses suggests that the role of RNA may be secondary to that of the protein whose synthesis is *governed* by RNA. Although puromycin blocks protein synthesis, present knowledge indicates that it does not in any way interfere with RNA synthesis. Further research is needed to clarify this problem.

ELECTROPHYSIOLOGICAL STUDIES

Such studies, usually conducted with chronically implanted electrodes, show that there are widespread changes in the response of brain regions to a stimulus during learning. These changes involve many anatomical systems in the brain. The data suggest that, early in learning, the stimulus exerts marked effects on the mesencephalic reticular formation. Later in learning, the thalamic reticular system seems to play a dominant role, and the mesencephalic reticular formation seems to be inhibited, perhaps by hippocampal influences interacting with the cortex.

Among the useful electrophysiological techniques are the biasing of local excitabilities by polarization (so-called dominant focus), studies of evoked potential changes to intermittent conditioned stimuli, and conditioning to direct electrical stimulation of specific points in the brain. Such methods—combined with such chemical techniques as spreading depression, classical ablation methods, and the more recent split-brain technique—can be expected to provide a steady increment in understanding of memory storage and retrieval mechanisms.

Electrophysiological studies with intermittent conditioned stimuli have revealed that the brain seems to possess the capability to reproduce previously experienced, temporal patterns of activity. Under particular conditions, the electrical activity of the brain seems to contain two components: exogenous activity, arising from stimulation of sensory receptors, and endogenous activity, related to previous experience. Endogenous activity is particularly noteworthy in nonsensory specific regions of the brain. Various writers have suggested the existence of a coincidence detector system, in which exogenous activity in sensory specific pathways is compared to endogenous activity released in nonsensory specific regions by the afferent input from the stimulus.

Neutral stimuli have been reported to release endogenous activity patterns, together with concomitant behavioral performance of previously acquired responses. Such released patterns can arise at different anatomical levels and do not appear to be a property of a localized region. Evidence of this sort suggests that memory may be mediated by a widely distributed mechanism capable of initiating particular patterns of activity in large neural aggregates. Much further work will be necessary to evaluate the functional significance of such phenomena.

REFERENCES

Diamond, I. T., and Chow, K. L. Biological psychology. In *Psychology: A Study of a Science*, S. Koch, editor, vol. 4, p. 242. McGraw-Hill, New York, 1962.

John, E. R. High nervous function: brain function and learning. Amer. Rev. Physiol., 23: 451, 1961.

John, E. R. Neural mechanisms of decision making. In *Information Storage and Neural Control*, W. S. Fields and W. Abbott, editors, p. 243. Charles C Thomas, Springfield, Ill., 1963.

John, E. R. Studies on learning and retention in planaria. In *Brain Function*,

M. A. B. Brazier, editor, vol. 2, p. 161. University of California Press, Los Angeles, 1964.

    Lashley, K. In search of the engram. In *The Neuropsychology of Lashley*. F. A. Beach, D. D. Hebb, C. T. Morgan, and H. W. Nissen, editors. McGraw-Hill, New York, 1960.

AREA B

Basic Psychological Sciences

CHAPTER 12

Perception

CYNTHIA P. DEUTSCH, Ph.D.

DEFINITION

P ER CE P TI O N, according to a generally acceptable definition, is "the process of organizing and interpreting sensory data by combining them with the results of previous experience." This definition contains several elements that give it its distinction. First, the term "process" implies that perception is not the name of a static structure or property of an organism but of an activity. Thus, perception is something that is going on. The second element to be noted is the naming of the process that is going on: "organizing" and "interpreting." These words indicate that the process is an active one and one that involves the organism in acting on something. The third element tells what that something is: "sensory data." Sensory data, in turn, may be defined as the uninterpreted product of the stimulation of end organs or receptors, such as the eye or the ear. The last element is the entire last phrase of the definition, "by combining them with the results of previous experience." The "combining" again indicates that it is an active process that is going on. The "results of previous experience" brings in another activity: memory. This element in the definition implies, then, that, without memory and without bringing the memory to bear on the sense data, there is no perception. It also implies that without previous experience there is no perception. This last point will be discussed again in the examination of some theories of perception; for now, however, let its implication stand.

This definition indicates, then, that perception is a complex process involving the past as well as the present and involving an external stimulus as well as an internal response. This fusing of past and present, of external and internal, makes perception a complex area, and its complexity accounts for the fact that many different theories of perceptual processes have arisen.

SCOPE

Perception, like the science of psychology itself, stretches from the biological sciences on one side to the social sciences on the other and includes data and ideas from physics and philosophy as well. The study and understanding of perceptual processes include these four broad fields.

Epistemology, that branch of philosophy that asks the question "How do we know?" sets the question that the study of perception endeavors to answer. The answer involves the physical properties of stimuli, the individual's nervous system, and his background and experiences. The physical properties of stimuli—wave lengths of light, frequencies of sound, and the like—are fundamental in determining the nature of the sense data. The individual's nervous system is the locus of the sensation and the perception, and its functional strengths and deficiencies relate to what is sensed and what is perceived. And the individual's family background and general social milieu and experiences contribute to his interpretation of his sense data.

For example, say a group of people, one by one, look through a small aperture at a green light. Afterward, each one is asked what he saw. One person says, "I saw a light, but I can't say any more about it." What might be the explanation? It could be explained by any of the aspects described above. For example, it might be that, when he looked through the aperture, something went awry with the transmitting apparatus, the wave length of the light changed several times, and he experienced a variety of colors subjectively. Or it might be that he was color-blind, having a physiological or anatomical disorder involving certain of the sense cells of the retina. Or it might be that he had never been taught color names or the differences between colors, an example of social factors at work. Just as the descriptions of an elephant by several blind men were determined by which part each man felt, so a view of perception could be determined by which aspect is emphasized. The goal must be to mesh all aspects into an understanding of the whole. Especially is this important when one is attempting to evaluate an individual's perceptions and aberrant perceptions.

EXTERNAL STIMULI

In considering the external stimulus, we must first of all be aware that there are various sense modalities through which organisms are stimulated and that the sense organ stimulated yields only a particular type of sensation. This last point was enunciated first as the doctrine of the specific energy of nerves by Johannes Müller in the nineteenth century. This was an important milestone in the path to modern considerations of perception, as it spelled the end of the concept of the transmission of entire images from the external environment to the brain. As long as the idea was generally held that an object such as a pencil was transmitted, as it were, whole from the external world into the brain, there was little opportunity to investigate the components of sensation and of perception and the components of the attribution of meaning to sense data. When that idea was replaced by the notion that each set of nerve fibers transmits impulses that are consistently and characteristically sensed in particular ways, it became clear that what was received was a set of sensations having to do with dimension, form, color, and similar attributes of the object. Through experience, the individual learns that that particular configuration of attributes is called a pencil. With this understanding, the whole area of sensation and perception as we now know it was opened to study.

Deriving from the doctrine of the specific energy of nerves is the categorization of adequate stimuli for each sense modality. Thus, sound is the adequate stimulus for the ear and the acoustic nerve complex, light for the eye, and so forth. A physical analysis of a given environment could determine the particular modality that would be stimulated in it.

VISUAL STIMULI

A great deal of the work on the influences of the stimulus field in perception has been done in the visual area. This is probably because what is perceived visually is strongly determined by the ordering of the stimulus components in space, and this is rather easy to manipulate. For example,

* * * * * * * * * * * * * * * *

is a row of sixteen asterisks. By manipulating the spatial relationships, one can enhance the probability that they will be seen as eight pairs of asterisks:

** ** ** ** ** ** ** **

In this pairing, the first and second, the third and fourth, and so on, constitute pairs. It is quite difficult to see the first as a single asterisk, with the second and third, and the fourth and fifth, and so on, being the pairs. Yet this perception can be encouraged by changing the spaces again:

* ** ** ** ** ** ** ** *

It can also be done by adding another formal element and returning to the earlier spacing:

* *···* *···* *···* *···* *···* *···* *···* *

In simple experiments such as these, what is perceived depends on and varies greatly with the grouping and the spacing of the individual stimuli. Analogies can be drawn in audition. The same set of tones are heard as different melodies, depending on the timing and spacing of their presentation.

Motion pictures provide another example of how perception is determined by the organization of the stimulus field. The stimulus of the motion picture is, of course, not motion per se but a series of still pictures taken at very short intervals. The intervals between the pictures taken determine how fast the movement appears to be: the longer the interval between pictures during filming, the faster and the less smooth the movement seems when the pictures are projected. Slow-motion films are actually those in which the camera action is the fastest; there is, for instance, the least excursion of a moving extremity between successive pictures. Seeing the subjects of the pictures move is a perceptual phenomenon called Phi phenomenon or apparent motion. Another example of apparent motion is the moving sign in which a light appears to go around the edge of a marquee, but the physical stimuli are really a great many electric bulbs being switched on and off in sequence.

Such situations, in which what is perceived is based on physical stimuli but is different from them, led to the enunciation of a principle to the effect that *the whole is different from the sum of its parts.* One explanation of this principle defines stimulus organization or Gestalt as an additional property of the stimulus field.

SELECTIVITY

Since man has receptors for many types of stimuli and since he lives in a complex environment in which there are numerous varieties of stimuli, he is constantly being stimulated. In fact, in the usual environment, far more stimuli than the individual can be aware of or respond to are impinging on him at any given instant. Although these stimuli are impinging simultaneously through many different channels—sound through the ear and along the acoustic nerve and its connections to the central auditory projection areas, light through the eye and along the optic pathways, etc.—the *perceptual* process is a central one, and only a limited amount of this vast information can be processed at one time. Therefore, a process of selectivity becomes operative. Some stimuli are perceived and some are not; some that are perceived are responded to and some are not.

Some objective and many subjective factors govern the operation of this selectivity; both the stimulus field and the attributes of the perceiver determine what will be perceived. One important objective factor is the strength of the stimulus. Typically, a strong stimulus is more likely to be perceived than a weak one. When two noises are present in the environment at the same time, the louder noise masks the softer one. And usually, though not inevitably, a stronger stimulus in one modality is perceived in preference to a weaker one in another modality. Thus, a very bright light may diminish the perception of a low sound. Another objective factor that governs what is perceived is timing. A stimulus that begins an instant before another may be perceived at the expense of the second, although the relative intensity of the two stimuli must also be considered. And there is a paradigm visual perceptual experiment that demonstrates that a particular type of stimulus can distort the perception of a *preceding* stimulus so that the earlier one is not perceived as it was presented. The nature of the fibers that transmit the impulse can also determine the order in which stimuli are perceived. If one touches a very hot surface, he will usually feel the heat first and then the pain because the fibers that transmit the heat sensation carry impulses faster than do the pain fibers.

Other factors that determine which of a variety of impinging stimuli are perceived have to do with the neurophysiology of perception and sensation and with individual experience and learning.

NEUROPHYSIOLOGY OF PERCEPTION

In the exploration of the neurophysiology of perception, we move away from emphasis on the stimulus field as a determiner of what is perceived. The first step is the response of the end organ to stimulation from the field. It is not appropriate here to discuss the anatomy or the basic physiology of the sensory pathways or to do more than note in passing that the intactness of the sense organs and tracts is a necessary condition for accurate perception. As noted in an earlier example, color blindness interferes with the perception of color. Similarly, diminished auditory sensitivity to particular frequencies distorts the perception of sound. The nature of such distortions and their relationship to various types of sensory disabilities will not be discussed here.

However, the perception of physical stimuli involves more than simply the sensory pathways specific to a particular modality of stimulation. Recent work has placed considerable emphasis on the role of the reticular formation in the perception of stimuli. This activating system is apparently essential to the arousal of the organism, which must precede the reception of a stimulus from any modality. The work of Magoun and his associates indicates that, when the reticular pathways of an animal are cut, the animal is rendered insensitive to stimuli that normally produce arousal and response. The full role of the reticular activating system is not yet known, but the evidence is such that it can be safely accepted that this system plays a critical role in the perception of stimulation, probably through its effect on general arousal and on attention.

Neurophysiological factors, it has been hypothesized, enter into the selectivity of perception through the reticular activating system. An experiment by Hernández-Peón illustrates this. He placed electrodes in a cat's cochlear nucleus in the brain stem and recorded the evoked potential in response to the presentation of clicks. That the cat's sensory apparatus was being stimulated by the clicks was evident from the evoked potential record. However, when a mouse was placed in the cat's visual field, the evoked potentials disappeared from the electrographic record, even though the clicks were still being presented. The cat's visual attention to the mouse—a very compelling stimulus for a cat—superseded its aural attention to the clicks, which were apparently not even noted in its brain. In one interpretation, this experiment shows the importance of the activating system in the perception of stimuli and indicates that selectivity in perception can have a strong neurophysiological component. There has been some theoretical argument about the strength of this interpretation, but the facts of the experiment are unassailable.

A different type of experiment relating to the selectivity of perception was done by Cherry. He presented differing stimuli to each of the subjects' two ears and asked them what they heard. He found that irrelevant information is rejected in favor of relevant information. The subjects could not report the irrelevant stimuli fed to one ear, but they could follow the directions presented to the other ear. However, he also found that a noisier noise masks the perception of a more meaningful one.

INDIVIDUAL DEVELOPMENT AND EXPERIENCE

Let us now consider the influences on perception that arise from individual development and experience. One tends, for example, to perceive the more important stimuli rather than the less important. Since the attribute of importance is based on individual experience and interests, two people in the same situation may perceive very different things, and yet both may be accurate. What each perceives is a function of his own learning and experience. This is true in terms of both long-term and short-term experience. For example, the letter "A" would be simply a collection of lines for someone who does not know how to read. But for someone who does, seeing the "A" as a letter would inhibit perception of the letter's individual lines. A particular experience could invest the percept with additional meaning, as, for instance, the special meaning of the letter "A" to Hester Prynne in *The Scarlet Letter*.

The short-term influence of experience on perception can be illustrated by an experiment that presented the same rather ambiguous figure to two groups of subjects. The figure could be seen as most resembling either a pair of eyeglasses or a dumbbell. On the initial presentation, one group of subjects was told that it was a picture representing eyeglasses; the other group had its attention called to the dumbbell characteristics of the figure. When both groups were later asked to reproduce the figure, the first group emphasized the eyeglass properties, and the second emphasized the dumbbell characteristics. Since the figure presented to the two groups was the same, the differential interpretation of it—the different perceptions of it —could be attributed only to the differential short-term experience.

An experience that predisposes an individual to certain types of perceptions is called a set. The influence of set on perception has been quite extensively studied, and several groups of principles have emerged. One large group of principles concerns the properties of the stimulus. The prototype principle here is that the more ambiguous the stimulus, the more its perception is determined by the set or proclivities of the subject. Another group of principles concerns the properties of the respondent. The prime example here is that the stronger the set of the individual, the more it determines his perception. When the two groups of principles interact, what emerges is the proposition that the meaning attributed to a particular stimulus by an individual is a function of the ambiguity of the stimulus and the strength of the individual's set.

APPLICATION OF PRINCIPLES

These principles have been extensively applied in studying individuals. By presenting unambiguous stimuli and analyzing incorrect responses, one can get a rough measure of the strength and nature of sets of particular subjects. This technique has its greatest application in the evaluation and study of individuals who show considerable distortion in their perceptions of the world around them.

PROJECTIVE TESTS

The major application of these principles, however, has been in projective testing, in which ambiguous stimuli are presented to individuals and their responses are analyzed in terms of their emphasis and patterning. Extrapolated from this analysis is a description of the individual's personality in terms of his perceptual proclivities. Perhaps the best-known projective test is the Rorschach test, which is a collection of ten inkblots. These are, of course, highly ambiguous stimuli that are in themselves meaningless. The individual is shown each inkblot and is asked the question, "What does this remind you of?" His responses are categorized according to a developed system and then interpreted in terms of his personality structure. Hermann Rorschach, the originator of the test, considered it a perceptual experiment, and it does, indeed, make use of one of the basic assumptions about the determination of what is perceived: that a percept is a function of the ambiguity of the stimulus and the strength of the individual's set.

The needs of the individual also influence the content of what is perceived. A classic experiment in this area presented ambiguous pictures to a group of college students one, three, six, and nine hours after eating. The incidence of food and food-related perceptions was lowest one hour after eating and increased in their reports three and six hours after eating; it decreased somewhat at the nine-hour testing but remained higher than at the one-hour test. Another experiment showed that hungry subjects judged food objects as larger than other ambiguously structured stimuli.

Overall psychological needs as well as immediate physical needs influence perception. Another well-known projective test, the Thematic Apperception Test, is based on this proposition. The stimuli for this test consist of pictures of people in various situations. The situations are ambiguous enough to allow for a variety of interpretations. The subject is asked to tell a story about each picture, and his story is interpreted in terms of his particular needs and drives. The test yields information about the individual's personality through an analysis of his need structure.

STUDIES OF INDIVIDUAL PERCEPTION

Emphasis on analysis of responses to stimuli as a means of learning about the individual is seen in a now classic series of experiments by Witkin and his associates. The basic experimental task in the series was adjusting a rod so that it would be exactly vertical within a frame. The experiment was usually carried out in the dark, with the rod and the frame painted with luminous paint. Numerous variations were introduced. For instance, in some experiments the frame was presented at an angle; the subject could then adjust the rod to make its position consistent with the presumed verticality of the frame or with other cues to the dimensions of the environment, such as his own bodily orientation in space. These latter variables were also manipulated; in some experiments, the subject sat in a tilting chair. By comparing the rod's direction and degree of deviation from the vertical, the experimenter was able to determine which cues the subject used. A series of studies then investigated correlations between personality traits and types and the cues relied on to adjust the rod. Subjects who relied mainly on the position of the frame to judge the vertical were labeled field-dependent; those who relied in the main on cues coming from their own body position were called field-independent. The field-dependent subjects tended to make greater errors in the estimation of the vertical than did the field-independent subjects. Also, the field-dependent subjects were found to be generally more dependent as people, to lack self-insight, to be more suggestible, and to have more inferiority feelings.

This work is an example of the approach to the understanding of individual personality through a study of individual perception. It is a particularly good example because it managed to avoid a major pitfall in this area: reliance on the subject's report to learn what he perceived. By using an objective physical manipulation, the adjustment of a rod to the vertical, it avoided the problem of determining whether the subject's report of his perceptions was an accurate one. A variety of motives besides the desire to report sensation accurately can influence what a subject says he saw. Many experiments have indicated that people can be influenced in their own perceptual judgments by the judgments of others. For instance, a point of light in an otherwise pitch dark room will appear to move, probably because of natural eye movements. When a subject is asked to judge the distance of the excursion of the light and then is permitted to hear the judgments of others, his own subsequent judgment will be closer to the other judgments. The degree of modification depends on an assortment of variables, including the consistency of others' judgments, the status of the other judges with respect to the subject, and the expertise attributed to the other judges.

In terms of the definition of perception, what is being manipulated here is, of course, the interpretation of sensory events by the individual. Since the light in the dark room does not in fact move, the sense data are somewhat ambiguous, and the subject is more prone to influence by social factors. Other experiments, however, indicate that, even with a more concrete sensory event, subjects are highly susceptible to suggestion in their reports of perceptual experience.

LEARNED BEHAVIOR

Much of perception is learned behavior. How much is actually learned and how much occurs as a result of the intrinsic organization of the nervous system is an issue that has occupied theorists ever since perception was first studied. Information pertaining to early perception is difficult to obtain because infants are not able to report what they see or hear. Some experiments on sensory deprivation, however, do yield information about what kinds of ability are lacking when sensory experience is lacking. In a sensory deprivation experiment, the subject is removed from all stimulation possible. In experiments reported by Riesen, chimpanzees were raised wholly in the dark from birth until certain predetermined testing times. The chimps' vision was tested after varying periods of rearing in the dark; in this way, the importance of visual sensory experience in the development of visual perception was studied. Riesen found serious decrements in visual perception on the part of the chimps and also found that the length of time the animals were reared in the dark determined the possibility of reversing the decrements.

Although such experimentation is not possible with human subjects, nature on occasion supplies relevant experimental conditions. Senden reports a series of studies of people who were blind from birth and who, at varying ages, underwent successful surgery for the removal of cataracts. Studies of their visual perception indicated that they had great difficulty in perceiving objects and even greater difficulty in distinguishing one object from another. Those who had learned to differentiate a square from a triangle by feeling the forms found that vision disrupted their recognition of the objects. What many became able to do was to count the corners of the figures in order to distinguish them. Most of the younger subjects were able to acquire adequate visual perception with time and practice, but many of the older subjects sustained an apparently permanent visual handicap.

These experiments are interpreted by some as evidence of the importance of experience in the development of visual perception. But others point to the evidence that the timing and duration of sensory deprivation influence its effect on perception and argue for the possibility of innate or intrinsic factors in perception. Their argument is that perhaps certain abilities develop in the absence of stimulation at certain very early periods in life but do not develop after those critical times. However, recent research supports the position that learning and experience exercise very strong influences on perception. For instance, Krech, Rosenzweig, and Bennett report that perceptual discrimination ability can be enhanced by enriching the normal environment of rats.

PSYCHOPATHOLOGY AND PERCEPTION

If the motivational and need states of the organism influence his perception of his environment, then it follows that psychopathological disturbance has a profound effect on perceptual functioning.

Some experimentation in an area called perceptual defense makes this clear. A central experiment in this area was done by Postman, Bruner, and McGinnies. They found that words related to the highly valued areas of a subject's concern were recognized-more quickly than were words related to areas of little or negative value to the subject. The term "perceptual defense" derives from the idea that the subject defends himself against the perception of words that have negative connotations for him; he takes much longer to recognize them when they are presented. This was illustrated in another experiment by McGinnies in which he found that subjects took a longer time to recognize taboo words than neutral words.

An individual who has a pathological fear or need to avoid certain categories of people or experience may, therefore, be expected to block.out perception of the threatening stimuli. It is possible that the mechanism by which this is done will ultimately be found in the neurophysiological processes by which Hernández-Peón's cat no longer perceived the clicks being presented when a mouse entered its visual field. It is also possible that future experimentation will reveal chemical changes in the brains of people with psychopathological disturbance and will reveal that these changes influence perception. It can be shown now that some drugs influence perceptual functioning and that different drugs influence it in different ways. Here the influence must be directly on the neural functioning underlying the apprehension and interpretation of stimuli. Some experimentation relevant to both the effects of drugs on perception and the effects of severe psychopathology on perception concerns differential effects of the same drug on schizophrenics and on nonschizophrenic subjects.

Schizophrenics Versus Nonschizophrenics

The literature on the differences in perception between patients and normal subjects is voluminous, and much of it is contradictory. To review this field is a task far beyond the scope of this chapter, and no attempt will be made even to summarize it. A few examples should suffice to indicate the kinds of experiments and findings reported in the literature.

Whether one views serious mental illness as functional or in some measure organic, the perceptual studies relate to the influence of the perceiver and his needs and state on the content of the perception. Many of the studies have taken some objective behavior, such as reaction time, and studied its attributes in a patient population and in a nonpatient, presumably normal population. In this way, schizophrenics, especially, have been compared with nonschizophrenic groups on a variety of perceptual measures—figure-ground differentiation, perceptual constancies, differential reaction times, and the like. It has been found, for example, that schizophrenics have a consistently and significantly slower reaction time than do nonschizophrenic subjects. However, attentional impairments can confound much research with schizophrenics. It may be that one is simply defining a difference in how much attention is being paid to the stimulus rather than a difference in the actual perception or speed of perception between schizophrenics and normal subjects.

Sutton and his colleagues, using a quite ingenious technique, avoided this problem of differential attention by first comparing the various aspects of the performance of a single individual and then comparing this relationship among parts to the same relationship obtained in the performance of nonschizophrenic subjects. Using this method, Sutton found that schizophrenics took relatively longer than normals to shift from one sensory modality to another. Since one of the prevalent clinical signs of schizophrenia is a kind of stickiness and perseveration, it is possible that this research is building a basis for objectifying and ultimately quantifying some clinical observations. This is an example of the way in which an attribute of perception can be used to study differences between groups of subjects and then to make hypotheses about the disease process.

Although much of the work in this area of perception and psychosis is done simply to define differences, at least one theory of psychopathology is used to predict the kinds of similarities and differences that may be found both between patient populations and normal ones and between the various groups and types of subjects within the patient population. Eysenck postulates a theory based on assumptions as to the state of the brain in various types of disturbances. For example, he says that a hypermanic individual has a cerebral cortex that is in a state of inhibition and that a depressed individual's cortex is in a state of excitation. From this, Eysenck postulates that the hypermanic person will be much more difficult to condition than will the depressed individual. Experiments done on these assumptions have yielded conflicting findings. This is another example of how the perceptual processes have been used to reflect the properties of individuals.

This very brief discussion of the highly complex area of perception is meant to give a general orientation to the field and to its importance in the determination and the measurement of human behavior. Many important topics and areas have been omitted; for a presentation of them and for a fuller explication of those touched on here, the reader is referred to the references below.

REFERENCES

Carmichael, L., Hogan, H. P., and Walter, A. A. An experimental study of the effect of language on the reproduction of visually perceived form. J. Exper. Psychol., 15: 73, 1932.

Cherry, C. Some experiments upon the recognition of speech, with one and with two ears. J. Acoust. Soc. Amer., 25: 975, 1953.

Dember, W. N. The Psychology of Perception. Holt, Rinehart and Winston, New York, 1960.

Hernández-Peón, R. Reticular mechanisms of sensory control. In Sensory Communication, W. A. Rosenblith, editor. Wiley, New York, 1961.

Hoch, P., and Zubin, J. Psychopathology of Perception. Grune & Stratton, New York, 1965.

Hochberg, J. E. Perception. Prentice-Hall, Englewood Cliffs, N. J., 1964.

Koffka, K. Principles of Gestalt Psychology. Harcourt Brace, New York, 1935.

Krech, D., and Crutchfield, R. Elements of Psychology. Alfred A. Knopf, New York, 1961.

Krech, D., Rosenzweig, M. R., and Bennett, E. L. Relations between brain chemistry and problem-solving among rats raised in enriched and impoverished environments. J. Comp. Physiol. Psychol., 55: 801, 1962.

Levine, R., Chein, I., and Murphy, G. The relation of the intensity of a need to the amount of perceptual distortion: a preliminary report. J. Psychol., 13: 283, 1942.

McGinnies, E. Emotionality and perceptual defense. Psychol. Rev., 56: 244, 1949.

Moruzzi, G., and Magoun, H. W. Brain stem reticular formation and activation of the EEG. In Basic Readings in Neuropsychology, R. L. Issacson, editor, p. 253. Harper & Row, New York, 1963.

Postman, L., Bruner, J. S., and McGinnies, E. Personal values as selective factors in perception. J. Abnorm. Soc. Psychol., 43: 142, 1948.

Riesen, A. H. The development of visual perception in man and chimpanzee. Science, 106: 107, 1947.

Ruch, F. Psychology and Life. Scott Foresman, Chicago, 1953.

Sayers, B. McA., and Cherry, C. Mechanisms of binaural fusion in the hearing of speech. J. Acoust. Soc. Amer., 29: 973, 1957.

Senden, M. von. Raum-und Gestaltauffassung bei operierten Blindgeborenen vor und nach der Operation. Barth, Leipzig, 1932.

Sutton, S., Hakerem, G., Portnoy, M., and Zubin, J. The effect of shift of sensory modality on serial reaction time: a comparison of schizophrenics and normals. Amer. J. Psychol., 74: 224, 1961.

Vandenberg, S. G. Behavioral methods for assessing neuroses and psychoses. In Drugs and Behavior, L. Uhr, and J. G. Miller, editors, p. 463. Wiley, New York, 1960.

Witkin, H. A., Lewis, H. B., Hertzman, M., Machover, K., Meissner, P. B., and Wapner, S. Personality Through Perception. Harper & Row, New York, 1954.

CHAPTER 13

Cognition

MARTIN DEUTSCH, Ph.D.

INTRODUCTION

IN HIS SEARCH for proof of his own existence, Descartes arrived at a satisfactory basis on which he could accept his own reality: *Cogito, ergo sum.* "I think; therefore I am." This became a cornerstone of Cartesian philosophical doctrine, which has had a profound effect on modern science. What concerns us about Descartes' statement is that he affirmed his own existence in terms of the basic human process of thinking.

Cognition as a word is generally used to refer to more than thinking processes; for many theorists it includes sensation, perception, and learning processes. However, in contemporary usage, the main aspect of cognition is considered to be thinking and problem-solving. Perhaps the very importance and inclusiveness of the area have made its margins somewhat fuzzy; exactly where cognition begins and perception or sensation ends, for example, is not entirely clear. For purposes of this chapter, however, we will discuss cognition mainly in terms of thinking and problem-solving, with only brief references to perception and learning.

First of all, cognition develops, and it develops in interaction with the circumstances of the individual's life. A number of theorists have defined stages in cognitive development. Most of these sets of stages have one particular progression in common. Cognitive development proceeds from the more concrete to the more abstract, from being more dependent on the actual presence and the sensing of stimuli in the environment to being relatively more independent of concrete stimuli and operating, instead, with the symbolic representations of stimuli in memory. In essence, these progressions represent the change from having to manipulate objects in physical space to solve a problem to being able to manipulate the symbols of objects in one's mind in order to arrive at a solution. And here is where man emerges as the superior, symbolic animal, the one most capable of problem-solving on the highest level.

When any part of man's symbolic language system is impaired, as by psychopathology in its many forms, his thinking or problem-solving process is adversely affected. Disturbed thought processes characterize most forms of mental illness. Through analysis of these thought processes, much insight can be gained into the nature of the individual's pathology and, by extrapolation from many such studies, into the nature of various types of disturbance.

Studies of thought processes and methods of problem-solving in the nondisturbed individual also yield information that relates to personality organization and type. This is an area of study and theory called cognitive style. One aspect of individual differences is in their capacity to solve problems, sometimes referred to as intelligence. Although intelligence is one of those too-encompassing words, one of its frequent definitions has to do with skill in problem-solving.

From the discussion so far it can be seen that what is referred to as cognition or cognitive process is a function related to problem-solving, to symbolization, to the field of learning, and generally to a kind of aptitude called intelligence. Even this string of definitions and associations, however, does not quite explain the area referred to by the term "cognition." Perhaps an example used by William James provides the best description. In talking about the inception of cognitive life, James said that the point when it begins is when one is able to say, "Hello! Thingumbob again." In a sense, a discussion of cognition must revolve about the various skills and processes that make that exclamation possible. These would include recognition, recall, and symbolization (labeling). Implied in these skills is the development of the individual in interaction with his environment.

LANGUAGE

Let us begin with language. In a sense, language may be considered the currency of cognition, at least for humans. We manipulate objects symbolically by labeling them. There is even a theory, proposed by Benjamin Whorf, that the structure of thought is determined by the structure of language. Essentially, such a theory means that, if there were a culture in which language did not include a past tense, it would be a culture without historical discussion. The Whorfian hypothesis has given considerable impetus to the study of semantics. Its enunciation has served in the behavioral sciences to place more emphasis on research into linguistic processes and the acquisition of language by the child.

The Whorfian position represents an extreme point on the continuum of theories relating language to thought. A somewhat more moderate theory was suggested by Vygotsky, a Russian psychologist who studied both language acquisition and thought processes. His book *Thought and Language*, which was only recently translated into English, has considerably influenced this area of research and theory. Essentially, Vygotsky discusses thought as the progressive introjection of speech, and he regards thought and words as quite inseparable. He said: "The relation between thought and word is a living process; thought is born through words. A word devoid of thought is a dead thing, and a thought unembodied in words remains a shadow."

VERBAL MEDIATORS

Many experiments have shown that adding language to apparently nonlinguistic problems facilitates their solution. For example, when labels are given to nonsense figures, it takes less time to learn their sequence.

Similarly, when prepositions are interjected between pairs of words that are to be learned, the number of repetitions needed to learn them decreases. For example, if the subject is to learn to say "table" after the experimenter says "hat," he learns the association faster if he adds, "on the" to himself; "hat on the table" is learned faster than simply "hat . . . table." This finding has been verified with many different groups of subjects, including those who are mentally retarded. According to some recent work of Jensen, the difference between retarded and normal subjects is that, if the normals are given the words to interpose on one occasion, they will make up such words on the next occasion; the retarded subjects, however, have to be supplied with the words each time. But for all of them, the use of interposed prepositions—called "verbal mediators"—speeds the learning of the word associations.

The field of verbal mediation in problem-solving is receiving much attention at the present time. The assumption is that verbal mediators and labels play a very important role in the learning of even nonverbal material. For instance, learning to tell different bacteria apart is not essentially a verbal skill; it is a visual perceptual one. Yet, if one can label particular shapes verbally, it helps him remember and differentiate them.

This area of work has served to place much emphasis on the acquisition of language by children and on the study of their progressively greater familiarity and ease with it. It has stimulated a great many studies in language and the use of language. This work has implications for an understanding of cultural factors in thought and of linguistic factors in mental disturbance.

ACQUISITION OF LANGUAGE

Language and its forms come to the child from his environment. He learns to speak the language of the people who surround him, even though his *capacity* for language learning and use are a part of his biological endowment, anatomical and neurophysiological. It becomes apparent that, if language plays a major role in thought and if language is environmentally stimulated and its content environmentally determined, then environmental stimulation has much to do with thought.

As indicated earlier, Jensen found that all his groups of subjects for learning studies, except the mentally retarded, learned to supply their own mediators for remembering verbal stimuli. For some of these groups, however, he had to supply the mediators in the beginning; they did not supply their own mediators spontaneously. What, then, of the child who is reared in a largely nonverbal environment in which he neither spontaneously learns to use mediators nor is specifically taught to use them? Such a child may be perfectly capable of learning as fast as a more privileged child, but without the verbal facility he may be handicapped in the solution of many different types of problems.

Use of Language

Social levels. That environmental and social factors play a large role in language usage is attested to by a number of investigators. Bernstein, in England, has done a substantial series of studies in this area and has concluded that social class designations—or, rather, the kinds of occupational, social, and environmental conditions that go along with certain social class levels—define also the type of verbal behavior seen in people.

Lower-class families tend to show what Bernstein calls "restrictive speech codes," and middle-class families tend to speak in what he designates as "elaborated codes." The two speech types differ from each other in the complexity of syntax, sentence length, richness of vocabulary, and several other categories used for linguistic analysis. What this means in everyday terms is that the lower-class families have a less rich speech, and the middle-class groups have a more complicated syntax and, therefore, a means for expressing more complicated thoughts.

The language of science, for example, is an elaborated code, but the language of the simple transaction in a store is a restricted code. This is not to say that children from lower-class families who speak in restricted codes cannot become scientists; it is only to say that, according to this theory, they will have to develop a more elaborate language system, one that the middle-class child is more likely to start school with in the first place.

Bernstein's results were obtained from studies he carried out in London, where the social class lines are much more rigidly drawn than in America. But investigators here have obtained data generally consistent with his findings. At the Institute for Developmental Studies in New York, investigators are discovering a more limited syntax for lower-class children as compared with middle-class children. Hess and his associates in Chicago are reporting similar findings.

Child-rearing techniques. Hess's studies also attempted to relate language systems to child-rearing techniques, and here is another point of direct contact between language systems and personality organization. He found that the mothers who speak in restricted code are more likely to be what he calls status-oriented in their relationships with their children, but the mothers with the more elaborated speech codes tend to be what he defines as person-oriented. The status-oriented mother, for example, disciplines her child in terms of "because I say so" and refers to the necessity for certain things to be done because "they say so" or because "the President says children should drink milk." On the other hand, the person-oriented mother is more likely to give reasons for actions and for discipline that are within the child's experience and his own motivations: "You should drink your milk because you want to grow up to be strong and healthy."

These differing kinds of child-rearing techniques can have very differing effects on the development of children's personalities. And these examples are only some of those available to illustrate the profound effect the variables labeled cognitive can have on personality development. These are not one-way effects; they are part of an interacting feedback by which personality and emotional factors also influence cognition.

LANGUAGE DEVELOPMENT

Many of the special programs designed to help disadvantaged children reflect the emphasis on linguistic influences in thought and the corresponding emphasis on social factors in language development. These programs are, in general, cognitive-enrichment efforts. They are directed toward the improvement of many cognitive skills, but a prime emphasis is language and language development. One of the reasons for the language enrichment is to improve the children's social communication skills; another reason is to influence their problem-solving abilities.

Irwin found substantial positive effects on children's language development simply from having their mothers read to them for half an hour every evening. Of course, when an adult reads to a child, there is usually a verbal interchange as well as the simple reading, so the effects are probably attributable to these other related language activities as well.

DEVELOPMENT OF COGNITION

Many theorists define a series of stages in cognitive growth. Usually, these theories indicate that one stage grows out of the next and that the stages follow a certain invariable sequence. Most but not all of the theories include the supposition that each succeeding stage expands on and replaces the prior one, though there can be vestigial remnants of the previous stage.

PIAGET'S THEORIES

A major theorist in this regard is Jean Piaget, a Swiss psychologist whose exhaustive and ingenious observations of his own three children provided the foundation for an entire elaborated developmental theory, with cognitive development at its base. For a long time in the United States the scientific *Zeitgeist* was such that the works of Piaget languished in libraries, with many of his books not even translated into English. This ignoring of Piaget stemmed from the American emphasis on emotional rather than cognitive development and the American stress on large-sample, controlled experimental studies in preference to Piaget's naturalistic and small-sample method. The growth of interest in cognitive development sparked a renewed interest in the work of Piaget, and a series of controlled experiments with children has verified some of the generalizations he made from his own observations. In turn, the theories and research stimulated by Piaget's work are coming to be regarded more and more as basically relevant to an understanding of the relationship between higher thought processes and emotional and social development and disability.

Schemata. During the entire' developmental period, according to Piaget, the child is involved in building schemata, which are organizations of behaviors relevant to each other. Thus, there can be a schema of sucking, which would include all the activities related to sucking: apprehension of the object to be sucked, activities of the mouth, lips, and hands during sucking, etc. The child's responses to the world are made up of schemata, though not exclusively. Piaget speaks more about schemata in the earlier, simpler cognitive periods than in the later periods.

Schemata are acquired by the dual processes of assimilation and accommodation. The first refers to the introjection of knowledge about the environment, which is then incorporated into the child's existing body of knowledge. In this incorporation, the existing body modifies somewhat to accommodate the new elements. It is by this continuing dual process that schemata are organized and changed, that concepts are built and expanded.

Stages of development. Piaget postulated a series of stages in cognitive development, beginning with what he designated the sensorimotor, progressing through the preoperational thought period to the stage of concrete operations into the period of formal operations. Age equivalents for these cognitive levels are very rough ones, with, presumably, fairly wide individual differences. A characteristic of the progression of levels is that the child becomes less and less dependent on particular external stimulation and more and more able to function in terms of symbols without concrete referents.

In the first period, the sensorimotor stage, the infant begins as a reflexive organism that responds to its environment in an undifferentiated manner. Later in this stage he becomes an organism that displays, as Flavell put it, "a relatively coherent organization of sensory-motor actions vis-à-vis his immediate environment."

The next stage, the preoperational thought period, is preparation for the stage that follows, the stage of concrete operations. In the preparatory stage, the child first begins to understand and use symbols, though he is able to do so only in unitary ways; double classifications elude him. For example, though he can understand that a particular person can be another child's mother—and, in fact, sees her in those terms: as "Johnny's mother" and not as "Mrs. Smith"—he is unable to see the same person in another classification as well—as "Mary's teacher."

By the end of the preoperational stage, the child is able to think in terms of classes, to see relationships, and to handle number concepts. He is still egocentric in his thought—he relates everything to himself, and his judgments are subjective—but the basis has been laid for the development of logical operations.

The stage of concrete operations includes the increasing ability to handle numbers, the development of a real logic, and an ability to relate external events to each other, independent of the self. The child can now classify the same person or object along more than one dimension. This period of from 7 to 11 years of age is one of massive intellectual and conceptual development. Interestingly, this period roughly corresponds to that defined in psychoanalysis as latency, a period of relative overt quiescence in psychosexual development.

The last developmental stage that Piaget defined is the period of formal operations, from about 11 to about 15 years. This is when the child develops true abstract thought and is able to make hypotheses and test them logically. He has achieved conceptual independence from the concrete and can operate wholly with symbols, with no need to introduce the concrete objects they represent.

Within all these stages are many substages and the development of particular concepts and conceptual frames, such as concepts of time and size. Included in Piaget's system are accounts of the development of perceptual, linguistic, mathematical, and moral concepts. It is a developmental system, and it is an interactive one, in the sense that development is seen to take place as a function of the contact between the child and his environment. None of these functions is presumed to progress as described in the absence of environmental contact and interaction; the basic processes by which the development proceeds are accommodation and assimilation.

This point is emphasized, as it was in the discussion of language, because it contributes to a view of the individual as plastic in his development and responsive to his surroundings. Although the neural substrate must be responsible for the *possibility* for cognitive development to take place, it is the relationship between this neural substrate and the stimuli that act on it that promotes the actual development. Such an understanding occupies a central place in modern behavioral science; it offers the possibility of influencing man's development in the most basic sense. For fields that deal primarily in attempting to teach and to change people, such as psychiatry and education, it offers an optimistic view of potential success for both prevention and remediation of disability.

Stimulation and Cognition

Intelligence.   There has been a popular assumption that intelligence
—which, in the context of this chapter, is the aptitude for cognitive development and cognitive functioning—is quite resistant to change by external intervention. The evidence does not bear out this assumption. There
is, however, a consistency in scores on intelligence tests at age 8 and at
adulthood in the absence of any special educational or interventional experiences in the interim. The consistency in intelligence test scores at age
2 and at age 8 is much less definitive.

The concept that intelligence is determined by the operation of internal
processes, presumably genetically determined, is no longer current. Some
theorists still hold to portions of it, but the evidence favors those who view
intelligence as a function that develops in the relationships between the
individual and his environment; that draws on various tools, such as language, that are developed in the same manner; and that grows or declines
as a consequence of the amount and nature of environmental encounters.
At the same time, these properties of change are relatively long-term ones.
Slight variations in living conditions or very temporary ones do not appre-
ciably affect cognitive abilities.

Enrichment programs.   Over the last thirty years, many programs
have been mounted to attempt to enhance cognitive functioning. Many
have been successful. Skeels, for example, found that the adoption of children from very poor and difficult institutional circumstances into more
favorable ones enhanced their intelligence test scores substantially. In a
follow-up study he reported maintenance of the positive changes associated with adoption. A control group of children, who were not adopted
and who were studied at the same times, showed a maintenance, on the
whole, of the lower functional levels.

Wellman reported positive changes in intellectual functioning as a result of a special nursery school experience. More recently, Kirk reported
significant improvement of cognitive skills of mentally retarded youngsters
enrolled in a special preschool program. Although the improvement did
not continue after the end of the special program, the gains acquired were
not lost.

Current attempts to enhance cognitive development with special programs are also focused on the preschool years. The long-term programs
that begin for 4-year-olds and continue for several years are as yet too new
to show definitive long-term results, but the short-term gains they report
are significant in terms of raising functional cognitive levels and intelligence test scores.

On the basis of these results, large-scale short-term programs are being
mounted all over the country with support granted under the antipoverty
legislation. This is just one example of how both theory and research from
the behavioral science field are applied to current social problems. This

application, in turn, can be expected to stimulate more research and experimental programs in the cognitive area.

Reading. The general ferment about stimulation of cognitive processes has also affected thinking about the skill of reading. For many years, the educational dogma stated that teaching children to read too early could be harmful to them and that the appropriate age to learn reading was approximately 6. This emphasis on the potentially harmful effects of earlier teaching effectively stopped experimentation with reading at earlier ages, even though Davidson in 1931 was able to make substantial progress in teaching reading to children who had a mental age of 4, including some retarded 5-year-old children.

Now interest in early reading has been reawakened, and many educators are rethinking their earlier opposition. As with other cognitive skills, there are vast individual differences in the ages at which children can acquire reading skill, but there is no scientific basis to any assertion of inevitable harmful effects from early teaching. Not all children are able to learn before 6, but apparently the only harm that comes from earlier attempts to teach them is caused by coercive methods used, rather than by such attempts per se.

Effects of environment. There is evidence that, in the absence of special intervention, children in a nonstimulating environment show a drop in intelligence test scores over years. This was reported in 1924 by Gordon, who studied gypsy children in Europe whose schooling and cognitive stimulation were highly irregular because the families lived on traveling barges. Gray and Klaus refer to this phenomenon as progressive retardation, and Deutsch and Brown call it cumulative deficit.

The influence of environment on intelligence can also be positive, even in the absence of specific programs of stimulation. Klineberg did a classic study that showed significant intelligence test score increases for Negro children who moved from poor and unstimulating environments in the South to better living conditions and better school situations in the North.

PERSONALITY AND COGNITION

Interrelationships among cognitive processes affect the individual's intercorrelated modes of thinking, problem-solving, and perceiving, which in current literature are referred to as cognitive style. Kagan and his associates studied the development of such styles in children and defined certain consistencies over time. They also found relationships between the styles of analyzers and nonanalyzers and their motoric impulsivity, with the nonanalyzers being much more impulsive and generally motoric in their reactions.

The Authoritarian Personality

A book by Adorno and his associates, *The Authoritarian Personality*, represents one of the first systematic attempts to relate certain personality characteristics, attitudes, and cognitive orientation. The studies reported in that book and elsewhere were oriented toward the personality and cognitive correlates of particular political attitudes, but part of the approach involved study of the relationships among perception, cognition, and personality. In general, those studies report a correspondence among fascist political attitudes, a status-oriented view of interpersonal relationships, and a cognitive rigidity.

This series of studies has been criticized because of the involvement with the definition of an authoritarian personality—although that was the aim of the studies in the first place—and the correspondingly lighter emphasis on definitions of other personality types and their cognitive correlates. However, the authoritarian personality studies set the pace in this area and provided an impetus for work that is still being felt. In the criticism and discussion of the book, many theories were formulated, and many investigators were stimulated to carry out related work.

Some interpretations of the data contained in the authoritarian personality studies have quite direct relevance to the process by which individuals can be influenced to alter their behavioral modes. For instance, Brown suggested that the person with the authoritarian mind can be classified in terms of the kinds of information that influence him to alter his thinking about particular topics. Brown said that the more authoritarian an individual's orientation is, the more he can be induced to change his mind because of the statements of authority or high-status figures alone. As the individual approaches the nonauthoritarian point on the continuum, the more he needs other kinds of evidence to change his thought or attitude.

The Open and Closed Mind

Following in the tradition of the authoritarian personality studies but avoiding many of the pioneering pitfalls, Rokeach reported a series of studies in a book entitled *The Open and Closed Mind*. According to his studies, the closed-mind person is dogmatic and rigid and is characterized by the operation of many mechanisms of defense, which serve to shield him from uncomfortable conflicts in his belief systems. The open mind, on the other hand, is just that: open to external stimuli and more apt to be probing the world of knowledge, seeking more information.

Almost the same type of dichotomy was enunciated by Witkin and his associates under the field-dependent versus field-independent rubric. Goldstein and Scheerer—in work that antedated the authoritarian personality studies and that was oriented less to attitudes and more to pure cognitive abilities, which they related to the presence or absence of central nervous system disability—defined two groups as concrete thinkers and abstract thinkers. Many other investigators have come to similar conclusions, albeit in different words.

Allport summed up the individual characteristics defined by all these investigators: "Some people are chronically unable to change their sets when objective conditions demand it; others, by contrast, are flexible."

What is most relevant about this work to the general field of psychiatry is its union of the cognitive and the emotional—the relationship defined among belief systems, cognitive rigidities, and personality orientations. This is perhaps best enunciated by Rokeach in *The Open and Closed Mind*:

> Many important aspects of intellectual functioning in particular and cognitive functioning in general can be attributed to personality rather than to intelligence. . . . It is possible to investigate many spheres of activity—ideological, conceptual, perceptual, and esthetic —via the common structural bond that ties them all together in the person's belief system. . . . A person's cognitive functioning is not a thing apart from his affective or emotional functioning. They are seen to be different facets of a person's total behavior.

Kagan, Shaffer, and Frenkel-Brunswik all indicated that these systems or styles develop early and are influenced by child-rearing practices.

PSYCHOPATHOLOGY AND COGNITION

The relationship between development and cognitive style and between the cognitive and the emotional has provided the basis for extensive inquiry into the thought processes of persons who are emotionally disturbed.

COMPARISONS WITH CHILDREN AND PRIMITIVES

One of the most specific discussions of the relationship between development of cognitive skills in children and their dissolution in the mentally disturbed is in Werner's book *Comparative Psychology of Mental Development*. The book presents a system of mental development that includes stages not too different from those enunciated by Piaget. Werner, however, is concerned with the entire life span and is more concerned than Piaget with brain function. Werner propounds a complex theory of mental development and cognition that includes comparisons among cultures, among individuals at different points in the life span, and among individuals with different types of organic and psychological pathology.

The fact that children, individuals with brain damage, and those with various forms of psychopathology are all concrete in their thought processes has tempted many theorists to compare these clinical groups to children. Cross-cultural studies, too, at times relate primitive concrete thought to the concretism found in children in our culture. Werner labeled all these comparisons false and disposed of them by pointing out that there is an essential difference between the concretism of the developing child and the regression to concretism that characterizes the disturbed or organically impaired adult. With regard to equating the primitive thought of psychopathology with primitive thought in primitive cultures, he said, "The primitive man lives in a world to which he is admirably adjusted; the pathological individual tries to adjust himself by means of primitive behavior to a world for him inadequate and nonprimitive." He also pointed out that any developmental stage contains elements of the preceding one and, therefore, that the primitive and concrete thought of the mentally ill adult contains vestiges of his earlier, more abstract, and intact functioning.

Schizophrenic Cognition

There is voluminous literature on thought processes in mental disease. About the only common point of departure for most researchers in this area has been the conviction that schizophrenic thought is somehow different from normal thought.

Investigators in this area have operated from different theories of cognition and from varying theories and definitions of mental illness. The experimental results are inconclusive and often contradictory. The reliability of these results is further confounded by the widespread experimental use of either heterogeneous schizophrenic populations or differently classified populations. The classical diagnostic categories of hebephrenic or paranoid schizophrenia have been used, as have newer categories, such as process-reactive, chronic-acute, and good and poor premorbid schizophrenics. Also, schizophrenic cognition or conceptual ability has been measured by a wide variety of tests, ranging from I.Q. and simple learning tests to higher-order tests of concept formation and deductive, inductive, and abstract reasoning.

Conceptual ability. Experiments concerning schizophrenic conceptual ability have yielded results that range from no conceptual deficit in schizophrenia to specific deficits associated with the type of psychosis to significant differences between *all* schizophrenic and normal subjects. Although the issue is still controversial, recent research has indicated that schizophrenics are not necessarily unable to form concepts and that the concepts they form are not significantly concrete or infantile. Rather, it has been pointed out that schizophrenics may be concerned with bizarre and personal concepts that they are unwilling to communicate or that they communicate in a private language. Other theorists have demonstrated that schizophrenic concept-formation ability can be raised to a normal level by decreasing the number of distracting stimuli and that their conceptual performance can be significantly lowered by increasing the number of stimulus distractions.

Conceptual functioning. Schizophrenics have often been observed to include irrelevant and extraneous factors in their response to a conceptual task, a phenomenon termed overinclusion. Such a phenomenon has been explained on the basis of a schizophrenic inability to select only those stimuli that are relevant to the task being performed. The results in this area are controversial and are not easily fitted into a single or simple theoretical framework. But the results may be summarized in the following way. Although some schizophrenics may form bizarre or personal concepts and may exhibit the phenomenon of overinclusive thinking, all schizophrenics, including the chronic population, have performed normally on a variety of conceptual tasks when time pressure and distractions were eliminated and when the levels of stimulus input (cue information) and motivation were increased.

Several major theoretical approaches have attempted to account for schizophrenic conceptual performance. One theory, presented by Goldstein and Scheerer in 1941, characterized schizophrenic thought as concrete; schizophrenics, like brain-damaged patients, are seen as having lost the ability to think in the abstract. Although early results with the Goldstein-Scheerer and Vygotsky blocks tests tended to support this view, research in the last decade has generally tended to disprove it.

Another theory was presented more recently by Arieti, who characterized schizophrenic thought as paralogical, dreamlike, and primitive rather than logical. He suggested that the schizophrenic is unable to handle stress and, therefore, regresses to a less-advanced level of personality integration. The schizophrenic then uses his thought processes to isolate himself from a threatening social environment. This withdrawal or desocialization takes place together with or even because of a concomitant process of cognitive desymbolization. In this state, objects assume a different and highly personal meaning to the schizophrenic.

Williams attempted what he regarded as a test of Arieti's theory, but the tasks he used did not yield differences in logical and syllogistic reasoning between schizophrenics and normals. This should by no means be considered a definitive disconfirmation of Arieti's theory, as the tasks Williams used may not have been adequately reflective of the kinds of logical difficulties that schizophrenics have. It is also possible that the testing situation influenced the performance of the subjects. There is some evidence, for example, that the conditions set for task performance influence the functioning of schizophrenics in predictable ways. This would mean that at least some persons with schizophrenia are still related enough to the world around them to be influenced by it, at least in cognitive functions.

A number of theorists have suggested that the apparent cognitive deficit observed in schizophrenia is a function of a high anxiety level, impaired attentional and time-reaction abilities, a lowered motivation level, and an oversensitivity to distractions. Some experiments in the area have tended to support these theories.

It is becoming fairly clear that the cognitive styles in schizophrenia are not necessarily stable and irreversible ones. Experiments have demonstrated that the abstracting and interpreting ability of mildly disturbed schizophrenics can be improved under conditions of enriched stimulus information. Schizophrenic concept-formation ability can be significantly improved and raised to normal levels under avoidance learning conditions by presenting subjects with a noxious stimulus that can be terminated by the correct conceptual response. In general, these results tend to support other experiments concerning less complex cognitive and learning tasks in which the schizophrenic response improved under conditions of punishment, censure, or failure threat.

The relationship of schizophrenic functioning to the nature of the task presented is supported by evidence, reported by Hunt and Cofer, that the schizophrenic functional deficit becomes greater as the complexity of the task increases. Mednick used this concept to reconcile the differing views of various investigators with respect to the thinking disorder seen in schizophrenia. He pointed out that "thinking is perhaps the most complex behavior in which man can engage" and indicated, therefore, that this would be a focus for schizophrenic dysfunction. Although theorists differ, Mednick believes that they all acknowledge that the thought of the schizophrenic can be described as disordered and that this disorganization results from irrelevant, fragmented, and competing associations.

One view of the genesis of such disorder is that it represents a reaction to stress. This assumption underlies one view of delusions, a prominent characteristic of certain types of schizophrenia. McReynolds, for example, said that a delusion may be viewed as a form of cognitive reorganization that desensitizes threatening and anxiety-producing thoughts by reinterpreting them. Thus, a delusion should be a less threatening organization of information for the schizophrenic. McReynolds and his associates later made a somewhat oblique test of his view of a delusion and confirmed his earlier theorizing. No experiment should be regarded as definitive, but this one does represent a promising line of investigation of cognitive functioning and cognitive deficits in schizophrenics.

MEMORY

Memory is an integral part of all thinking and learning, but it has also been studied separately in a variety of ways. First of all, it is well-known that memory plays tricks—in the sense that one does not always remember accurately what one learned or experienced—and that these inaccuracies are, in part, a function of individual experience. Different individuals in the same situation later remember different aspects of it and are likely to remember the same aspects differently. A portion of these differences can be attributed to their differential apprehension of the experience in the first place. But another portion can be related to vagaries of memory function and to the influence of the individuals' varied experiences subsequent to the experience being recalled.

INTERVENING EXPERIENCES

Experimental studies of memory indicate that what is remembered is related to the experience that intervenes between the initial learning and the recall. The closer the intervening experience is to the learning situation, the more interference there is with the initial learning, and, therefore, the more data are lost in the recall or are confused with the subsequent learning. For example, if one were to learn the names of all the rivers in Africa and then learn the life cycle of the snail, the chances are that he would do better on a subsequent test of his knowledge of African rivers than if that learning had been followed by the learning of the names of African mountains.

TESTING METHODS

Accuracy of memory varies also with the method used to test it. The most difficult circumstance in which to remember something is in response to an open-ended question that gives no information itself; for instance, "Name the rivers of Africa." If one were asked to name four rivers in Africa that begin with the letter "N," the task would be somewhat easier. The simplest form of the task would be to pick out the African rivers from a list that includes rivers of other continents.

TIMING

There are also differences between immediate memory and memory for events that occurred longer ago. The memory defect in senility is so well-defined, in fact, that it is used diagnostically; the senile person has a much better memory for remote events than for recent events.

DRUGS

Certain drugs apparently enhance or interfere with memory functions. Scopolamine, for example, seems to cause forgetfulness, and some of the hallucinogens, such as lysergic acid diethylamide (LSD), seem to heighten both sensation and memory. The effects of drugs on memory and on other cognitive functions provide a promising line of investigation into the nature of the cognitive process and its deficit in various forms of psychopathology.

SUMMARY

Cognition includes many points of relationship between cognitive and emotional processes and their subsequent interaction and relationship with that individual orientational entity called personality. However, relationship does not imply causation. From the data reported and discussed, it is not possible to say that cognitive processes *cause* particular emotional reactions or that those reactions *cause* particular cognitive perceptions or distortions. Rather, the functions are related and interrelated, and all owe their genesis, in one degree or another, to the relating of the individual to his environmental and social circumstances. Vygotsky said with respect to language, "Words play a central part not only in the development of thought but in the historical growth of consciousness as a whole. A word is a microcosm of human consciousness." The same could be claimed for each of the elements discussed here.

REFERENCES

Adorno, T. W., Frenkel-Brunswik, E., Levinson, D. J., and Sanford, R. N. *The Authoritarian Personality*. Harper & Row, New York, 1950.

Allport, G. W. *Pattern and Growth in Personality*. Holt, Rinehart and Winston, New York, 1961.

Arieti, S. *Interpretation of Schizophrenia*. Robert Brunner, New York, 1955.

Bernstein, B. A socio-linguistic approach to social learning. In *Social Science Survey*, J. Gould, editor. Pelican Books, London, 1965.

Bloom, B. S. *Stability and Change in Human Characteristics*. Wiley, New York, 1964.

Bruner, J. S. The course of cognitive growth. Amer. Psychol., 19: 1, 1964.

Davidson, H. P. An experimental study of bright, average and dull children at the four-year mental level. Genet. Psychol. Monogr., 9: 119, 1931.

Deutsch, M. The role of social class in language development and cognition. Amer. J. Orthopsychiat., 35: 78, 1965.

Deutsch, M. Some psychosocial aspects of teaching the disadvantaged. Teachers Coll. Rec., 67: 260, 1966.

Deutsch, M., and Brown, B. R. Social influences in Negro-white intelligence differences. J. Soc. Issues, 20: 24, 1964.

Flavell, J. H. *The Developmental Psychology of Jean Piaget*. D. Van Nostrand, Princeton, 1963.

Frenkel-Brunswik, E. Patterns of social and cognitive outlook in children and parents. Amer. J. Orthopsychiat., 21: 543, 1951.

Goldstein, K., and Scheerer, M. Abstract and concrete behavior: an experimental study with special tests. Psychol. Monogr., 53: No. 5, 1941.

Gordon, H. Mental and scholastic tests among retarded children. London Board of Education Pamphlet, 44: 92, 1924.

Gray, S., and Klaus, R. A. An experimental preschool program for culturally deprived children. Unpublished paper given at American Association for the Advancement of Science. Montreal, 1964.

Hess, R. D., and Shipman, V. Early experience and the socialization of cognitive modes in children. Child Develp., 36: 869, 1965.

Hunt, J. McV. *Intelligence and Experience*. Ronald Press, New York, 1961.

Irwin, O. C. The effect of systematic reading of stories. J. Speech Hear. Res., 3: 187, 1960.

Jensen, A. Verbal mediation and educational potential (Unpublished manuscript).

Kagan, J., Moss, H. A., and Sigel, I. E. Psychological significance of styles of conceptualization. In *Basic Cognitive Processes in Children*, J. C. Wright and J. Kagan, editors. Society for Research in Child Development, Monograph No. 86, 1963.

Klineberg, O. *Race Differences*. Harper & Row, New York, 1935.

McReynolds, P., Collins, B., and Acker, M. Delusional thinking and cognitive organization in schizophrenia. J. Abnorm. Soc. Psychol., 69: 210, 1964.

Piaget, J. *The Language and Thought of the Child*. Harcourt Brace, New York, 1926.

Rokeach, M. *The Open and Closed Mind*. Basic Books, New York, 1960.

Skeels, H. M. Effects of adoption on children from institutions. Children, 12: 33, 1965.

Skeels, H. M., Updegraff, R., Wellman, B. L., and Williams, A. M. A study of environmental stimulation: an orphanage pre-school project. Univ. Iowa Stud. Child Welf., 15: 4, 1938.

Vygotsky, L. S. *Thought and Language*. M.I.T. Press and Wiley, Cambridge, Mass., and New York, 1962.

Werner, H. *Comparative Psychology of Mental Development*, rev. ed. Follett, Chicago, 1948.

Whorf, B. L. *Language, Thought and Reality*. Wiley, New York, 1956.

Williams, E. B. Deductive reasoning in schizophrenia. J. Abnorm. Soc. Psychol., 69: 47, 1947.

Witkin, H. A., Lewis, H. B., Hertzman, M., Machover, K., Meissner, P. B., and Wapner, S. *Personality Through Perception*. Harper & Row, New York, 1954.

CHAPTER 14

Learning

ARTHUR J. BACHRACH, Ph.D.

INTRODUCTION

LEARNING IS BASIC to every form of psychological theory. As Hilgard observed: "Psychologists with a penchant for systems find a theory of learning essential because so much of man's diverse behavior is the result of learning. If the rich diversity of behavior is to be understood in accordance with a few principles, it is evident that some of these principles will have to do with the way in which learning comes about." When Hilgard asserted that learning theory is critical "if the rich diversity of behavior is to be understood in accordance with a few principles," he was stating an assumption completely in keeping with a scientific method designed for explanations of events in terms of lawfulness and a striving for a minimal set of rational, demonstrable principles to account for these events. In a laboratory science such as experimental psychology, the search for laws of learning has been carried on with just such methods. The leaders in formulating theories of learning—Hull, Tolman, Skinner, Spence, Thorndike, Pavlov, and Guthrie—have all been, to one degree or another, laboratory scientists committed to research. A major part of their efforts and those of their colleagues has been the definition of learning variables.

The definition of learning has always been a difficult problem. Kimble has suggested that the roads to definition are two—factual and theoretical. The factual definitions relate learning to observable events in the physical world. The theoretical definitions are concerned with descriptions of basic processes that the learning theorist believes to be necessary in order for learning to occur. Hebb illustrated the theoretical definition when he discussed central nervous system (CNS) activities, the neural messages that occur in the CNS pathways: "Learning means a change in the direction of messages in the CNS." Skinner, in discussing response probability as a basic datum in the learning process offered a factual definition: "We may define learning as a change in the probability of response, but we must also specify the conditions under which it comes about." Hebb was postulating changes in the CNS that may be difficult to observe. Skinner concentrated on the frequency and altered probability of a specific observable response under specified observable conditions.

There is, withal, a general agreement that somehow learning is a change in behavior that results from practice, with learning representing an intervening process or variable that links organismic states before and after a change in behavior occurs. As Kimble observed, the definition of learning always assumes a relatively permanent change in behavior, excluding changes resulting from maturation, sensory adaptation, and fatigue.

The central question has always been one of differentiating learning from performance. Learning is inferred from observed performance. Kimble saw learning as a change in behavior potentiality. The organism may acquire capabilities to perform some act through learning, but the act itself may not occur. He stated, *"Learning* refers to long-term changes of the organism produced by practice. . . . *Performance* . . . refers [to the] translation of learning into behavior." At this point Kimble introduced another aspect of the definition in observing that practice alone does not produce learning; it is necessary for some maintaining event to occur, and so it is necessary to add reinforcement. Sidman defined reinforcement as "any event, contingent upon the response of the organism that alters the future likelihood of that response."

Learning, then, is defined as a change in behavior potential resulting from reinforced practice. Reinforcement, as so considered, becomes an example of an empirical law of effect that is basic to much of contemporary learning theory. The law of effect, as stated by Thorndike in 1931, says: "Acts followed by a state of affairs which the individual does not avoid, and which he often tries to preserve or attain, are selected and fixated, while acts followed by states of affairs which the individual avoids or attempts to change are eliminated." The following year, 1932, Thorndike modified his law and indicated that rewarded responses were always strengthened but that punished responses did not always diminish in strength, thus leading to an emphasis on reward as a primary determiner of behavior.

CONDITIONING

It is fairly traditional to view conditioning as a case of learning. Hull in many of his writings described the classical Pavlovian conditioned reflex as a special case of the law of effect, assuming reinforcement to be operative in such simple learning examples as well as in higher-order learning. Most theorists accept a rough dichotomy between two types of conditioning: classical (Pavlovian) and instrumental conditioning.

CLASSICAL CONDITIONING

Ivan Pavlov, the Russian physiologist, observed in his work with gastric secretions in dogs that stimuli that were often present at the time the dogs were offered food came to evoke salivation in the animals even in the absence of food. For example, the footsteps of the experimenter as he entered the room came to evoke salivation in dogs, even though the dogs could not see or smell food. Pavlov assumed that the stimulus of the footsteps came to be associated with food. His research was directed toward an analysis of this event, which he called the "conditional reflex" (the reflex would occur, given certain conditions), later somewhat mistranslated as the more familiar "conditioned reflex" or "conditioned response."

In a typical Pavlovian experiment, a stimulus that, prior to training, had no capacity to evoke a particular type of response becomes able to do so. To illustrate: Under normal circumstances, a bell sounded near an animal probably does no more than evoke exploration, such as a turning of the head toward the sound or, at most, a startled response. Also, under normal circumstances, a hungry animal may be expected to salivate in the presence of food. Pavlov's conditioned reflex experiment was a training experience in which the previously neutral stimulus of a bell was made, by pairing it with the food, to evoke the response of salivation, which it normally would not do.

To diagram this:

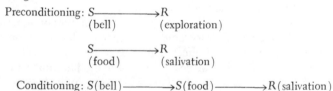

Preconditioning: S————————→R
            (bell)   (exploration)

S————————→R
(food)   (salivation)

Conditioning: S(bell)————————→S(food)————————→R(salivation)

Bell sounds are followed by the presentation of food. The animal salivates at the sight of the food and ultimately pairs S (bell) and S (food).

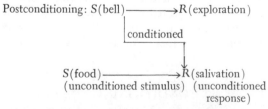

Postconditioning: S(bell)————————→R(exploration)

conditioned

S(food)————————→R(salivation)
(unconditioned stimulus) (unconditioned response)

Because the food naturally produces salivation, it is referred to as an unconditioned stimulus. Because the bell was originally unable to evoke salivation but, by pairing with the food, came to do so, it is referred to as a conditioned stimulus.

INSTRUMENTAL CONDITIONING

In contrast to classical conditioning, in which the organism is usually restrained—in a Pavlovian harness, for example—and in which the response is elicited by the experimenter, instrumental conditioning is an experimental technique in which a freely moving organism emits behavior that is instrumental in producing a reward. For instance, a cat in a Thorndike puzzle box must learn to lift a latch in order to escape from the box; a monkey in an experimental chair must press a lever to effect the presentation of food.

Sanford lists four kinds of instrumental conditioning:

The simplest kind is called *primary reward conditioning*. The learned response is instrumental in obtaining a biologically significant reward, such as a pellet of food or a drink of water. In *escape conditioning* the organism learns a response that is instrumental in getting him out of some place he prefers not to be. *Avoidance conditioning* is the kind of learning in which a response to a cue is instrumental in avoiding a painful experience. A rat on a grid, for example, may avoid a shock if he quickly pushes a lever when a light signal goes on. *Secondary reward conditioning* is that in which there is instrumental behavior to get at a stimulus which has no biological utility itself but which has in the past been associated with a biologically significant stimulus. For example, chimpanzees will learn to press a lever to obtain poker chips, which they insert in a slot to secure grapes. Later they will work to accumulate poker chips even when they are not interested in grapes.

Generally, it is assumed that most learning occurs as a result of instrumental responding rather than as an elicited consequence of classical conditioning. But both classical and instrumental conditioning techniques have begun to occupy a central place in the theoretical and practical behaviors of a growing group of clinicians who consider their methods to be clearly based on experimental laboratory procedures, therapists who derive their techniques and principles from learning theory as based in the laboratory. The clinicians—represented by such theorists as Mowrer, Wolpe, and the followers of methods developed by Skinner—refer to themselves as "behavior therapists," "learning therapists," and "conditioning therapists," such appellations being virtually interchangeable and synonymous.

The most influential contemporary theories of learning have been advanced by Hull (upon whose theoretical structure much of Wolpe's work is based) and Skinner (whose methods are basic to operant conditioning techniques in treatment). These theorists fall within the group of learning theorists espousing a reinforcement model of learning. The two-factor learning theory espoused by Mowrer, in which classical conditioning and reinforcement theory are considered, has also been influential.

HULL'S LEARNING THEORY

Clark Hull's approach to learning theory is strongly mathematical and neurophysiological. He sought to establish a theory of behavior, which he equated with learning, that could be quantified and tested in accordance with scientific method. In his book *Principles of Behavior*, Hull described the learning process this way: "Just as the inherited equipment of reaction tendencies consists of receptor-effector connections, so the process of learning consists in the strengthening of certain of these connections as contrasted with others, or in the setting up of quite new connections." For Hull, these connections occurred internally and were mediated by nervous system stimulation. The establishment of a connection occurred as follows:

$$S \to s \to r \to R$$

where an external stimulus, S, has as its function the stimulation of an efferent system, s, which, in turn, effects a motor impulse, r, within the nervous system. The final response, external R, does not have to occur for learning to take place; the critical connection is the s-r connection, leading to a habit.

HABIT FAMILY HIERARCHY

The habit, for Hull, is an established connection within the nervous system, but these connections are not limited. The concept of the habit family hierarchy allows for transfer of learning or generalization to occur. Thus, a given stimulus, S, may evoke a number of different responses in varying levels of strength, but this stimulus, as we have noted, evokes a response or set of responses within the nervous system that anticipate a goal response. For Hull, the goal response is antedated by fractional responses in the establishment of a habit. Thus, r may become a fractional response, an element of R, called a "fractional anticipatory goal response" or r_G, which in itself is stimulating. Said Hull:

> A fractional anticipatory goal reaction must produce continuously a stimulation (s_G) characteristic of the point of reinforcement or goal situation . . . s_G becomes a guiding stimulus leading to its own realization, to the final complete act of which it is a part. As such, the fractional goal reaction (r_G) is a *pure stimulus act*, i.e., an act whose only biological or survival function is that of producing a stimulus for the control of other action of a more direct adaptive value.

The fractional response, r_G, then becomes a mediating element between S and R. An example of this is salivation occurring before the consummatory goal response of eating.

Because there is variability in response sequences leading to a goal as a result of varying environmental conditions, Hull postulated that "since all the alternative behavior sequences have led to the same goal, all of the component acts of all the sequences will alike be conditioned to the same fractional anticipatory goal-reaction stimulus (s_G), and in this sense will constitute a *family*."

The habit family hierarchy, noted Bugelski, proposes that "any of a number of S's can eventuate in the same R_G goal response." There is a common fractional goal reaction (r_G) to all the elements in the series and hence in the habit family, but some of these will be weaker than others in excitatory potential. Hull suggested that this results from being more remote from the final R_G at the beginning of the sequence. Therefore, they form a hierarchy of strength. This conceptualization forms an important basis for the therapeutic application of this learning theory, inasmuch as it allows for an analysis of behavior clearly in terms of adaptation through alternative response conditioning.

HULL'S CONCEPT OF DRIVE

Thorndike's law of effect used the concept of satisfaction to account for reinforcing effects of certain responses. Hull attempted to make the satisfying element less subjective by stating the law of effect as he understood it to be:

> If the central afferent receptor discharge (s_c) of a stimulus element (S_c) of a stimulus compound is active in the central nervous system at the same time that a reaction (r_u) is evoked and if at about this time there occurs a "reinforcing state of affairs," there will result from this conjunction of events an increment to a habit (sHr).

The "reinforcing state of affairs," for Hull, represented the "diminution in a need (and the associated diminution in the drive (D))."

This principle of primary reinforcement is clearly a drive-reduction approach; attaining the goal response reduces the drive associated with the aroused need, strengthening the behaviors that led to the reduction in tension. This strengthened sequence becomes the habit.

INHIBITION

Hull postulated that neural impulses (afferent receptor discharges) "occurring at about the same time interact and so modify each other." He called this afferent interaction and viewed this as a basis for the reduction or elimination of a response through the presence of an "extra or alien stimulus in a conditioned stimulus compound which can reduce the excitatory potential." An example of this is the interference of "irrelevant stimulations resulting from an emotional upset" that may disrupt a child's classroom performance.

Hull saw this as equivalent to Pavlov's external inhibition. Pavlov's concept of internal inhibition is similar to Hull's conditioned inhibition

$(_sI_r)$, which resulted from reactive inhibition, a "negative drive state" similar to fatigue or physiological impairment resulting from activity. Hull's conditioned inhibition is an interfering set of events.

This brief summary of salient features of Hullian learning theory indicates that Hull's theoretical position was largely based on neurophysiological postulates and concerned itself with drive and drive reduction as basic to reinforcement. Let us turn now to Wolpe's behavior therapy and briefly examine its Hullian bases.

WOLPE'S CONDITIONING THEORY

Wolpe defined neurotic behavior as behavior that "consists of persistent habits of learned (conditioned) unadaptive behavior acquired in anxiety-generating situations." It is no coincidence that Wolpe invokes the term "habit" to describe neurotic behavior in this regard. The Hullian influence becomes clear again in the following observation about anxiety responses: "They necessarily produce anxiety drive (with concomitant central neural excitation) as an antecedent." He also reflects this neural approach to learning when he notes that "learning is subserved by the development of conductivity between neurons in anatomical apposition." Here we see the Hullian concepts of learning as being mediated by central nervous system activity, the neurophysiological basis of drive, and anxiety as a drive leading, presumably, to activity aimed at drive reduction.

Reciprocal Inhibition

Wolpe also reflected a Hullian orientation in his important principle of reciprocal inhibition, which may account for anxiety drive reduction: "If a response inhibitory to anxiety can be made to occur in the presence of anxiety-evoking stimuli, it will weaken the connection between these stimuli and the anxiety responses." Relaxation, for example, is considered to be incompatible with and, therefore, inhibitory to anxiety.

Anxiety Hierarchy

Wolpe also used Hull's concept of habit family hierarchy in an interesting clinical fashion when he established anxiety hierarchy relationships among anxiety-evoking stimuli. Assuming that varying stimuli may evoke the response of anxiety, Wolpe asks his patient to imagine, usually under hypnosis, the least disturbing item of a list of potential anxiety-evoking stimuli, then to proceed up the list to the most disturbing stimuli. For example, a patient with a fear of death might rank the sight of a coffin lower in the hierarchy than a corpse (highest intensity), with perhaps a tombstone ranked somewhere in between.

Wolpe's technique of desensitization is a counterconditioning technique in which responses designed to inhibit the anxiety response are evoked at each level along the hierarchy. Reciprocal inhibition of the fear response is thus conditioned.

SKINNER'S LEARNING THEORY:
OPERANT CONDITIONING

Proponents of an experimental analysis of behavior based on operant conditioning techniques and also reinforcement theorists form a group of behaviorists who tend largely to minimize theoretical considerations and to concentrate on an analysis of the functional relationships among events. For example, instead of dealing with the repression of unacceptable thoughts, as psychoanalysts do, Skinner suggested that it is more important to avoid the inner causes and to emphasize the questions that ask "why the response was emitted in the first place, why it was punished, and what current variables are active."

The term "operant" refers to a class of responses that are emitted by the organism rather than elicited by some known stimulus. Operant responses are also frequently referred to by such terms as "voluntary," as opposed to "involuntary" or reflex behavior. Reflex responses are elicited, as in classical conditioning, and are termed respondents. Thus, respondents, such as pupillary reflexes, are differentiated from operants. An example of an operant response is reaching for a telephone. An operant has some effect on the environment. Keller observes:

> Respondents, right from the start, are evoked by their own special stimuli. Food in the mouth will bring salivation. . . . In the case of operants, however, there are at the beginning no specific stimuli with which we can evoke them. Rather, we are compelled to wait until they appear before we can do anything about them. . . . It is for this reason we may speak of operant behavior as emitted ("sent out") rather than elicited.

Skinner in his first major work, *The Behavior of Organisms*, differentiated two types of conditioning, which he called type S and type R. Type S conditioning "is defined by the operation of the simultaneous presentation of the reinforcing stimulus and another stimulus." In type R conditioning, the reinforcing stimulus "is contingent upon a response." This distinction between classical (respondent, involuntary, type S) and instrumental (operant, voluntary, type R) conditioning is not entirely accepted by many learning theorists, on the grounds that the criteria are too ambiguous. Psychophysiological interactions, for example, are not clearly differentiated into operant or respondent. For most purposes, however, the distinction can be useful if one avoids the tendency to let theoretical niceties restructure the nervous system.

REINFORCEMENT

A key concept in operant conditioning is that of reinforcement, which, as was noted earlier, Sidman defined as "any event, contingent upon the response of the organism that alters the future likelihood of that response." In operant conditioning the term "positive reinforcement" is used to describe an event consequent upon a response that increases the probability of that response recurring. A negative reinforcement is an event likely to decrease the probability of that response's recurrence. A negative reinforcement is an event that strengthens the response that removes it; for example, if a punishing consequence attaches to a response, any behavior that avoids or escapes the punishment will be strengthened —that is, increased in probability.

RESPONSE FREQUENCY

Another important concept is the use of response frequency as a basic datum. The frequency with which a response is emitted is a clear, observable measure of behavior. Skinner has observed that personality descriptions are couched in frequency terms; to say that a person is "an enthusiastic skier," "an inveterate gambler," or "hostile" reduces to a statement of a perceived frequency with which a certain class of behavior is emitted, presumably with some normative conceptualization in mind. Aggressive behavior is emitted by most people; to say that a person is "hostile" suggests that this class of response occurs with a higher level of frequency than is usually expected.

SHAPING BEHAVIOR

The concept of shaping is also of importance in discussing operant conditioning. Working with a freely moving organism, the experimenter selects the final response he desires to produce. Sidman describes the shaping process this way:

> Shaping is accomplished by reinforcing successively closer approximations to the behavior with which the experimenter ultimately wants to work. The experimental situation, for example, may be one in which a monkey is to be reinforced with food for pressing a lever. If the monkey just sits quietly at first, the experimenter will wait until the animal moves and will then immediately deliver the food. By continuing to reinforce all movements, the experimenter will soon have an active animal with which to work. He then reinforces only those responses which bring the animal closer to the lever, as if drawn by an invisible string. The experimenter now directs his attention to the animal's hand. He delivers the food whenever the hand moves closer to the lever, and it is not long before the animal places its hand on the lever and depresses it. The experimenter can then turn the rest of the job over to his automatic apparatus, which will deliver the food only when the animal actually depresses the lever.

This successive approximation, by steps, toward the final terminal behavior is a critical aspect of the experimental method. But it is necessary to specify the response desired, not in general terms but by specific behavioral criteria. One of the key factors in operant conditioning is the frequency with which a carefully specified response occurs in an equally carefully defined environment.

Control of the environment does not necessarily mean the rigorous controls of an experimental laboratory. Skinner, in a paper on teaching animals, observed that it takes a controlled laboratory situation to work out full learning experiments but that a great deal can be accomplished under informal home conditions, provided that the elements of reinforcement, such as food for the family dog, and a conditioned reinforcer, such as a snap cricket, are present.

OPERANT PARADIGM

A summary statement of basic concepts in operant conditioning has been presented by Goldiamond, who noted that Dollard and Miller listed the four variables of learned behavior as drive, response, cue, and reinforcement and who suggested that these are identical to the variables stated in the following paradigm:

$$\ldots\ldots\ldots SV \text{ (state variables)}$$

controlling stimuli:

$$
\left.
\begin{array}{l}
S^D - S^\Delta \text{ (discriminative)} \\
SS^c \text{ (constant)}
\end{array}
\right\}
\qquad
-- R \text{ (response)} \;--\; S^r - S^0 \\
\text{(differential} \\
\text{reinforcement)}
$$

Bachrach, Erwin, and Mohr have presented the following explanation:

To modify Goldiamond's explanation of this paradigm somewhat, presenting a discriminative stimulus (S^D) in the presence of other constant stimuli (SS^c) will occasion a response (R); whether this response recurs is contingent upon the consequences (S^r) of that response (under these specific conditions) and the state variables (SV), usually referred to as "needs," "motivation," "deprivation," and the like, which make the consequences of the response effective in controlling it. Assuming that behavior is governed by its consequences under specified conditions, discriminative behavior can be produced, maintained, and altered if the constant stimuli, the discriminative stimuli, the response contingencies, and the state variables are specified and controlled.

This paradigm was used in a clinical case described by Bachrach, Erwin, and Mohr in which the experimental therapy program was planned according to the variables. The patient was an anorexic whose eating behavior was restored through operant conditioning techniques.

MOWRER'S TWO-FACTOR LEARNING THEORY

O. H. Mowrer in a paper in 1939 offered, as Hilgard has observed, "the first clear statement of the anxiety-reduction or fear-reduction theory of reinforcement." Mowrer then theorized that much learning could be explained on the basis of acquired fear (anxiety) and that responses that reduce this anxiety are learned and maintained.

Contiguity and Drive Reduction

Mowrer suggested that anxiety responses are learned by contiguity. An adventitious association of a neutral stimulus with a painful stimulus conditions fear by contiguity in a fashion related to stimulus substitution in classical conditioning. In other words, a stimulus that in itself is not fear-evoking is accidentally presented at the same time as a painful stimulus; by simple conditioning, what Mowrer then called sign learning, the neutral stimulus becomes a conditioned aversive stimulus.

Any response that results in the avoidance or elimination of such a conditioned aversive stimulus, as an anxiety-producing event, is reinforced, even in the absence of other reinforcement, because the response reduces anxiety (drive). Once learned, these avoidance responses persist.

Mowrer believed that these were different from other types of conditioned responses in that there was no need for continued reinforcement to maintain the response. Other conditioned responses would extinguish in the absence of reinforcement; Mowrer felt that conditioned anxiety responses did not need the reinforcement of repetition of the original trauma. Although the responses were conditioned by contiguity, they were maintained by the reinforcing effects of drive reduction; classical conditioning of fear by contiguity was maintained by the subsequent conditioning (instrumental) of avoidance behavior by drive reduction.

Autonomic Responses

Another differentiation Mowrer assumed in his two-factor theory was that fear responses are entirely autonomic. Emotional responses are involuntary and largely autonomic; instrumental responding is voluntary and largely under the control of the central nervous system. The classically conditioned fear response learned under contiguity (sign learning) was, therefore, physiologically differentiated from the instrumentally conditioned avoidance responses maintained by anxiety reduction, what Mowrer came to call solution learning. The operant-respondent, type S-type R dichotomy is clearly in evidence here.

Some experimental evidence supported Mowrer's position that drive reduction is important in solution-learning (instrumental conditioning) but that it is not crucial in the autonomically controlled anxiety response. Studies such as those reported by Mowrer and Solomon tended to support such a position, although Solomon and Wynne suggested that fear responses are more than autonomic, involving such events as visceral and neuroendocrine responses as well as skeletal motor discharge. Thus, central nervous system functions and voluntary behavior are also involved.

Mowrer has also invoked a model in which the stimuli conditioned to the onset of painful events acquire certain drive (anxiety) characteristics, but those stimuli associated with the avoidance of or escape from pain become positively reinforcing. These two events Mowrer described as responses of fear and hope. In recent years Mowrer's theorizing has centered largely around the development of neurosis and, in particular, the centrality of guilt and anxiety in emotional disorders.

CONCLUSION

In the application of some of the laboratory procedures derived from learning research, the behavior therapies have fallen heir to the very problems that beset the research scientists. Foremost among these is the problem of definition; the precise definition of such crucial concepts as stimulus, response, and reinforcement remains a theoretical and experimental problem. It is true, for example, that the definition of reinforcement when an experimenter is working with deprivation variables—deprivation of food or water, for instance—is a relatively uncomplicated experimental manipulation, although even here there are problems. But these problems are enormously complicated when the reinforcements are based on socially acquired drives, such as approval or attention, vaguely defined social events that appear of importance in human behavior. The precision with which experimental contingencies can be stated in both the laboratory and the clinic, then, is a continuing theoretical and research issue. A dedicated and meaningful interaction between research and clinical scientists in the development of learning theories and their application appears to be a most important and fruitful enterprise.

REFERENCES

Bachrach, A. J. Operant conditioning and behavior: some clinical applications. In *The Psychological Basis of Medical Practice*, H. Lief and N. R. Lief, editors, p. 94. Hoeber Medical Division, Harper & Row, New York, 1963.

Bachrach, A. J., Erwin, W. J., and Mohr, J. P. The control of eating behavior in an anorexic by operant conditioning techniques. In *Case Studies in Behavior Modification*, L. Ullmann and L. Krasner, editors, p. 153. Holt, Rinehart and Winston, New York, 1965.

Bachrach, A. J., and Quigley, W. A. Direct methods of treatment. In *An Introduction to Clinical Psychology*, I. A. Berg and L. Pennington, editors, ed. 3, p. 482. Ronald Press, New York, 1966.

Bugelski, B. R. *The Psychology of Learning.* Holt, Rinehart and Winston, New York, 1956.

Goldiamond, I. Perception. In *Experimental Foundations of Clinical Psychology,* A. J. Bachrach, editor, p. 280. Basic Books, New York, 1962.

Hebb, D. O. *A Textbook of Psychology,* ed. 2. W. B. Saunders, Philadelphia, 1966.

Hilgard, E. R. *Theories of Learning.* Appleton-Century-Crofts, New York, 1956.

Hull, C. L. Conditioning: outline of a systematic theory of learning. In *The Psychology of Learning,* 41st yearbook, National Society for the Study of Education, Part II. University of Chicago Press, Chicago, 1942.

Hull, C. L. *Principles of Behavior: An Introduction to Behavior Theory.* Appleton-Century-Crofts, New York, 1943.

Keller, F. S. *Learning: Reinforcement Theory.* Random House, New York, 1954.

Kimble, G. A. *Hilgard and Marquis' Conditioning and Learning,* ed. 2. Appleton-Century-Crofts, New York, 1961.

Mowrer, O. H. A stimulus-response analysis of anxiety and its role as a reinforcing agent. Psychol. Rev., 46: 553, 1939.

Mowrer, O. H. On the dual nature of learning—a reinterpretation of "conditioning" and "problem-solving." Harvard Educational Rev., 17: 102, 1947.

Mowrer, O. H. Two-factor learning theory reconsidered, with special reference to secondary reinforcement and the concept of habit. Psychol. Rev., 63: 114, 1956.

Mowrer, O. H. *The Crisis in Psychiatry and Religion.* D. Van Nostrand, Princeton, 1961.

Mowrer, O. H., and Solomon, L. N. Contiguity vs. drive-reduction in conditioned fear: the proximity and abruptness of drive-reduction. Amer. J. Psychol., 67: 15, 1954.

Sanford, F. *Psychology: A Scientific Study of Man.* Belmont, Wadsworth, 1965.

Sidman, M. *Tactics of Scientific Research.* Basic Books, New York, 1960.

Skinner, B. F. *Science and Human Behavior.* Macmillan, New York, 1953.

Skinner, B. F. Some contributions of an experimental analysis of behavior to psychology as a whole. Amer. Psychologist, 8: 69, 1953.

Solomon, R. L., and Wynne, L. C. Traumatic avoidance learning: the principles of anxiety conservation and partial irreversibility. Psychol. Rev., 61: 353, 1954.

Thorndike, E. L. *Human Learning.* Appleton-Century-Crofts, New York, 1931.

Wolpe, J. The genesis of neurosis. South Afr. Med., J., 24: 613, 1950.

Wolpe, J. *Psychotherapy by Reciprocal Inhibition.* Stanford University Press, Palo Alto, 1958.

Wolpe, J. The experimental foundations of some new psychotherapeutic methods. In *Experimental Foundations of Clinical Psychology,* A. J. Bachrach, editor, p. 554. Basic Books, New York, 1962.

CHAPTER 15

Motivation

ROBERT B. MALMO, Ph.D.

INTRODUCTION

UNDER THE GENERAL TOPIC of motivation are many subtopics that are of interest from the psychiatric point of view, and this chapter focuses on these instead of attempting to touch on all points in the general area. For example, the topic of experimentation on drug dependency in animals has been selected not only because it is relevant for theories of motivation but also because these observations on animals have proved invaluable in placing the human problems of drug dependency in much clearer perspective. The second part of this chapter, drawing on data from human subjects, summarizes various clinical and experimental approaches to problems of human motivation. In addition, some current theoretical issues in this field are discussed. For example, the relevancy of data at the physiological level is considered. The affirmative point of view is in part documented with references to observations on neurological patients with operations on their frontal lobes and on psychiatric patients suffering pathological anxiety. The activation concept, which is introduced in the subsection on animal motivation, is also brought to bear on the human problem of anxiety.

The reader may well ask what some of these subtopics have in common and how they differ from those aspects of behavior dealt with under other headings, such as perception and learning. First of all, it should be pointed out that these topics are not mutually exclusive. For example, learning is

Preparation of this chapter was supported in part by grants from the Medical Research Council, National Research Council, and Defense Research Board of Canada, and from the National Institute of Mental Health and National Science Foundation of the United States.

certainly involved in becoming addicted to a drug, and, when the drug is withdrawn, the resulting bodily changes are clearly perceptual phenomena. But given an organism with certain perceptual capacities and with a particular learning history, what is called motivation determines the nature and intensity of the behavior that occurs under certain conditions of environmental stimulation.

ANIMAL MOTIVATION

BIOLOGICAL MECHANISMS AND HOMEOSTASIS IN MOTIVATION

In the mediation of learning and perception in mammals, the cerebral cortex plays a major role. But the limbic system, the hypothalamus in particular, appears to hold the main keys to understanding basic biological mechanisms responsible for motivating behavior. Neural and glandular processes mediated by this system as they appear to relate to motivation are the subject of extensive investigation at the present time. So numerous are these studies that even listing various lines of attack on basic biological motivational mechanisms is not feasible here, and this discussion, therefore, is highly selective.

Homeostatic mechanism for water regulation. In order to provide a concrete reference point for the discussion that follows, we briefly describe the homeostatic mechanism for water regulation. This mechanism has been chosen as an illustration because most of its aspects are well understood and because its principles of operation are typical of other homeostatic mechanisms.

Everyone knows that, for the mammal to remain alive, it must have water. When it has not had water for a period of time, its behavior is dominated by search for water and relief of thirst. But the whole problem of water regulation requires analysis at more than one level.

At the physiological reflexive level, water deprivation causes a release of antidiuretic hormone (ADH), which in its action on the kidneys reduces urine flow to a minimum, thus conserving water. Crucial for understanding this mechanism and other fluid-regulating homeostatic mechanisms is the *milieu intérieur* concept of Claude Bernard. In the case of water regulation, *milieu intérieur* refers to critical physicochemical relations between internal conditions of certain cells, called receptor cells or sensors, and the extracellular fluids, chiefly the blood supply, surrounding them.

Three questions are generally raised when the detailed workings of any homeostatic mechanism are being sought: (1) What critical changes in physicochemical conditions represent a significant departure from the optimal *milieu intérieur* or other steady state? (2) What sensor detects this departure from the optimum? (3) What is the line of transmission from sensor to the mechanisms responsible for effecting return to more optimal conditions? For water regulation, the answers are these: (1) The critical physicochemical changes are increments in effective osmotic pressure in extracellular fluids and intracellular volume changes. (2) The known sensors are neurons in the supraoptic nucleus of the hypothalamus, called osmoreceptors because their rate of firing increases with treatments that increase effective osmotic pressure in the extracellular fluids—for example, injection of hypertonic sodium chloride. Ishikawa, Koizumi, and Brooks, whose experiments with unit recordings established this fact, also found that the osmosensitive neurons responded to injections of hypertonic sodium chloride by an acceleration of firing, even after isolation from surrounding brain tissues. (3) It has been established beyond question that the supraoptic nuclei of the hypothalamus are involved in the production and release of antidiuretic hormone from the posterior lobe of the pituitary. The resulting conservation of water by the kidneys completes the reflexive chain, effecting return to more optimal physiological conditions.

At the reflex level, then, the picture is relatively complete. But renal water conservation is only a temporary measure, and, of course, the animal must seek and ingest water in order to avoid fatal dehydration. What is known about neurophysiological mediation of these *behavioral mechanisms?* Water intake, as well as renal water conservation, is increased by tiny intrahypothalamic injections of sodium chloride. This indicates that, generally speaking, the sensors for reflexive and behavioral mechanisms share the same general area of the brain. But much more investigation is required on the behavioral aspect of this problem.

Other innate homeostatic mechanisms. The homeostatic mechanisms for regulation of temperature and of food intake have sensors in the hypothalamus. Microelectrode studies of cells in the hypothalamus— their reactions to changes in the *milieu intérieur* and their relations with other structures in the brain—are actively proceeding at the present time, with prospects of gaining important information in the next few years.

These innate homeostatic mechanisms serve to maintain an equilibrium essential to the health and survival of the animal, and their role in the motivation of animals is obvious.

Homeostatic mechanism for drug addiction. Drug dependence, though acquired and detrimental rather than beneficial, also appears to involve some kind of homeostatic mechanism. At least, the hypothesis that it is an acquired homeostatic mechanism seems useful in investigating this problem.

The physiological and behavioral aspects of morphine addiction, the most thoroughly studied addiction in animals, may be considered with reference to the following questions.

1. HOW IS THE HOMEOSTATIC MECHANISM ACQUIRED? Considering the gaps in knowledge concerning the innate mechanism for maintaining the constancy of the water content of the blood and the even greater gap in knowledge of other innate mechanisms, it is not surprising that much less is known about acquired homeostatic mechanisms, such as

the one mediating dependency on morphine. Still, animal studies have thrown considerable light on the problem of how morphine dependency can be produced.

It does not matter whether the morphine is self-administered or administered by the experimenter. The only requirement for establishing dependency on morphine is that the administration be kept up regularly, day after day, until some objective criterion of dependency has been reached, usually the appearance of withdrawal symptoms. In Spragg's investigation of morphine addiction in chimpanzees, a typical course of morphine injections was 0.1 mg. per kilogram twice a day for the first three weeks, thereafter gradually raised to 2 mg. per kilogram and continuing at that level for several months.

When a dose was skipped or delayed for a few hours, some early signs of mild withdrawal were noted: slight rhinorrhea, drops of perspiration on the face, unusually large quantity of feces in the cage, heightened irritability, and yawning. Animals differed in the time required to produce the first clear (withdrawal) signs of dependence from as early as two and a half weeks in one animal to seven weeks in another.

When the animal sought out the injection on his own initiative, which happened after as long as five months of injections, Spragg called the animal addicted. Examples of such purposeful goal-seeking behavior, usually after some break in the continuity of dosing with the drug, were: showing eagerness to be taken from the living cage by the experimenter when doses were needed, in clear contrast to behavior exhibited when taken from the living cage at other times; tugging at the leash and leading the experimenter toward and into the room in which injections were regularly given; exhibiting frustration when led away from the injection room and back to the living cage without having been given an injection; showing eagerness and excitement when allowed to get up on the box on which injections were regularly made; cooperating eagerly in the injection procedure; choosing a syringe-containing box, whereupon injection was given, in preference to a food-containing box.

2. WHAT SENSOR SIGNALS A NEED FOR THE DRUG? To put the question concretely, does the acquired homeostatic mechanism underlying dependence on morphine have a sensor resembling the osmoreceptor cells in the hypothalamus, which help maintain constancy of the water content of the blood? It is conceivable that certain hypothalamic cells, not already specialized for detecting dehydration or other such primary need states, may somehow undergo modification during the course of continuous morphine administration, thereby acquiring a sensitivity to the physicochemical conditions that underlie withdrawal symptoms in the morphine-dependent individual. This possibility would be susceptible to experimental attack if, by means of microelectrode recording, a search could be made for cells in the hypothalamus that fire at a faster rate just prior to a needed injection and reduce their rate of firing immediately

after injection. At present, this notion is speculative.

3. WHAT PHYSICOCHEMICAL CONDITIONS STIMULATE THE SENSOR? That is, what are the physicochemical conditions in drug dependency that correspond to the blood osmotic pressure in hydration constancy? According to Sourkes, the nature of the cellular adaptations in states of drug dependence and tolerance is an unsolved problem that presents a challenge to the physiologist and biochemist. Two kinds of theory about dependency may be distinguished. Both models postulate a form of cellular adaptation, and they are not mutually exclusive. According to one theory, the mechanism of adaptation requires that the drug be present on the neuron itself. According to the other theory, it is simply necessary that neurohumoral input be reduced; in other words, the reduction of nervous activity per se and not the exposure of neurons to the drug itself is directly responsible for the development of withdrawal hyperexcitability.

4. WHAT CENTRAL NERVOUS SYSTEM MECHANISMS ACT TO RESTORE EQUILIBRIUM? A reflex such as renal water conservation can work for a limited time only. Eventually, the animal must engage in purposive or goal-seeking activity in order to maintain conditions essential for life. For example, the dehydrated mammal must seek water. Similar goal-seeking activities are observed when an animal acquires an addiction, although they are not essential for maintaining life. Examples of purposive activity in chimpanzees suffering morphine deficiency have been mentioned. Such activities reflect at least two things: the strength of the dependency and the fact that the animal has learned the connection between his withdrawal symptoms and the means to eliminate them. It will be recalled that this learning did not occur until several months after withdrawal symptoms first appeared.

It was once believed that lower mammals like the rat could not become addicted to morphine. Compared with the chimpanzee, the rat is obviously limited in its range of responses instrumental to obtaining morphine. But after dependency, as shown by physiological withdrawal symptoms, had been produced by continuous injections over a period of several weeks, rats drank more fluid containing a morphine substitute than they drank prior to this period of morphine administration. Furthermore, Beach has shown that, after dependence was established, rats exhibited a preference for stimuli associated with the effects of morphine. Recently it has been shown by Weeks that, after dependence on morphine had been established, rats would press a bar to inject themselves with morphine by means of an indwelling injection device. A plastic tube was passed under the skin from behind the ears to the front of the neck, where it was connected to a silicone-rubber cannula inserted into the rat's jugular vein, leading to the heart. All these data indicate that taking morphine away from an addicted rat elicits goal-seeking behavior.

EXPERIMENTAL ALCOHOLISM IN ANIMALS

Continuous administration of alcohol to animals for periods sufficiently long to produce dependence has rarely been carried out. Richter succeeded in producing dependence in three wild rats by restricting their fluid intake to a 10 per cent alcohol solution for a period of about forty days. At the end of the period of force-feeding with alcohol, the rats continued to drink large quantities of alcohol, even though plain water was made available to them. One animal drank progressively more alcohol and less plain water, ate less and less, and died thirty days later. The course was one that closely parallels that of some human alcoholics.

In domesticated rats, however, Richter states that, even with more prolonged periods of forced feeding of alcohol, no such clear signs of dependence were ever observed. It is possible that dependency in the domesticated rat could be demonstrated with still longer periods of exposure to alcohol. But Richter found no such difference between wild and domesticated rats when force-fed for three to six months on diets supplemented with increasingly higher concentrations of morphine sulfate. Wild and domesticated rats showed very similar withdrawal symptoms when the morphine sulfate was removed from the diet. Other workers have also reported clear-cut dependency on morphine in domesticated rats. Again, absence of reports in the literature of dependency on alcohol in the domesticated rat may simply be due to the failure of investigators to administer alcohol in sufficient volume and over a long enough period of time. Still, the available evidence from animals is in line with clinical knowledge that dependency on morphine is much more readily established than is dependence on alcohol. That dependence is much more common in the case of tobacco than alcohol has been commented on recently by Brain.

It may be supposed that alcohol (or acetaldehyde) per se does not act on a receptor site in the nerve cell. In cases where dependency does occur after long-continued heavy alcohol intake, the effect of alcohol may be much less direct than the effect of morphine. Recent research suggests such a possibility and is cited as an example of what *might* occur, although this suggestion is highly tentative. It seems possible that continuous ingestion of large quantities of alcohol may cause a deviation in the metabolism of norepinephrine and that in this process ethanol or acetaldehyde may promote the formation of catecholamine catabolites that resemble morphine. If dependency after heavy drinking of alcohol does turn out to involve some indirect process such as this, the fact that moderate drinking does not ordinarily produce dependency would be understandable, since moderate drinking would not ordinarily cause sufficient deviation of norepinephrine metabolism to promote the formation of morphine-like catabolites and subsequent dependency. Apparent proneness of certain individuals to dependency on alcohol might also be understandable in terms of their norepinephrine metabolism being more prone to interference, resulting in more rapid appearance of the addicting catabolites.

Or it may be that, compared with morphine, ethanol is a less effective blocking agent. Furthermore, it is logical to consider that individual differences in effectiveness of ethanol as a blocking agent may account in part for differences between individuals in their susceptibility to dependence on alcohol.

However, these are highly tentative suggestions. The nature of neural or other cellular adaptations in *all* states of drug dependence is still an unsolved problem, a problem urgently in need of further experimental work.

IMMEDIATE EFFECTS OF DRUGS VERSUS EFFECTS OF WITHDRAWAL SYMPTOMS

The fact that even sated rats developed a preference for the goal box where they were injected with morphine was interpreted by Beach as evidence that the drug's immediate effects, after many exposures, had reinforced learning. Beach and others have demonstrated a second kind of reinforcement, that of relief from withdrawal symptoms in dependent animals. Unfortunately, some authors, perhaps through failure to be explicit, cause confusion in the minds of readers between immediate effects of the drug on nondependent animals and the relief from withdrawal symptoms in dependent animals.

It appears that there are two motivational mechanisms involved, one mediated by the immediate reinforcing nature of alcohol or morphine and the other mediated by the relief of a *need* for the substance in the homeostatic sense. In the first case, when the animal chooses to drink alcohol, the alcohol is most probably not fulfilling a homeostatic need; instead, it has gustatory or postingestional effects that are reinforcing. In the case of an addicted animal, however, the ingestion of an addicting substance is necessary to keep from becoming ill.

The literature dealing with alcohol ingestion by animals particularly suffers from confusion of these two mechanisms. Sometimes it is implied that conditions that strengthen the animal's preference for an alcohol solution *necessarily* make him significantly more prone to chronic dependency on alcohol. This, of course, is clearly wrong. As Richter's work has shown, domesticated rats can drink relatively large quantities of alcohol over long periods of time without showing withdrawal symptoms or other signs of dependency.

It is important, therefore, to distinguish between a shift in the *nondependent* animal's preference for alcohol and the *dependent* animal's intake of alcohol to relieve withdrawal symptoms. With this distinction clearly in mind, however, it is of considerable interest to investigate the question of what conditions, other than dependency, do increase preference for alcohol in animals.

Mammals below chimpanzee and man on the phylogenetic scale usually reject solutions of alcohol, with the exception of an inbred strain of mice that for some reason, as yet unknown, prefers certain alcohol solutions to water. Special conditions, however, have been shown to raise the animal's preference for alcohol solutions relative to plain water. Sex and strain differences are examples of constitutional variables that have been studied. Experiential variables have usually involved some kind of stress. In a recent study by McEwen at McGill it was found that alcohol intake patterns in rats could be modified under a number of conditions. These modifications were not due to simple correlations between intensities of stress in the variety of situations; they were dependent on complex interactions between strain, sex, and particular experiences.

Results of recent experiments on chimpanzees by Fitz-Gerald at the Yerkes Regional Primate Research Center are consistent with McEwen's findings of sex differences. Fitz-Gerald's data also indicate that chimpanzees resemble man in their enjoyment of alcohol. Unlike lower mammals, including rhesus monkeys, they drink alcohol voluntarily, without special inducements. It may be that a large brain with a relatively high proportion of cortex is required for accumulation of residual tensions that are pleasantly relieved by alcohol.

ACTIVATION CONCEPT IN MOTIVATION

The activation concept in its multifactor empirical form states that the level of physiological activation is determined by the interaction of internal and external factors. The changes in the *milieu intérieur* produced by water deprivation are examples of internal factors. In this situation the external cue factors interacting effectively with the internal ones to raise level of activation are, for example, perception of water or of other cues associated with the procurement of water.

Bélanger et al., at Université de Montréal have found that heart rate (HR) increases progressively with hours of water deprivation or food deprivation when the recordings are made under appropriate conditions of cue stimulation. The HR curve for rats in Figure 1 is a typical finding: HR in rats bar-pressing for water showed progressive increment as a function of increasing hours of water deprivation. HR increment may also be regularly produced by depriving the animal of food. But food deprivation and cues associated with food must be operative *together* for HR to show a rise. Even though the animal is deprived of food or water, HR does not increase in the absence of appropriate external cues. This observation provides important clues to the kind of neural mechanism that mediates goal-seeking, motivated by deprivation of a basic need.

In the previous discussion of the mechanisms for water regulation, it was noted that the osmoreceptors in the hypothalamus react to changes in

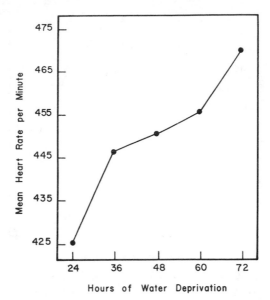

FIGURE 1. Heart rate level in relation to duration of water deprivation in rats. The rats were subjected to an increasing order of deprivation. (Data are from article by Bélanger, D., and Feldman, S. M. J. Comp. Physiol. Psychol., 55: 220, 1962.)

the *milieu intérieur* by acceleration of firing rate, even after isolation from surrounding brain tissues. The conditions producing that acceleration are different from those accelerating HR because, obviously, afferent inputs are not required for accelerating the firing rate of the osmoreceptor cells, which appear to be under the sole control of the *milieu intérieur*. It may be that these osmoreceptor cells are specialized for taking part only in the reflex mechanism through which water is conserved by the kidneys.

It is possible that for a goal-seeking mechanism, where environmental cues are of critical importance, there are other cells, probably also in the hypothalamus, that accelerate firing in reaction to both internal (*milieu intérieur*) and external cue factors. This question can be attacked experimentally by recording from single cells in the hypothalamus of awake animals, following the paradigm of the Bélanger and Feldman experiment illustrated in Figure 1. Finding, under these conditions, that neural cells respond in a lawful quantitative manner, like HR, would provide strong support for one of the basic neural assumptions underlying the activation hypothesis.

The relation between hours of deprivation and frequency of bar-pressing, as shown in Figure 2, takes the form of an inverted U. This finding is consistent with the prediction that there is a level of activation

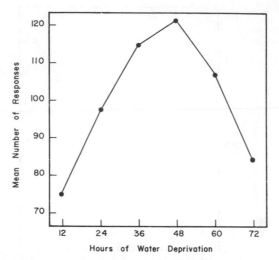

FIGURE 2. Number of instrumental responses in relation to duration of water deprivation in rats. The rats were subjected to an increasing order of deprivation. (Data are from article by Bélanger, D., and Feldman, S. M. J. Comp. Physiol. Psychol., 55: 220, 1962.)

that is optimal for performance and that, on either side of this optimum, there is a performance decrement; the greater the departure from the optimum, the greater is the decrement in performance. It is probable that the freezing reaction in frightened animals represents impairment of normal motor sequences by overactivation. In any event, it is a good illustration of why it is important not to confuse overt activity and activation. Though inactive, an animal paralyzed with fear is nevertheless highly activated.

According to the activation or arousal concept, the kind of neural activity considered here feeds impulses into organized neural cell assemblies, supporting the firing of their units in delicately timed sequences. According to this conception, optimal level of activation is that level of background firing—for example, of neurons in the hypothalamus—that provides the optimal facilitations of the organized neural activities—for example, in the cerebral cortex. It follows that too little or too much background firing of cells in the arousal system is deleterious with regard to organized neural firing (mediating performance).

NONHOMEOSTATIC MECHANISMS OF MOTIVATION

When an animal is very hungry or very thirsty, his behavior is largely dominated by cues associated through learning with these organic needs. However, when the animal's basic needs are satisfied, his behavior is often directed by cues that have nothing whatever to do with seeking food or water or escaping from painful stimulation. Thorough experimental documentation of this point comes from extensive work on the curiosity drive in monkeys in Harlow's laboratory at the University of Wisconsin. Harlow et al. demonstrated that monkeys work for hours on mechanical puzzles with no reward other than solving them. Butler's experiments at Wisconsin showed that monkeys work hard, hour after hour, just to have a small door open, allowing them the opportunity to look at objects in another room. They worked hardest to see another monkey there, but they worked nearly as hard to see an electrical train running.

This, of course, is one line of conclusive disproof of the drive-reduction theory in its original form. As a matter of fact, these and other findings, such as Hebb's, show that, far from seeking reduction in level of activation or arousal, animals look for excitement. Even lower mammals like the rat manifest exploratory behavior that seems to have little or nothing to do with food-seeking.

Another strongly motivated activity that does not depend on the animal's being in a deprived state is the Olds-Milner phenomenon of intracranial self-stimulation. Electrical stimulation of certain areas of the brain is clearly rewarding. Much remains to be learned about the mechanisms responsible for this remarkable phenomenon and the equally remarkable aversion to stimulation in other parts of the brain, first discovered by Delgado, Roberts, and Miller. But it is already clear that animals do seek positive stimulation. It is perhaps more correct to say that interactions between the relatively unactivated organism and its environment are often such that behavior is engaged more by stimuli that have activating effects than by stimuli that have quieting effects.

Following the pioneering work of Hess and later refinements in technique by Delgado, current investigations are showing that rather complicated, well-directed patterns of behavior can be elicited by means of stimulation through chronically implanted electrodes in the brains of awake animals. Of particular interest to psychiatrists are the recent brain stimulation experiments by Flynn, Glusman, von Holst, and others on offensive-defensive behavior.

The importance of viewing motivated behavior as the product of complex, though potentially decipherable, interactions between external stimulation, hormonal influences, and neural influences is clearly illustrated in the work of Lehrman et al. on the reproductive behavior of ring doves. Normally, external stimuli are effective in eliciting a particular behavior only if the bird's reproductive cycle has progressed sufficiently far. But the behavior can be induced very much earlier in the cycle by injecting a hormone, provided the hormone is selected with knowledge of the succession of hormone secretions during a normal reproductive cycle. For example, if eggs are introduced into the cage before the doves have engaged in courtship behavior for five to seven days, the birds do not sit on the eggs. Instead, they ignore the eggs while they engage in courtship. However, injecting both members of the pair with the ovarian hormone progesterone almost always elicits incubation behavior within three hours after the introduction of the eggs into the cage, instead of five to seven days later.

An important key to an understanding of the neurophysiological aspect of these interactions lies in the fact that the activity of the pituitary gland, which secretes gonad-stimulating and other hormones, is largely controlled by the nervous system through the hypothalamus.

In the higher mammals, especially in the chimpanzee but to some extent even in the dog, copulatory behavior is more complicated than the stimulus-bound subcortically mediated behavior in lower mammals. The relative importance of the cerebral cortex in mating behavior increases in the mammalian series from rat to man.

HUMAN MOTIVATION

ACTIVATION

From the psychiatric point of view, it is a matter of great concern when a patient's work efficiency is chronically impaired by excessive tension. It is important, therefore, to try to gain a deeper understanding of the neurophysiological mechanisms underlying tension and its interactions with efficiency of performance.

Continuity from animal to human experiments on activation is illustrated in Figures 1, 2, and 3—graphs from two reference experiments, one

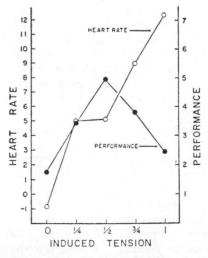

FIGURE 3. Heart beat and performance levels in human subjects under tension. (From article by Wood, C. C., and Hokanson, J. E. J. Personality Soc. Psychol., 1: 506, 1965.)

with rats and one with human subjects. In both cases the curve for heart rate (HR) rises continuously, and the curve for performance takes the form of an inverted U. For the human subjects, different HR levels were produced by having the subjects squeeze a hand dynamometer, applying different degrees of force under the various conditions; the stronger the squeeze, the higher the HR. The performance measure was the score on a digit-to-symbol code translation task. Despite the great differences in subject, task, and means of producing HR change in the experiments with humans and with rats, the graphic functions obtained are remarkably similar from experiment to experiment. These findings are typical of results in a substantial number of similar experiments.

In other experiments with human subjects, graded verbal incentives have been used successfully by the experimenter in place of induced muscular tension to produce different levels of physiological activation. Performance on tasks of motor skill has been shown in some but not in all instances to vary predictably with the different activation levels. The physiological measures themselves are only imperfect indicators of central nervous (arousal) system action.

In all experiments with human subjects employing band-pass filters and integrators for quantification, electroencephalographic (EEG) changes concordant with the peripheral physiological changes have been found. It is presumed that the peripheral measures reflect activation level because the arousal system seems to have strong facilitation on peripheral effector mechanisms in both autonomic and somatic spheres. It is not to be concluded, however, that a high level of activation is merely a state of extreme dominance of the sympathetic nervous system.

EEGs recorded along with various peripheral physiological measures, such as HR, respiration, and electromyograms (EMGs), have also been very useful in revealing an important difference between the rising functions just considered and a superficially similar but quite different kind of progressively rising physiological function called physiological gradient. Unlike the rising activation level curves, where EEGs show progressive changes, too, there are no systematic EEG changes accompanying the physiological gradients. These physiological gradients accompanying mental activity have been found in skeletal-motor and autonomic recording, commencing with the onset of the behavior sequence and terminating at its conclusion. Although it has been shown that these gradients do not represent increasing motivation or the like *during* the task, there is strong evidence indicating that the *steepness* of the gradients is a function of motivational level. It is presumed that there is some kind of mechanism that ensures the running off of a behavior sequence. Whatever the mechanisms are that furnish the support for continuous productive mental activity, they seem to depend partly on normal exteroceptive sensory stimulation, since, under prolonged conditions of sensory isolation, mental activity suffers markedly.

ACHIEVEMENT MOTIVATION

There are individual differences in the plans of men. What are the conditions that make one man determined to achieve certain goals in a lifetime, and how are they different from those that operate to make another man content with a low level of achievement?

The hypothesis that the strength of achievement motivation can be gauged in a meaningful and useful way by analyzing the content of stories told from pictures, like those in the Thematic Apperception Test (TAT), underlies the extensive investigative work of McClelland et al. The research began with a demonstration that college students given instructions designed to heighten their intensity of motivation to perform well on certain tests produced, in the stories they wrote from the TAT pictures, more responses having to do with future achievement than students who were in a relaxed state at the time of writing TAT stories. The next stage in the experimental program was guided by the general hypothesis that individuals who obtain high TAT need (n) achievement scores under controlled conditions are normally more intensely motivated to achieve than persons who obtain low n achievement scores under the same conditions.

From the results of investigations so generated, it was concluded that intensity of motivation to achieve at any task in any particular situation is determined by at least two factors: (1) the achievement motive—that is, desire to achieve—and (2) expectancy of probable success or failure. McClelland has recently been engaged in highly successful field research, including some in underdeveloped countries, that has demonstrated that it is possible to teach businessmen to acquire n achievement and thereby to advance in business.

Expectancy × value.   The further development of this general line of attack has been pursued by Atkinson et al. in the expectancy × value approach to motivation. The value factor refers to the common observation that there are marked individual differences with respect to values placed on certain objects or goals. Some students strive for A's, for example, and others depreciate the importance of grades, placing high values mainly on intellectual satisfactions or on extracurricular activities. The expectancy factor refers to the subjective probability that with expenditure of sufficient effort the object may be acquired or the goal reached.

It is appropriate here to call attention to the aphysiological character of Atkinson's theory and to suggest that theorists who look at neurophysiological data are probably able to construct a more comprehensive and useful theory than theorists who choose to ignore those data. Atkinson states that his approach is not "explicitly guided by any preconceptions concerning neurophysiology." However, Hebb has argued that behavior theorists who disregard contemporary neurophysiology and neuropsychology may unconsciously fall back on outmoded neural conceptions in their theoretical formulations. Aphysiological theorists are disinclined to speculate or to deal with data from two levels of description, neurophysiological and behavioral. But it seems there should be a two-way street here. Not only is behavioral research enriched by an appreciation of neurophysiological discoveries and observations in neurological clinics, but tracing relations between the behavioral and neural levels of description must inevitably be heuristic for research at both levels.

For example, the expectancy × value theory surely would be enriched by observations of neurological patients, especially those showing motivational deviations. Milner has found that frontal lobe patients break test rules more often than other patients do. For example, in performing a stylus maze test, they pushed ahead instead of going back to the point where they made an error, or they moved along diagonals (against the rules). It was not that they didn't realize these things were wrong; it seemed they just couldn't control their impulsiveness. When progress toward the goal came into conflict with rules, the value system normally respecting rules was shown to be abnormally weak in the frontal lobe patients. What is there about frontal lobe mechanisms that make them essential for such value systems to have normal control over behavior? This question seems highly relevant for the expectancy × value theory of motivation, and the theory should gain considerably in scope if it takes such data into account.

Drive (D) × Habit Theory

As in the case of the activation concept, so, too, in the D × habit theory, there are points relevant to the general problem of anxiety in its effect on performance. Using manifest anxiety scores (MAS) from a questionnaire to divide human subjects into high MAS and low MAS groups, Spence and Taylor have compared the two groups with respect to performance on various tasks. The main general finding is that high MAS scorers are favored over low scorers on simple tasks in which potential competition between conflicting responses is low and that low MAS scorers are favored in more complex tasks. These authors are careful not to extrapolate their findings to psychiatric patients suffering pathological anxiety. Their subjects were usually university students.

Their work stemmed from the drive × habit formulation of Clark Hull, according to which habit strength is increased with an increase in drive, such as that produced by food or water deprivation (and later, following Mowrer's work, also anxiety). In Hull's terminology, D represented general drive, the combined effects of various specific drives. Hull proposed a multiplicative relation between the nonspecific general drive (D) and the behavioral manifestation of habit strength; the greater the D, the stronger the response.

In an extensive series of experiments with human subjects, Spence and Taylor have attempted to verify the $D \times$ habit (H) strength hypothesis, earlier investigated with animals, and they have accumulated a certain amount of supporting evidence for better performance going along with high D. When high D, as measured by the MAS questionnaire, is found associated with *lowered* performance, the performance decrement is accounted for in terms of competing responses interfering with the correct response. But some very simple responses show the inverted U relation to drive strength instead of the monotonic relation predicted by the $D \times H$ hypothesis. These cases seem impossible to account for in terms of the competing response notion of the Hull-Spence formulations; they seem to require some kind of explanation like that provided by the activation concept.

CURRENT MOTIVATIONAL CONCEPTS

Certain terms appear frequently in the literature on human motivation. The concept denoted by each term gains clarification by reference to the experimental procedures employed in investigating each specific problem. Therefore, the main purpose of the brief remarks that follow is to indicate in each case the kind of experimental approach employed.

Dependency. On the basis of studies with children, Sears regards dependency as an acquired drive, one that is or may be developed very early in a child's life. The topic has received relatively little systematic study with adults.

Level of aspiration. This term has been used by Lewin and his students and involves a procedure in which the subject is asked to say how he will do on the next trial of a task. For example, a subject engaged in a dart-throwing task may be asked before his first throw what number he expects to hit. After the throw and before the next trial, he is asked again to predict his performance, and so on for several trials. The relation of level of aspiration to achievement motivation is discussed in detail by Atkinson.

Ego involvement. The term ego involvement in the investigative sense refers to observations of the individual in situations where persons, groups, or values with which he identifies are called into question. This topic is discussed by Cofer and Appley.

Cognitive dissonance. This is Festinger's term, and it means incongruity or disharmony with respect to such matters as expectation and actuality. An A student who makes a B experiences a tension not experienced by a B student making the same grade. In general, dissonance occurs when there is a palpable disparity between two experiential or behavioral elements. It is postulated that cognitive dissonance produces a tension state, like hunger, that is motivating. The kinds of experimental investigation generated by the theory are illustrated by the following question: How does dissonance in different degrees affect the individual's inclination to seek out or to avoid new information? What are the reactions of persons who are forced to consider information or propaganda they would normally have avoided?

Perceptual defense. The concept of defense here resembles that of repression, unconscious resistance against the perception of things that are disagreeable or disturbing. Attempts to demonstrate such a phenomenon in the laboratory have invariably been challenged by critics who offer what they consider to be more parsimonious explanations of the reported observations. Probably the most promising line for future investigation is in the study of idiosyncratic perceptual defensive reactions—that is, in the study of individual differences in perception rather than in the study of average reactions from groups of individuals.

Intrinsic motivation. Hunt defines intrinsic motivation as being "inherent in the organism's informational interaction with circumstances through the distance receptors and in its intentional, goal-anticipating actions." Promising new experimental work with human infants by Hunt et al. is concerned with the possibility of hastening certain aspects of development by providing the infant with interesting and varied exteroceptive stimulation.

PSYCHOANALYTIC MOTIVATION THEORY

From the historical point of view, Freud's contribution to the psychology of human motivation should come first, of course. Freud's writings were probably the most powerful single influence initiating scientific investigations of human motivation. The whole course of experimental psychology was changed by the combined attack of Freud and the behaviorists on structural psychology, which had become lost in sterile introspective exercises. From Freud's observations it was plain that a full understanding of the causes of human behavior could not be gained from conscious introspections. Clearly, much of behavior is determined by unconscious mental activities, activities that the person is unaware of and consequently cannot report on.

Atkinson points out that Freud, the scientist, regarded his conceptions as tentative. An appropriate concluding statement to this consideration of the study of motivation is provided by the following quotation from Freud (cited by Atkinson):

> We must be patient and wait for other means and opportunities for investigation. We must hold ourselves too in readiness to abandon the path we have followed for a time, if it should seem to lead to no good result. Only such "true believers" as expect from science a substitute for the creed they have relinquished will take it amiss if the investigator develops his views further or even transforms them.
>
> For the rest we may find consolation in the words of a poet for the slow rate of progress in scientific knowledge:

"Whither we cannot fly, we must go limping.
The Scriptures saith that limping is no sin."

REFERENCES

Atkinson, J. W. *An Introduction to Motivation.* D. Van Nostrand, New York, 1964.

Beach, H. D. Morphine addiction in rats. Canad. J. Psychol., *11*: 104, 1957.

Bindra, D. *Motivation. A Systematic Reinterpretation.* Ronald Press, New York, 1959.

Brown, J. S. *The Motivation of Behavior.* McGraw-Hill, New York, 1961.

Butler, R. A. Curiosity in monkeys. Sci. Amer., *190*: No. 2, p. 70, 1954.

Cofer, C. N., and Appley, M. H. *Motivation: Theory and Research.* Wiley, New York, 1964.

Flynn, J. P., Wasman, M., and Egger, M. D. Behavior during propagated hippocampal after-discharges. In *EEG and Behavior*, G. H. Glaser, editor, p. 134. Basic Books, New York, 1963.

Glusman, M., Won, W., Burdock, E. I., and Ransohoff, J. Effects of midbrain lesions on "savage" behavior induced by hypothalamic lesions in the cat. Trans. Amer. Neurol. Assoc., p. 216, 1961.

Hebb, D. O. *A Textbook of Psychology*, ed. 2. W. B. Saunders, Philadelphia, 1966.

von Holst, E., and von Saint Paul, U. Electrically controlled behavior. Sci. Amer., *206*: No. 3, p. 50, 1962.

Hunt, J. McV. Intrinsic motivation and its role in psychological development. In *Nebraska Symposium on Motivation*, D. Levine, editor, p. 189. University of Nebraska Press, Lincoln, 1965.

Ishikawa, T., Koizumi, K., and Brooks, C. McC. Activity of supraoptic nucleus neurons of the hypothalamus. Neurology, *16*: 101, 1966.

Jaffe, J. H. Drug addiction and drug abuse. In *The Pharmacological Basis of Therapeutics*, L. S. Goodman and A. Gilman, editors, p. 285. Macmillan, New York, 1965.

Lehrman, D. S. The reproductive behavior of ring doves. Sci. Amer., *211*: No. 5, p. 48, 1964.

Malmo, R. B. Activation. In *Experimental Foundations of Clinical Psychology.* A. J. Bachrach, editor, p. 386. Basic Books, New York, 1962.

Malmo, R. B. Physiological gradients and behavior. Psychol. Bull., *64*: 225, 1965.

Malmo, R. B. Studies of anxiety: some clinical origins of the activation concept. In *Anxiety and Behavior*, C. D. Spielberger, editor, p. 157. Academic Press, New York, 1966.

Malmo, R. B., and Bélanger, D. Related physiological and behavioral changes: What are their determinants? Res. Publ. Ass. Res. Nerv. Ment. Dis., *46*: 1966.

McCleary, R. A., and Moore, R. Y. *Subcortical Mechanisms of Behavior.* Basic Books, New York, 1965.

Milner, B. Visually-guided maze learning in man: effects of bilateral hippocampal, bilateral frontal, and unilateral cerebral lesions. Neuropsychologia, *3*: 317, 1965.

Olds, J. Hypothalamic substrates of reward. Physiol. Rev., *42*: 554, 1962.

Richter, C. P. Production and control of alcoholic cravings in rats. In *Neuropharmacology*, H. A. Abramson, editor, p. 39. Josiah Macy, Jr. Foundation, New York, 1957.

Sourkes, T. L. *Biochemistry of Mental Disease.* Harper & Row, New York, 1962.

Spragg, S. D. S. Morphine addiction in chimpanzees. Comp. Psychol. Monogr., 15: Whole No. 79, 1940.

Valenstein, E. S. Problems of measurement and interpretation with reinforcing brain stimulation. Psychol. Rev., 71: 415, 1964.

Weeks, J. R. Experimental narcotic addiction. Sci. Amer., 210: No. 3, p. 46, 1964.

CHAPTER 16

Ethology

ECKHARD H. HESS, Ph.D.

INTRODUCTION

SINCE MODERN-DAY PSYCHIATRY, psychology, and ethology can all trace their origins to work carried out in the last decades of the nineteenth century, it seems rather paradoxical that psychiatry has been more sympathetic to and made greater use of ethological concepts than has psychology.

The deep chasm that has existed until recently between ethology and psychology can be attributed to several factors. One is certainly the cavalier use of the term instinct by psychologists such as McDougall early in the twentieth century; such usage eventually reduced the concept of instinct in the United States to a catch-all explanation for behaviors that could not be easily understood in other terms. Concurrently, J. B. Watson attracted attention with his behavioristic theory, which appealed to psychologists because of its parsimony and its promise of explaining behavior on the basis of simple relationships between the individual and his environment. The third major factor leading to the negative relationship between psychology and ethology was a fundamental lack of communication between researchers in Europe and in the United States, which lasted until the late 1940's.

In contrast, ethology and psychiatry have their roots deep in the same soil. Initial developments in both areas stem from the work of Europeans, and ethological ideas were familiar to many psychiatrists who transported them to this country in the period before World War II. Besides, there were no disrupting factors for psychiatrists in adapting ethological concepts to the phenomena with which they were confronted.

DEVELOPMENT OF ETHOLOGY

Some of the basic principles of ethological research can be traced back for several hundred years. So the modern study of animal behavior, rather than implying that ethology is a new approach to behavior, seems to reflect a rediscovery of the relationship of the concepts and orientation of ethology to present-day problems in behavior.

NATURAL BEHAVIOR

Basic to the ethological approach to the study of behavior is the emphasis on familiarity with the natural behavior of the organism to be studied. Once the observer is acquainted with the functioning of the animal in its natural environment, he can vary the environment and learn with certainty how it influences the animal's behavior. This principle is well illustrated in the work of Baron von Pernau, a German zoologist whose major treatise was published in 1716 and who provided detailed descriptions of behavior peculiar to each of many different species of birds—what we now call species-specific behavior.

His most important finding was that in some songbirds the species-specific vocalizations of the adult are learned early in the life of the animal but that in other species these vocalizations are completely innate. To reach this finding, he used a technique known to present-day ethologists and to those dealing in psychological research as the deprivation experiment. Once familiar with the normal behavior of these species, von Pernau raised birds of several such species in an environment in which they were deprived of contact with other members of their own species. Under these conditions, songbirds of some species exhibited species-specific vocalizations at the proper time in development; but birds of other species grew to adulthood employing the vocalizations and songs of the nonspecies members with which they had been raised. They retained these vocalizations even though they were later given an opportunity to live with their own species.

SPECIES-SPECIFIC BEHAVIOR

Instinctive behavior. The next major contribution to ethology was provided by the work of the French naturalist and scientist Reaumur in the middle eighteenth century. Reaumur wrote of innate behaviors in a wide range of species, observing that many species-specific behaviors occurred even though the young animals were removed from the mother shortly after birth and reared without the companionship of species members.

Innate complex behavior. Reaumur was also the first to point out that, in some cases, rather complex behaviors involving the use of special organs must be innate, since the behavior patterns adapted for the use of these organisms are performed before the organ has developed and cannot have been learned through experience. An example may make this clear. Young goats push each other with their heads before they have horns, and young boars try to slash each other with sideways blows of their heads long before their tusks have developed.

Evolution of behavior patterns.   The concept of innate or unlearned behavior was given a great impetus by the work of Charles Darwin. He wrote of complex behavior patterns that were characteristic of a species and required no learning, since they appeared full-blown immediately after birth or after hatching. Darwin's major contribution in this area was his approach to behavior from the genetic point of view. He treated innate behaviors in the same way that morphological characteristics were dealt with and found ample evidence for the evolution of behavior patterns.

Blind behavior.   Another person prominent in the study of instinctive behavior during the nineteenth century was D. M. Spaulding. As a result of observing the behavior of many animals, he felt that instinctive behavior patterns were fundamental in the behavior of many species and was the first to call attention to the blind aspect of certain instinctive behaviors. Spaulding noted that, when he presented himself to newly hatched chicks in place of the mother, these animals followed him and reacted to him in the same way that chicks normally do to their natural mother. In this case, the young animals had a built-in response (following) that was released by the first object encountered after hatching, but the animals did not have an innate conception of what this object should look like.

Writing in the early 1870's, before Mendel's work on genetics had been widely recognized, Spaulding emphasized the genetic transmission of instinctive behavior patterns and hypothesized that this transmission took place in the same way that physiological characteristics are passed on from generation to generation. Spaulding's work was the precursor of the concept of imprinting.

Umwelt.   Jacob von Uexküll, whose writings encompass a twenty-five-year period from the early 1900's to the middle 1930's, developed the concept that each organism has its own particular *Umwelt*, which means essentially that, of the vast complex of physical stimuli in an animal's environment that could possibly affect his behavior, he may respond to only a few. It was also demonstrated in von Uexküll's work that instinctive behavior is specifically geared to the survival of the individual and of the species.

The behavior of simple organisms clearly illustrates these concepts. The common woodtick, for example, apparently responds to only three environmental stimuli during the greater part of its adult life. First, as a result of photosensitive receptors in its skin, it goes to the brightest part of its environment. This leads the tick to climb a bush or tree. Second, it responds to the scent of butyric acid, which is given off by warm-blooded animals, by releasing its hold and dropping from the branch. Third, on encountering a temperature of approximately 37° C., such as that of a mammal, it attaches itself to the spot and gorges itself on blood before falling to the ground to lay its eggs sometime later. The relationship between these stimuli and these responses is innate in origin, and certainly each is designed to ensure survival of the species.

In more-advanced organisms, these relationships are not so easily seen. At the human level, any study of instinctive behavior mechanisms is confounded by the complexity of the physical and social environment that man has created for himself. Since man's technology has developed much more rapidly than he has changed through genetic adaptation, it may be necessary to ask how a bit of behavior, which we suspect is innate, fitted into the environment of primitive man and contributed to his survival.

Appetitive behavior and consummatory responses. Wallace Craig brought out this complexity in the behavior of more-advanced species when he made the distinction between appetitive behavior and consummatory responses. Appetitive behavior is essentially variable, though goal-directed, and can be changed through experience with the environment. The consummatory response, however, is stereotyped in form and instinctive in nature. This distinction has illustrated that behavior may vary from species to species as the two components vary.

Instinct-training interlocking. Among contemporary ethologists, Konrad Lorenz has contributed to the greater understanding of instinctive behavior and has both clarified earlier concepts and presented new ones concerning the functioning of instinctive behavior mechanisms. Lorenz amplified Craig's idea of appetitive behavior and consummatory responses into a system he has called instinct-training interlocking. This term implies that the behavior of a particular organism is a continuous process of smooth integration of learned aspects of behavior with the instinctive components. Those behaviors that are learned lend a flexibility to behavior and lead to greater adaptability in varying environmental situations. Those components that are instinctive ensure that certain reactions to certain stimuli will be made without the necessity of learning; instinctive components are most clearly seen in cases in which, if learning were required, the possibility of survival would be greatly diminished.

Action-specific energy. Another major contribution of Konrad Lorenz was the concept of action-specific energy. He observed that, with repeated performance, there was a waning in the ease with which instinctive behavior patterns could be elicited and that this waning was not related to general fatigue of the animal. After an interval of nonelicitation, however, the suitable environmental stimulus would again lead to the instinctive response. Lorenz concluded that for each instinctive response there was a certain amount of energy available and that, when this energy was depleted, the response would no longer be exhibited but that, with rest, the energy reservoir would be replenished. It should be kept in mind that studies of action-specific energy are carried out under circumstances that do not simulate the normal environment of the animal, since under natural conditions the function of the response is served the first time it is released by the environmental stimulus.

Vacuum activity. Lorenz's belief in the existence of action-specific energy was strengthened by observing behavior he termed vacuum activity. In the absence of the appropriate environmental stimulus, an animal showed a precise instinctive response, just as though the stimulus were present. Since this occurred primarily in animals deprived of their natural environment, where the stimulus appropriate to the response would be encountered, Lorenz interpreted this behavior as a spilling over of action-specific energy into behavior when this energy had built up as a result of the long period of response inactivity.

Displacement activity. One of the first books devoted exclusively to the study of instinctive behavior was written by Niko Tinbergen and appeared in 1951. Tinbergen emphasized the relationship between internal factors, such as hormonal conditions, and external factors, such as distinct environmental stimuli, in leading to instinctive responses.

Another concept discussed in Tinbergen's first book is displacement activity, which had been noted previously by other ethologists. This behavior is most clearly seen in situations where there is a conflict between two instinctive behavior patterns and the expression of one or the other pattern is physically prevented or overwhelmed by ambivalence. As a consequence, the animal exhibits a third instinctive behavior, usually quite unrelated to either of the behaviors in conflict with each other. It is as though, when blocked, the neurological activity generated by the two conflicting behavior patterns sparks over into the third behavior, which is inappropriate to the situation. For example, a chicken faced with an opponent that it would like to attack but that is clearly superior in size or weight may, instead, start to peck at nonexisting food.

Neurological mechanisms. Until recently, the concepts of action-specific energy and displacement activity have been in the realm of hypothetical constructs, together with such psychoanalytical ideas as sexual and aggressive energy systems. The research of Erich von Holst has done a great deal toward solidifying the position of neurological mechanisms that function in association with both types of behavior.

The basic technique used by von Holst involves the implantation of electrodes in the brain stem of chickens. Through electrical stimulation of various points in the brain stem, von Holst has been able to elicit almost all the simple and complex behavior patterns normally exhibited by the species. Activation through electrical stimulation seems to simulate the activities of these areas in the same way as normal neurological processes.

The finding of centers in the brain stem directly related to behavior patterns in chickens supported some of the ethological ideas about the organization of behavior. Further support came from results that appeared to simulate action-specific exhaustibility. In these cases, von Holst found that, with repeated stimulation, the threshold for the response rose rapidly and there was repeated response evocation until the point was reached where even a large amount of current would not evoke the response. However, after the chicken had a period of rest, it was again possible to get the response with the normal voltage. Von Holst, in a way, was artificially replicating those results that had been obtained by others, who elicited and exhausted the response with an external stimulus.

Of even greater consequence were experiments in which antagonistic drives and responses were simultaneously stimulated. This sort of experimentation fits the paradigm of displacement activity as exhibited by an animal in its natural environment. Although, in some cases under electrical stimulation, one response would supersede the other, there were also cases where, just as with displacement activity, a third response, completely unrelated to the two stimulated, was evoked during the experimental session. And whenever the two particular responses were stimulated simultaneously, it was always the same displacement response that was shown by the animal, indicating the same type of lawfulness found in nature.

Innate releaser and fixed-action pattern. The innate releaser is a stimulus in the environment that serves to trigger a specific innate behavior on the part of the animal. This stimulus can be received by the organism through any of the sensory modalities, although the most common are visual and auditory stimuli. The response elicited by an innate releaser is stereotyped in manner and does not vary from one elicitation to another. For this reason, these instinctive responses have been termed fixed-action patterns.

To the inexperienced or casual observer, the relationship between innate releasers and innate responses looks like a stimulus-response relationship based on learning. However, a response must meet several criteria before it can be called a fixed-action pattern and thus qualify as an instinctive response. These are: (1) the behavior involved in a response must occur in exactly the same way each time the stimulus is presented; (2) the complete response must occur at the first presentation of the releaser, before there has been a chance for learning to take place; (3) the response must occur in all members of a species; and (4) the response must occur in individuals raised in isolation from species members.

ETHOLOGY AND PSYCHIATRY

Since the middle 1950's, a number of articles in the psychological and psychiatric literature have used ethological concepts to support certain psychiatric hypotheses that have developed over the years. The ethological concepts of action-specific energy, displacement activity, and imprinting have, apparently, been the most useful to the psychiatrist.

The basic phenomena with which the ethologists have concerned themselves and the hypotheses that relate these phenomena to human behavior
and human development represent an effort to solve some of the behavioral problems that have confronted psychiatrists. In this effort, man is
viewed as a member of the animal world rather than as a separate and
distinct species exempt from developmental and behavioral regulations applied to the behavior of other animals. Clearly instinctive behavior patterns are designed to maximize the biological survival of the individual as a
species, and this function is implicit wherever instinctive mechanisms are
postulated as operating at the human level. Just as clearly, studies involving the concepts of action-specific energy and displacement activity have
provided working hypotheses as to the internal control and organization of
instinctive behavior patterns.

ACTION-SPECIFIC ENERGY

Relation to Freud's psychic energy.   Freud's use of psychic energy as
the basic force in human behavior has probably been one of the most
difficult of his theories to accept. Psychic energy, obviously, cannot be
visibly seen and studied but must be inferred from actions of the individual. The independent development of the concept of action-specific energy associated with instinctive behavior patterns has given great support
to Freud's theory. There is a strong similarity between the two concepts,
and action-specific energy can be precisely studied at a behavioral level,
even though its physiological bases are just beginning to be elucidated.

Mechanisms and function.   Konrad Lorenz presented the underlying
mechanisms and function of action-specific energy in two of his earlier
papers (1935 and 1952) and gave examples of how the concept operates
at the behavioral level. Basically, action-specific energy serves both as a
factor that energizes instinctive behavior patterns and as a motivational
factor so far as the behavior is concerned. As the term implies, Lorenz felt
that there is at any given time a quantifiable amount of energy available
for the activation of a particular bit of instinctive behavior. Once this
reservoir of energy is completely drained or depleted as a result of continuous activation of the response, a time interval is required in order for the
supply of energy to be replenished.

The clearest example of this aspect of action-specific energy can be seen
in behavior patterns that are used in nature with relative infrequency. For
example, a bird, the whitethroat, has a characteristic response of feigning
injury in order to lure a predator away from the nest. As the predator
approaches the nest, the bird hobbles away with one wing hanging, as
though it had been seriously injured. When a safe distance away from the
nest, however, and certainly before being caught by the predator, the
whitethroat takes to the air and returns to the nest. This response appears
in complete detail the first time the experimenter approaches the nest.

Should the experimenter approach the nest again shortly after the bird has settled, the response is made again but to a lesser degree. And on the third approach, immediately after the bird has resumed its brooding, no response is made at all. If the entire process is repeated several times, with an interval of a few days between sets of trial, exactly the same thing happens each time the response is tested.

The draining of the energy available for such responses is not due to general physical fatigue, since other responses are readily performed when the innate response in question can no longer be elicited. The phenomenon is due neither to adaptation to the eliciting stimulus nor to fatigue but, rather, to the depletion of the energy used specifically for that response.

DISPLACEMENT ACTIVITY

Kaufman has pointed out the similarity between Freud's model of libidinal energy and the concept of action-specific energy. For a clearer picture of how action-specific energy might be applied at the human level, it is necessary to go into a more detailed account of the closely allied phenomenon of displacement activity.

As noted earlier in this chapter, displacement activity refers to a response that occurs out of its normal environmental context. In other words, the response, which is instinctive in nature, appears in the absence of the usual stimulation normally associated with the response. However, in contrast to vacuum activity, displacement activity can be directly related to an environmental situation.

Conflict of drives. Tinbergen outlines two situations in which displacement activity is most likely to occur. The first one is a conflict of two strongly activated drives that are antagonistic to each other. Displacement activity of this type is seen commonly in a fish, the male three-spined stickleback, when fighting behavior and escape behavior are simultaneously activated. In this species, each male has his territory containing the nest, which is closely guarded against the encroachment of another male. The sight of another male coming into the territory serves first as a sign stimulus for the male to respond with a threat posture. In some cases, this posture alone is sufficient stimulus to cause the strange male to leave the territory. At other times, if the strange male has no territory of its own and he is motivated by a strong internal drive to establish a territory and start nest-building, he may not leave the established territory when threatened this way. The established male then attacks the strange male, but, as he approaches the edge of his territory, this attack response weakens and starts to conflict with his flight tendency. At this point, when the conflict between the two drives is such that each is at about the same intensity, the stickleback exhibits a third instinctive behavior pattern, displacement digging, which is completely out of the context of the situation. The movements involved are exactly the same as those seen during the time the male is building the nest. This, of course, clearly belongs to a set of innate responses that have nothing to do with either fighting or fleeing behavior.

In effect then, when behavior is blocked by the conflict of drive states and motor patterns involving those drive states, pressure is released by running off into a third behavior pattern. This is, of course, a purely conceptual way of dealing with the phenomenon.

Lack of external stimulus. The second situation in which it is common to see displacement activity occurs when there is a strong internal motivation for a consummatory act but the external stimulus necessary to release the act is lacking in the environment. This is most commonly seen in sexual responses, with hormonal levels acting as the internal stimulus and certain social responses in fellow species members serving as releasers for the sexual behavior.

Physical implications. Both action-specific energy and displacement activity suggest that there is an energy system controlling behavior, which under certain conditions must be discharged in overt activity, and that there is a built-in neurological relationship between internal excitation and the stereotyped fixed-action patterns of instinctive behavior. Both types of situations leading to displacement activity indicate that, when the appropriate channel for the discharge of action-specific energy is blocked, the energy spills over into another channel as the result of activity in the central nervous system, rather than leading to random activity.

Social implications. The transition from instinctive behavior, as we have discussed it in relation to action-specific energy and displacement activity, to the traditional psychoanalytic concept of instinct as outlined by Freud primarily involves a shift from purely physical relationships at the animal level to physical and psychic relationships at the human level. At the animal level, there is a specific, genetically determined relationship between internal excitation, a releaser in the environment, and the response, and this relationship cannot be altered through experience. At the human level, there is a certain amount of genetic determinism regarding psychic energy, which may be invested in the sexual and the aggressive drive, but the stimulus objects to which this energy is cathected can be the mental representations of these objects and may be determined through individual experience.

The possibility exists that, without the complex sociological pressures to which man has been subjected, there would be a lawfulness in the development of human behavior similar to the organization found in animal behavior. In fact, it can be predicted from what we know about the genetic determinants in the behavior of men that without civilization man would nevertheless exhibit behavior and behavior patterns that would make him little different, to the best of our present knowledge, from the socially organized small groups of other primates. The blocking of the discharge of sexual and aggressive energy into natural channels, due to society's not permitting the individual certain modes of instinctual gratification, could be analogous to the situations leading to displacement activity in the examples from animal behavior.

Psychiatric implications. Contemporary psychiatrists have used the ethological concept of displacement activity in at least three ways in relating ethological principles to human behavior. Although each approach is somewhat different, each seems to provide a valid working hypothesis at the human level.

The fact that many displacement activities at the animal level do not serve to maximize the survival of the individual or species has been emphasized by Weigert. In a way, this relates displacement activity to neurotic anxiety, which Freud considered to be the result of a frustrated libidinal impulse and which is, of course, basically detrimental to the individual. This interpretation of displacement activity emphasizes the nonfunctional aspect of neurotic behavior. At the same time, it must be kept in mind that the conflict situation experienced by the individual may, under certain circumstances, result in the sublimation of libidinal energy into activities condoned by society. This has been pointed out by Freud.

Kaufman has postulated that, in addition to the sexual and aggressive instincts in men, there may be an instinct for flight. He has drawn heavily on work with displacement activity, since many such behaviors are the result of a conflict between aggressive and flight reactions. Kaufman points out that at the animal level sexual behavior, aggression, and flight are all built-in tendencies and that the same thing is likely to be true of man. He feels that this theoretical paradigm would be beneficial in the treatment of patients whose shyness and timidity (low-intensity manifestations of a flight tendency) would not have to be construed as a reaction to hostile or sexual impulses but could be interpreted as a drive in its own right.

A third way of viewing displacement activity is that taken by Ostow. After drawing some parallels between the psychoanalytic concept of instinct and the ethological concept of instinct, he used displacement activity to illustrate a logical progression of development in man. Dealing only with the sexual instincts, he hypothesized that gratification of these instincts takes different forms during different periods of development and that the mechanism that leads from one form to another functions in the same way displacement activity functions in lower animals. As one mode of gratification is inhibited, the instinct accepts another mode of gratification. In this way, he traces the sexual aims in psychic development through oral, anal, phallic, and genital stages.

Imprinting

Research on early experience has shown that the environment of an animal early in life can play an exceedingly important role in later adjustment and later adult behavior. This point is made most clearly in the phenomenon that has become known as imprinting, derived from the German term *Prägung*, which is attributed to Konrad Lorenz.

Species recognition. Lorenz observed the behavior of newly hatched geese both with the natural parents and with himself when he presented himself to the young animals as a parental object before they had an opportunity to associate with their parents. Later in life, the animals treated members of that species to which they had first been exposed as fellow species members. Lorenz concluded that this species recognition was imprinted onto the nervous system of the young animal during the first period of exposure after hatching.

FIGURE 1. Imprinting-test apparatus. The apparatus used in the study of imprinting consists primarily of a circular runway, around which a decoy duck can be moved. In this drawing a duckling follows the decoy. The controls of the apparatus are in the foreground. (Reprinted by permission from Hess, E. H. Imprinting. Science, 130: 134, 1959.)

As a functional piece of instinctive behavior, imprinting serves its purpose well. Under normal conditions, the first object seen is, of course, the natural parent, and the rapid attachment of the young to the parent is necessary for the survival of the young animal. During the first days of life, the parent broods the young, protects it from predators, leads it away from dangerous situations, and takes the animal to food objects in the environment. None of this would happen if the young animal did not almost immediately become highly attached to the parent and follow it under all circumstances.

Contrasts with association learning. Since the early 1950's, imprinting has been studied in the laboratory, particularly in the United States. Ramsay and Hess in 1954 showed the feasibility of studying imprinting in a laboratory situation, and their work has been reviewed in papers by Hess in 1959 and 1964. The results of their laboratory work can be stated in five points that seem to make imprinting quite different from the association learning commonly studied by the experimental psychologists.

In the waterfowls studied, there is a critical period that is sharp and distinct. In the case of mallard ducks, for example, there is a peak of sensitivity to the imprinting phenomenon at about sixteen hours after

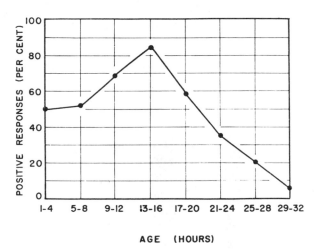

AGE (HOURS)

Figure 2. Critical age for imprinting ducklings. Ducklings are most effectively imprinted at the age of 13 to 16 hours, as depicted by this curve, which shows the average test score of ducklings imprinted at each age group. (Reprinted by permission from Hess, E. H. Imprinting. Science, 130: 135, 1959.)

hatching, and this sensitivity drops rapidly thereafter. By thirty-two or forty-eight hours after hatching, the increased fear response of the animal appears to interfere with further imprintability. Similar critical periods have been found for other animals as well. Although not all the critical periods are within the first day, they have all been found to occur in the very early life of the organism.

The use of certain drugs, particularly muscle relaxants, interferes completely with the acquisition of the imprinting effect. These same drugs do not interfere at all with the normal acquisition of a discrimination such as one would experimentally study in a psychological laboratory.

Massed practice is more effective than spaced practice as far as imprinting is concerned. In addition, by the law of effort, the imprinting effect is positively related to the amount of energy expended by the animal in going to or in attempting to go to the imprinting object. In this case, too, there is a difference between imprinting and association learning.

In imprinting, primacy and recency work in a way completely different from the way they work in association learning. In imprinting, it is clearly the first thing learned that is retained, whereas in association learning the animal tends to respond to the last meaningful stimulus.

The effect of punishment or painful stimulation in imprinting has a result quite the opposite of what occurs in an association-learning situation. This study is perhaps of particular interest to psychiatry.

In this study (Kovach and Hess, 1963), data are reported on groups of chicks at an age close to the critical period, eighteen hours, and well beyond the critical period for imprinting, forty-eight hours. At each age, chicks were given electrical shocks while in an imprinting apparatus with a blue ball (parent object); control chicks received no shock. At the age of forty-eight hours, those chicks receiving shock avoided the parent object,

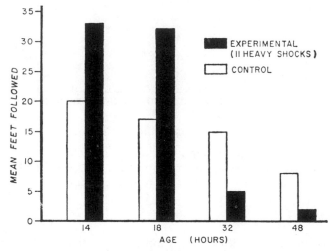

FIGURE 3. Effects of punishment during imprinting. This chart shows the number of feet that chicks of two major treatment groups, one shocked and the other not shocked, followed the imprinting object and their age at first exposure to the imprinting situation. The shocked chicks were given 11 heavy shocks of 3-milliampere intensity, ½-second duration, during the imprinting experience; the nonshocked control chicks were given none. (Reprinted by permission of Holt, Rinehart and Winston from Hess, E. H. Ethology. In *New Directions in Psychology*, Chapter 3, 1962.)

which was evidently associated with the shock. However, those animals that were shocked in the same way during the optimum period for imprinting actually followed the parent object significantly more than the control animals, which had not received shock.

This result may be perplexing from the standpoint of association learning, but it is not unreasonable from the standpoint of instinctive behavior and the normal survival value of such behavior. For example, if in the natural situation the young animal was stepped on by the parent before he left the nest, it would not be biologically useful to have the young avoid the parent, leave the nest, and die. If anything, there seems to be an overcompensation for any punishment associated with the parental object, since the animals receiving shock did follow better than the control animals. The animal, in a painful situation at that moment when it depends on the parent to a tremendous degree to survive, seeks to get even closer to the parent object.

At least one paper published in the psychiatric literature seems to tie in this phenomenon with behavior in young children, where there is also a dependency relationship between the child and parent. In discussing ethological concepts as they might apply to moral masochism, Menaker takes the position that psychic development is as important to the child as physical development and that, when the mother is "unloving, powerful, exploitative, and dominating" in relation to the ego needs of the child, the child, as the weaker member of the pair, becomes submissive. At the same time "it creates an idealized image on which it can then be nourished for purposes of identification, ego formation, and ultimate survival." Menaker relates this type of behavior to innate mechanisms of submission that prevent species members from killing each other. It appears that the child, who is essentially in a punishing relationship with the parent and who reacts by idealizing the parent and picturing her as all-powerful and loving, is doing exactly the same thing a young chick does during its critical period, when it follows a parent object even more closely after being punished in the presence of that object. It is not impossible that both mechanisms are operating on the unconscious level, are vital to the survival of the organism, and parallel each other on some phylogenetic basis. Just as nature has ensured that the chick will stay with the parent under the most adverse conditions, a similar mechanism must operate with the child, who obviously could not survive alone.

The fact that most modern societies have made provisions to give children adequate physical care may obscure the functioning of a mechanism that binds the child to the parent during his period of dependency, even when physically punished. However, as Polt suggests, it seems as though the normal parent-child relationship implicitly assumes that something of this sort operates. When a parent physically punishes a child for some misdemeanor, the purpose of the punishment is to deter the child from repeating the act with which the punishment is associated, not to lead the child to avoidance of the parent. If the normal association-learning laws were operative in the situation, the parent would be the object most closely associated with the punishment, and avoidance of the parent, rather than deterrence of the child from continuing the misdemeanor, would result.

Development of social behavior. The basic imprinting phenomenon implies that in a number of species there is a specific time in the development of the animal when it is most susceptible to the formation of primary social bonds with fellow species members and that this period usually occurs quite early in the life of the animal. In addition to adding a certain degree of substance to Freud's theory of developmental periods early in the life of the human child, imprinting research has served to reinforce and, in some cases, generate studies, such as those done by Spitz in 1945 and Goldfarb in 1943, that indicate the effects early institutionalization can have on later behavior. Very clearly, the environment of the human infant must satisfy certain minimal requirements during the first year of life if he is to show the psychological development required or expected by the society in which he is living.

One of the strongest supporters of ethological concepts as applied to the development of social behavior in humans has been Bowlby, who has viewed smiling in the human infant as an instinctive behavior pattern and who has drawn certain analogies between imprinting and the human mother-child relationship.

In outlining the similarity between smiling in the infant and innate behavior patterns found at the animal level, Bowlby presents the hypothesis that the smiling response increases the infant's chances of survival, since it makes the infant more appealing to the mother. He further suggests that there is a possibility that in the evolutionary history of man there has been a selection factor favoring this response and that infants without this response had a much higher mortality rate. Besides, there is a specific stimulus that elicits smiling in the infant—the schema of the human face—and this can be considered a releasing stimulus in the ethological sense. And the smiling response is said to be stereotyped and occurs in all members of the species. Ambrose, an associate of Bowlby's, points out that there also seems to be a critical period for early smiling, which is terminated by wariness of strangers, very much like the fear of strange objects that cuts off following in an imprinting situation. This application of ethology to human development has led Bowlby to conclude that other instinctive behaviors may also exist at the human level.

Perhaps of greater importance to psychoanalytic theories of the development of personality is the idea that clinging and following in the human infant are instinctive behaviors. This also has been outlined by Bowlby. It is his contention that, when the child is capable of locomotion, his following of the mother or mother object is like imprinting in other animals and that certain irrevocable bonds are formed through this behavior. On the basis of his observation and treatment of disturbed children, Bowlby has concluded that there is a high degree of correlation between emotional problems in childhood and complete lack of a mother object or lack of one that permits sufficient exercise of the child's responses of clinging and following.

The research on imprinting and the effects of early experience that has been carried out in a rather massive fashion with a variety of animals from the lower vertebrates to birds, mammals, and even primates has added substantially to an ethological approach to the problem of such bond formation, even at the human level. This research suggests the possible effects of an inadequate relationship and inadequate exercising of certain abilities.

PUPILLARY CHANGES

Another area of research that has recently been developed in psychology uses some of the basic techniques of ethology and may prove to be of value to the psychiatrist. First reported in 1960 by Hess and Polt, this technique bypasses verbal questioning of a human subject and relies on changes in pupil size as the subject reacts to stimulation. Briefly, Hess and Polt found that subjects looking at pleasing or interesting visual material had enlargement of the pupil. Looking at neutral material, they showed no change. Looking at pictures that were distasteful in some fashion caused contraction of the pupil. The amount of brightness of visual stimulation was, of course, controlled. Just as the ethologist depends on his knowledge of the behavior of a species under normal conditions to judge what is not normal in the behavior, this technique uses observation of the pupil of the eye to determine what might be called the mental behavior of the person under observation.

CONCLUSION

The contribution already made by ethology to psychiatry is only a beginning compared to its potential. Thus far, ethology can be said to have contributed in three ways. First, it has given rise to concepts, such as displacement activity and fixed-action patterns, that have been taken up by psychiatrists and used in their interpretation of normal and aberrant human behavior. Second, a large body of experimental data has been accumulated in regard to effects of early experience and imprinting, and it has been possible to draw parallels to human behavior and, in at least some respects, to test the hypothesis generated from the animal work in relation to how they fit human early behavior. Third, the methods and techniques of ethology can be and to a degree already have been used in psychiatry. Knowledge of normal behavior and normal development of behavior are cases in point. The use of schematic representations to determine whether or not sign stimuli or releasers are operating at the human level, as in the case of the smiling response to schematic representations of the human face, allows us to come to grips with certain aspects of early human behavior. And the use of techniques that do not involve verbal responses, such as the pupil phenomenon technique described previously, may allow us to gain information about the development of attitudes and perceptions in the infant and developing child, either before verbal responses are possible or where verbal responses may, perhaps, not be trusted.

There is one great over-all value that ethology and what might be called ethological psychology can bring to psychiatry. This is the rediscovery that man is a biological organism, that man must have a background and bring to present-day species members an ancient repertoire of behaviors that have some bearing on the problem of human behavior today. From the ethological point of view, the human infant is not a completely naive, innocent being. He has a legacy of potential behavior patterns that at one time assured the survival of the organism. Some of these innate behavior patterns must assuredly involve sexual behavior, aggressive behavior, and innate social responses. The realization that these potentials are present and that many of these potential behavior patterns must be channelled into quite different directions in our present-day civilized world may make a great contribution to an approach to the problems of man and could have a tremendous impact on the search for mental health. To assume, for example, that aggression is somehow the result of bad aspects and environment is to close one's eyes to the evolutionary usefulness and biological survival value of aggression, which surely must have a place in the make-up of man, as it does in all other organisms. If, in this one case alone, aggression were recognized as a normal and useful biological consequence, ethology would have made a major contribution to the field of psychiatry.

REFERENCES

Ambrose, J. A. The concept of a critical period for the development of social responsiveness in early human infancy. In *Determinants of Infant Behavior*, B. M. Foss, editor, vol. 2, p. 201. Wiley, New York, 1963.

Bowlby, J. Symposium on the contribution of current theories to an understanding of child development. Brit. J. Med. Psychol., 30: 230, 1957.

Bowlby, J. The nature of the child's tie to his mother. Int. J. Psychoanal., 39: 350, 1958.

Goldfarb, W. The effects of early institutional care on adolescent personality. J. Exp. Educ., 12: 106, 1943.

Hess, E. H. Imprinting: an effect of early experience, imprinting determines later social behavior in animals. Science, 130: 133, 1959.

Hess, E. H. Imprinting in birds. Science, 146: 1129, 1964.

Hess, E. H., and Polt, J. M. Pupil size as related to interest value of visual stimuli. Science, 132: 349, 1960.

Kaufman, I. C. Some ethological studies of social relationships and conflict situations. J. Amer. Psychoanal. Ass., 8: 671, 1960.

Kaufman, I. C. Symposium on "Psychoanalysis and ethology." III. Some theoretical implications from animal behavior studies for the psychoanalytic concepts of instinct, energy, and drive. Int. J. Psychoanal., 41: 318, 1960.

Kovach, J. K., and Hess, E. H. Imprinting: effects of painful stimulation upon the following response. J. Comp. Physiol. Psychol., 56: 461, 1963.

Lorenz, K. Der Kumpan in der Umwelt des Vogels. J. Ornithol., 83: 137 and 289, 1935.

Lorenz, K. Die Entwicklung der vergleichenden Verhaltensforchung in den letzten 12 Jahren. Verh. Deutsch. Zool. Ges. Freiburg, Akad. Verlag, Leipzig, 1953.

Menaker, E. A note on some biologic parallels between certain innate animal behavior and moral masochism. Psychoanal. Rev., 43: 31, 1956.

Ostow, M. The erotic instincts: a contribution to the study of instincts. Int. J. Psychoanal., 38: 305, 1957.

Polt, J. M. *The Effects of Social Experience on Imprinting*. Unpublished doctoral dissertation, University of Chicago, 1966.

Ramsay, A. O., and Hess, E. H. A laboratory approach to the study of imprinting. Wilson Bull., 66: 196, 1954.

Spitz, R. Hospitalism. Psychoanal. Stud. Child., 1: 53, 1945.

Tinbergen, N. *The Study of Instinct*. Clarendon Press, Oxford, 1951.

Uexküll, J. v. *Umwelt and Innenwelt der Tiere*, ed. 2. Jena, Berlin, 1921.

von Holst, E., and von St. Paul, U. Electrically controlled behavior. Sci. Amer., 206: No. 3, p. 50, 1962.

Weigert, E. Human ego functions in the light of animal behavior. Psychiatry, 19: 325, 1956.

CHAPTER 17

Social Communication

JURGEN RUESCH, M.D.

INTRODUCTION

DURING THE NINETEENTH CENTURY, physiologists talked about system-functions such as circulation, respiration, and digestion. The more behavior-oriented physiologists and psychologists added such considerations as locomotion, perception, expression, and motivation. Psychiatrists were mostly concerned with aberrations of thinking, feeling, and action. Anthropologists constructed cultural typologies. The linguists studied language codes. And the sociologists analyzed social structure. The tendency of scientific research was to study progressively smaller areas of structure and function. But, as Kety stated, "We do not always get closer to the truth as we slice and homogenize and isolate—that which we gain in precision and in the rigorous control of variables we sometimes lose in relevance to normal function, and . . . in the case of certain diseases or problems, the fundamental process may often be lost in the cutting."

The twentieth century departure from the older scientific procedures of slicing structure and function into progressively smaller parts can be traced in the field of communication to the introduction of the concept of steersmanship or cybernetics, which, based on the notion of feedback, enabled engineers to integrate part functions into a whole. The advances made in the field of communication engineering soon spread to the field of human behavior, with the result that scientists no longer confined themselves to the study of single human beings in isolation from one another. The emphasis switched from the person to the message, making it possible to trace communications as they pass from one individual through institutions and machines, to their ultimate destination in another person.

Communication can be defined as the process that links discontinuous parts of the living world to one another. It is made possible by three basic properties of living organisms found at all levels of organization, from the single cell to complex societies. In organisms, these properties are called perception, evaluation, and expression; in research, they are sometimes referred to as input, decision-making, and output. In spite of the fact that these functions constitute an organizing principle of nature, there does not exist as yet a unified theory of communication. Instead, each discipline has developed its own theoretical position. A brief survey of the various approaches to communication is presented in Table I.

BASIC SOCIAL PROCESS

When individuals communicate with each other, they engage in a social process that is controlled by three sets of determinants. The organs of communication—sensory system, effector system, and central nervous system—and the urge to use these organs are part of the individual's genetic endowment. The environment to which a person is exposed and the people by whom he is surrounded represent the social determinants. And the manner in which his experience influences his knowledge, his skills, and his ways of adaptation can be considered the psychological determinants. Thus, communicative behavior is influenced by biological, social, and psychological factors.

When all these complex and interwoven patterns are reduced to a few fundamental premises, we arrive at a description originally formulated by Cantril, who stated that man requires the satisfaction of his survival needs and seeks security in a physical and psychological sense; he craves sufficient order and certainty in his life to enable him to judge with fair accuracy what will or will not occur; he seeks to enlarge the range and to enrich the quality of his satisfactions; and, being a creature of hope, he is not inclined to resign himself easily. Since man has the capacity to make choices, he desires freedom to exercise this capacity. He wants to experience a sense of his own worthwhileness, and he wants to share a system of values or beliefs to which he can commit himself. Also, he needs to live in a society that holds out a fair degree of hope that his aspirations will be fulfilled.

In implementing these needs and in seeking to realize his potentialities, man engages in a social process that can be described as follows:

Man is a herd animal, and distinct or prolonged separation from the group is frustrating to him. Therefore, every individual strives to prevent separation from the group at the same time that he attempts to remain a distinctly separate entity within the group. The individual achieves this balance by controlling the type and magnitude of social differences that exist between himself and others.

Excessive differences that may produce tensions can be decreased (1) through equal exposure of people to things, persons, and situations (simi-

TABLE I

Approaches to Communication[a]

Discipline	Field of Specialization	Source
History		
History of language	Development of language over the centuries	Hoselitz, Pei, Revesz
History of communication engineering	Development of communication technology and codes	Cherry
Theoretical disciplines		
Cybernetics	Steersmanship and feedback in biological and social systems	Wiener
Mathematical theory of communication	Information theory	Shannon and Weaver, Brillouin, Pierce
Communication engineering	Computers, automata, and control devices	George, Latil, Licklider
Scientific philosophy	Assumptions made in scientific procedures	International Encyclopedia of Unified Science, Ruesch and Bateson, Horowitz
Unified theory	Communication as general systems theory	Ashby, Bertalanffy
Behavioral sciences		
Neurophysiology	Communication and the central nervous system	Horrobin; MacKay; Miller, Galanter, and Pribram; Rosenblith
Neuropsychology	Perception, transmission, decision-making, memory	Broadbent, Churchman, G. A. Miller, J. G. Miller
Ethology	Animal communication	Sebeok, Hess
Social sciences		
Social organization	Organization of social networks	Argyris, Kahn
Group process	Communication in small groups	Collins and Guetzkow, Homans
Mass media	Television, radio, press	Dexter and White, Klapper, Schramm
Language and codes		
Linguistics	Phonetics, language codes	Saporta, Osgood and Sebeok

[a] For the pertinent works by the authors listed in the third column of this table, the reader is referred to the reference section at the end of this chapter. Complete bibliographic references for the sources cited may be found in other publications of the author.

TABLE I (*Continued*)
Approaches to Communication[a]

Discipline	Field of Specialization	Source
Signifies	Meaning of signs and signals	Berelson, Morris
Symbolic systems	Verbal and nonverbal codes	Hall, Skinner, Whorf
Biological codes	Genetic code	Beadle
Commercial disciplines		
Propaganda and advertising	Influencing people to act	Packard
Political thought reform	Influencing people to believe	Lifton, Hinkle and Wolff, Schein
Business organization	Efficiency of communication	Redfield, Haney, Haire
Clinical disciplines		
Family psychiatry	Communication difficulties inside the family	Ackerman, Bell, Howells
Individual psychiatry	Disturbed communication	Bateson, Jackson, Haley, and Weakland; Ruesch
Group therapy	Group analysis	Foulkes, Slavson
Psychoanalysis and psychotherapy	Communication with patients	Feldman, Haley, Meerloo, Ruesch
Mental hygiene	Community organization	Bellak, Duhl, Leighton
Neurology and neurosurgery	Pathology of organs of communication	A.R.N.M.D. Proceedings (1962), Pribram
Psychopharmacology	Influence of drugs on communication	Kalinowsky and Hoch, Sargant and Slater
Speech disorders	Aphasia, reading disability	Brain, Hermann
The arts		
Painting and sculpture, dance, theatre, music	Expression of inner events through shape, color, movement, texture, and sound, resulting in the creation of nonverbal signals and signs to which others respond	Gombrich, Ostwald, Stanislavsky
Arts and crafts		
Architecture, decorative arts, cabinetmaking, handcrafts, interior decoration, fashion design	Shaping of the material environment embodies the assumptions and conventions of a particular period and person; architectural structures and objects may	Gorsline, Hall, Hogben, Larousse Encyclopedia of Mythology, Ruesch and Kees, Laver

TABLE I (Continued)
Approaches to Communication[a]

Discipline	Field of Specialization	Source
	become symbols for communicative exchange of people with each other and with posterity	
Social games		
Law, politics, sports, special and social situations	Stylized message exchange by participants who assume certain roles and abide by well-established rules can be analyzed as if it were a game or a play	Berne, Neiman and Hughes, Jackson, Sarbin

[a] For the pertinent works by the authors listed in the third column of this table, the reader is referred to the reference section at the end of this chapter. Complete bibliographic references for the sources cited may be found in other publications of the author.

lar experience); (2) through social interaction, thereby establishing correspondence of information and behavior (communicative exchange); (3) through shared explanations to justify existing differences (interpretation); and (4) through coercive action or threat of coercive action in case of deviance (social exclusion, imprisonment, hospitalization).

Insufficient differences may also produce tensions. Differences between people can be increased (1) through isolation from the group and exposure to self (solitude); (2) through exposure to new groups (culture change); (3) through the acquisition of knowledge or skill not possessed by others (achievement); and (4) through unusual life experiences not shared by others (illness, adversity, adventure).

If a balance cannot be achieved between personal identity and group membership, the ensuing tension usually exerts a disruptive influence on both individuals and group. This tension can be reduced to a tolerable level if one or more persons adapt pathologically, in neglect of their own needs, or if the disruption of the group leads to new group formations.

ASSESSMENT OF SOCIAL NETWORKS

The social process that connects person with person or the social conflict that disrupts relationships can be studied best through observation of the ways and means of message exchange. The following questions may serve as a guideline in the assessment of groups: Who? (status, role, identity) said What? (content) to Whom? (status, role, identity) When? (chronological, biological, elapsed time) Where? (situation) How? (codes) with what Effect? (feedback).

The questions *who* and *to whom* must be answered in terms of role, status, and identity. Out of a pool of thousands of people, the persons who actually sent and received a given message must be selected. The clues here may be found not only in the social characteristics of the sender but also in the message itself. The manner in which a communiqué is coded, phrased, and timed frequently identifies the sender, a fact used in detective and intelligence work. These explanatory or instructional aspects, which help in deciphering the main content of a message, have been referred to as the metacommunicative aspects of communication. For example, a certain signal given by a uniformed traffic officer is a command; the same signal given by a ten-year-old child may be interpreted as play. Or a poorly constructed letter containing errors in grammar and orthography may be assumed to have been written by a person with relatively little education.

The *what* of a communication refers to the events that signs and symbols stand for. Proper usage presupposes the existence of a dictionary or legend. Unfortunately, people use, in addition to the standard dictionary, a multitude of other informal and usually unprinted dictionaries. Mothers and babies, husbands and wives, industrial and work crews, and sports teams develop private vocabularies. Thus, a message can be interpreted in many ways, according to which legend is used. The study of the broad conventions that regulate this process of attributing meaning is the domain of cultural anthropologists. The narrower conventions are studied by language experts and psychologists. And in the case of patients and their relatives, the psychiatrist and the psychoanalyst are the professionals who specialize in deciphering idiosyncratic and particularistic language.

The *when* of a message refers to different aspects of time and timing. Clues must be found that indicate the historical period, the point in the development of the situation, the age of the participants, and the nature of other messages that preceded or followed the message under study.

The *where* of a message deals with the social context in which the communication takes place. The situation or occasion (wedding, traffic accident, lunch) usually furnishes a label that enables the participants to identify the pertinent rules. These, in brief, indicate who can talk to whom, about what, for how long, where, and in what manner—and the consequences if the rules are violated.

The *how* of a message refers to the code in which it is phrased. In the exploration of this area of communication, speech and language experts are joined by the gesture experts and all those other artists and craftsmen who specialize in nonverbal codes. In addition to written languages, there exist many auditory and visual codes, such as semaphore, Morse code, jungle drums, and the sign languages of the Indians and of the deaf and dumb.

The *effect* of a communication can be evaluated by studying the change it produces. An initial statement by one person or group is usually followed by a reaction on the part of another person or group. During the exchange, the identity of the participants, the schemes for interpretation, the rules of procedure, and the referential properties of the symbols are clarified. A message may be said to have had an effect if it has changed the parameters of the system. The chances of relating subsequent effects to the information contained in a given message are better if the interval between message and reaction is short. If the interval is long, intervening factors blur the cause-and-effect relationship. Large-scale evaluations of effects are undertaken by advertisers, propagandists, government agencies, and public health experts.

DISTURBED COMMUNICATION

Disturbances of communication arise when messages are too intense, are perceived in a distorted way or not at all, arrive too early or too late, or are inappropriate to the situation. The therapeutic measures vary with the circumstances under which the disorders occur and the ways in which they affect the participants.

Disease, trauma, or malformation of the organs of communication may lead to distortions of perception, evaluation, and expression. In such conditions, the therapeutic intervention is predominantly somatic.

Perception, evaluation, and expression may be quantitatively altered because of overload or underload, incorrect timing, and other factors subsumed under the term "stress." Here the therapeutic intervention is designed to program the individual in such a way that he no longer exposes himself to stress. Sometimes large-scale social reorganization may reduce human stress.

Perception, evaluation, and expression may be qualitatively distorted in that these functions do not provide for correct information or response. Because of one-sided experience or lack of social skills, a person may be ill-prepared to communicate in the setting in which he finds himself. Therapeutic intervention here is directed at reeducation or at helping the person find a more suitable environment.

The communicative process may be distorted because actual or imagined content is threatening to the participants. In this case the therapeutic intervention is directed at the correction of erroneous perceptions and evaluations or at helping the patient accept circumstances that cannot be altered.

Communication may be disturbed if feedback processes are not functioning properly. Lack of acknowledgement, delayed response, replies that are not relevant to the original statement, and failure to reach agreements may all exert a disorganizing effect on both individual and group. Also, if the participants have an erroneous model of what is going on, they cannot behave appropriately. In dealing with distorted images of reality, the most significant therapeutic measure consists of exposing and discussing the unrealistic assumptions. If the processes that stabilize distortions have been rendered inoperative and corrective feedback has become rewarding, a more realistic image of the world is likely to develop.

THERAPIES BASED ON COMMUNICATION

Once the presence of disordered communication has been established, the psychiatrist must decide what type of intervention is appropriate in order to restore functioning. The psychiatrist may influence his patients by intervening with the human instruments of communication, as in psychosurgery, electroshock, and drug therapy. He may attempt to change the patient's body of information by means of the psychological therapies. Or he may try to alter the ways of responding, as in the social therapies, either through direct retraining or through changes brought about in the environment or in the relationship between the patient and the environment. These interventions may all be conceived of as being based on two central features, communication and organization.

As a therapeutic tool, communication may be used to help the individual increase his awareness of himself and of the ways he fits into the existing social and cultural patterns, acquire communicative skills and the ability to get along with people, abandon unnecessary assumptions that restrict effectiveness, and modify his attitudes in the direction of understanding and tolerance of behavioral differences.

Within the small group, communication is used to clarify the roles of the participants, to specify the rules that the group observes, to verbalize the assumptions of the various participants, and to formulate goals of action acceptable to all.

Reorganization of the social system that surrounds individuals may consist of (1) introduction of new organizational structures or removal of obsolete ones (agencies, committees, associations, laws, and regulations can be created to take care of social needs as they arise; this is a task of social planning); (2) alteration of existing networks of communication (the flow of messages, the place of decision-making, the organization of checks and balances can be changed; this is a task of management); and (3) adaptation of technological procedures to fit the needs of individuals (treatment methods can be adapted to blend with the political, economic, and ethnic values and practices of the local population).

In practice, the therapies aimed at improving the social communication of people are known under a number of different names.

The term "community psychiatry" refers to a complicated set of operations aimed at changing the attitudes and tolerance limits of a given group to insure the best treatment of their sick members. Once this goal has been achieved, psychiatric treatment methods and procedures can be adapted to that particular community (rural, metropolitan, military, industrial, academic, etc.), and the necessary resources and facilities can be mobilized.

The term "therapeutic community" refers to carefully managed relationships between patients and staff in an institutional setting, whereby the patients have time-limited and often controlled contact with the area and the people surrounding the hospital.

Group therapy, group psychotherapy, analytic group psychotherapy, and psychodrama—all utilize the group setting for therapeutic purposes. Depending on the particular method chosen, the main efforts are directed toward guidance, counseling, lecturing, inspiration and exhortation, activity and play, or the acquisition of insight.

Family therapy involves the treatment of an entire family by the same therapist or by different therapists. The family members may be seen interacting with each other in the presence of the psychiatrist or the therapeutic team, or they may be seen separately.

Occupational therapy and work, play, music, drama, or dance therapy are oriented toward skilled activities, and human interaction is subordinated to the physical task at hand.

Social programming refers to the discussion of specific social tasks individually or in groups. The technical aspects of how to get a job, how to behave at a social gathering, or what side effects to watch for when taking medications can be reduced to step-by-step operations and taught to the patient and his relatives.

Regardless of whether the psychiatrist deals with organization, somatic therapies, psychotherapy, or group therapy, he has to deal with people. He relies on the built-in desire of the individual to seek human contact, and he gains leverage and exerts his influence through three fundamental processes: understanding, acknowledging, and agreeing. Understanding involves the establishment in the mind of the therapist of an accurate model of the patient's behavior; to be understood is a rather pleasant experience for the patient. Acknowledging refers to the therapist's receipt of the patient's purposive or involuntary messages; to be acknowledged is even more gratifying for the patient. Agreeing implies the isolation of a certain aspect within the universe of discourse and the establishment of corresponding views or bodies of information regarding this aspect; to reach an agreement is most satisfying.

COMMUNICATION ENGINEERING AND PSYCHIATRY

The phenomenal advances made in communication engineering have left their mark on psychiatry. The psychiatrist's functions of perception, scanning, memory, computation, reasoning, decision-making, expression, and action can be vastly expanded through the use of communication technology. Mass education and perhaps even mass treatment will become more significant as further technological advances are made. Some of the applications of communication engineering that may affect the work of the psychiatrist have been sketched in the following paragraphs.

Computers

Information storage and retrieval. Procedures are now available for storing the information contained, for example, in books or periodicals. Any page in such a collection could be located in a fraction of a second. It is possible that in the future computer storage and retrieval of information will be cheaper than the present system of libraries.

Computation and statistics. Complicated mathematical operations that would take human beings years to work out can be solved in seconds. Budget computations, logistics, and other administrative tasks are greatly facilitated by computers.

Data-processing, decision-making, and problem-solving. Computers can scan, translate, combine data, and perform many other functions of the human mind. As aids in decision-making, they can weight factors properly and can consider more material in a shorter period of time than the human brain can. For example, results of blood, urine, spinal fluid, X-ray, and other examinations can be quickly combined to yield a medical diagnosis. Similar procedures can probably be used for the assessment of personality as better measurements of behavior become available.

Computers as scientific models. Computers can be used as models of organisms or society. The program for a computer that reenacts a process is becoming just as acceptable a theory of that process as the equation describing it. With such a procedure, more precise definition of various functions can be achieved than has been possible up to now. Reenactment or simulation of natural phenomena is the path on which scientific advances are currently made.

PROGRAMED INSTRUCTION

Texts. Textbooks can now be written in very much the same way that teaching machines operate. A question is presented, and, if the student answers it correctly, he proceeds to the next one. However, if he answers incorrectly, he is advised to do more studying on that specific point.

Mechanical teaching machines. In a variety of semiadaptive teaching machines that are operated by hand or electrically, questions and answers are presented serially. The next question is not revealed if the previous one has been answered incorrectly. This forces the student to find the correct answer if he wishes to continue.

Computerized teaching programs. A computer can present questions to a student by way of television or on a typewriter. The student then types out his answers, and this serves as input to the computer. If the answer is wrong, the computer gives the student more training on the spot. If the answer is correct, the computer presents the next question. Such computerized programs can be used with a variety of psychiatric patients—for example, the mentally retarded, the brain-diseased, and the emotionally disturbed slow learner.

Therapy machines. With automatic control devices, suitable machines can carry out tasks formerly performed by people. Psychiatry has made little use of this aspect of technology, but in the future it should be possible to program computers to interact with patients or to rehearse certain behavioral features with which the patients have difficulty. For example, a patient can be given an opportunity to learn and abreact at his own speed; if he is slow and redundant, the machine has more forebearance than the human being.

MASS MEDIA

Broadcast television, closed-circuit television, and radio. These media facilitate the delivery of lectures at any time, practically anywhere. Taped lectures can be preserved, evaluated, and sold, and for this reason they are generally more carefully prepared. The mass media approach is particularly significant in teaching students, training personnel, addressing relatives of patients, and informing boards of hospitals or public health agencies of current trends and needs in psychiatry.

PERCEPTION AND ACTION BY REMOTE CONTROL

Microphones and television cameras can now be placed in difficult locations that formerly were not accessible to observation—for example, inside an organism or in a social group. Recording observations in this way obviates the presence of the scientist. The observations can be preserved over time, and all the scientist has to do is evaluate the tapes. Psychiatrists use closed-circuit television to monitor two-person and larger group sessions. With this method the psychiatrist or the patient can be confronted with his own behavior, which he may never have seen or heard.

In the technological age the psychiatrist will progressively make more use of modern communication machines in teaching, research, and treatment. And in all probability the future training of the psychiatrist will include some aspects of communication engineering.

REFERENCES

Bellak, L., editor. *Handbook of Community Psychiatry and Community Mental Health*. Grune & Stratton, New York, 1964.

Berne, E. *Games People Play*. Grove Press, New York, 1964.

Broadbent, D. E. *Perception and Communication*. Pergamon Press, London, 1958.

Cantril, H. The human design. J. Indiv. Psychol., 20: 129, 1964.

Coulson, J. E., editor. *Programmed Learning Computer-Based Instruction*. Wiley, New York, 1962.

Feigenbaum, E. A., and Feldman, J. editors. *Computers and Thought*. McGraw-Hill, New York, 1963.

Feldman, S. S. *Mannerisms of Speech and Gestures in Everyday Life*. International Universities Press, New York, 1959.

Hollander, E. P., and Hunt, R. G., editors. *Current Perspectives in Social Psychology*. Oxford University Press, New York, 1963.

Horrobin, D. F. *The Communication Systems of the Body*. Basic Books, New York, 1964.

Hoselitz, B. F., editor. *A Reader's Guide to the Social Sciences*. Free Press of Glencoe (Macmillan), New York, 1959.

Kent, A., and Taulbee, O. E., editors. *Electronic Information Handling*. Spartan Books, Washington, 1965.

Kety, S. S. A biologist examines the mind and behavior. Science, 132: 1861, 1950.

Pierce, J. R. *Symbols, Signals and Noise*. Harper & Row, New York, 1961.

Rioch, D. McK., and Weinstein, E. A. Disorders of communication. Res. Publ. Ass. Nerv. Ment. Dis., 42: 1964.

Ruesch, J. *Disturbed Communication*. W. W. Norton, New York, 1957.

Ruesch, J. *Therapeutic Communication*. W. W. Norton, New York, 1961.

Ruesch, J., and Bateson, G. *Communication: The Social Matrix of Psychiatry*. W. W. Norton, New York, 1951.

Ruesch, J., Brodsky, C. M., and Fischer, A. *Psychiatric Care*. Grune & Stratton, New York, 1964.

Ruesch, J., and Kees, W. *Nonverbal Communication.* University of California Press, Berkeley, 1956.

Saporta, S., editor. *Psycholinguistics.* Holt, Rinehart and Winston, New York, 1961.

Wiener, N. *Cybernetics, or Control and Communication in the Animal and the Machine,* ed. 2. Wiley, New York, 1961.

AREA C

Basic Sociocultural Sciences

CHAPTER 18

Anthropology and Psychiatry

ANTHONY F. C. WALLACE, Ph.D.

INTRODUCTION

WHAT IS RECOGNIZED as pathological in behavior is usually a matter of common consensus within a society. But the standards of consensus vary from one society to another. In the United States, for instance, hallucinatory experience is generally regarded as prima facie evidence of at least temporary mental disorder. But in many primitive tribes hallucination is not regarded as evidence of pathology at all; rather, it is an experience deliberately sought and prized for its presumed value as a communication from supernatural beings. The anthropologist, who studies human societies in an evolutionary and cross-cultural perspective, explains such differences as the results of differences in culture.

Culture, in the anthropologist's sense, is the sum of what the individual members of a community—be it a small band of hunters or a large industrial nation—have learned from generations of accumulated social experience. It includes manners, customs, tastes, skills, language, beliefs, and all the other patterns of behavior that are part of organized social life. Just as cultures differ in technology, kinship practices, and religious belief, so they differ in the behaviors classified as normal and abnormal.

HISTORY OF PSYCHOANALYTIC ANTHROPOLOGY

The involvement of anthropology with studies of personality and psychopathology began in earnest with the efforts of psychoanalysts to apply their insights to cultural data. This tradition in Freud's work is best known in *Totem and Taboo*, *Moses and Monotheism*, and *The Future of an Illusion*. Psychoanalytic anthropology has been developed and refined by a number of later scholars who combined anthropological training and field work, particularly Geza Roheim, Weston LaBarre, Abram Kardiner, and George Devereux.

The main stream of the culture and personality studies, however, springs from a combination of the American ethnographic tradition, as developed by Franz Boas and his students, and a variety of psychological and psychiatric traditions, of which psychoanalysis is only one. Margaret Mead and Ruth Benedict, both students of Boas, are perhaps the best-known representatives of this eclectic and humanistic tradition. In this tradition, psychological insights from a variety of sources infuse and illuminate ethnographic description.

A more systematic approach relies on tests, measurements, and formal models of analysis of values, communication processes, personality structure, and psychopathology. This approach is found in the work of Hallowell, Kluckhohn, Whiting, Spindler, Bateson, Opler, and Wallace. But many of the most significant contributions have been made by anthropologists who are not primarily identified with culture and personality. For instance, Malinowski's analysis of the important role of the mother's brother in many primitive societies suggested modification of the simpler forms of the Oedipus formulation. The work of anthropologists in these areas has been collected or reviewed by Honigmann, Kluckhohn, Murray, Schneider, Barnouw, Hsu, and Kaplan.

CORRELATIONS WITHIN A CULTURE

Cultural anthropologists have worked from intensive case studies of individual cultures and from statistical cross-cultural studies to explore the degree to which various aspects of culture are correlated. These studies show that change in any one sector of culture—for instance, in technology or economic system—is apt to produce a series of changes in other sectors, such as family structure, religious belief, and values. The studies also show that certain assortments of culture elements are more congenial than others and are most likely to be found together in a society; for instance, strong belief in witchcraft tends to occur in societies with poorly developed governmental systems of social control.

The statistical associations in such findings are not impressively high. However, the implication for psychiatry is that the folk definition of behavior disorder; the precise symptoms of that disorder; the stresses contributory to its development, onset, and course; and the methods of social response to the disorder are likely to be more or less direct functions of many cultural factors, such as economic system, family structure, political organization, and religious belief and practice.

Several generalizations can be made about behavior in cultures. (1) There are always folk criteria for distinguishing behavior that is normal from that which is abnormal. (2) Abnormal (as distinct from merely wrong or criminal or even pathological) behavior is always explained as a result of interference, by disease or by supernatural agencies, with the normal functioning of the organism. (3) Conventional therapeutic or extrusive procedures are always available and believed to be effective to end any unwanted interference and thereby to restore the victim's behavior to normal or at least to minimize its disrupting effect on the community. (4) There are no human societies in which mental disorders, of one sort or another, never occur. (5) In most human societies, both primitive and civilized, both Western and non-Western, the same major symptom clusters can be recognized: schizophrenias, depressions, conversion reactions, dissociative reactions, obsessions and compulsions, phobias, and psychosomatic ailments.

SIMILARITIES OF PSYCHOTIC PROCESSES

Despite the difficulty of securing adequate statistical data, societies do seem to differ markedly in preferred style of symptoms, in the incidence and prevalence of major types of disorder, and, slightly, in total psychiatric census. Furthermore, societies exotic to Western eyes may display dramatically different ethnic psychoses, whose symptoms may, at first glance, appear strange to Western eyes: *amok* in southeast Asia (a homicidal rampage), *latah* in Malaya (echopraxia), *piblokto* among the polar Eskimos (an endemic convulsive disorder).

For example, the windigo psychosis, repeatedly described among the Algonkian hunters of northeastern North America, is superficially unique. These people, although recurrently faced by starvation, do not condone cannibalism. The victim of the windigo psychosis, however, gradually becomes convinced that he is possessed by a supernatural monster, the windigo, whose taste for human flesh is notorious in mythology. He himself experiences an increasingly imperious urge to satisfy a cannibalistic appetite. He attempts to control it, to withdraw from tempting contacts with family and friends. Finally, he may attempt suicide or urge others to kill him, lest he actually become a cannibal. Indeed, he may be physically restrained or even killed by a terrified community when they learn of his fears.

However, these unique delusions and occasional accompanying hallucinations appear to follow the same sort of mental process that in Western society may accompany fears of homosexuality (as in Freud's analysis of the Schreber case) or of heterosexuality (as in the panics among medieval nuns over seduction). In other words, the basic structure of a paranoid process involving fear, defense against the fear, and powerful but disallowed impulses in a progressively delusional set of defense mechanisms is apparent in the supposedly exotic windigo syndrome.

VARIETIES OF PSYCHOTIC CAUSES

Causes, in fact, appear to be more diverse than the basic symptomatic structures. The variety of social structures displayed in the archives of ethnography provides a vast spectrum of possible emotional stresses to which individuals may respond with psychopathological behavior. In regard to the household in which the child lives, for instance, there is the Western European ideal model of the nuclear family, in which mother, father, and children live together in an apartment or house of their own. There are also polygynous societies in which each child lives with his mother and siblings, and the husband and father only occasionally or never spends the night with his wife and their offspring. There are societies in which a number of nuclear families live under the same roof, the affiliating genealogical connection being sometimes matrilineal, sometimes patrilineal. There are societies in which a woman has several husbands. There are societies in which the mother's brother plays some of the roles played by the natural father in our own culture. There are societies in which the infant is cared for by a large number of mature females. The list could go on and on. The patterns of identification, love, and hate that are most likely to arise in these different domestic arrangements are diverse.

Even the political structure provides different opportunities for stress and for particular kinds of symptomatic relief. Societies in which there are no political institutions that can maintain social control by invoking effective sanctions against wrongdoers are apt to be rife with fears and accusations of witchcraft. This is less apt to happen in those societies in which the individual can seek protection and legal recourse by appeal to human authority. The fear of witchcraft as a cause of illness or even death functions in politically weak communities as a principal deterrent to interpersonal aggression.

Religious beliefs, too, are notoriously variable from culture to culture. They condone, reward, or taboo human impulses in a remarkably irregular way.

NATIONAL CHARACTER

Many observers, both anthropologists and psychiatrists, have suggested that each culture is associated with a common or, at least, widely shared national character or basic or modal personality structure. This character is particularly adapted to the prevailing social structure and belief system and is, at the same time, particularly vulnerable to certain stresses.

From this point of view, the type of neuroticism (focusing on an Oedipus conflict involving a nuclear family in which the father holds the position of supreme authority and the mother is the nurturant figure) that Freud was able to define as common among his patients is by no means universal. On the contrary, it is specific to a few cultures, including that of central Europe at the end of the nineteenth century. Even if some sort of triangular libidinal relationship among child, adult male, and adult female is universal in mankind, it is argued that the course of character development and of neurosis differs from culture to culture. Thus, where the father appears to the child as marginal or ineffectual in comparison with the mother, the growing male may find it difficult to identify with a male figure. The child may, therefore, have to accomplish a male identification by undergoing a dramatic puberty ritual, as among Australian aborigines, or by compulsive display of external symbols of masculinity, as among American Negroes.

In this connection it should be pointed out that large modern states like the United States are polycultural; they display a diversity of socioeconomic classes, geographic regions, and ethnic origins. The psychologist or psychiatrist cannot assume that a single American culture or American personality exists in a sense comparable to *the* culture and *the* national character of a small primitive tribe.

INSTITUTIONALIZED SYMPTOMS

Most societies, even the most complex, have traditional means for accommodating themselves to episodes of disturbed behavior. In a sense, the task of the culture is to institutionalize and channelize the symptoms of an endemic disease in such a way that the symptoms are not disruptive of orderly community life. Such institutionalization minimizes the costs of extruding the sick person from the community by confinement or execution. It also minimizes the cost of maintaining the sick person in the company of his family and associates.

The means of institutionalization seems to be of three kinds: the denial of illness; special roles for the chronically ill; and therapeutic rituals for those, who may number most of the community, whose disturbances are occasional and episodic.

Denial of Illness

There is a tendency in our own society for families to ignore or deny even gross symptoms in a member. Although this may be deplored where more effective means of treatment are available, such a procedure at least has the probable advantage of not adding to the sick person's difficulties the burden of being publicly branded as incompetent. Where the condition is widespread, where there is no reliable and inexpensive treatment, and when the symptoms are episodic and not severely threatening to community welfare, such a policy has even more merit.

In our own culture, the ignoring of emotional disorders associated with menstrual periods seems to be dictated by such considerations. Among the polar Eskimos, *piblokto*, fits of convulsive hysteria whose cause is not fully understood, is apparently treated with a similar indifference. On the other hand, in some other cultures, menstruating women, whether or not they suffer from premenstrual tension, are taboo and physically isolated because of beliefs concerning the dangerous nature of menstrual contamination. And, in our culture, episodic convulsive disorders are often regarded as serious, requiring heroic measures of treatment.

SPECIAL ROLES FOR THE ILL

In many societies, including sectors of our own, a person suffering from a chronic condition such as schizophrenia is allowed to take on or is even encouraged to take on the role of shaman. He is regarded as a person who has a special skill in communicating with or manipulating supernatural powers and beings and who performs for a fee such services as divining the location of missing objects, foretelling the future, curing illness, and persuading a divinity to bestow benefits on a client. The shaman's delusions and hallucinations are channeled and institutionalized in a definite pattern of behavior. He secures the support of the community in return for ritual services that the community believes will be helpful. Even in a person who has not undertaken the role of shaman, the occurrence of occasional or repeated hallucinations may give him a recognized role as prophet. His visions and voices are interpreted by the community as communications from the spiritual world. Whatever its impact on public policy or its consequence in the creation of new cults or social movements, the prophetic role has often been an important institutionalized niche for the delusional or hallucinating person in many societies.

RITUALS FOR EPISODIC ILLNESS

Religious rituals in almost all societies may give symptomatic relief in episodes of acting out to individuals suffering from chronic but not necessarily grossly disabling emotional conflicts. In many cultures, rituals are cathartic; impulses that cannot be readily satisfied in the workaday world may find expression in ritual. For instance, in some African Negro societies, voodoo rituals encourage individuals to become possessed by supernatural beings and to act out the variously gratifying roles associated with them. These roles, performed in a dissociated state, permit the dancer to satisfy impulses by temporarily assuming an alternate personality. Rituals under religious sanction may provide occasions for the satisfaction of sexual wishes disallowed under ordinary circumstances, such as incest and adultery. The Iroquois Indians believed that dreams were the language in which the soul expressed its unconscious wishes. They had an elaborate panel of procedures by which frustrated desires could be identified and satisfied.

Not all such rituals are cathartic; they may also be repressive, intended to strengthen the capacity of the individual to reduce the anxiety of conflict by supporting defense mechanisms. For instance, rituals in which a scapegoat is condemned and destroyed have the effect of enabling the conflict-ridden person to say, "It is not I, but he, who is guilty of such and such wishes." Rituals of confession and absolution similarly permit the individual to feel—temporarily, at least—that guilt has been removed.

THERAPEUTIC AND PROPHYLACTIC RITUALS

The line is thin between rituals intended generally to provide symptomatic relief for any and all members of a community who wish to take advantage of them and those rituals aimed at therapy and prevention for particular persons or classes of persons.

THERAPEUTIC PROCEDURES

Specific treatment of mental disturbance in primitive societies commonly involves one of four principles: exorcising a possessing spirit, recalling the victim's wandering soul, making reparations for the violation of taboo, or countering the spell cast by witchcraft.

The ritual procedures by which the shaman or the group undertake such a therapeutic task may indeed be based on a faulty conception of the nature and causes of mental illness, but such procedures are not necessarily inefficacious. Sharing a belief system with the shaman that defines his ritual as effective, the victim is apt to be relieved of the fear that his case is hopeless and must end in death or the destruction of his identity. Indeed, as Cannon has pointed out, this fear may itself be lethal if the physiological stress accompanying it is not relieved. Furthermore, some shamans interview the patient in order to discover the nature of the taboo violation or the possible occasion for witchcraft. In the interview, the shaman may directly encounter the patient's unconscious conflicts, help him to verbalize them, and thus, in the manner of any good psychotherapist, bring them into a state of consciousness, where the ego can begin to deal with them. To the extent that he is able to do this, the shaman may be able to accomplish real psychotherapy.

Gillin, for instance, describes a Maya Indian shaman in Guatemala who was treating a woman for presumably hysterical conversion symptoms. The native theory of the disease (*susto*) was soul loss, and the ritual treatment was arbitrary and, in a sense, irrelevant to the psychodynamics of the case. However, the shaman did spend a good deal of time talking with the patient in order to find out what emotional shock had frightened her soul away. This discourse rapidly converged on a discussion of precisely those matters a trained psychotherapist would have been attentive to: her unhappiness with an unfaithful husband; her poverty; her memories of her father, whom she loved.

PROPHYLACTIC RITUALS

In what may be called preventive psychotherapy, most primitive societies tend to rely on what are called rites of passage. These are the rituals, often supported by more or less elaborate religious beliefs, in which a person is separated from an earlier social role and introduced to a new one. They are performed on occasions of life crisis: birth, puberty, marriage, military undertakings, bereavement, and so on. The particular pattern of occasions selected for ritual treatment and the content of the rituals vary, of course, with the culture.

Puberty ceremonies. The rites of passage most relevant to the interests of modern psychiatry are the puberty ceremonies performed on youths and girls, usually in the early stages of puberty, to mark the transition from childhood to adolescence or even adulthood. What is involved is usually more than a mere celebration of the change in social role. In the classic instances, such as the initiation rituals of the Australian aborigines and the bush schools of West Africa, a class of initiates, particularly males, is physically removed from the community and imprisoned in a special compound. There they are instructed in the secrets of manhood and are subjected for days or weeks to prolonged and various forms of hazing at the hands of elder males. The climax of the ritual is the public occasion on which genital mutilation—generally circumcision but among some Australian aborigines subincision also—is performed on the youth. This marks the completion of the process of transformation. The child is considered to have died, to have been reconceived and held in embryonic isolation, and, finally, to have been reborn a man. Comparable ceremonies are, more rarely, also conducted for girls.

The unconscious meanings of the acts performed in such rituals are subject to multiple interpretations. The Australian circumcision and subincision ritual has been interpreted as a symbolic castration by jealous elders of young males who potentially compete for their women. It has also been interpreted as the satisfaction of an unconscious womb envy on the part of the males, who by the operation of subincision acquire the simulacrum of a vagina.

Functions of rituals. Every society has communal rituals when a major transformation of role in that society's terms is required of an individual or a class of individuals. It is a reasonable inference that a major function of such rituals is to minimize the duration and depth of internal psychic conflict accompanying major changes in social role by taking the matter out of the individual's hands and, as it were, ritually brainwashing him.

For instance, the primary function of the puberty rituals described above is to facilitate the transformation of children into adults by separating them physically from the parental household, encouraging appropriate changes in knowledge and motivation by a combination of stress and suggestion, and reintroducing them to the community in a new role. The community is expected to respond in complementary fashion. Just as it is obligatory for the child to forsake childish things and behave as an adult, so the adults of the community are enjoined to respond to the initiate as an adult and no longer a child.

The agonizing conflicts concerning roles, values, motives, and responses commonly observed in many members of Western societies at times of life crisis seem to be, in part, a consequence of the unavailability of *effective* rites of passage. Granted, the price a society has to pay for the advantage of such rites is heavy. They exact a relatively high degree of uniformity. Perhaps the price is too heavy for large, complex societies that are organized for rapid and continuous change in both technology and social structure. If individuality, diversity, and creativeness are prized, then ritualization of psychic maturation may be so costly that it cannot be tolerated. Viewed in these terms, the various individualized psychotherapeutic and counseling techniques developed in industrial societies in the nineteenth and twentieth centuries seem to be the necessary functional alternative to standardized rites of passage. And the continuous outcries against the demands of conformity and the threats to identity imposed by industrial urban society should not be regarded as a sign that modern society is becoming more and more ritualized and uniformitarian. Rather, they are a sign that more and more people are becoming aware that this kind of society cannot function successfully if conformity and uniformity are too highly emphasized.

STUDIES OF HOSPITALS AS CULTURAL SYSTEMS

In recent years many social scientists, including anthropologists, have studied the social and cultural milieu of the mental hospital. Indeed, a number of psychiatric administrators have encouraged anthropologists to study the social system of the mental hospital, its customs and procedures, and their possible unintended effects on patients. The social scientists have worked on the assumption that the course, symptoms, and outcome of psychotic and neurotic disorders are heavily influenced by the nature of the hospital environment.

SOCIAL CONFLICTS

One result of such studies has been the demonstration of characteristic types of social conflict built into the social system of the hospital staff: the castelike division of the line staff into such hierarchically ranked categories as physician, nurse, attendant, and maintenance personnel, with mobility blocked between categories (a nurse, for example, cannot become a doctor without leaving the organization); the military-like pattern of authority, characterized particularly by the phenomenon of multiple subordination (a nurse, for example, is expected to respond to orders from a number of other nurses and also from physicians, who may or may not be in communication with the nurse supervisors); the tendency for the patient to be so effectively stripped of his outside identity as spouse, parent, worker, and citizen that the reconstruction of a new outside identity or the reassumption of the old one is made very difficult, even if the patient's psychiatric condition permits it, and he comes instead to display the syndrome of hospitalism (his new identity becomes that of the good, passive, chronic patient).

It is difficult to estimate how much therapeutic benefit would accrue from instituting the changes in hospital organization and practice suggested by such observations. There is no clear understanding of the causes of the functional psychoses or of the relative efficacy of the various therapies available; therefore, the weighting of any one factor must be problematical. But, whatever method of treatment is undertaken, the patient's response must depend partly on his confidence in his physician and the physician's apparatus, which in this case is the hospital itself, and partly on what confidence the physician and staff communicate to him.

COMMUNICATION PROCESSES

Anthropologists doing research in psychiatric settings are also interested in the nature of the communication process between patient and staff and between patient and family. For instance, studies have used the techniques of linguistic and kinesic analysis in order to understand better the exchange of feelings and attitudes that goes on below the surface of the content of speech. Such studies tend to confirm clinical impressions that, however indispensable rational conversation may be to the therapeutic process at some points, much of the emotionally significant interchange between therapist and patient and, for that matter, between healthy individuals involves the mutual communication of affects by autonomic signs, culturally patterned gestures and postures (kinesic communication), and paralanguage (intonation, voice quality, and so forth). The availability of multiple modes of communication also facilitates those ambiguous and contradictory exchanges described by such terms as the double bind and the identity struggle, which some investigators have regarded as possibly pathogenic.

ALIEN CULTURES

The services of anthropology may be useful in clinical settings to evaluate the meaning of the patient's symptoms and his attitudes toward treatment. This is particularly likely where the psychiatrist and other psychiatric personnel are confronting persons from a cultural background alien to their own. To some extent, this may be true even when both patient and staff come from the same country or even the same region or metropolitan area. Marked differences in social class, education, and ethnic background may directly interfere with communication because the staff simply doesn't know what the patient is talking about and may more subtly block agreement on the goals and nature of treatment because the patient's tacit expectations are at variance with the physician's. Segregated ethnic minorities, such as some American Negroes and American Indians, may entertain a world view very different from the middle-class psychiatrist's.

This cultural gap is even more obvious where the psychiatrist is responsible for persons of sharply different cultural background. This may be the case when he is treating visitors from a foreign country or people in underdeveloped areas, such as African tribal societies or United States Trust Territory native populations. Even where there superficially appears to be a familiarity with Western technology and medical belief, certain values, attitudes, and beliefs may baffle the Western physician when he first encounters them in symptom formation or in the therapeutic negotiations. Beliefs about possession, witchcraft, the efficacy of rain-making ceremonies; values concerning the expression of pain, grief, or affection; the obligations of kinship and other social ties; attitudes toward white men and white medicine—all these may be difficult to accept or to interpret. A sensitive and intelligent physician can, of course, learn a great deal from his own patient, from casual association, and from reading the relevant social science literature. But it may sometimes be helpful to consult an anthropologist whose intensive study of the group enables him not only to answer particular queries but to provide a general framework that anticipates future dilemmas. Since anthropologists tend to specialize in particular culture areas, it is necessary to communicate with an expert on the particular group in question.

EVOLUTION OF PSYCHIATRIC DISORDERS

One of the traditional contributions of anthropology has been to disabuse modern man—in particular, modern Western man—of various popular ideas about human nature and the evolutionary development of human behavior.

"HAPPY PRIMITIVE" MISCONCEPTION

One popular delusion is probably inherited from romantic Rousseauistic notions of the happy primitive. This, in turn, harks back to the ancient doctrine of the Golden, Silver, Bronze, and Iron Ages, with the Golden Age being an era of blissful simplicity, a Garden of Eden, and subsequent ages more and more sophisticated and also more and more evil. In such theories, mental disorder is regarded as a disease of civilization, one that regularly increases in frequency as the civilization progresses. Occasionally, remote tribal populations or isolated utopian communities are cited as places where, because of the uniformly high quality of mother love or the absence of contradictory role expectations or whatnot, functional mental disorders are rare or nonexistent. These psychiatric paradises regularly turn out to be, on closer examination, no more immune to mental disease than other human groups. The inference, of course, is that mental difficulties are not recent afflictions of mankind. They could probably be traced, if records were available, far back in the human phylogeny to a time when technological and social simplicity, comparable to that of modern primitives, was the general condition.

"SICK SOCIETY" MISCONCEPTION

A related popular misconception is that whole societies can be diagnosed as suffering from paranoid or other psychoses. This pseudoscientific attitude is apt to flourish most exuberantly when scientists feel the need to condemn their or their nation's enemies without seeming to exhibit unscientific prejudice.

"INHERITED NEUROSIS" MISCONCEPTION

In a similar vein, there is little to support the argument that neurotic guilt and the consequent Oedipus neurosis began with some primal parricide, as suggested by Freud, and that the nucleus of the Oedipus conflict is a genetically inherited constant in human nature. There are some startling uniformities in symbolism and mythology across otherwise widely differing cultures. But these can readily be interpreted as the consequences of common features of the human condition, such as prolonged infancy. Or they may be the results of the historical diffusion of culture content. They are far less likely to be the results of inherited modifications of the genetic material. Nor can one support the idea that in neurosis and psychosis the human mind regresses phylogenetically as well as ontogenetically, recapitulating the stages of barbarism and savagery through which our ancestors passed thousands and tens of thousands of years ago.

Vulnerability to emotional conflict seems to be as much a general characteristic of the human central nervous system as its vulnerability to physical and chemical insults. In view of the extraordinary complexity of experience and, therefore, of learning that the human brain is capable of, it is hardly remarkable that so many persons in all cultures at one time or another suffer more or less severe episodes of mental disorder. It is more remarkable, indeed, that so few remain chronically ill. There probably are no model cultures that immunize their members against emotional difficulty, either in the present or in the future.

EVOLUTION OF SOCIAL REACTION TO THE MENTALLY ILL

What is readily demonstrable is a long-term change in the reaction of society to the disordered behavior of those who are mentally ill. Here, a general evolutionary trend is evident.

Hunting and gathering cultures have a work rhythm characterized by periods of days or weeks of intense, exacting effort alternating with similar periods of rest and relaxation. A person's contribution to the welfare of such groups is better measured by what he can do when he is at his best than by how constantly he remains at a standard level of performance. Thus, simple societies can and do tolerate episodic disorders more readily than the more complex societies do. Occasional episodes of hallucination, convulsive seizures, bursts of rage, or depression can be tolerated because the person can be expected to emerge and carry out his role effectively at the next period of intense activity.

Agricultural and, particularly, industrial societies depend far more heavily on continuous, reliable, day-after-day performance of routine tasks, frequently involving intricate machinery and complexly arranged social relationships. Here, reliability of performance over long periods of time, even at a mediocre level, may be more important than the high peaks of efficiency during occasions of intense effort. The interruption of the routine by episodes of behavioral disorder in such societies may present serious problems and attract therapeutic efforts or sanctions far more intense than in the hunting and gathering societies. In complex societies, therefore, episodic illness is likely to be treated as a chronic problem because the threat it poses is chronic. This is true even where the differentiation of labor and the demand for innovation make uniformity less important as a social value.

Along with this change in the evaluation of episodic disorder, there has occurred the other major change in the response of society to mental disorder. This is the progressive removal of responsibility for prevention and treatment from the religious sphere to the secular sphere, particularly the scientific, medical sphere. So far, medical science has been able to do little more than chip away at the edges of the vast and recalcitrant conglomerate of disorders. Various organic conditions have been discovered that are responsible for behavior disorder. As these are discovered, they are separately classified and treated. But the poorly understood mass of functional neuroses and psychoses—a mysterious amalgam of biological, psychological, and social determinants—still awaits penetration by research. A milestone in cultural evolution will have been reached when valid understanding and quick, effective treatment of mental disorders are achieved.

REFERENCES

Barnouw, V. *Culture and Personality*. Dorsey Press, Homewood, Ill., 1963.

Cannon, W. B. "Voodoo" death. Amer. Anthropol., 44: 169, 1942.

Caudill, W. *The Psychiatric Hospital as a Small Society*. Harvard University Press, Cambridge, Mass., 1939.

Devereux, G. *Mohave Ethnopsychiatry and Suicide: The Psychiatric Knowledge and the Psychic Disturbances of an Indian Tribe*. Bureau of American Ethnology, Bulletin 175. United States Government Printing Office, Washington, 1961.

Eaton, J. W., and Weil, R. J. *Culture and Mental Disorders*. Free Press of Glencoe (Macmillan) New York, 1955.

Gillin, J. Magical fright. Psychiatry, 11: 387, 1948.

Honigmann, J. *Culture and Personality*. Harper & Row, New York, 1954.

Hsu, F. L. K., editor. *Psychological Anthropology*. Dorsey Press, Homewood, Ill., 1961.

Kaplan, B., editor. *Studying Personality Cross-Culturally*. Row, Peterson, Evanston, Ill., 1961.

Kardiner, A. *The Individual and His Society*. Columbia University Press, New York, 1939.

Kluckhohn, C., and Murray, H. A., editors. *Personality in Nature, Society, and Culture*. Alfred A. Knopf, New York, 1953.

Linton, R. *Culture and Mental Disorders*. Charles C Thomas, Springfield, Ill., 1956.

Opler, M. *Culture, Psychiatry, and Human Values*. Charles C Thomas, Springfield, Ill., 1956.

Opler, M., editor. *Culture and Mental Health*. Macmillan, New York, 1959.

Teicher, M., editor. *Windigo Psychosis*. University of Washington, Seattle, 1960.

Wallace, A. F. C. *Culture and Personality*. Random House, New York, 1961.

CHAPTER 19

Sociology and Psychiatry

IRVING SILVERMAN, Ph.D.

INTRODUCTION

THAT MEDICINE involves social science as well as biological science is by now a widely accepted idea. The purpose of this chapter is to relate one of the social sciences, sociology, to one of the medical specialties, psychiatry. The exposition is in three main parts: first, what sociology is and how it fits in among the various social sciences; second, some of the main concepts of sociology and how they may apply to psychiatry; third, three major research projects as examples of empirical studies done at the intersections of sociology and psychiatry.

WHAT SOCIOLOGY IS

Sociology is an empirical science that studies human relations. Its domain of problems spans two levels of analysis among superorganic (behavioral) systems: the interactional level and the organization level.

The superorganic is the level of symbolic meaning. It is above the organic, the level of life, which, in turn, is above the suborganic, the level of matter and energy. These levels of analysis are logical housekeeping rules for handling concepts so that they may share a common degree of generality at a common level of abstraction. It would violate these rules, for example, to explain a war in terms of molecules or to explain a hurricane in terms of hostility.

Presumably, there are distinct emergent levels of organization in nature that underlie the need for distinct levels of analysis in discourse. But, as tools of analysis, levels are designated for their usefulness—and not without arbitrariness—especially in the division of main levels into subordinate levels (such as those of cell, tissue, and organ within the organic level). For purposes of this chapter, there are four subordinate superorganic levels: individual, interactional, organizational, and institutional.

Take this as an example of how these levels might emerge: Robinson Crusoe, alone on his island, presents behavior at the individual level. With the appearance of his man Friday, there are situations for behavior at the interactional level. From these interactions emerges a mutual recognition of differences in position—Crusoe as master and Friday as servant; and that is a rudimentary social structure that may be studied organizationally. Insofar as these two organized men come to institute ways of doing things —ways that are learned, shared, and transmittable to others—they could be studied institutionally, culturologically.

Some confusion may exist between common usage and present sociological use of some terms. It is common for a particular place, such as a hospital, to be called an institution. Technically, a particular hospital, such as Bellevue, is an organization; but *the* hospital—that is, the generic idea of such a place as a way of doing things—is an institution, a part of our culture. And culture refers not only to high or highbrow pursuits— such as art, science, and philosophy—but to a society's way of life, including every mundane detail. Moreover, a social organization may be formal, like a school or a government, or it may be informal, like a friendship clique or a society.

The term "system" is familiar enough in such usages as "solar system," "heating system," and "digestive system." The general idea is that of a whole composed of parts (organs) that are interrelated (organized). When we refer to relations among things that we construe as parts of a whole, we are thinking of that whole as a system.

The distinctive thing about a discipline is its area of problems. For an applied discipline, it is a substantive (content) area. For a basic discipline, such as sociology, it is a conceptual domain of problems. To identify a problem in science, one must have something to explain, taken as problematic, and something to explain it by, taken as given. One must be exempted from explaining the givens; otherwise, one would either go on explaining forever or end up in a circle.

Sociology, then, may be defined as the basic discipline for the study of superorganic systems in which two levels of organization are taken as problematic, that of social interaction and that of social organization. This straddling of at least two levels of problems, a source of manifold confusions, is usual among disciplines in the behavioral sciences. Psychology straddles the organic and the individual sublevels of the superorganic. Social psychology straddles the individual and the interactional levels. Anthropology, in practice, extends over all levels.

Another source of confusion in the behavioral sciences that is related to the straddling of levels of organization is the duplicity of meanings among concepts. Many a single concept, such as role, is useful for reference at each level of organization; but at each level it must be invested with a somewhat different meaning, depending on the system reference that is intended. If the system reference is not clear, the term is ambiguous. Thus, the role of mother may characterize the personality of an individual (motherliness) or the nature of an interaction (mothering someone) or a part in a social organization (mother in a family) or a set of cultural norms for a pattern of behavior ("like a mother to me").

Among the social sciences, sociology covers two superorganic sublevels as problematic, social interaction and social organization. The sociologist, of course, may concern himself with the relations between things sociological and many other types of things—individual, cultural, meteorological, etc. But the basic discipline of sociology builds its own distinctive propositions with its own distinctive concepts.

As a presentation device, we shall use some general ideas in introducing and organizing the material. Based on a rough definition of a system—a whole that consists of interrelated parts—the discussion is divided into four main sections. The first two sections focus on the organizational level, first from the standpoint of how the parts maintain the whole, and the second from the standpoint of how the whole maintains the parts. The remaining two sections focus on the level of interaction, on the guidance of each part and on complementarity between parts.

SOCIAL ORGANIZATIONS

A system is an instance of orderliness in the universe, a negation of randomness. In studying any system, one may ask: "How did such order originate? How is it maintained?" Questions of origination may be bypassed here. It is questions on system maintenance, on how a system works and endures, that will be considered. Some of the main concepts in systematic sociology, their meanings, and the ways in which they may be relevant to psychiatry will be explored. Many of the concepts that follow may be viewed as quite general ideas that have been adapted to sociology's particular domain of problems.

Large-scale behavioral systems may be vastly complicated affairs of wheels within wheels within wheels. A social organization, such as the Daughters of the American Revolution or Macy's department store, can do many of the things that a person does in society. It can join organizations, enter into contracts, pay and receive money, etc. These corporate individuals, like an individual person, can operate with stability and reliability. How is that possible? Insofar as the answer lies within the boundaries of the system itself—apart from its external relations, foundations, or broader context—two analytic perspectives are useful: In what ways do the member parts maintain the system as a whole? In what ways does the whole maintain the parts?

PARTS MAINTAIN THE WHOLE

Insofar as an organizational system works, each of its parts must, in a patterned way, be somewhere to take its part in a structure, do something as its function, and develop somehow—for example, generate or degenerate—to bring about systemic change. Social systems, then, embody concepts applicable to social structure, social function, and social change.

Structure. The concept of social position is used to describe a social structure. A social position, often called a "social status," is defined by a set of rights and a set of duties. That is to say that the coordinates by which a position in social space may be located are rights, referring to what an incumbent of a position may expect of others, and duties, referring to what others may expect of him. These expectations are social norms or standards of conduct, based ultimately on moral values. The study of values per se belongs to philosophy and theology. But the study of valuations, the ways in which values are formed and held in the course of human behavior, is not merely allowed in scientific sociology but essential. It must be stressed that there is virtually unanimous agreement among sociologists today that a social order is distinctively a normative order.

If the structural parts of a social system are positions, where, then, does the individual come in? He comes in by taking various social positions. He may do so by ascription (if it is given to him—for example, his religious affiliation at birth) or by achievement (if he earns it—for example, a foremanship in a plant). There is, of course, no one-to-one correspondence between individuals and positions. One individual usually fills many types of positions, and each type of position is usually filled by many individuals. A specific position in an organization may be held by several people in succession or by no one when it is vacant.

What holds a position in position in a social structure is largely a matter of mutual support among positions, mutual recognition, and enforcement of rights and duties. Feelings of humiliation, for example, may be appreciated in psychological terms; but to humiliate means literally to reduce to a lower position. There is some evidence that the upsets of everyday life, considered by many as an important concern for preventive psychiatry, are very often positional upsets due to violations of vested expectations.

Function. A social role, as Linton puts it, "represents the dynamic aspect of a status." When a role is performed, the rights and duties of a social position are put into effect, and a social system functions.

Role strains for the individual may be patterned in various ways. One example is a high-performance role, such as concert violinist or marathon runner, in which it is expected that the performer will go to marvelous extremes of taxing himself. Other types of strains are due to conflicts, in which two or more roles carried by one individual make too heavy a load or impose conflicting demands, such as home and career.

Illness itself, in its sociological aspect, has been conceptualized under the heading of "the social role of the sick person" or just "the sick role." It is a societal device for exempting an individual from his regular role demands, and it usually carries additional rights (secondary gains) to receive care and solicitude. But the sick role imposes the duties of wanting to get well, of seeking necessary help, and of cooperating in treatment. The physician plays a special part as the one who can formally pronounce that any particular taking of the sick role is legitimate or not legitimate (malingering). Failure to meet role demands carries the stigma of deviant behavior if the failure is not covered by the sick role; and the sick role must include the above-mentioned signs of good motivation if it is to secure exemption for nonperformance.

Professional helpers also appreciate good motivation in their cases as a factor in eventual success, and they may often reject some types of cases, such as alcoholics or drug addicts, for apparent lack of motivation to get well.

The public stigma that attaches to mental illness in this culture is notorious, and it is a great detriment to afflicted individuals. People generally allow the sick role to mental patients but do not stop defining them as deviants. Indeed, many symptoms of mental disorders are acts that deviate from social norms; and many mental patients are not so earnest and cooperative as the sick role requires.

Compliance with social norms, however, is rarely demanded in absolute terms. There are various ways for allowing toleration of deviation, and there has been evidence of growing tolerance for and even acceptance of the mentally ill by the public at large.

Change. Socialization and social mobility are concepts that apply to ways in which individuals change and thereby contribute either to social stability or to social change.

Socialization is the process by which the individual learns to perform social roles. It applies not only to children but to recruits at any age. Anticipatory socialization refers to learning that goes on before a role is actually taken.

Social mobility refers to a change in social positions, usually the occupational position of the head of the household, taking occupation as the prime indicator of social rank for a family or single adult. It may be measured as intergenerational mobility (difference between parent and offspring) or as career mobility (the individual's own movement as an adult). Geographic mobility refers to moving one's residence from one place to another.

Reference individuals and reference groups are two sources of orientation for learning content and style in new roles.

Each age cohort within a given group is socialized in a singular historic situation by a parental generation that was formed in another type of situation, such as a time of depression or of war. How do these shifting patterns affect the processes of child development and of adult adjustment in consequence? They seem to be a source of confusion and consternation for those who experience these processes and for those who study them.

The effects of social change on mental well-being have been investigated. Findings by Leighton and his associates in the Stirling County study were consistent with their hypothesis on the ill effects of social deterioration in an area. Ruth Benedict's concept of cultural discontinuities postulates that the culturally normal life course may be costly to the individual's well-being if it contains sharp breaks, as does the transition in this culture from adolescence to adulthood. Syme and his associates found associations between rates of coronary heart disease and four patterns of change: increasing urbanization of a stationary population and all three types of individual mobility—geographic, intergenerational, and career mobility. They postulate cultural mobility as the common factor, referring to external changes in the way of life to which the individual must adapt. In addition to the hypothesis that mobility induces illness, there is the drift hypothesis that illness induces movement of certain kinds. Both processes seem to occur, but it is usually hard to measure their respective contributions to observed rates of illness.

THE WHOLE MAINTAINS ITS PARTS

Structure, function, and change have been discussed as aspects of a system in which the whole depends on its parts—where they are, what they do, how they develop. A system thus dependent on its parts must somehow manage to maintain them in working order if it is to endure. Parts can go out of order in a number of ways, each way corresponding to a positive process (in parentheses, below) that keeps it from happening: The parts must not lose their distinctness, for instance, by fusing together (differentiation); they must not perish for lack of sustenance (allocation); they must not detach themselves from the whole (integration); and they must not underdo or overdo whatever they do, at least not beyond tolerable limits (regulation).

Differentiation. Social differentiation refers to the variety of positions that make up a social system. Leveling is a type of dedifferentiation in which individual rights tend to sameness, and role-blurring refers to situations in which duties tend to sameness.

Dedifferentiation may occur suddenly in a situation where there is panic, such as in a fire in a crowded theatre. Role distinctions between house staff and audience are lost, as are the distinctions among men, women, and children. Exits become blocked with masses of undifferentiated humanity.

Logically, dedifferentiation reduces variety among parts (social roles) and thereby sets limits on capacity to function. In practice, of course, society defends some differences more strongly than others. For example, we strongly control social differentiation by sex; transvestitism is made a crime and is considered a sign of illness.

Allocation. Social allocation refers to the socially patterned ways in which the needs and wants of an individual are met. Economics studies these processes insofar as they involve production, exchange, and consumption of goods and services by market mechanisms. Sociology projects these matters onto a wider screen. The kinds of rewards that can be had from a social system are placed under these main dimensional headings: class, status, and power.

Class is based on life chances in the market place. Status, here a synonym for prestige, is based on one's embodiment of the fulfillment of social values, as through a respected family name or by occupational attainment. Power is based on being in a position of control over events. These three dimensions are conceptually independent. Empirically, they can be discrepant, but they tend to be highly associated.

Differential allocation in these three dimensions produces social differentiation of an invidious kind, called social stratification. A stratum includes persons of roughly the same social rank. Social surveys often use a composite measure of overall social rank called socioeconomic status, or SES, based on such indicators as education, occupation, income, rent, and area of residence. SES tends to be one of the strongest variables in social surveys on whatever topic; that is, it tends to show wide and strong empirical relationships.

For some empirical comparisons, it is valuable to consider the various indicators of SES separately. And for some conceptual comparisons, it is valuable to consider class, prestige, and power separately. Moreover, the concepts of class, status, and power can be used to distinguish not only types of rankings but also types of interactions. The ways of dealing for money or prestige or power tend to be distinctive. Also such dealings may blend in distinctive ways, as in the contrast between class politics and status politics.

Relations between social rank and mental disorder have been studied by various investigators in various ways. There is remarkable agreement on the finding that, the lower the social rank, the greater the risk in most nosological categories of mental disorder and in most symptomatic indicators. All three dimensions of social rank appear to contribute to the general finding insofar as they can be separated by empirical indicators. Moreover, there seems to be an interaction effect from discrepancies in rankings among an individual's social positions, such as occupation of high rank but an ethnic background of low rank or vice versa. Jackson found such departures from status consistency to be associated with psychosomatic symptoms.

Hollingshead and Redlich among others reported direct associations between quality of care received for mental disorders and social class rank of patients. There are many issues of measurement and interpretation on which such findings may be questioned, but if differences in quality (subtle or gross) are recognized in a thing, those differences tend to affect the allocation of the thing. How that happens depends on how the dealings in that thing are organized. The allocation of care for the mentally ill may be organized along lines of one or another of the dimensions discussed—class, prestige, and power.

If care is organized predominantly on a fee-for-service basis, it is basically a market matter; and we may expect class differences in care. In the model used by the military services, access to care is a right of membership that applies to private soldiers and general officers alike; but generals do better than privates in that regard, not by issuing commands but because, by the value structure of the military, they have more prestige than privates. Finally, there are those who, viewing the care of mental health problems in a community context, see it as a matter of mobilizing the power of affected groups to win improvements in their conditions of life.

Integration and regulation.   Integration refers to the act or process of making whole or entire. Social integration of an individual in a group refers to the extent to which he is joined (united, bound) to the group. It is a highly generalized conception that may be analyzed in many ways. Regulation refers to processes of keeping events within the limits set by some rule or standard. Social regulation of the individual by the group refers to the ways in which he is kept within the limits set by group norms.

The concepts of integration and regulation are discussed together to emphasize their conceptual distinctness while pointing to their closely intertwined empirical relations. A classic juxtaposition of these two concepts occurs in Emil Durkheim's study of suicide, in which he marshalled evidence to adduce four types of suicide in sociological terms: egoistic, due to underintegration; altruistic, due to overintegration; anomic, due to underregulation; and fatalistic, due to overregulation.

Acts of regulation by a group tend to foster the integration of the group; that is, the norms are strengthened by exercise. Thus, some deviant behavior is normal and perhaps necessary for group solidarity. Scapegoating and segregation of outgroups by ingroups are ways of activating these mechanisms.

Acts of regulation may be aimed to correct the malintegration of an individual. They may succeed, or they may boomerang by producing feelings of social alienation. Some degree of malintegration, as in a marginal member, may be of value to a group. Such members, because they are usually not as parochial or square as highly integrated members, can be valuable sources of innovation and criticism.

The concept of alienation and its correlates has been receiving much popular and scholarly attention. Seeman, in a much-quoted article, has suggested five types of alienation: powerlessness, meaninglessness, normlessness, isolation, and self-estrangement. Dean has compiled the following suggested correlates from the literature: apathy, authoritarianism, conformity, cynicism, hoboism, political apathy, political hyperactivity or personalization in politics, prejudice, privitization, psychosis, regression, and suicide. In general, the concept of alienation appears in the thick of the efforts to study the processes by which the individual seeks a modus vivendi with society—his provocations, compensations, and decompensations—affected especially by processes of social integration and social regulation.

Empirical attitude measures have been devised for many aspects of alienation, notably the F (authoritarianism) scale from the seminal study of Adorno and his associates and Srole's A (anomia) scale.

SOCIAL INTERACTIONS

A social organization operates through the actions of its members with one another and outsiders. Saying that a firm or a group or a society does this or that summarizes the resultants of patterns of events at another level of analysis, that of social interaction. Interactions are more accessible than are organizations to everyday observation and common sense interpretation.

At the level of social interaction, it is still the case that individuals take parts, but these are not necessarily parts in organizations, formal or informal. Interactional roles may be demarcated in terms of the structure of the situation in which they are played: the role of a stranger, a nonmember, a third party, a spoiler, a conciliator, an innocent, a clown.

Interactions between individuals are guided by each of the participants' definition of the situation. In the words of W. I. Thomas, "Things that people define as real, are real in their consequences." Inasmuch as definitions may be highly subjective, people may not know what to expect of each other in the absence of a common culture to establish the rules of the game. Moreover, because social processes sometimes operate perversely, prediction may be hazardous, even under a common cultural umbrella. Some things that otherwise would not have happened may happen because they were predicted (self-fulfilling prophecy); and some things may fail to happen because they were predicted (boomerang effect).

An interaction system is marked by complementarity of expectations— that is, some way in which the parts complete a whole; but the valence of complementarity in any situation is not necessarily positive (cooperation). It may be negative (contention) or null (suspension).

Guidance of Each Part

A guidance mechanism may be analyzed for three kinds of functions. It must get relevant information (cognitive), match that information to an appropriate mode of response (affective), and check the response against governing standards (evaluative).

Cognitive. Social clues are guides to social positions. A married woman wears a wedding band on the third finger of her left hand or of her right hand in the European fashion. A manual occupation is symbolized by a blue collar. An aristocrat is expected to distinguish himself by dress, bearing, and soft hands.

Social cues are guides to expected conduct. Our culture provides a clear signal for the ending of a formal interview: The person behind the desk stands up. If it is an informal visit, then the host must wait for the guest to decide to leave. There are tales of excruciatingly long visits by newly arrived Indian students, in whose culture it is the host who must say when a visit has ended.

Behavior problems of school children are often attributed to cognitive difficulties, such as a deficiency in sight or hearing or cultural deprivation.

Affective and evaluative. An individual enters interaction situations with certain guidelines: beliefs, which are positions on questions of fact; affects, which are feelings pro or con toward things; and values, which are commitments to standards, especially moral standards.

Interaction may be considered the interplay of the set of wants (affects) and musts (values) of its several participants. But the structure of the game of interaction consists of more than the sum of such parts. This is illustrated by the story of the permissively managed nursery school children who asked, "Must we do what we want?"

The individual composes his guidelines and poises himself for interaction by his postures or attitudes toward things and issues.

Insight into the functions of attitudes and values in social interaction is gained by referring to two of the ways in which role performance may break down: embarrassment and scandalization.

Gross and Stone write: "Embarrassment occurs whenever some central assumption in a transaction has been unexpectedly and unqualifiedly discredited for at least one participant. The result is that he is incapacitated for continued role performance." They describe "role as consensual attitudes mobilized by an announced and ratified identity." In short, part of one's presentation of self for interaction is the projection of attitudes, perhaps not the same ones from situation to situation; if they are discredited, the interaction may suffer mortally.

Scandal occurs when someone is caught failing to uphold the values for which his position stands. It is a violation of prestige that hurts the reputation of the individual who fills the position and also of the organization that contains it. If no one of high prestige can be assigned responsibility, then even very grave malefactions are not scandalous. Scandal is an alarm reaction at a failure of responsibility for social regulation. Because rank has its privileges, some may deliberately scandalize others as a way of asserting rank. But a scandal often severs role relations and, therefore, can make a position untenable.

The relations of expressed attitudes to actions, interactions, and organizational positions may be studied by social survey techniques. The concept of value homophily refers to the observed tendency of friends to see things in the same way or stop being friends. Consensual validation refers to mutual confirmation of shared attitudes (sentiments) in a group. Cross-pressures arise when an individual finds that a conforming opinion for one of his major social positions contradicts that of another.

Expressed attitudes that are extremely rigid or extremely fluid may, of course, be indicators of personality dysfunction or breakdown. It is a vast area for the study of the interplay of psychodynamics and social dynamics.

COMPLEMENTARITY BETWEEN PARTS

Personal relations between individuals may be, grossly speaking, positive, negative, or indifferent. That is to say that, in terms of their feelings, they may like or dislike each other or fail to do either one. The same gross possibilities apply to the nature of their interactions, independently of their feelings, depending on the complementarity of their role performances. Individuals may cooperate with or contend with or suspend their attentions to each other. These possibilities at the level of interaction are logically independent not only of the individual level of feelings but also of the organizational level of social eufunction or dysfunction. Competition, for example, may be required between some members of an organization in order to foster heightened performance among them. Empirically, however, there is usually a positive association between good personal feelings, cooperative role relations, and organizational eufunction.

Cooperation. Cooperative relations may serve mutual personal ends directly, as when one hand washes the other. Or, if their direct purpose is organizational, they may serve personal ends indirectly through the fostering of group morale. At its highest levels, morale seems to create conditions in which the individual accepts organizational interests as his own, and the various ways in which the whole maintains the parts—differentiation, allocation, integration, and regulation—seem to be taken for granted or ignored.

Juveniles and senior citizens are two social categories that have gained special psychiatric notice. In this social system, neither group normally has important roles to perform. Thus, they are blocked from chances for prestige (organizational) or esteem (interactional), with presumptive damage to self-esteem.

Contention. Many of the institutional spheres normally operate by an adversary system: competition in the economic sphere, opposing counsel in law courts, and opposing candidates for elective office. It is taxing to be a contender and dispiriting to be a loser. For the individual, contention may help to develop strength and stamina, but it may be costly through strain of effort, conflict of motives, and punishment from the opposition. It is very difficult, even in imagination, to engineer an optimal role for contention in a social system.

Suspension. In social life, one is expected to be his brother's keeper in many ways but not limitlessly. There are some areas that, under most conditions, are subject to suspension of interaction. The individual is accorded rights of privacy and also duties of decency. An analysis of these complementary concepts turns on the concept of social visibility, which is a far more portentous matter than it may seem offhand. Visibility refers to exposure to public notice. For certain ends, like finding customers in a market or being appreciated for one's affluence (Veblen's conspicuous consumption), visibility is a necessary condition. But where freedom from attention is desired, invisibility is to be prized.

Privacy rights are analogous to property rights in that they extend to delimited areas, they allow of exceptions, and one may refer to their violation as invasion. A *right of privacy consists in the enjoyment of social invisibility*. It may be extended to things, like dandruff or a physical handicap, that are perfectly visible in a physical sense.

There are social norms governing the underexercise of privacy rights. In other words, the individual has obligations to keep certain things of his socially invisible. These norms come under the heading of decency. Things like billboards and sound systems in public places have been fought as invasions of privacy, on the grounds that privacy consists in the right to be left alone. But the latter is only one means of being accorded privacy and not an essential means. A public nuisance violates decency by failing to keep things invisible that should be so. It invades one's attention but not one's privacy, which is one's own right to invisibility.

Norms of privacy and decency are of extreme importance to psychiatry because the psychiatrist works with patients under conditions of extreme liberalization of these norms as they apply in other spheres, even that of the family. These liberties are legitimate yet somehow suspect. Part of the public stereotype of the psychiatrist is that he can penetrate privacy, seeing what was intended to be invisible and creating feelings of indecency. When a psychiatrist goes outside of the clinical setting to practice community mental health, he may have to overcome such feelings in the people, such as community leaders, with whom he must deal on matters of policy.

RESEARCH IN SOCIOLOGY AND PSYCHIATRY

The following summaries of three research projects are meant to convey what sociological research in psychiatric problems has been like. These were chosen—omitting from consideration studies that are described elsewhere in this volume and seeking variety of subject matter—from among the best-known work in the field.

SOCIAL CLASS AND MENTAL ILLNESS

Hollingshead, Yale's chairman of the department of sociology, and Redlich, chairman of the department of psychiatry, studied the urbanized community of New Haven, Connecticut, consisting of that city and five surrounding towns, during parts of 1950 and 1951.

Design. The research project was multiplex, consisting of five main parts: (1) a census of psychiatric patients, (2) a sample survey of the population at large, (3) a study of psychiatrists, (4) a study of the community, and (5) a controlled case study.

The psychiatric census, the heart of the project, aimed to identify all persons who, as residents of the study area, entered a course of psychiatric treatment anywhere and were in that course for any of the interval from June through November 1950. To be included, a treatment facility had to be a private psychiatric practice, a psychiatric clinic, or a mental hospital; but it did not have to be in the study area. Thus, the private hospital search included all licensed institutions in seven contiguous states and some others farther afield.

Who escaped this net? Persons who may have been ill but received no treatment or else received some treatment that was under the auspices of a specialty other than psychiatry—such as social work, clinical psychology, or pastoral care—were omitted by design. Some others may have been omitted through clerical error or because they went to a remote facility. Finally, a large group was known to be missing because their agent of treatment refused cooperation. All the 22 hospitals and 7 clinics that were approached did cooperate. Out of 66 private practitioners known to have eligible patients, 20 practitioners, who earlier had reported a total of 31 eligible patients, refused to share data. Of those 31 patients, 30 went to New York City for treatment. The researchers estimated that 40 to 50 patients from the intended target group were left out of the census; that amounts to about 2.5 per cent of the total target group, the census having found 1,891 patients.

The instrument for data collection was a patient schedule. It was divided into a sociological part, focused on the patient's social and family history, and a psychiatric part that covered the therapeutic history, including the types of treatment the patient received and a diagnostic impression by his psychiatrist. A sociologist and a psychiatrist abstracted their respective parts from the clinical records of the institutional patient. Each private practitioner gave the information on his patients in an interview with a project psychiatrist.

The sample survey described the composition of the entire population from which the patients came. It allowed comparisons between the patients and the rest of the population, and it provided denominator figures for calculating patient rates.

The study of psychiatrists allowed comparisons between aspects of psychiatric practice and characteristics of the practitioner. It also was relevant to the description of psychiatric facilities for the study area and to characterization of types of treatment that patients received.

The community study gathered historic and contemporary information on matters pertaining to psychiatric care for the community and on the social class structure of the community. The measure of social class status for the study was Hollingshead's index of social position, which is based on the individual's education, occupation, and area of residence. Each indicator is valued numerically, and the three are combined into a score by standard operations. A detailed knowledge of the particular community is needed to map and evaluate residence areas as indicators of social status. All the persons under study—patients, sample-survey respondents, and psychiatrists—were placed in a scheme of five classes from class I, the highest, to class V, the lowest. Because class I was relatively small, the two highest classes were often combined as class I–II in the presentation of findings.

The controlled case study included 50 patients, selected by criteria of age (22 to 44), color (white), class (III and V only), and diagnostic category (25 psychoneurotics and 25 schizophrenics). These same criteria, when applied to the patient census, showed that the selected cases were not significantly different, with respect to such other variables as age and sex, from the pools from which they were drawn. The case study, the researchers said, "was designed to explore systematically interrelationships between sociocultural and psychological factors in the development of psychoneurosis and nuclear schizophrenia in two nonadjacent social classes."

What did the researchers want to accomplish by this battery of interrelated operations? In general, they wanted to bridge a gap between sociology and psychiatry. They chose social class status on the sociological side and treated mental illness on the psychiatric side as their focal variables. Their central interests were in the relation of social class to occurrence of mental illness treatment methods.

They formulated five major hypotheses, to be tested by their data: Position in the class structure is related to (1) prevalence of treated mental illness, (2) types of diagnosed psychiatric disorders, (3) types of psychiatric treatment administered by psychiatrists, and (4) social and psychodynamic factors in the development of psychiatric disorders. The final hypothesis was that (5) mobility in the class structure is a factor that is related to development of psychiatric difficulties.

Class status and cultural characteristics. The authors sketched the distinctive styles of life that they found in each class.

Class I, containing the community's business and professional leaders, has two segments: a long-established core group of interrelated families and a smaller upward-mobile group of new people. Members of the core group usually inherit money along with group values that stress tradition, stability, and social responsibility. Those in the newer group are highly educated, self-made, able, and aggressive. Their family relations often are not cohesive or stable. Socially, they are rejected by the core group, to whom they are, however, a threat by the vigor of their leadership in community affairs.

Class II is marked by at least some education beyond high school and occupations as managers or in the lesser-ranking professions. Four out of five are upward-mobile. They are joiners at all ages and tend to have stable families; but they have usually gone apart from parental families and often from their home communities. Tensions arise generally from striving for educational, economic, and social success.

Class III males for the most part are in salaried administrative and clerical jobs (51 per cent) or own small businesses (24 per cent); many of the women also have jobs. Typically, they are high school graduates. They usually have economic security but little opportunity for advancement. Families tend to be somewhat less stable than in class II. Family members of all ages tend to join organizations and to be active in them. There is less satisfaction with present living conditions and less optimism than in class II.

In class IV, 53 per cent say .they belong to the working class. Seven out of 10 show no generational mobility. Most are content and make no sacrifices to get ahead. Most of the men are semiskilled (52 per cent) or skilled (35 per cent) manual employees. Practically all the women who are able to hold jobs do so. Education usually stops shortly after graduation from grammar school for both parents and children. Families are much different from those in class III: Families are larger, and they are more likely to include three generations. Households are more likely to include boarders and roomers. Homes are more likely to be broken.

Class V adults usually have not completed elementary school. Most are semiskilled factory workers or unskilled laborers. They are concentrated in tenement and cold-water-flat areas of New Haven or in suburban slums. There are generally brittle family ties. Very few participate in organized community institutions. Leisure activities in the household and on the street are informal and spontaneous. Adolescent boys frequently have contact with the law in their search for adventure. There is a struggle for existence. There is much resentment, expressed freely in primary groups, about how they are treated by those in authority. There is much acting out of hostility.

Paths to the psychiatrist. A person entering psychiatric treatment for the first time may be seen as passing through four stages: Abnormal behavior occurs; it is appraised as a psychiatric matter; there is a decision that help is indicated; and the decision is implemented. The authors discussed class differences in all four stages. Their figures on source of referral apply only to the fourth stage, where they found clear and strong associations with social class. For example, among those classified as neurotics entering treatment for the first time, the referrals by private physicians were much greater in class I–II (52.5 per cent) than in class V (13.9 per cent). The police and the courts referred no one from class I–II, but they referred 13.9 per cent of class V patients. Social agencies referred 1.4 per cent of class I–II and 36.1 per cent of class V.

Class and prevalence of disorders.   In confirmation of their first hypothesis, the researchers found "a distinct inverse relationship does exist between social class and mental illness." In terms of treated psychiatric illness per 100,000 of the population, the rates are 798 overall, 556 for class I–II, 538 for class III, 642 for class IV, and 1,659 for class V. Thus, the really sharp dividing line is between class V and the classes above it.

The relationship between the two major variables—class and treated prevalence—was explored by the use of five social background variables as controls. These were age, sex, race, religion, and marital status. It was shown that these other social variables, either singly or in pairs, did not explain away the relationship of major interest in the study design. The analysis did not dwell on any social variables other than class—that is, the index of social position—as interesting in their own right in relation to the patient rates.

Class position and types of mental illness.   The second hypothesis, relating social class to types of disorders, was also supported. A simplified diagnostic scheme drew a major distinction between neuroses, divided into seven subgroups, and psychoses, divided into five subgroups. The overall prevalence rates for the neuroses were highest in class I–II and tended to fall as class level fell; but for the psychoses the rates rose sharply as class level fell; and they rose very sharply from class IV to class V—from 518 to 1,504 per 100,000. The analysis by class of the diagnostic subgroups, especially among the neuroses, shows considerable variety of patterns. The same applies to the division of the total prevalence rates into components of incidence, reentry, and continuous rates.

Treatment process.   The researchers confirmed their third hypothesis by showing that social class was related to where and for how long patients were treated and what kind of therapy they received.

The analysis of this material was relatively complex. It involved three previously discussed variables—social class, diagnostic group, and components of prevalence—and four new ones—type of facility, type of therapy, length of therapeutic sessions, and duration of treatment.

The facilities covered in the study were 42 private practitioners, 10 private hospitals, 7 public clinics, 6 state hospitals, and 5 veterans' hospitals. Two out of three patients were in the state hospitals and nearly one in five with private practitioners. Consider the relation of social class to type of facility among neurotic patients treated for the first time: With private practitioners were 85.7 per cent of class I–II and 9.8 per cent of class V; in state hospitals were 19.7 per cent of class V and none of class I–II.

The major treatment types distinguished were various types of psychotherapy, organic therapy, and custodial care. Neurotic patients in classical analysis or analytic psychotherapy were 46.9 per cent of class I–II versus 4.9 per cent of class V.

Length of sessions among neurotic patients treated by private practitioners varied greatly by class. In class I–II, 94.3 per cent had the longest session—50 to 60 minutes—versus 45.4 per cent of class V; and 36.4 per cent of the latter had the shortest session length—15 to 30 minutes— which was more than ten times the percentage of any other class.

Median number of years in treatment varied by class directly and moderately among neurotics. It varied by class inversely and sharply among psychotics.

Expenditures on treatment. The researchers found that "expenditures on treatment are linked in highly significant ways with class status in each type of psychiatric facility." In private mental hospitals the higher classes, with longer terms of hospitalization, spent more in toto but spent less per day as a result of having better access to discounts. In clinics, on the other hand, fees tended to be equal, but total value of treatment rendered varied directly with class. "The clinics spend eight times as much treating each class II patient as they do each class V patient."

Psychiatrists. Psychiatrists were divided into two main classes: (1) those with an analytic and psychological orientation, called the A-P group, and (2) those with a directive and organic orientation, called the D-O group. The division was based on type of training for therapy and on types of therapy employed by the practitioner. Admittedly, it was a somewhat arbitrary distinction, allowing of considerable variations. And yet, empirically, it turned out to be a most powerful discriminator of broad clusters of traits of various kinds, amounting virtually to a division of psychiatry into two separate fields of practice.

In the study area, the university psychiatrists were largely A-P and the public hospital psychiatrists largely D-O.

The D-O psychiatrist, in contrast to the A-P, wore a white coat rather than a business suit in a clinical setting. He did not use a couch. He made house calls, worked uneven hours, accepted emergencies as a daily occurrence, usually saw his patients for short periods—15 to 30 rather than 50 to 60 minutes—and saw them weekly or monthly rather than daily. He charged less a visit but averaged about $25,000 a year to the A-P's $22,000.

All the psychiatrists in the community were in class I, except for 5 per cent in class II. The A-P group tended to be much aware that social stratification existed, but the D-O group tended to deny it and to be embarrassed by questions about it. Only 8 per cent of the A-P group were of old American stock, compared with 44 per cent of the D-O group; 58 per cent of the A-P group were first or second generation, compared with 38 per cent of the D-O group. A related finding was that 83 per cent of the A-P group were from Jewish homes, compared with 19 per cent of the D-O group; and 12 per cent of the A-P group were of Protestant background, compared with 75 per cent of the D-O group. The A-P group showed far more social mobility than the D-O group.

Conclusions. The researchers, focusing on relations between social class and mental illness, pointed out that Americans prefer to avoid the two facts of life they had chosen to study. Actually, they did not them-selves encounter mental illness head on. They studied, by indirect observa-tion, patients under the care of psychiatrists. Carefully stressing that lim-itation, they offered only tentative inferences.

The empirical findings of the study amply bore out the hypotheses on relations between class position and how many cases were treated, of what diagnostic types, and by what types of psychiatric treatment.

In a discussion of the neuroses, this terse generalization was offered: "The class V neurotic behaves badly, the class IV neurotic aches physi-cally, the class III patient defends fearfully, and the class I–II patient is dissatisfied with himself."

On the phenomena of mental illness and social class, the authors offered these inferences: (1) "Each type of mental and emotional disor-der occurs in all classes, but in different proportions." (2) The fact that psychiatric facilities differ in the status level to which they cater seems to be related to the differential distribution of disorders by class. Extremely regressed schizophrenics, for example, are rarely seen in good private hos-pitals. (3) The content of mental illness reflects social and cultural condi-tions. (4) Perceptions of mental health are class-related. (5) Observed relations between sociocultural variables and the prevalence of treated dis-orders do not establish that the former are the essential and necessary conditions in the causes of mental disorders.

In suggesting some applications for their study, the authors stressed the need for more knowledge of social factors in psychiatry, new treatment methods, new approaches to professional training, better public mental hospitals, evaluation of psychiatric care ("Class V needs help most—social and psychiatric—and gets it least"), and improved public health education in mental health.

Psychiatric Hospital as a Small Society

William Caudill studied a small psychiatric hospital attached to the medi-cal school of a large university. He gathered his data as a participant inves-tigator during 1951 and 1952. Before that, in 1950, he had been a con-cealed observer in the same hospital, posing as a patient. That venture caused some shock to the hospital's members when the impersonation was made known.

Caudill, an anthropologist, sought to develop a distinctively sociological thesis in his book. He was "concerned with a search for an understanding of the broad context of the therapeutic process in a psychiatric hospital." He believed and sought to show by the evidence of multiple interrelation-ships that that broad context constitutes a social system. The functioning of that system, moreover, "affects the behavior of the people who make it up in many ways of which they are unaware."

Design. The research consisted of three interrelated studies: (1) A ward observational study, based on detailed daily observations in two eight-week periods, covering first the men's locked ward and then the open wards for both sexes. Each of these periods consisted of more than three hundred hours of observation. (2) A small group study, covering the daily administrative conference, that began before and continued through the sixteen-week period of the ward studies. The data for this conference study consisted of an essentially verbatim record of more than 120 consecutive conferences. (3) An attitude survey, which began in the fourth month of the project and lasted for seven months. The respondents were both patients and staff. The questions were based on a series of specially drawn sketches that depicted everyday situations of life in the hospital.

One type of data was missing from the project, much to the regret of the researcher. He was not able to get regular and reliable reports on what happened during the psychotherapeutic hours. He was especially interested in relative progress or regress in therapy as a variable that might show relations to events in the broad social context. Such data would have allowed a direct test of a ground-swell theory, which posits that a majority of the patients on a ward do well or poorly at a particular time.

Small-group findings. The daily administrative conferences were held each morning except Sunday, usually lasted some twenty minutes, and usually included thirteen persons, divided among senior staff, residents, the supervisor of nurses, charge nurses, and other specialized personnel.

One of the findings of this study, though very simple, was remarkably consistent and strongly supportive of the main thesis of the book. It was found that the amount of talking each person did was a function of rank in the hospital. Everyone in a higher-status group talked more than anyone in a lower-status group, the most passive resident more than the most extroverted nurse. Within each role group, the amount of talk was in order of rank. Among the five residents, nominally of equal rank, there was a consistent order within each of three series of twenty-one conferences. When the senior staff members were asked to rate the five residents in order of clinical competence, it was found that the ratings corresponded almost perfectly with the rank order on amount of talk during the conferences.

Attitude findings. The attitude study, based on sketches of hospital life, showed many discrepancies in patterns of perceptions among role groups. Surprisingly, the senior staff and the patients showed very similar patterns. It was surprising in that it was found that the senior staff were often unfamiliar with physical aspects of the ward because they were so seldom there. Residents and nurses had different distinctive patterns. Nurses, for example, tended to be optimistic about patient contacts that were administrative but pessimistic about those that were therapeutic. Patients showed exactly the reverse pattern.

Ward findings. The findings from the ward observation study involved much narrative material. The findings pointed to such things as unintended consequences of administrative decisions, failure of communication, and conflicts between administrative and therapeutic objectives. One highlight was an account of a collective disturbance that centered about a television petition by the patients. It was marked by tension among patients and staff, mainly as a result of poor communication. The author was able to analyze the incident into a sequence of four phases, and he speculated that it may be possible to develop monitoring techniques to predict the tenor of events on the wards. The disturbance illustrated the author's conception of "a covert emotional structure underlying the overt formal and informal structure of the hospital."

Conclusions. The author pointed to some distinctive social-structural features of the psychiatric hospital as being especially relevant to its effectiveness. There is dual control, a division between administrative and therapeutic functions that has a high potential for causing conflicts. The author questioned the assumption that these two kinds of functions are incompatible and suggested that they may beneficially be combined in one person. Another similar source of conflict is multiple subordination, where several independent chiefs have authority over the same worker. Another feature, one that pertains to hospitals in general, is the use of mobility-blocked roles. The levels of personnel are marked off by lines, which personnel do not cross within the system. Attendants do not rise to become nurses, and nurses do not rise to become physicians. This feature induces formalized relations and greatly affects the content and flow of communications.

The author called for greater openness among persons who operate existing psychiatric hospitals and greater self-examination, comparable to that demanded of the psychiatric patients, if the goal of a therapeutic community is to be reached. And he called for a willingness to consider new departures and new models for the physical and organizational structure of psychiatric hospitals.

CLOSED RANKS

John Cumming is a psychiatrist, and Elaine Cumming, his wife, is a sociologist. In 1951 they conducted an intensive six-month educational campaign in Blackfoot, a Canadian town with a population of 1,500, attempting to modify public attitudes toward mental illness. They used a variety of media—such as lectures, the press, radio, and films. Their presentations involved concepts and materials that were then generally available. They were very careful and hard-working in their efforts to achieve good community relations.

Design. They employed an experimental design to evaluate the effectiveness of their campaign. That involved a second town, 150 miles from the first and similar to it, as a control community. In both towns, there was one wave of interviews before the educational campaign in Blackfoot and a second wave after it. The control community received no stimuli from the researchers other than the interviews. Two attitude scales, a social distance scale and a social responsibility scale, were the intended means of measuring before-and-after conditions in the two communities.

Results.   Before the educational campaign, the scores in both communities tended to be low in both scales, indicating much prejudice against the mentally ill and little acceptance of responsibility toward them. After the campaign, the researchers found no trend of change. The two communities remained at about the same level as each other and unchanged from the first wave.

The researchers met an effect in the experimental community that compounded their chagrin. As the educational campaign went on, the community reacted with growing hostility and aggression that was, for the most part, aimed not at the educators but at the second-wave interviewers. Some six years after the experiment, the authors published their report on what happened, giving their reflections on what it all may have meant.

Findings.   The project was designed to allow not only an experimental test of the educational campaign but also an exploratory analysis of data on public attitudes toward mental illness. Some interesting findings emerged.

The researchers put together a series of attitude questions that they thought belonged to a single dimension of constructive versus nonconstructive attitudes. But they found that the items fell into two dimensions: social distance (for example, "I would be willing to room with a former mental patient") and social responsibility (for example, "I would feel partially responsible if a member of my family had a serious mental breakdown"). Each dimension was measured by a scale that reflected responses to several questions. It was found, surprisingly, that these two scales were statistically independent of each other and bore different patterns of relations to other variables. Social distance (nonacceptance) scores varied directly with age and inversely with education. Social responsibility scores were unrelated to either age or education, but they did relate to the respondents' ideas about the causes of mental illness. Those who saw social or economic causes scored highest on social responsibility. Next came those who saw personality causes. Lowest were those who saw either moral or biological causes for mental illness.

Conclusions.   Why were the research findings on the educational campaign negative? Was it, perhaps, simply a result of faulty research methods? The authors acknowledged that their campaign was uneven in its coverage and that their sample in Blackfoot (540 respondents, equal to 60 per cent of the adults in the community) was biased. Lower-class persons were underrepresented. Also, the design allowed only trend measures of net change in the group and not turnover measures on actual changes by persons. Finally, the design did not include any measures of how much each person may have been exposed to educational material from the campaign or other sources. It seems hardly likely, however, that these or any other methodological points can explain away the experimental evidence of resistance to attitude change.

The authors tried to explain what happened by means of a theoretical discussion. They discussed "the patterned reaction to mental illness in our society." From a societal viewpoint, mental illness is a form of deviance from social norms. Any deviant behavior upsets the equilibrium of the social setting in which it occurs, and the way in which the deviant person is treated may be expected to serve the function of helping to restore social equilibrium. It is this societal function that lies behind the postulated patterns of values, beliefs, and actions. The pattern is characterized by themes of denial, isolation, and insulation of mental illness in this society. Confronted by irrational behavior due to mental illness, the citizen's first tendency is to normalize the behavior. When this denial of illness is no longer tenable, the next step is physical and social isolation of the deviant. Finally, there is insulation of the entire problem by additionally denying that these elements of the pattern may have posed any civic problem.

The project induced hostility, the authors believe, because of the intensiveness of their campaign. Theirs was a highly concentrated assault of high social visibility. It was not so much a matter of arousing anxiety in individuals as of posing a threat to the equilibrium of the community. The community responded by asserting the solidarity of the same. It closed ranks against the intruders.

REFERENCES

Adorno, T. W., Frenkel-Brunswik, E., and Levinson, D. J. *The Authoritarian Personality.* Harper & Row, New York, 1950.

Benedict, R. Continuities and discontinuities in cultural conditioning. Psychiatry, 1: 161, 1938.

Caudill, W. *The Psychiatric Hospital as a Small Society.* Harvard University Press, Cambridge, 1958.

Caudill, W., Redlich, F. C., Gilmore, H. R., and Brody, E. B. Social structure and interaction processes on a psychiatric ward. Amer. J. Orthopsychiat., 22: 314, 1952.

Clausen, J. A. Social factors in disease. Ann. Amer. Acad. Polit. Soc. Sci., 346: 138, 1963.

Cumming, E., and Cumming, J. *Closed Ranks: An Experiment in Mental Health Education.* Harvard University Press, Cambridge, 1957.

Dean, D. G. Meaning and measurement of alienation. Amer. Sociol. Rev., 26: 753, 1961.

Durkheim, E. *Suicide.* Free Press of Glencoe (Macmillan), New York, 1951.

Goffman, E. *The Presentation of Self in Everyday Life.* Doubleday, Garden City, New York, 1959.

Gross, E., and Stone, G. P. Embarrassment and the analysis of role requirements. Amer. J. Sociol., 70: 1, 1964.

Hollingshead, A. B., and Redlich, F. C. *Social Class and Mental Illness: A Community Study.* Wiley, New York, 1958.

Jackson, E. F. Status consistency and symptoms of stress. Amer. Sociol. Rev., 27: 469, 1962.

Leighton, A. H., *et al. The Stirling County Study of Psychiatric Disorder and Sociocultural Environment.* 3 vols. Basic Books, New York, 1959–1963.

Linton, R. *The Study of Man.* Appleton-Century-Crofts, New York, 1936.

Mechanic, D. The concept of illness behavior. J. Chronic Dis., 15: 189, 1962.

Merton, R. K. *Social Theory and Social Structure.* Free Press of Glencoe (Macmillan), New York, 1957.

Myers, J. K., and Roberts, B. H. *Family and Class Dynamics in Mental Illness.* Wiley, New York, 1959.

Parsons, T. *The Social System.* Free Press of Glencoe (Macmillan), New York, 1951.

Seeman, M. On the meaning of alienation. Amer. Sociol. Rev., 24: 783, 1959.

Srole, L. Social integration and certain corollaries: an exploratory study. Amer. Sociol. Rev., 21: 709, 1956.

Syme, S. L., Hyman, M. M., and Enterline, P. E. Cultural mobility and the occurrence of coronary heart disease. J. Health Hum. Behav., 6: 178, 1965.

CHAPTER 20

The Role of the Family in Psychiatry

STEPHEN FLECK, M.D.

INTRODUCTION

THE FAMILY is the universal, primary social unit and, therefore, must occupy a central position in any consideration of social psychiatry. As current psychiatry and medicine encompass the study and understanding of the cell and its elements, of cellular organization and integration into organs and organ systems, and of their orchestration into a biopsychological whole that is the organism, so is that organism's behavior in and interaction with its environment important for the understanding of health and disease. Knowledge of the social elements and parameters of this environment is as essential to diagnosis and treatment as is reliance on laboratory data on body chemistry and the nature of food, water, and air supply.

The first social environment for every human being is his biological family or its substitute. If the latter, it is ideally adoptive parents, who take over at the earliest possible time after birth. Usually, however, one family provides an offspring with both his biological and cultural heritages.

The family is, therefore, an important sociocultural institution, the keystone of society, and every human group has devised traditional prescriptions and proscriptions to ensure that the family fulfills its biological and enculturating tasks. In this way the family is both the link between generations that ensures the stability of the culture and also a crucial element in cultural change. The biological functions of the family are usually left to the nuclear family, especially to the mother, but the enculturating functions may be assigned to members of the extended family or even to nonrelated persons in the community. In Western society both of these tasks have rested with the primary family, although not always with the primary nuclear family, as is most usual today.

HISTORY OF FAMILY STUDIES

Sociocultural Studies

Scientific study and knowledge of the family have a rather recent history, especially in the context of psychiatry, but preoccupation with the family as a sociocultural institution is as ancient as human history. Three of the Ten Commandments specifically concern family relations, and every religious doctrine contains many specific rules and taboos about family structure and family duties. Equally ancient are concerns about family dysfunctions. Athenians deplored the alleged decline of family tradition and cohesion as endangering the state and society; the decline of the Roman Empire has been attributed, among other causes, to the family's failure to inculcate the earlier moral standards and discipline. Throughout history major social upheavals have been examined in the light of changes in family life. Today this age-old thesis finds expression in more scientific endeavors, such as the current interest in cross-cultural comparisons, which seek precise correlations between national characteristics and family practices.

The causal relationships between family characteristics and social change or human history are circular and complex rather than unidirectional. Because of the family's central importance in human development, not only historians and social anthropologists but also legal scholars, economists, philosophers, and sociologists have studied and written about the family. However, some of our most perspicacious insights derive from literature—for instance, *Oedipus Rex, Hamlet*, Strindberg's *The Father*, and O'Neill's *Long Day's Journey into Night*.

Psychiatric Studies

Although the medical profession has prided itself on its family physician, this designation is based on his identical role with all members of a family and not, until recently, on any formal knowledge of family dynamics and their institutional characteristics. Historically, such endeavors in Western medicine can be measured in decades. Freud, although aware that his discoveries pertained primarily to family processes, chose to study and treat family pathology only in individuals. He concentrated on the investigation and conceptualization of his patient's psychic apparatus, isolated from its usual environment in the stark setting of the analyst's office. He thereby limited the social parameters to the analyst-patient dyad, a situation in which a person can relive family experiences through the phenomenon of transference.

Not until twenty-five years after Freud's first accounts of family-related unconscious processes—such as his rediscoveries of Oedipus and Electra, of the family romance and incest—did the first psychoanalytic effort to conceptualize family processes appear in print. At about the same time, investigation and clinical consideration of family members began in the American child guidance clinics. But, in clinical medicine and psychiatry, family histories have continued to focus mostly on familial incidence of disease and on hereditary patterns, not on family dynamics. In psychiatry some investigation of sociocultural constellations in families of patients according to diagnosis began in the 1930's, but direct clinical and research study of the family as a group did not begin until the 1940's. Despite the existence of an extensive sociological literature on family life, despite scholarly studies of family law, and despite anthropologists' preoccupations with non-Western family systems during this century, medicine and psychiatry continued to focus on the individual patient and the doctor-patient relationship. Only in the last twenty years has there been rapidly increasing clinical scientific interest in and appreciation of the family as the most significant social force in human development, specifically in personality development, and hence as a potent agent in personality disorders. The family, therefore, is not only the keystone of society but also a key to understanding the humanness of the human being, including his failures as a human.

MARRIAGE

Marriage is, of course, an integral part of and constitutes the basis for the family in most societies. But it needs to be considered also as an institution somewhat apart from the family, and it must be evaluated in each instance along a range of sociocultural and idiosyncratic contingencies.

PURPOSES OF MARRIAGE

A universal biopsychosocial need for completion and fulfillment of oneself through the intimate life with another exists among humans and some other species, and two people may undertake marriage solely for their mutual satisfaction, without intent or capacity to establish a family. In Western society today this definition of mutual satisfaction could be exclusively that of the two partners, although their definitions would necessarily reflect the cultural and psychological norms or deficiencies they have absorbed into their personalities during their respective developments. Western society would not interfere with such decisions or plans to produce no offspring, the needs or demands of spouses' parents or collateral relatives to the contrary notwithstanding. Other cultures may dictate in these matters. In extended family systems, parents may achieve neither full independence in these respects nor full authority over their own offspring, and failure to produce offspring can lead to dissolution of the marriage by either partner or by outsiders. On the other hand, marriage may also be undertaken in our society solely for the purpose of procreation, and in some religions it is indeed so prescribed, even if not always practiced.

Subconscious purposes. From the clinical vantage point, most marriages fall somewhere between these extremes of intent and purpose, one extreme being nonfamilial and the other 100 per cent family-oriented. It is most important for the clinician to appreciate that the spouses' respective explicit intents and beliefs may be at variance with the implicit or subconscious intents and wishes that lead them to marriage. For instance, one spouse may agree to marriage determined not to have children, and the other spouse may accede to this condition, quite prepared not to honor the agreement after marriage, or the other way around. Such behavior need not be a conscious or a designed betrayal; both spouses may intend to honor such agreements but later find that they cannot resist their own subconscious opposite desires or needs. For instance, Catholics may have increasing guilt feelings over birth control, or one or more of their parents who aspire to the status of grandparents may exert pressure on the couple.

Depending on the partners' culture, they unite in marriage because they want to, because it has been arranged for them by their parental families, or because of a combination of these prescriptions. In the West, partners choose each other by and large on the basis of their feelings and hopes, be they realistic or not. Among the less-conscious motivations and unrealistic factors that lead to marriage are many neurotic tendencies and needs. Most common among these is probably the use of marriage to achieve independence from the family of procreation, which the young person cannot accomplish as an individual. This brings to the marriage certain dependency needs, which are likely to result in expecting parental care from the spouse. Another such factor is social pressure, especially on girls, from one's family or peers that marriage at a certain age is an essential earmark of success.

Not all unconscious or external determinants need be unsound. The choice of a marital partner is a complex process, and a certain intuitive sense of personality fit between two people seems to operate effectively at times, even if neither spouse can account for it explicitly. There are many paths to marriage, sound and unsound foundations for family life, but spouses can build sound relationships even if they have united for ill-considered reasons. One of the chief criteria for a successful marriage is that it furthers individual growth and growth as a unit.

Changes in industrialized societies. The personalities and the sociocultural values two individuals bring to marriage determine the nature of their relationship more than do their hopes, dreams, and intentions during courtship. This is particularly so now in industrialized societies, where marriage and offspring have shifted during this century from being economic advantages and even necessities to being economic liabilities. The basis for marriage and for marital continuity has changed from tangible issues to the intangible necessities and requisites of companionship, encompassing physical, intellectual, affectional, and social facets. Although the partners can share the economic burdens, they can rarely do so side by side, as they would in dividing complementary tasks on the farm. Maintaining a house and household can be reduced to a minimum of labors, leaving as the major shared goal family life itself, together with the care of the offspring.

Sharing family responsibilities, however, has been made much more difficult by the absence of the husband from home during working hours, and, if he is ambitious, working hours may approach the entire waking hours of the family on many days. Hence, when there is concern in present-day America about the husband's declining role in the family, these sociocultural givens of an industrial society are probably more responsible and pertinent than speculative clichés about the decline of masculinity or the ascendency of masculine strivings on the part of women. It must be appreciated that a boy of our age, after his school day with women teachers, does not return to a home where a father works. Such a youngster may hardly ever see his father at work, the nature of which may be very difficult for a young child to comprehend. The burden of making an absentee husband a live and appropriate image for the children often falls on the wife and depends, therefore, on the marital relationship.

MARITAL COALITION

The marital coalition may be defined as those interactional patterns that the spouses evolve to provide, at first, for their mutual satisfaction. Later, in the structure and dynamics of the family, this coalition must serve the age-appropriate needs of the children and still maintain an area of exclusive relationship and mutuality between the parents. One of these parental sectors is sexual activity, interdicted to children in our society. Mutuality denotes the spouses' interactive patterns on implicit and explicit levels, the sharing of feelings, and the conveying of respect and appreciation of the spouses to each other and to others.

Sex-linked roles. An important function of this coalition in family life is the mutual reinforcement of the spouses' complementary sex-linked roles. As parents, they represent culture-determined masculinity and femininity, not only as individuals but also through the other spouse's support and approval. Another facet of the coalition is the conjugal role divisions and reciprocities the spouses establish for themselves. These role allocations and the decision-making methods vary with each socioeconomic class. According to Bott and to Rainwater, upper-class spouses believe that their role divisions are equal and complementary but that husbands make more decisions. Lower-class spouses, except for the lowest group, also state that their role allocations are joint and complementary but that wives make more decisions than husbands.

Effects of isolation.   Industrialization and social and geographic mobility have isolated the nuclear family, adding to the critical importance of the marital coalition in the life of the family. Newlyweds may well seek isolation initially, but, in the process of adjusting to married life, they find that friends and relatives can be useful. Nowadays marriage is often followed by a move to new surroundings, strange for both partners. Whereas living apart from one's family of origin is considered desirable, letters are not the forum in which one inquires about a recipe for tonight's supper or in which one reports and gains perspective about the first marital altercation. These items may seem trivial, but professional experience with marital problems indicates otherwise; minor problems and disharmonies can easily accumulate and fester. Physicians can help as marriage counselors, but young people have few occasions to seek out health resources until pregnancy occurs. Prenatal care, therefore, offers an important opportunity for remedial marital counseling and for the prevention of future marital and family disorders.

Because the marital partners usually become the sole or at least the major sources of identification for their young, the spouses' personalities and the marital coalition are much more critical today for the personality development of the children than in the past. In extended family systems a child has many adults of his sex to use for identification. This is still true to some extent in subcultures where grandparents and the parents' collaterals live nearby, albeit in separate households. Living isolated from close relatives deprives the spouses of the advantage of sharing parental functions with an extended family group and leaves each child with little alternative but to view his parents and their relationship as exemplary. Spouses must depend on each other in crises without ready availability of a relative to assume the tangible household or income-producing duties of a disabled partner. In this sense, the demand for individual adjustment and maturity and for effective role complementarity are more stringent than in earlier times. Moreover, most offspring have no other adult models at home in a continuing way to compensate for model deficits in one or the other parent. Problems in the isolated nuclear family, therefore, tend to become circular: Marital difficulties affect children adversely, and a difficult or ill child strains the marital coalition.

Individual adjustments.   In a free society, spouses depend still more critically on their inner resources because, compared with other cultures, a free society has relatively few social rules or rituals concerning marriage. In the West, society and religion concern themselves primarily with the beginning of marriage and with death and divorce. Aside from registration of the newborn, society intervenes with a family only if gross undercare or mistreatment of the young is made evident. Otherwise, marital partners are on their own to mesh their personalities into the kind of bond and coalition they desire and are capable of, but their capabilities may fall short of their desires. If this happens, they may seek help through counsel-

ing, which is available only to a very limited extent, or they may live on in
conflict and disharmony, or they may seek divorce.

MARITAL PROBLEMS

Marriage in the United States now depends primarily on the personalities
the spouses bring to it. Their personalities are shaped largely by their
parents and by the marital modes to which they have been exposed, modes
that often do not serve or suit a younger generation of newlyweds. From
these circumstances, plus the greatly prolonged duration of the average
marriage, derive some specific burdens of marriage in current industrial
societies.

Whether the prevalence of marital maladjustment is absolutely greater
or only proportionally so compared to other periods is uncertain. Because
the marriage now depends so greatly on the partners' personalities, the
high prevalence of individual emotional maladjustment must be taken
into account. If every tenth person spends some time in a mental hospital
and if the prevalence of symptomatic personal maladjustment is still
higher, marital adjustment, which depends so largely on personality factors, obviously carries a commensurate incidence of instability. Of course,
marriage can also lend support and stability to an unstable partner. But
the doubling of the marriage-life span also requires that the marital relationship be adaptable to more stages and to the challenges of longer lives.

Counseling.   Because marital and familial maladjustment tends to be
so encapsulated, the parents must seek help actively outside the family. In
extended family systems, remedial influences may have arisen spontaneously from within the group through the efforts or the mere presence of
one or more of the other adults. In this way the marital problem as such
may have been contained and never have become quasipublic and statistical.

From the clinical standpoint a marriage should be evaluated as a singular undertaking of two people. It should be examined in the contexts of
their respective personalities and motivations for marriage and family and
of the family they have already created. Their sociocultural milieu must be
taken· into account, and their coalition evaluated according to the class-
specific modes of marital interaction.

Although a marriage between two disturbed partners can be satisfactory
to them, this does not ensure a good prognosis for a healthy family. Furthermore, a marital coalition adequate for the nurturance of a few children may deteriorate if the family enlarges every year. Family planning
through contraceptive control to avoid offspring, to plan and space them,
or to limit family size is, therefore, an essential element of marital counseling and health care and of preventive psychiatry.

Premarital sexual activity.   Premarital and extramarital sexual intercourse is difficult to assess statistically and cannot be discussed meaningfully as a single phenomenon. In particular, these practices must not be

confused with morality, as societies that permit complete freedom of sexual activity after puberty are no less stable or less successful in living up to their cultural norms and preserving their continuity. The same is true of societies that condone extramarital sexual activity implicitly or explicitly.

The changes in premarital sexual activity in this society may be less marked in practice than are the attitudes toward such practice. Young people have gained freedom in recent decades to know and talk about sexual matters; they also expect tolerance with regard to their activities. This has led to the present-day demand of adolescents for their elders to take an open and nondefensive stand about rules and guidelines for sexual behavior outside marriage. There are serious advocates of complete license in this respect, and there are equally serious advocates of Victorian rules of behavior and thought.

The physician, however, should not take positions of generalities. When called on to advise or educate on matters of sex and marriage, it is incumbent on him to inform about sexual matters and reproductive control, but it is also incumbent on him to consider to whom he is talking and why. The patient's health needs, his or her life situation, and the capacity of the individual or couple for mature relationships, be the goal marriage or not, should concern the physician, who must be especially aware in this part of his work that the patient is apt to attribute to him a parental role. He must use such transference elements for the welfare of his patients in these emotionally charged instances just as skillfully as in any other facet of doctor-patient interactions.

Clinically, there is no evidence that premarital sexual relationships either promote or detract from successful marital adjustment. However, one reason for early marriage seems to be the desire for legitimate sexual union, even though emotional and socioeconomic independence may not have been achieved by the couple. This can create special problems if they become parents while still dependent on others; also, they may not be as mature and certain in their identities as they might be a few years later, when they might seek different partners.

DIVORCE

Divorce is popularly considered a kind of barometer of marital and societal stability, but divorce, too, must be understood in appropriate context. Divorce as a social phenomenon is susceptible to customs and legalistic vogues and to changes in the law, and it is also subject to religious codes. It is fashionable to point out that the divorce rate in this country has tripled in this century from 0.7 to 2.2 per 1,000 population and that the number of divorces has risen more than seven-fold. But these figures must be considered in the light of the changed basis for marriage, the modern risks to marital stability, and the freer attitudes toward the dissolution of marriages so beset by problems and suffering that present-day counseling and therapeutic agencies find them beyond salvage.

In particular, the marriage counselor must examine critically a common rationalization designed to avoid divorce for the sake of the children. Children's needs and how they are served by a particular marital pair must be carefully assessed, without assuming a priori that two parents under the same roof are better than one. In the past a very disturbed marriage may have been continued because there was no avenue open to dissolve it except through desertion, and economics often dictated its continuance. Even today severe economic liabilities are usually imposed on the divorcing parties by circumstances or by the court or by both.

The peak divorce rate in the United States of 3.5 per 1,000 occurred in 1945, when many hastily undertaken war marriages were dissolved, often by spouses whose life together could be counted in days or months. But, from the overall statistical standpoint, the divorce-risk time has doubled because, with an increased life expectancy in this century from forty-seven to seventy years, the duration of marriages, over 90 per cent of which take place before the age of thirty, has more than doubled. The tripling of the divorce rate for the population represents an increment of between 30 per cent and 50 per cent if the rate is corrected for risk. The lowering of the average marriage age requires a further correction, so that the properly corrected rate increase is about one-third, which is quite different from the uncorrected figure of thrice the gross rate. Considering that 10 per cent of the population will require temporary psychiatric hospital care and that most but not all divorces involve one or two emotionally unstable partners, the present divorce rate is far from commensurate with the estimated prevalence of emotionally disturbed individuals.

FAMILY STRUCTURE AND DYNAMICS

In this and the following sections, the term "family" refers to the Western nuclear family, the isolated family of industrial society, unless otherwise specified.

From the sociodynamic standpoint the family is a small group to which most small-group dynamics apply, but it is also a very special group. The special group features pertain to the family's biosocial evolution in a particular culture and to its axial divisions into two generations and two sexes. These axes are important psychological and behavioral boundaries. The parents form the generation that leads, and they are implicitly obligated to relate sexually to each other. Sexual relations, however, are interdicted to all other members by the archetype of all taboos, that against incest. The generation of offspring follows and learns from the parents as gender-typical models.

As a group, the family moves from the parental dyad to a triad and larger group and later contracts again. Because the family is divided into two generations, each child's relationship to the parents is to some degree exclusive and unique and can be represented by an inverted triangle. The family consists of a series of overlapping triangles, each child forming a triangle with the parents, and these triangular relationships are not identical. It cannot be overemphasized that no child lives in the same family as his siblings in a dynamic sense, sometimes tangibly so because of changing family fortunes. Even identical twins are ascribed different roles and characteristics by parents, by siblings, and eventually by themselves, so that each has different relationships with the parents and with the parental unit.

The family as a whole also constitutes a structural and functional unit. It has already been pointed out that one important task of the marriage consists in mastering the family's evolutionary transitions or crises. Besides the arrival of children, such critical phases include each child's oedipal phase, school beginnings, puberty, adolescence, and eventual emancipation as he leaves his family of origin physically and emotionally. Adversities, such as illnesses and economic or political misfortunes, may produce other crises and even temporary or permanent separations.

These evolutionary crises can also be viewed as a succession of separations, which all family members must learn to master. These separations can be tangible or intangible; that is, they may be on only an emotional plane, as when a child in early adolescence withdraws from closeness to parents. The evolutionary expansion of the family also involves issues of emotional separation and lessened dependency gratifications for the older members in the family. Family life, therefore, requires the capacity to forego individual gratifications for the sake of the group, whose cohesion depends on the example being set by the parents' foregoing some degree of their individuality and certain gratifications for the marital coalition and for the family. Each evolutionary step or crisis results in a new equilibrium and realignment of the family's emotional forces, and sometimes this leads to role changes and different task distributions.

ROLE DIVISIONS

The image of a strong authoritarian patriarchy of the Victorian age has been overdrawn, but it cannot work in modern democratic society. Compared to the Victorian prototype, the father in present-day America has weakened, but more in appearance than in substance. Typically, the father's role is still that of the leader; his activities, his productivity, and his education determine the position of the family in the community and larger society, and these same factors also correlate with the character of the marital coalition. He provides the instrumental model of how things are done in society in matters of acquisition and survival. It is true that he can be pushed by his spouse's ambitions or even be overshadowed by her accomplishments in all these respects, but such a family may pay a price in suffering, disturbance, and pathology. The fact that the father's activities today occur mostly away from home, unshared and unobserved by the family, is a disadvantage.

The mother's primary role concerns the affective life of the family, and she also tends to its biological needs in health and sickness. Her role is expressive in that she not only tends to affective needs but identifies them and helps the children to learn about and understand feelings and, therefore, is more responsible for their self-expressive communication. She also guides the child toward self-awareness. This is distinct from instrumental communication—how to get things done—which is more the father's domain.

These divisions are not absolute; they only indicate the dominant role of each parent. However, it must be appreciated that the mother's ability to help a child gain self-awareness and body consciousness and perceive and establish boundaries between himself and the world outside him is more crucial than the father's ability to do this, whereas the father's role as a leader and activator in matters of communal relationships is more important to the family than the mother's social competence and instrumental skills outside the home.

These role divisions are not only important for reasons of example but also essential in the children's acquisition of communicative skills. For instance, a father working away from home cannot be relied on to teach about intimate feelings in a detailed way, but he can bring to this and other family tasks a perspective that a mother, harassed by the demands of young children throughout the day, cannot maintain around the clock.

Parental role divisions should be flexible and complementary rather than fixed because, in crises, role complementarity may be essential, and temporary role reversal may even be necessary. Permanent role reversal of the spouses occurs, too. It may be mutually satisfactory to the parents, but it provides offspring with unsuitable models for their future life in society. Parental role reversals are particularly disadvantageous to the child if the reversal is covert but desired by both parents. Parents must provide gender-typical role models that are in harmony with the larger society in which they live, lest the child fail to acquire and incorporate role attributes and expectations of himself that have utility when he moves into the community.

FAMILY STRUCTURE AND PERSONALITY DEVELOPMENT

Dynamically, the triangular structure of the family is epitomized by the oedipal phase of each child. Its adequate and appropriate resolution, which determines important salients of the child's psychic structure, depends more on the family structure and behavior than on biological determinants, as postulated by Freud. This appears to be true of all phases of psychosocial development, although parental attitudes and behavior are both reactive and interactive with the child, so that a child's equipment at birth, his temperament, and the parents' capacity to cope with infantile needs all coincide to establish the family's interactional patterns. From these patterns derive much of what the child sees and observes in terms of what kind of people his parents are—indeed, how they are human. Personality development, proceeding through identifications and imitations, depends as much on the parents' individual characteristics as on their correlated marital and familial interactive behavior. The child observes and absorbs the defensive modes of those around him, and in this way secondary processes are acquired from familial examples and interaction.

After a child has learned body awareness and body management, including the correlated communicative facility, his relational learning begins. The task for the family is to help each child establish his place in the family and to make him feel sufficiently secure in it so that he can begin to move beyond the family circle without undue anxiety. To attain this place of nearly equal emotional distance from both parents, not only must he master body competence and competence in feeding, clothing, and toileting himself, but he has to master the oedipal issues of desexualizing his close primary object relations to his parents. Only then can he turn to peers as an increasingly important source of relationships. This step, in one sense the internalization of the incest taboo, the family must accomplish with him. The family accomplishes much of this not only nonverbally but almost unconsciously. The personalities, especially the degree of security in sexual identity that the parents bring to their union, and their coalition are more crucial to this task than in any other phase of family life, most of which can be more explicit and verbally directed.

Further personality development of the child is less directly dependent on family structure and dynamics. But in subtle and not so subtle ways, the oedipal issues are relived in adolescence in terms of dependence-independence issues. These problems begin with the internal imbalances of puberty and continue into the prolonged path toward heterosexual competence and personal identity. The parental models play a role during this phase, often as an antipodal fulcrum for the offspring. To achieve a workable ego integration and identity, the offspring must be able to overcome his negativistic stances, which serve for separation from his elders but do not serve in themselves the reintegration of an independent and inwardly directed personality. If the antipodal position is very ambivalent and remains emotionally charged, it may become fixed. The child then remains partially identified with a parent he also rejects, a shaky foundation for ego integration and ego ideal.

FAMILY FUNCTIONS

Although it is artificial to separate structure, relationships, and functions, clarity may be served by the different emphasis of the sections. Indeed, the formation of a family structure is one of its inherent functions for its own sake, but it is also an implicit charge from the larger community. Society expects the family to prepare children for their lives as adults in the wider community, enabling them, in turn, to procreate and form their own families. Procreation is essential to the survival of any species, but the human species must also teach its heritage and thus ensure its continuity and future development. The family as the basic sociocultural unit is the embryo of social organization, and the parents are the sociocultural gametes.

The biological heritage demands a set of vital family tasks to be performed for the infant, such as feeding, sanitation, and teaching him body management and the utilization of survival tools. All this animals do for their young, and social organization is also a characteristic way of life of many species. For the human race, another dimension is added through the development of the culture-typical symbols and their utility, not only in the survival tasks but in planning for the future through an understanding of one's individual past and the group's collective past. Moreover, the symbolic communication among humans does not require physical proximity of the communicators in time or space, a prerequisite to communication among animals.

For the purpose of discussion, family functions will be separated as follows: (1) marital, (2) nurturant, (3) relational, (4) communicative, (5) emancipative, and (6) recuperative—keeping in mind that in vivo they all overlap and to some extent are continuous. Also, all except the marital interaction itself involve educational tasks, even though formal education is assigned to extrafamilial institutions in many industrial and other societies.

MARITAL FUNCTIONS

Marriage must serve the respective needs and satisfactions of the spouses and enable them to effect an appropriate family constellation in order to fulfill their tasks. Beyond the familial obligations, the marital partners must jointly prepare to renounce their close ties to their children when they are ready to emancipate themselves physically and emotionally from the family. The family ultimately becomes a dyad again and must turn its concerns from productive engagement in the community to issues of retirement and the concomitant aging processes.

NURTURANT FUNCTIONS

The nurturant functions of the family encompass more than nursing and food supply, although these are basic at first. Beyond nursing, there are the other forms of physical care that the helpless infant needs. Their performance requires the mother's motivation and some degree of security on her part in performing these tasks. This security derives from her quasi-instinctual propensity for mothering, coupled with the almost symbiotic union with the newborn, such as the mutual and simultaneous relief of the baby's hunger and the mother's breast turgor, and from the support of her spouse and other family members, if any. The less specific nurturant activities of the mother continue throughout the life of the family. Eating together as a family at least once a day is not only a caloric ritual but a significant landmark in family life for communication, learning, interacting as a group, and relaxing together.

The psychological and symbolic aspects and overtones of nursing and feeding grow from and with the earliest mother-infant interaction. Here the infant acquires his initial trust in his human environment. Because the entire family is involved, their interaction with the mother-infant unit determines much of the nursing atmosphere. The broader nurturant tasks concern almost every aspect of the young child's development as he acquires body awareness and learns body management, sphincter competence, and self-care with regard to feeding and clothing. All these myriad activities—feeding with its symbolic significance, caring for the baby, helping the child to walk and to talk, getting things he cannot reach, supplying him with appropriate visual, auditory, and kinesthetic experiences—can at times be carried out by any family member or by other substitutes.

RELATIONAL FUNCTIONS

Weaning. Weaning is part of nurturing but implies more than withdrawing bottle or breast. The intricate physical closeness with the mother must be weaned, and an essentially nonphysical intimacy must be established with all family members. Weaning involves still more, in that both the process of weaning and its accomplishment are foundation stones in the acquisition of ego boundaries. In reverse, a mother may fail to wean a baby adequately and at the appropriate age because her ego boundaries are blurred and because she overidentifies with the infant. She also violates the generation boundary. In all these functions the mother plays the dominant role, but the entire family atmosphere and interaction are also crucial. For instance, parents already locked in an energy-consuming struggle with each other or with one child necessarily neglect another child proportionally. It should be noted in passing that, in terms of ultimate mental health, the underattended child may fare better than the overinvolved one.

Weaning, the cessation of sucking in the narrow sense, has important relational implications as the prototype of a succession of separation crises that characterize personal development and family life evolution. Nurturant competence on the part of the parents implies not only providing for needs and their satisfaction but also the capacity to frustrate and deny the child without provoking undue feelings of rejection and without undermining his natural propensity to grow and master problems, often painful problems. When frustrated or punished, the child may find his anger and hostility quite overwhelming, and he may lose faith in a parent temporarily. Nurturant and weaning competence in the family teaches the child that his temper tantrum does not overwhelm others in the family and that he is separate but not alone. In reverse, a parent's anger and frustration with a child teaches him the limits of his provocative power and is another essential lesson in grasping limits between himself and others and in establishing his own ego boundaries. Here the parental coalition counts. Ideally, the uninvolved and nonangry spouse supports both the upset parent and the child.

Mastery of separation can be defined as the child's experiencing the pain of acute loss of good feeling toward or of dissatisfaction with another significant person, the parent, without losing faith and trust in the continuity of the relationship and the ultimate restoration of good feeling. Through these experiences he also learns and grows, becoming more able to avoid the same impasse and less vulnerable to and threatened by subsequent separations or emotional distance from others. This mastery must be facilitated by the opportunity to observe, imitate, and eventually internalize how other family members cope with frustration and this kind of separation anxiety.

The relational issues involved in the feeding and weaning experiences culminate in each child's oedipal phase. Its successful passage includes the central issue of effecting the incest taboo as a rather unconsciously directed inhibitory force within the child and within the family. Conscious incestuous preoccupations beyond the oedipal phase interfere with subsequent successful personality integration and growth, especially in adolescence. The child's omnipotent sense of exclusive relationship with the mother must be curbed and frustrated, enabling the child to wish to grow up like the same-sex parent and to relate to both parents as individuals and as a unit.

Peer group relationships.   After the child has been helped to find his place in the family, permitting him to feel comfortable and safe in intrafamilial relationships, his relational learning turns to peer groups. Here the familial guidance becomes more distant and indirect, but familial facilitation and support of peer relationships are as essential as restraint against undue familial intrusion into peer activities. After 6 or 7, the child's relational learning depends increasingly on extrafamilial examples and on the family's social activities with relatives and friends.

Not only are the culture-typical distance and closeness to various people in differing situations learned that way, but extrafamilial persons are important as alternate figures for imitation and identification. Such experiences complement the parents' unique examples as members of their gender and their society and provide alternate or corrective models for parental shortcomings as people. Even if such shortcomings are not severe, teenagers often find their friends' parents or other adults superior and preferable as examples to follow in the service of emotional separation from the family.

Parents and the family as a whole must be able to tolerate such disloyalties, lest the emancipating adolescent bear an undue degree of guilt, burdening him with an intense conflict between his needs and society's—that is, his peer group's—demands to be an individual on the one hand and parental demands to conform to their standards on the other. Such an impasse may occur because of his inner needs or of parental resistance to his independence or of both. The parents' respective values and expectations for their offspring must be in sufficient harmony that the child can integrate parental objectives and standards, and parents and children must reconcile these values and goals with the realities both of the child's capacities and of the community in which they live or wish to live.

Communicative functions. The central element in the family's educative mission concerns communicative competence. Talking with the child about his earliest internal and external experiences is essential to his beginning to talk and to communicate meaningfully. What he says and what is said to him must be meaningful to himself and to others so that, through such sharing, he comes to rely on the utility and consistency of language to express himself and to impress others. Only through language and the symbols basic to it does body awareness become body knowledge, and only through language can the basic trust of the mother-infant relationship be reinforced and broadened to include other family members and people outside the family. Without language or equivalent symbols, prediction and a grasp of the future are almost impossible. For instance, only by very rigid timing could a child feel assured that he will be fed when hungry. Language allows for flexibility, such as, "supper will be late," or "after your bath tonight instead of before."

Familial communication must, of course, be related to the communication styles and symbol usages of the family's community. It must be appreciated that language plays a role in personality and concept formation beyond its communicative utility. Language reflects the culture's conceptual heritage and determines thought and concept organization across the generations.

The jargon of any younger generation combines elements of both the emancipating striving for separateness and of changes in language and culture. In some immigrant families special problems arise because school-age children often surpass their parents in vocabulary and linguistic mastery, depriving both generations of certain communicative dimensions.

Emancipative functions. The ultimate goal for each child is to grow up and take his place as a full-fledged member in the society into which his family has placed him. In Western industrialized society this usually means that the offspring must attain physical, emotional, and economic independence from his family, being motivated and able to originate his own family.

In other societies the emancipative tasks may not be as stringent and extensive, but the family still serves to guide the child toward the position society expects him to occupy as an adult. The process of emancipation of each child demands a compensatory reequilibration of the family after each departure until the spouses return to a dyadic equilibrium, free to enjoy parental prerogatives as grandparents without the continuing responsibilities of the nuclear family. Obviously, each step toward emancipation poses the recurrent issue of separation until it is final and definitive.

The degree of mastery of the earlier and more limited separations—beginning with weaning and later the beginning of school, separate vacations, and possible hospitalizations of members—indicates and to some extent determines the ease or difficulty experienced by the family when a child leaves for college, to get married, for military service, etc.

But geographic separation is only a part of the issues to be mastered; more important are the emotional components, the sense of loss experienced by all involved, and the inner capacity of each member and the capacity of the family as a group to do the work of mourning appropriately without becoming pathologically depressed. The departing member must accomplish this alone or with his spouse; the remaining family group can work it out together, the parents demonstrating appropriate mourning, faith in everybody's ability to master separation, and faith in the continuity of life.

The modern family is handicapped with regard to total separation experiences, as the death of a parent or child within the life span of the nuclear family is now rare, whereas it would have been rather usual only fifty years ago. Often now the four grandparents are still living at the time a young adult emancipates himself from his family. And grandparents often live at a distance, so that the impact of their deaths on the nuclear family does not carry the immediacy and intensity of the permanent loss of a regular participant in family life. The time when the first child leaves may be the first occasion for all family members to mourn together, in contrast to the experience of a youngster of earlier generations, who usually would have shared mourning with his family incident to the death of a close relative.

Family bonds continue, of course, beyond the emancipation of the young. Rejoining one's family temporarily is a mutually enjoyable and relaxing experience, provided the family has done its tasks well. Opportunities for mutual support are also likely to arise after parents have become grandparents.

RECUPERATIVE FUNCTIONS

The family must provide for the relaxation of its members, relaxation of manners and behavior and even of defenses essential to interaction in the community. Most mothers are familiar with the need of an elementary school child for strenuous physical activity, even for a fight on his return from school, and the home must serve as a controlling environment for such socially nonadaptive, possibly regressive, relaxation.

In the family circle parents shed formal attire, actually and symbolically. If a man's house is his castle, his family is the one group in which he can be king or at least president and in which he can also exhibit dependency needs. For such mundane reasons alone, the family might have to be invented if it did not exist, as no other living arrangements could provide for so many individuals these opportunities to forego formal behavior and recover energy for the work in the community, which requires more formal and defensive interpersonal demeanor.

To some degree the family also permits its members to engage in creative or other activities that afford relief by contrast with the monotony of many jobs. By setting limits on relaxing activities, the family as a group also demands and teaches impulse control—in games, for instance—and all members may have to defer individual hobbies to family group activities at times. Children experience discipline in this way as with other frustrating experiences, first as outer control and eventually as inner restraint.

If the family is so burdened by its own tasks that relaxation and enjoyment as a group become jeopardized—either because of emotional conflicts and ill health or because its size overtaxes its emotional, nurtural, educational, or tangible resources and reserves—indications for family limitation and for outside assistance with family tasks are at hand.

FAMILY PATHOLOGY

Psychiatric entities with a familial incidence based on chromosomal and inborn defects, whether hereditary or not, will not be considered here. Correlations between family pathology and psychiatric syndromes are seen on all the many levels of human and social integration, and the conceptualization of these processes is difficult and complex. At this time there is much need for further clinical investigation and for standardization of conceptual terminology. Here, correlations among family disorders, psychopathology, and psychiatric syndromes will be outlined only in general terms, relating these phenomena to deficiencies and difficulties in the family's task performances, including the failure to evolve a workable structure.

Broken Families

Broken families are the grossest but not necessarily the psychiatrically most devastating form of family pathology. Broken families are disproportionally frequent in the backgrounds of sociopaths, unmarried mothers, and schizophrenics, regardless of whether the fracture is through death, desertion, or divorce.

Family Deficiencies

Parental psychoses and neuroses. Family deficiencies cover a wide range. Intrapersonal parental inadequacies form one large category. For instance, severe immaturity may lead one spouse to seek a dependent position in the family, akin to that of an offspring. Such a spouse expects a parent role of the partner or even of a child. Beyond this, almost any form of neurosis or psychosis in one parent is apt to produce a defective parental coalition, which in turn handicaps the nurturant and enculturating tasks on which the children depend. Parents with severe hysterical or obsessional or other neurotic characteristics are apt to produce offspring with like defensive structures if not symptoms.

Mental inadequacies. Mental subnormality tends to run in families, apart from genetic factors. Below certain intelligence levels, parental functioning, especially the communicative performance, does not suffice to accomplish the enculturation of offspring. Educational inadequacies and inferior social position in a given subculture can also result in ineffectual family structure and dynamics, especially if the family belongs to a group against which the surrounding community discriminates actively.

Inadequate gender models. Inability or failure of a parent to serve adequately as a gender model appropriate to the larger society leads to increased developmental vicissitudes, especially for the child of the same sex. This is even more true if, as is often the case, the posture of such a parent is further weakened and undermined by the mate's critical and even contemptuous attitudes. The insecure gender identity of a parent predisposes the same-sex child to gender uncertainty and confusion, leading to social ineptness or the development of perversions or schizophrenia.

Need for an extended family. Another form of family pathology peculiar to the nuclear family can be viewed as a surreptitious need for an extended family system. This occurs overtly or covertly when one parent or both remain primarily attached to and dependent on their parents or a parental substitute, and the center of gravity for authority, decision-making, and emotional investment rests outside the nuclear family group. This distorts family structure and functions, especially if both parents feel primarily beholden to their respective families of origin, and no workable coalition for the younger family becomes established. An extended family system is quite workable with differential role assignments across three generations, but it is damaging to a nuclear family that intends or aspires to such designation and that geographically lives as a nuclear family.

Overinvestment in children. Parental overinvestment in the achievement of children, especially the parents' social prestige aspirations, is related to the development of depression in offspring. Such parental attitudes are introjected, and they predispose the child to intense ambivalence and a sense of being loved and worthy only on the basis of superior performance and achievement. Punitive attitudes toward the self supervene when failure in terms of the internalized overstringent expectations occurs.

SCHISMATIC AND SKEWED FAMILIES

Probably more pathogenic than actual parental separation is family schism. Here, the family is divided overtly or covertly into warring camps, usually because of chronic conflict and strife between the parents. The children are forced to take sides, to the detriment of their personality development and integration. This type of family pathology is found in the background of schizophrenic patients.

Another form of family pathology related to schizophrenia is the skewed family, when a dyad other than the parental one dominates the group emotionally and often tangibly. A skewed marital relationship is different; here, one spouse expects the other to be a parent to him or her, or one disturbed parent dominates the other and family life absolutely and rigidly. Such a marital coalition preempts parental functions and emotional resources, and the children's affective and psychological needs are neglected.

In both schismatic and skewed families, violations of the generation boundary abound, and in both the intense relationship between one parent and one child may have seductive and incestuous components, an additional violation of sex-role requisites if not of the incest taboo.

Overt incest is evidence of gross parental psychopathology and of defective family structure. Father-daughter incest is commonest, but both parents are psychologically involved, since incest often bespeaks a tenuous equilibrium in a family that seeks to avoid overt disintegration. The involved daughter has often assumed many parental functions, but the parents maintain a facade of role competence. The family often breaks up after incest is brought out into the open, usually by the involved child.

FAULTY COMMUNICATION

Aberrant communication in the family is a common psychiatric finding. Although usually secondary to parental psychopathology, notably thought disorders, faulty communication also builds up a pathogenic autonomy of its own. Young children learn the defective communication modes, distorting their linguistic development, perception, and concept formation. If communication is confusing within the family and ineffectual as expressive or instrumental tools, children are deprived of a critical socializing instrument outside the family. They may never gain basic faith in and reliance on the utility of communication. The seeds of autism may be sown in this way. Severely amorphous or fragmented methods of communicating have been found among families of schizophrenic patients.

LEARNED ABERRATIONS

Parental examples of paralogic thinking and of fear and mistrust of their social environment affect offspring by creating confusion and anxiety, and children may internalize the faulty ideation and the mistrust of the world. This is the familial counterpart of Cameron's pseudocommunity, and paranoidal suspiciousness can be learned in this way.

Johnson and Szurek delineated another form of family pathology among sociopaths who carry out covert or overt needs or wishes of parents.

The child's asocial behavior may express directly such propensities of a parent in exaggerated form; in other instances, the child behaves like a sociopathic parental collateral whom one parent secretly, or not so secretly, admires.

CLINICAL EVALUATION

Besides the history of psychiatric disorders in the family, clinical assessment concerns family functions, but function and structure cannot be separated as neatly by the clinician as by the textbook writer. The observation of functioning and coping forces inferences about structure and vice versa. Just as the clinician can draw inferences about lung structure or pathology from breathing patterns, so also can he deduce on a statistical basis that chronic sociopathic behavior in an offspring, for instance, is related to structural functional family defects.

Symptoms aside, the clinician seeks information about the basic elements of family structure, notably the maintenance of the generation boundary and the gender-linked role divisions and complementarities, and about the manner in which the family copes with its major tasks and functions. He pays special attention to their communication modes.

Diagnostic investigation and therapeutic influences overlap in the establishment of family diagnosis, as they do in psychiatry generally. This section will not deal with techniques of assessment but will only outline the referential framework for evaluation through family history and direct observation.

INFORMATION SOURCES

Ideally, the individual histories and statements of all family members are combined and examined for congruent and contradictory data. These individual records are complemented by participant observation of the family as a group. There are many methods available for this, ranging from open-ended family interviews to more or less structured formats, including the possibility of having the family do specific tasks or tests together while being observed and, preferably, recorded.

THE SPOUSES

The referential framework begins with an examination of the marital relationships, the pertinent data concerning the spouses' respective backgrounds, their personal developments, educational levels, socioeconomic class positions, and the cultural and ideological value patterns of their respective families of origin. Significant discrepancies in these parameters should alert the examiner to potential conflict areas, and he should investigate the resolution of such discrepancies. For instance, he should investigate discrepancies with regard to religion, social class ambitions, desired family size, and rearing methods of and goals for the children.

FAMILY STRUCTURE

Data about family structure can be obtained through inquiries about living and sleeping arrangements, activities of the family as a group and as part groups, role divisions incident to various family tasks, and the decision-making processes. As far as possible, these items should also be examined directly through group observations, as should the possible existence and nature of dominant dyads other than that of the parents. In observing the family as a group, the diagnostician gains impressions about the extent and methods of parental leadership and whether it is united or not—that is, criteria about the effectiveness of the parental coalition and the integrity of generational division. Gender appropriateness in manners and in conversational content can be established impressionistically in family interviews, or inappropriate seductiveness can be documented, for example.

FAMILY COPING

This can be assessed by learning about crisis behavior. The normal crises of family evolution are important sources of understanding about the family's coping patterns, coping reserves, and coping deficiencies. Among such crises are possible resistance or reservation of the spouses' families to the marriage and how this was resolved; the first pregnancy; the original triad formation; subsequent pregnancies and births; economic misfortunes; deaths of relatives or friends. In psychiatric practice the examination often takes place in a crisis situation, such as that incident to the hospitalization of a family member as a mental patient.

SOCIAL NETWORK

The nature of the family's social network should be examined to establish social isolation or the nature of family relatedness within the community. The network must fit to some degree the class position and the patterns of the community and subculture of which the family is a part. The involvement with the spouses' families of origin and collaterals also must fit to some degree their cultural pattern, or conflict should be presumed and the resolution of it examined. A parent's intense attachment to either family of origin should alert the examiner to the possibility that a truly nuclear family has not been established.

THE CHILDREN

Evaluation of the children depends on their respective ages. Pediatric histories, including well-child-care data, may be the only source of information available outside the family. For older children, kindergarten and school adjustments, records from recreational agencies, and, when indicated, information from neighbors and friends as to the socialization of a child can be utilized. School phobias are a classic manifestation of deficient separation mastery in the family.

In families with older children, attention must be paid to their emancipating efforts and the parents' reactions to these. Adolescence, notoriously a family stage of uneasy truce in many respects, should be just that, a family dissolution process, at least on an emotional plane. Adolescents must experiment with greater independence, and each step carries a potential for disagreement and conflict for all concerned. Also, the adolescent's dissatisfaction with and opposition to parental standards are an intermittently necessary stance for him in his strivings for emotional distance and independence. Examining and evaluating the family with adolescent offspring are, therefore, especially difficult because of this evolutionary state of imbalance.

INTRAFAMILIAL COMMUNICATION

Here, recordings or films are essential if detailed analysis is to be attempted. But grossly or impressionistically, the clarity of communication or lack of it can also be seen and heard. Contradictory statements in the same verbal passage or discrepancies between verbal content and nonverbal communication may confuse rather than convey meaning or may have a double-bind effect. Scapegoating of a member becomes readily apparent, as do ambivalences, such as the more or less covert condoning of a member's behavior that also constitutes the family's complaint. Careful analysis of verbal passages or special tests given singly or to the group discloses thought disorders and ideational defects.

TOOLS

Questionnaires and schedules of family process items are available or can be composed for specific assessment modes, but, in general, they are ancillary diagnostic tools. They are most useful for the examiner who wants to standardize examinations for data-retrieving purposes, for research, or for didactic purposes. Their major value, therefore, rests with the organization of data and not with the information-gathering segment of clinical evaluation, which rests primarily with the clinician's skill and art.

REFERENCES

Ackerman, N. W. *The Psychodynamics of Family Life*. Basic Books, New York, 1958.

Ackerman, N. W. Family diagnosis and therapy. In *Current Psychiatric Therapies*, J. Masserman, editor, vol. 3, p. 205. Grune & Stratton, New York, 1963.

Bell, N. W., and Vogel, E. F. Toward a framework for functional analysis of family behavior. In *A Modern Introduction to the Family*, N. W. Bell and E. F. Vogel, editors, p. 1. Free Press of Glencoe (Macmillan), New York, 1960.

Bott, E. *Family and Social Network*. Tavistock Publications, London, 1957.

Bowlby, J. *Maternal Care and Mental Health*. World Health Organization, Geneva, 1952.

Erikson, E. *Insight and Responsibility*. W. W. Norton, New York, 1964.

Erikson, E. *Childhood and Society*, ed. 2. W. W. Norton, New York, 1964.

Fishbein, M., and Burgess, E. W., editors. *Successful Marriage*. Doubleday, Garden City, N. Y., 1948.

Fleck, S., Lidz, T., Cornelison, A., Schafer, S., and Terry, D. The intrafamilial environment of the schizophrenic patient: incestuous and homosexual problems. In *Science and Psychoanalysis*, J. Masserman, editor, vol. 2, p. 142. Grune & Stratton, New York, 1959.

Flugel, J. *The Psychoanalytic Study of the Family*. Hogarth Press, London, 1921.

Keniston, K. *The Uncommitted*. Harcourt, Brace and World, New York, 1965.

Kluckhohn, F. *Variants in Value Orientations*. Row, Peterson, Evanston, Ill., 1957.

Leighton, A. H. *My Name Is Legion*. Basic Books, New York, 1959.

Lidz, T. *The Family and Human Adaptation*. International Universities Press, New York, 1963.

Lidz, T., Fleck, S., and Cornelison, A. *Schizophrenia and the Family*. International Universities Press, New York, 1966.

Parsons, T. The incest taboo in relation to social structure and the socialization of the child. Brit. J. Sociol., 5: 101, 1954.

Parsons, T. *Social Structure and Personality*. Free Press of Glencoe (Macmillan), New York, 1964.

Parsons, T., and Bales, R. F. *Family, Socialization and Interaction Process*. Free Press of Glencoe (Macmillan), New York, 1955.

Rainwater, L. *Family Design*. Aldine Publishing Company, Chicago, 1965.

Richardson, H. B. *Patients Have Families*. Commonwealth Fund, New York, 1948.

Riesman, D. *The Lonely Crowd*. Yale University Press, New Haven, 1950.

Vygotsky, L. S. *Thought and Language*. Wiley and M.I.T. Press, New York, 1962.

Weinberg, S. K. *Incest Behavior*. Citadel Press, New York, 1955.

Whorf, B. L. *Language, Thought, and Reality: Selected Writings of Benjamin Lee Whorf*. Wiley and M.I.T. Press, New York, 1956.

Zimmerman, C. *Family and Civilization*. Harper & Bros., New York, 1947.

AREA D

Other Fundamental and Behavioral Topics

CHAPTER 21

Epidemiology

PAUL V. LEMKAU, M.D., and
GUIDO M. CROCETTI, B.Sc.

DEFINITION

Epidemiology is the study of health conditions in a population in relation to any conceivable factors existing in or affecting that population that may influence the origin of the health state or affect its distribution in that population. The object of such study is to ameliorate any factors that contribute to ill health, to enhance any that contribute to health, and to draw generalizations from studies that can be applied to other populations to contribute to health in general. From the point of view of pure or basic science, the objective of the promotion of health is not essential to epidemiology. But, as a derivative of the public health movement, epidemiology has always had a large element of applied science in its conceptual base. In practice, the promotion of health and the alleviation of disease states are accepted as parts of its logic.

HISTORY

The origins of the science of epidemiology are very ancient. Probably the first discovery was the fact that disease tends to be a greater threat when the wastes of human living accumulate. The importance of human feces in the spread of disease probably followed this general but vague notion and led, as much as esthetic reasons, to the invention of sewers and other methods of waste disposal.

Mosaic Laws

Certainly by the time it was possible to encode the Mosaic laws, about 1200 B.C., a great deal of epidemiology was already known. Not all the Mosaic laws are interpretable in the light of modern medical science, and it is impossible to know what sort of logic, superstition, or magic underlay many of the dietary and other laws. Yet it is clear that the interdiction of pork could have had to do with a fear of trichinosis and other diseases and that the interdiction of shell fish may have had to do with gastrointestinal diseases or induced reactions to products of decomposition.

The rules regarding the handling of the sick and of corpses are easily seen to be related to the recognition of the contact transmission of disease and of the importance of fomites. Similarly, the laws regarding the management of lepers, whatever disease or diseases the Biblical term leprosy may have included, show a recognition of the transmissibility of disease from the sick to the healthy. Such notions were considered important enough to be incorporated into the highest level of law in the theocratic organization patterns of the Israelites of that time. Indeed, in almost all civilizations prior to the Renaissance, health and disease were very closely bound to the religious systems of the people.

Epidemic Constitution

In addition to the more or less specific relationships implied in the Mosaic laws, used here as one of the earliest examples of applied epidemiology, there was much thought given to why waves of disease struck at particular times and intervals. These rather vague thoughts found expression in such terms as "epidemic constitution," into which were woven at different times and by different people ideas of the influence of climate and other cosmological factors. The name "malaria" (*mala aria* or bad air) is evidence of this, as is the propensity for keeping out the night air in malarious regions or the avoidance of low-lying land in favor of higher areas for the building of summer homes.

This sort of nonspecific but nevertheless effective action based on epidemiological concepts perhaps reached its highest point in the famous Broad Street pump incident in London in 1854. At that time John Snow realized that cholera was being spread by water from a particular pump and prevented the use of that water by dismantling the pump, thereby retarding the epidemic.

Incidents that involved no recognition of any specific causative factor but were nevertheless effective—Jenner's discovery of cowpox vaccination to prevent smallpox, for example—were accompanied by a great many ineffective actions. These are often forgotten in the congratulatory history of the successful ventures. But during the same period useless fires were built in the streets to arrest plague, and as late as the 1950's swimming pools were emptied and public assemblies forbidden to prevent the spread of poliomyelitis, although both actions were ineffective.

SPECIFICITY

The next step in epidemiology came with improvement in diagnosis. The most important figure in this was Sydenham, who distinguished many illnesses in the seventeenth century. He recognized that such broad generalizations as the epidemic constitution could not deal equally well with all questions of disease spread; each disease might well have its own laws of spread and, by implication, of control. This is a concept too late applied to mental diseases. There is still tendency to talk of the prevention of mental illness, as though the prevention of paresis, pellagrous psychosis, various postencephalitic states, alcoholism, mongolism, depression, and schizophrenia were all the same.

Sydenham's work led to the recognition that specific illnesses required specific preventive measures and that the concepts "infectious disease" or "exanthems" were useless in prevention for the most part. The same lesson of specificity is only now being learned in psychiatry. Too often, prevention is dealt with in terms of broad generalizations, as though there were some panacea to be found that would deal with all the variety of mental diseases. In every case in which a mental illness has been prevented, a clear-cut causative factor related to a definable syndrome had been discovered. Witness the decline of syphilitic psychosis with the emergence of effective treatment for syphilis, the decline of pellagra with improvement in knowledge of nutrition, the decline in frequency of toxic delirium with the introduction of the sulfonamides and the antibiotics.

The discovery of the importance of bacteria in disease led to the development of modern epidemiology, and this phase in the development of the science is only a few decades past its zenith. With the discovery of obligatory causative agents—first bacteria and then viruses, Rickettsia, mycobacteria, and others—the development of the epidemiology of the one overwhelming cause took place. For a number of years concern was almost exclusively on etiology and the control of etiological agents, either directly or through immunological reactions. This era is still underway and is still of outstanding importance; witness the control of poliomyelitis in 1955 and the still more recent immunizing procedures against measles. From the psychiatric point of view, a good deal remains to be done in this branch of epidemiology; there are unsolved problems in encephalitis, for example, the solutions to which will contribute much to the prevention of some psychiatric syndromes.

MULTIFACTORIAL ETIOLOGY

The golden age of epidemiology did not solve all the problems of epidemiology, however, and a new era of epidemiological study began with a familiar term in psychiatry, "multifactorial etiology." During the golden age just described, epidemiology was mostly concerned with obligatory factors in disease—that is, the causative agent in the absence of which no specific disease could occur. There could be no pneumococcal pneumonia without pneumococci, no leprosy without *Mycobacterium leprae*, no measles without the measles virus, no schistosomiasis without flukes, no syphilis without the spirochetes. These causative agents, however, were not enough to explain all problems. There were always individuals in the population who were known to be infected but who did not become ill. There were always those who recovered while others died. And there were many diseases in which the model of infection did not fit the cases, notable among them being some arthritic conditions, arteriosclerosis, and, among the mental diseases, schizophrenia, depression, neurosis, alcoholism, and the character disorders.

These unsolved problems led, under the leadership of Dubos and others, to a renewed consideration of the host factors in disease, those factors within the individual that determined his vulnerability. The disease that precipitated much of this thinking was tuberculosis. In this disease the obligatory cause, the mycobacterium, constitutes a smaller proportion of the total etiology than is the case in more acute diseases. But the other diseases listed above were also important in the development of this phase of epidemiological development. For the most part they are diseases for which no obligatory factor is as yet known. It is a matter, at present, of looking for all possible factors associated with the diseased state. Felix expressed the concept very economically by saying that schizophrenia is like tuberculosis without the mycobacterium entering the picture. Except for those mental illnesses known to have obligatory causes—and they are numerically small in proportion to the others—the epidemiology of the mental illnesses falls in the same category as the epidemiology of arthritis, coronary thrombosis, and arteriosclerosis.

Too often the accomplishments of the golden era of epidemiology for psychiatry are overlooked. The conquering of syphilis led to a decrease in psychiatric illness considerably greater than that in physical disease contributed by the prevention of poliomyelitis or measles. The antibiotics have tremendously reduced the psychiatric problem of toxic delirium. Furthermore, the control of infectious diseases has relieved much occasion for the emotional stress of grief in parents. The control of childbed fever has allowed a much higher proportion of children to be raised by their mothers than was the case earlier in human societies. The golden era of epidemiology contributed both directly and indirectly to mental health.

STUDY METHODS

DISEASES WITH OBLIGATORY CAUSES

Epidemiological theory has been concerned in part with the way epidemics rise and fall and the periodicity of these waves of illness. This part of epidemiological theory is concerned primarily with diseases with one overwhelming, obligatory cause.

The shape of the ascending epidemic curve depicting the proportion of a population affected by a disease over a period of time appears to depend primarily on such factors as the length of time between exposure and onset of disease for the particular illness under question and the method of transmission of the disease. The descending arm of the epidemiological curve depends on the exhaustion of the supply of susceptible persons in the population. Both ends of the curve depend, also, on the prior history of the disease in the population, the type of immunity resulting from having the disease, and any immunizing measures that may have been used. It is relatively easy to study the shape of epidemic curves by animal experiments, and it is also helpful to express the various possible shapes of curves in mathematical form. Particular shapes of curves are typical for certain groups of illnesses, and the epidemic curve may lead to the determination of the diagnosis in some epidemics and can lead to information useful in identifying the obligatory causative agent. Statistical devices are most useful in determining the significance of epidemiological data; that is, statistical tools allow estimation as to whether changes are due to chance or are related to a patterned sequence of events.

These experimental and mathematical methods have been useful in diseases that occur in waves and then disappear or reach a low ebb of sporadic occurrence. They have thus far been less helpful in the study of diseases that vary little in their rates over time or that do not result in death or recovery within a relatively short period.

CHRONIC DISEASES

Chronic diseases require other methods of study, particularly when no obligatory causative factor is known. Changes in rate of occurrence are likely to be rather slow, making them hard to interpret, particularly since medical science is likely to have changed in quality of diagnosis and treatment while any change in rate has been occurring. This is particularly true when the causative factor has to act over a long period of time to produce its effect.

The best example of this kind of problem is the association between cigarette smoking and lung cancer. Such an association could not be found until the diagnosis of lung cancer could be made quickly and accurately and until sociological methods to determine who smoked in the population had also become available. The cause of lung cancer as related to tobacco tars probably could not have been discovered without the development of surgery that offered the possibility for cure; it is hard to arouse interest in a disease for which there is no cure. The epidemiological success had to await developments in several other areas of medicine.

Life table. The tool most useful in studies of chronic illnesses for which no obligatory cause is known is the life table. Essentially, the life table is a composite of the experience of a group of people who share certain common factors considered to be related to a pathological process, in contrast to a group without these factors.

For many diseases the end point of the life table is death; in other diseases the end is a form of disability. In psychiatry the measure is often hospitalization, considered to be a measure of behavior disorder in that society will no longer tolerate the sick person in its midst. Some have termed this measure the point of social or productive death of the individual. Although the concept has certain advantages for dealing with psychiatric illnesses, the tolerance of societies does not stay constant, and advances in treatment may result in improved behavior without affecting the underlying disease process. Nevertheless, the life table method presents many still unexploited possibilities for the study of psychiatric illnesses and of factors in mental health.

Many mathematical tools have been developed for the interpretation of life table information. A modern and as yet uncompleted experiment dealing with what is essentially life table methods is the work on the relationship between diet and arteriosclerosis.

DISEASES WITHOUT KNOWN CAUSATIVE FACTORS

The life table method is also applicable in studying illness states in which no causative factor can be postulated. Various sorts of events occurring in people's lives can be used as the basis for forming contrasting groups, which can then be followed to some other event, such as the appearance of disease, social or productive death, or death itself. The method can be applied with some greater risks to retrospective data. Plummer and Hinkle used it, for example, in the study of the relation of ill health to certain social situations in female telephone employees and in relating ill health to events in the lives of migratory students. The studies of the types of families producing schizophrenic children are essentially life table studies, though the numbers reported are far too small to allow the use of the available mathematical tools for tests of significance. Although the life table method has not been applied rigorously enough to allow genuine evaluation, it is the concept that underlies most of the thinking relating childhood behavior disorder to later disease or health. At the present time the most rigorous studies tend toward a negative relationship, although the end of the story is not yet clear.

DISEASES WITH MULTIPLE CAUSES

It is clear that the life table method allows the testing of a very wide range of possible relationships between events and what follows them. In individual cases the method was introduced by Adolf Meyer as the life chart. Lorr and others have worked out various ways of evaluating behavior at successive points in time so that intervening events may be related to later behavior. From this sort of study of the lives of individuals, hypotheses arise that can then be tested by life table methods. How to quantify experiential events and the status of illness and health remains a persistent problem greatly deterring the testing of hypotheses in the area of psychiatry but at the same time offering inviting vistas for research.

MENTAL DISEASES

Reid has voiced many of the problems in the application of epidemiological methods to mental diseases. His conclusion is that the methods of epidemiology are applicable to psychiatric diseases, provided the data can be properly quantified. By this he means that diagnosis must be replicable, if not valid, and that life events involved in hypothesis testing must be somewhat quantifiable.

These desiderata are important, but helpful concepts may be developed through work done before they are fully met. Snow controlled cholera before he knew why the action he took worked, and he did it in the absence of any mathematical controls. Psychiatry has an equal basis for hoping that its studies may lead to serendipitous discoveries of a helpful sort before it is able to reach the level of excellence of data that will allow the application of the most highly developed epidemiological theory and methodology. Along with mistakenly building fires in the streets, psychiatrists may encounter some other kind of removal of the handle of the Broad Street pump.

Action cannot be delayed at many points. The clear-cut proof that a kind of retardation is associated with the absence of an enzyme necessary in the metabolism of phenylalanine logically leads to the testing of all infants and the inauguration of special diets for those lacking the essential enzyme. Meanwhile, the as-yet-unproved assumption that children deprived of a broad preschool experience contribute a high proportion of the mildly mentally retarded cannot be neglected. Preschool education for underprivileged children, like that going forward under the antipoverty program in the United States, may prove to be as ill-founded as building fires in the streets was for controlling plague. Yet there must be an effort to control the apparent deficiency in mental health, and preschool education is the best way presently known to accomplish the task. Epidemiology does not insist on absolute proof of relationship. But it does help place some responsibilities for selection of methods and for marshaling available facts concerning actions taken to relieve the problems of the various mental illnesses.

EPIDEMIOLOGY OF THE MENTAL ILLNESSES

For the most part the epidemiology of the mental illnesses is at a quite primitive level, particularly in regard to its most important problems—schizophrenia, depression, and the various neuroses. Depression and schizophrenia are better studied than the neuroses, probably largely because they are more reliably diagnosable, though they leave much to be desired in this area. Diagnosis of neuroses is far from reliable—that is, reproducible by equally qualified diagnosticians.

Studies of schizophrenia and depression have been largely descriptions of the prevalence of the illnesses in various populations and the comparison of the sick, by various characteristics, to the total population. Hypotheses have been based on such findings, but exceedingly few, if any, studies have been directed toward the testing of hypotheses. Leighton is in the process now of testing whether changing the social organization of a community will change its rate of symptoms of mental illnesses. This study is based on his earlier finding that less socially organized communities have a higher rate of symptoms than better-organized ones. This is one of the first attempts to test a hypothesis after formulating it on the basis of prior research into the distribution of symptoms. It is similar to the preschool education program already mentioned except that the etiological concepts involved are much better supported by data in the Leighton research than in the necessarily far-broader test of a less-well-documented hypothesis in the Head Start program.

Epidemics

The earliest publications on epidemiology of mental symptoms had to do with reactions sweeping through populations in ways familiar from the study of epidemics of infectious diseases. In Italy around the seventeenth century, an epidemic of very fast dancing ran through the country. The reaction was supposed to follow the bite of the tarantula, but it is clear that the need for this stimulus soon faded out, the reaction becoming psychogenic. The epidemic left its permanent mark in music, the tarantella form being that of a very fast dance.

William Sargant has continued the study of such epidemic psychological reactions, linking the tarantella with trancelike states appearing in every period of civilization, depicted on Greek vases and seen today in many religious sects, such as the dervishes and, in the United States, the snake-handlers. Such reactions have not been well-studied epidemiologically. It is not known, for example, what proportions of populations are actually involved or how many consciously put on an act while others are carried away by the various kinds of reactions. One of the best-studied of such epidemics is one reported from Louisiana in 1939 (Schuler and Parenton, 1943). An excellent bibliography on ancient psychological epidemics appears in The Milbank Memorial Fund publication on epidemiology (Jastak and Whiteman, 1957).

Genetic Illnesses

Perhaps the earliest modern studies of the epidemiology of mental illness were those of Luxenberger and Brugger in Germany, published about 1928. These studies were primarily designed to test hypotheses in the genetic area. A case of an illness was selected as a starting point, and all relatives of this patient were then investigated as to the presence or absence of psychiatric illness. Another person who was not ill was also selected and matched with the patient for certain characteristics. His relatives were similarly traced and examined. The results of such studies gave not only the differential rates between the two basic groups but rates in specific, defined populations as well, the first such rates in the literature. Studies allowing similar conclusions were done in other places as well. The genetic aspects of these studies form a legitimate subject for epidemiological research, and they have continued, largely as twin studies, under the leadership of Kallmann.

DIRECT RESEARCH IN TOTAL POPULATIONS

The next step in epidemiological studies was direct research in total populations to see what illness they had produced. Fairbank and Lemkau were leaders of groups in Baltimore and were probably the first to have skilled biostatisticians associated with them in such studies. Their group worked in the urban Eastern Health District of Baltimore; a companion group was working at the same time in a rural area of Williamson County, Tennessee.

The Baltimore group searched all available sources to find cases of psychiatric illness, from the mental hospitals to the police records to the records of social agencies. The cases were analyzed by geographic location, race, age, sex, and economic status. The Williamson County study was obliged to establish a diagnostic and treatment center in order to find and obtain diagnoses on cases, a technique later used by Leighton and his colleagues as well.

DEFINED POPULATIONS

Strömgren in Denmark began the study of defined populations. He used the total populations of relatively isolated islands for study, populations in which individuals who were ill could be traced. This research design was also used by Bremer in the study of an isolated fishing village in northern Norway. This study indicated for the first time that psychiatric symptoms were actually exceedingly common. His figure was 25 per cent of the population, of which he studied each member personally.

Ødegaard defined his population for study in another manner—by whether or not they had carried out a certain action. He studied the rates of mental illnesses among Norwegians who had migrated to the United States as compared with family members who had remained in Norway, coming to the conclusion that those who migrated were at greater risk of mental illnesses than those who remained behind. In general, this conclusion has stood up rather well in the light of later findings, though other patterns of migration may provide different findings.

Eaton and Weil studied the Hutterites, a group defined by their religious beliefs and a kind of communal social organization. The group lives in northwestern United States and southwestern Canada and is highly inbred. The legend that this group had no mental disease was exploded by the study. The rates for schizophrenia were not markedly dissimilar from those in other populations, and depressions seemed more common among the Hutterites than in other populations.

Another method of defining a population was used by Gruenberg in his studies in New York State. He used an age limit, interviewing all people over 65 and establishing rates according to certain social and economic parameters.

MENTAL RETARDATION

The epidemiological study of mental retardation began with a Scottish study of the early 1900's. The intelligence of a large number of children was evaluated by psychological tests; the state of mental retardation in adults was judged by social characteristics. The study probably missed very severely retarded cases, and its criteria for diagnoses left something to be desired. Nevertheless, this study represented a large step forward in methodology, and its main findings have often been replicated by others.

A more thorough, census-type of study was attempted by Jastak in the 1950's but, unfortunately, resulted in few publications. It did tend to show that Lewis's finding of high rates of mental retardation in rural as compared with urban areas was less marked in the 1950's than it was earlier in England. Studies by others have thrown light on many technical problems in the study of the epidemiology of mental retardation. Imre has conducted a very thorough study of a rural area, profiting from the improved methodology now available.

Gruenberg surveyed a New York county, using teachers as case reporters. He found that, using this technique, his reporters tended to include a wide variety of behavior disorders as retarded cases, even though their psychological test scores were quite high.

PROBLEMS ENCOUNTERED

In all these studies there are problems of definition of the illnesses counted, of severity of symptoms reached before a case is counted, of whose judgment is to be used if the case is not seen personally, and many others. There is also a problem of how to present the data. This matter has now reached a rather stable point; data are presented as incidence rates and prevalence rates. Incidence rate is that proportion of a population that becomes ill for the first time during a specified time interval, usually a year. Prevalence rate refers to the proportion of a population ill at any one period of time, regardless of time of onset. Prevalence rates may be given as of a single day or as the total number ill during a specified time, regardless of whether they were continuously sick throughout the period. In some studies it is assumed to be important to the future of the individual if he has ever been ill, and the figures are presented as cumulative, so that a prevalence rate not only includes those sick during a specific period but all those in the population who have been ill with a mental illness at any time and are still alive. Although these conventions are often violated by workers reporting studies, strict adherence to them allows comparisons between studies that are otherwise impossible.

STUDIES OF GROUPS OF PATIENTS

The analysis of groups of patients to find their characteristics was apparently begun by Esquirol about 1830, when he found a need to know what sort of people he was taking care of in his hospital. Studies of this sort are generally based on data gathered for official administrative reports, although more recently some have been done primarily for scientific purposes. Malzberg in New York and Dayton in Massachusetts have been most influential in the early period, and Kramer et al. represent more recent studies. The earlier types of studies are conveniently gathered in the books by Landis and Page and by Dayton, and in Malzberg's numerous papers and books.

These studies have brought out such facts as the very high rate for senile psychosis in the seventh, eighth, and ninth decades of life; the variation in risk of the two sexes in the different mental illnesses; and the differences in rates of illnesses of various sorts in groups when analyzed by national origin, race, and so on.

Data on hospitalized patients have also been used to attempt to answer the question of whether the mental illnesses are increasing or decreasing in populations. For the most part, the results remain equivocal. Goldhamer and Marshall were, however, able to present data extending over the century from 1840 to 1940 and reached the conclusion that there had been no increase in severe mental illnesses in the young adult age group during that period. Their data suggest that there may have been an increase in psychoses of the senium, though they were unable to separate disease from social factors influencing hospitalization in this group to their own satisfaction.

Kramer introduced studies of cohorts of patients into psychiatric epidemiology. Patients of a particular age group are admitted during a particular period selected, and their fate over a period of years is determined. He has shown the outstanding differences in mental hospital retention rates for different mental illnesses and, perhaps more than any other worker, has demonstrated that there is a high rate of turnover of patients in psychiatric hospitals, even though there is at the same time a large residual population in which there is minimal movement.

Bahn, Gorwitz, and Miles have recently added statistics regarding outpatient services to those on inpatients. Thus far, the data indicate that services vary in amount furnished to various segments of the population, with the elderly and those of the lower social status groups receiving disproportionately low amounts of service. As the data collection methods mature, firmer and more detailed conclusions will undoubtedly be reached.

Hollingshead and Redlich have studied the type and amount of psychiatric service available to persons of various socioeconomic groups. Their data tend to show that psychotherapy is offered far more often to more advantaged groups and that the low socioeconomic groups tend to be treated by means of physical methods—electroshock, drugs, and other forms of direct management. Furman, Sweat, and Crocetti found similar relationships in a study of outpatient services. Jaco, in a study of treatment practices in Texas, reached somewhat similar conclusions and dealt also with differences in availability of treatment in different racial groups —the "Anglos," the Spanish Americans, and the Negroes of that society.

Psychiatric register. Material on inpatients and outpatients is presently being combined by means of a new technical device, the psychiatric register. It will not only allow much more prompt and accurate reporting of a far larger variety of cases receiving services by a variety of service units but will also allow, for the first time, the study of the psychiatric management of behavior disorders over long periods of time. This will solve one of the most vexing problems of longitudinal studies—the Scylla of the danger of retrospective studies being influenced by the state of the patient when the study is made and the Charybdis of having to wait a very long time to see how cases mature. Although a relatively small amount of data can be preserved for each patient at each contact with a service, the register can be used as an index to existing case histories. With computer techniques, information can be very quickly analyzed and groups compared in an almost infinite variety of ways. The register technique will greatly facilitate some kinds of epidemiological research in the future.

The pattern on which registers are being developed has come to a considerable extent from the United Kingdom, where Brooke et al. have exploited the National Health Service's statistical data. Their interest has been, to a considerable extent, administrative. It is from their work that the United Kingdom projects a rate of psychiatric hospital beds of 1.8 per 1,000 for the future.

Lin's exhaustive and thorough studies in Taiwan have provided data for his review of psychiatric epidemiology, from which he concluded that approximately 1 per cent of populations are actively psychotic but that beds need be provided, at least in developing countries, for only one-tenth of these. These figures stand in contrast to those of Pasamanick and Lemkau, who found approximately 10 per cent of the population seriously impaired by psychiatric symptoms at any one time.

STUDIES BASED ON SYMPTOM-RECORDING BY PATIENTS

Alexander Leighton et al. conducted studies in a semirural agricultural, lumbering, and fishing area known as Stirling County. Thomas Rennie et al. conducted similar studies in a defined area on the east side of Manhattan. In both studies, although the methods were different in detail, the basis of the data was interviews with a relatively small sample of the total population. Questions asked were usually designed to ascertain whether or not patients had symptoms that might be regarded as psychiatric or psychosomatic. The interviews were scored by psychiatrists as to whether or not the patient was ill and to what extent illness impaired his functioning.

In general, the Leighton group exercised somewhat greater care in the scoring process than did the New York group. In neither study was any attempt made to establish specific psychiatric diagnoses.

Both studies reported high rates of symptoms in their populations, and the results of the two are so nearly alike that they can be presented together for the purpose here. Overall, both found about 30 per cent of the population to be rather seriously bothered by symptoms, another 30 per cent to be moderately symptomatic, and about 25 per cent to have mild and relatively inconsequential symptoms. Around 15 per cent were found to be symptom-free. The severity and extent of symptoms were found to vary among different groups within the population.

Neither study implies that the presence of symptoms indicates a disorder. However, both suggest that, of the three groups of symptomatic persons found, the group with the largest number of symptoms would undoubtedly receive a diagnosis of mental disorder if seen by a psychiatrist, with the probability decreasing as the frequency and severity of symptoms become less.

Leighton has used the presence of symptoms not as an indicator of psychiatric disease but rather as an index of the reciprocal of a state of health; that is, the fewer the number of symptomatic people, the healthier the population is. He then hypothesized that there is a relationship between the health of a population and the type of life in the communities in which it lives. Upon investigation of the communities his people came from, he found a number of parameters on which they could be graded, including the extent of social organization. He found that communities with a low state of organization—few and badly supported school and church groups, for example—tended to produce higher rates of symptomatic people than did communities that were well-organized. This technique has also been applied by the Leighton group to an African society, the Yoruba. The findings appear to support the hypothesis.

The Leighton group is now embarking on an experiment to test whether it is possible to change the pattern of social organization of some of the communities studied and whether, when such changes are accomplished, the rates for frequency and severity of symptoms fall. It is clear that these studies are of critical importance to the whole structure of the theory of sociodynamics in psychiatric illness. They open the way for the testing of a great many hypotheses presently being acted on rather uncritically—such as the relationship between psychiatric illness and industrialization, poverty, mobility, and education. They have not yielded significant results in previous investigations because sampling tended to be warped very strongly by differential availability of service.

REFERENCES

Bahn, A. K. *Outpatient Population of Psychiatric Clinics, Maryland 1958–1959*, Public Health Monograph No. 65, 1961.

Bremer, J. A social psychiatric investigation of a small community in Northern Norway. Acta Psychiat. Neurol., Suppl. 62, 1951.

Brooke, E. M. Factors affecting the demand for psychiatric beds. Lancet, 2: 1211, 1962.

Brugger, C. Psychiatrisch-genealogische Untersuchungen an einer Allgauer Landbevolkerung. Z. Ges. Neurol. Psychiat., 145: 516, 1933.

Dayton, N. A. *New Facts on Mental Disorders*. Charles C Thomas, Springfield, Ill., 1940.

Dubos, R. J. Molecules, social systems and dermatology. J. Invest. Derm., 33: 227, 1962.

Eaton, J. W., and Weil, R. J. *Culture and Mental Disorders*. The Free Press of Glencoe (Macmillan), New York, 1955.

Fairbank, R. E., and Cohen, B. M. Statistical contributions from the Mental Hygiene Study of the Eastern Health District of Baltimore. I. General account of the 1933 Mental Hygiene Survey of the Eastern Health District. Amer. J. Psychiat., 94: 1153, 1938. II. Psychosis in the Eastern Health District. Amer. J. Psychiat., 94: 1377, 1938. III. Personality disorder in the Eastern Health District in 1933 (with Elizabeth Green). Hum. Biol., 11: 112, 1939. IV. Further studies on personality disorder in the Eastern Health District in 1933 (with Elizabeth Green). Hum. Biol., 11: 485, 1939.

Furman, S. S., Sweat, L. G., and Crocetti, G. M. Social class factors in the flow of children to outpatient psychiatric facilities. Amer. J. Public Health, 55: 385, 1965.

Gardner, E. A., Miles, H. C., Bahn, A. K., and Ramano, J. All psychiatric experience in a community. A cumulative survey: report of the first year's experience. Arch. Gen. Psychiat., 9: 369, 1963.

Goldhamer, H., and Marshall, A. W. *Psychosis and Civilization*. Free Press of Glencoe (Macmillan), New York, 1949.

Gruenberg, E. M. A mental health survey of older persons. In *Comparative Epidemiology of the Mental Disorders*, P. H. Hoch and J. Zubin, editors. Grune & Stratton, New York, 1961.

Gruenberg, E. M., Goodman, M. B., Downing, J. J., and Rogot, E. A prevalence study of mental retardation in a metropolitan area. Amer. J. Public Health, 46: 702, 1956.

Hollingshead, A. and Redlich, F. C. *Social Class and Mental Illness*. Wiley, New York, 1958.

Jaco, E. G. *The Social Epidemiology of Mental Disorders*. Russell Sage Foundation, New York, 1960.

Jastak, J. F., and Whiteman, M. *The Prevalence of Mental Retardation in Delaware: The Nature and Transmission of the Genetic and Cultural Characteristics of Human Populations*. Milbank Memorial Fund, New York, 1957.

Kallmann, F. J. *Heredity in Health and Mental Disorder*. W. W. Norton, New York, 1953.

Kramer, M., Goldstein, H., Israel, R. H., and Johnson, N. A. *An Historical Study of Dispositions of First Admissions to a State Mental Hospital: The Experience of Warren State Hospital During the Period 1916–50*. Public Health Monograph No. 32, 1955.

Landis, C., and Page, J. D. *Modern Society and Mental Disease*. Farrar & Rinehart, New York, 1938.

Leighton, A. H., Lambo, T. A., Hughes, C. C., Leighton, D. C., Murphy, J. M., and Macklin. D. M. *Psychiatric Disorders Among the Yoruba.* Cornell University Press, Ithaca, 1963.

Leighton, D. C., Harding, J. S., Macklin, D. B., Macmillan, A. M., and Leighton, A. H. *The Character of Danger.* Basic Books, New York, 1963.

Lemkau, P., Tietze, C., and Cooper, M. Mental hygiene problems in an urban district. I. Description of the study. Ment. Hyg., 25: 624, 1941. II. Psychotics, the neurotics. Ment. Hyg., 26: 100, 1942. III. The epileptics and mental deficients. Ment. Hyg., 26: 275, 1942. IV. Mental hygiene problems in children seven to sixteen years of age. Ment. Hyg., 27: 279, 1943.

Lewis, E. O. *Epidemiological Aspects of Mental Deficiency, Being a Joint Committee of the Board of Education and the Board of Control. Parts I, II, III, IV.* H. M. Stationery Office, London, 1929.

Lin, T., and Standley, C. C. *The Scope of Epidemiology in Psychiatry.* World Health Organization, Geneva, 1962.

Lorr, M., O'Connor, J. P., and Stafford, S. W. Confirmation of nine psychotic symptom patterns. J. Clin. Psychol., 13: 252, 1957.

Luxenberger, H. Demographische und psychiatrische Untersuchungen in der engeren biologischen Familie von Paralytikerehegatten. Z. Ges. Neurol. Psychiat., 112: 331, 1928.

Malzberg, B. *Social and Biological Aspects of Mental Disease.* State Hospitals Press, Utica, N. Y., 1940.

Ødegaard, O. Emigration and mental health. Ment. Hyg., 20: 546, 1936.

Pasamanick, B., Roberts, D. W., Lemkau, P. V., and Krueger, D. C. A survey of mental disease in an urban population. Amer. J. Public Health, 47: 923, 1957.

Reid, D. D. *Epidemiological Methods in the Study of Mental Disorders.* World Health Organization, Geneva, 1960.

Rennie, T. A. C., Srole, L., Michael, S. T., Langner, T. S., and Opler, M. K. *Mental Health in the Metropolis: The Midtown Manhattan Study.* Blakiston (McGraw-Hill), New York, 1962.

Sargant, W. *Battle for the Mind.* Doubleday, Garden City, N. Y., 1957.

Schuler, E. A., and Parenton, V. J. A recent epidemic of hysteria in a Louisiana high school. J. Soc. Psychol., 17: 221, 1943.

Strömgren, E. Social surveys. J. Ment. Sci., 64: 266, 1948.

CHAPTER 22

Computers and Psychiatry

MAX FINK, M.D.

INTRODUCTION

DESPITE THE NOVELTY, complexity, and expense of modern high-speed computers, numerous applications have been developed in psychiatric research, teaching, and even clinical practice. An impetus for this interest rises from the increasing application of quantitative analytic methods in medical and biological investigations. Quantification has supplemented clinical impression and has stimulated increasing use of systematic tests of significance. The demand in computer usage for explicit instructions has forced physicians to increase the precision of their data and to prepare them in standardized, easily retrievable forms.

Applications of specific psychiatric interest are in information processing, data analysis and statistical operations, studies of language and the simulation of interviews, and model-testing. General applications of computers with relevance to psychiatry are in information retrieval and dissemination, automated clinical laboratory testing, and hospital and financial record-keeping.

Many of the present-day applications of electronic computers to psychiatric problems are extensions of techniques developed in other fields. As their use has been made more practical and shown to be related to psychiatric practice, the applications have rapidly increased. Some of the more-promising directions are listed here, but the most rewarding aspect of the use of computers in psychiatry is in the need for the scientist to modify his mode of thinking. The clinical impression is augmented by definitions of terms, by measurement, and by quantification. Processes as well as terms require exact definition, and computers are catalyzing a change in attitude from an impressionistic art to a quantitative science. Although little that is novel in modern psychiatry has yet been ascribed to computers, their use and the opportunities they represent herald significant changes in the clinical practice of psychiatry during the next score of years.

DESCRIPTION OF COMPUTERS

Computers are direct descendants of rapid calculating devices, with the additional facility for sequential operations (programing) and for retention of intermediate outputs (memory), thereby extending the range of possible calculations.

TYPES OF COMPUTERS

Modern computers are electronic instruments capable of performing numerical and logical operations. These are usually classed as analog, digital, or hybrid. Analog computers use physical, electrical, or mechanical models corresponding to some aspect of the original object for measurement or calculation. Digital computers perform operations on numeric representations of objects. Hybrid computers perform operations in both analog and digital modes.

In the application of digital computers, the operations may be controlled by program instructions stored in the console. Programs are sequential machine instructions written in special languages detailing each logical step of the required operations. The languages vary for each machine, and among the most common are Fortran, Cobol, and Algol. The operations are carried out with speed and accuracy and without fatigue. It is the combination of memory, variety of instructions, speed, accuracy, an indefatigability that provides the basis for the many and varied applications of digital computers.

HARDWARE

Configurations of digital computers include a central processor, a memory, and input and output devices. The central processor is the control instrument for all operations. The memory stores both instructions and data and may be core (directly accessible to the processor for operations) or peripheral (indirectly accessible), as in magnetic tapes and random-access disks.

Input devices—punch card and mark-sense card readers, punch-paper tape, magnetic tape, or typewriter—bring data and instructions into the processor. Output devices express the results of operations, and these may be either intermediate or final. Intermediate outputs include magnetic and punch-paper tape, punch cards, disks, and digital oscilloscopes. Final output devices are printers, typewriters, plotters, and photographic cameras.

Data for digital computers may be derived from input devices located at the computer center or from devices at remote locations with communication from the input device to the processor by telephone networks. Data may also be provided from specialized input devices, such as analog-to-digital converters, optical page readers, light pens, and digital oscilloscopes. The multiplicity of input devices is increasing rapidly, and many new devices have greatly extended the range of applications to psychiatry.

Computer hardware may also be classified as to location—within a single laboratory and devoted primarily to one application or centralized for many users. Laboratory computers are frequently small, highly specialized in their input-output modes, and hybrid. Their operations are often defined by the structural configuration of the instrument. The operations are usually modified by switches and dials in the console. These computers are operated by the individual investigator with short intervals (minutes to hours) between data collection and data processing. These include the average response computers, the LINC (Laboratory Instrument Computer), and the small, general-purpose computers located within one laboratory as in the studies of electroencephalographic (EEG) quantification using an IBM 1710–1620 system.

Centralized units are often large and varied in their peripheral components and usually operate in batch mode—that is, various programs for different investigators are serviced sequentially. In such units the time between data collection and data processing is apt to be long, perhaps days to weeks.

The varieties of equipment or hardware are great, but recent electronic developments in transistors, integrated circuits, and modular design have made the capacity and characteristics of the equipment of different manufacturers very similar.

SOFTWARE

The great range of computer operations depends largely on the programs that are written, the software, rather than the type of computer. The sequential instructions that must be written accurately and in complete detail and the facility and flexibility of the machine languages are the heart of every computer operation. As almost any design or picture can be printed or reproduced on film by combining many dots of different colors, so almost any set of mathematical or logical operations can be reproduced by combinations of program instructions in a digital computer. The limits of the operations are defined by the imagination of the scientist in picturing the problem, the ability of the programer to translate these visions into instructions, and the capacity of the memory of the machines. It is in these instructions, the programs, that the greatest energies and bottlenecks are now found.

APPLICATIONS IN PSYCHIATRY

STATISTICAL STUDIES

The early extensive use of electronic computers has been in statistical calculations and demographic studies. With their high speed and large memory for intermediate calculations and for complex programs, computers have made possible the general application of multivariate statistics. In demographic studies, the need for adequate definitions of illness, symptoms, and psychopathological signs has led to studies of psychiatric terms, classifications of illnesses, and an enhanced interest in symptom-rating scales. The data of population studies lend themselves to simple statistical tests.

It is in clinical trials and in the development of psychiatric typologies that the computer has had signal applications. The rapid success of clinical psychopharmacology in the treatment of psychosis stimulated interest in the early verification of clinical claims. Scientists examined the prevailing methods for therapy evaluation and found them based largely on unverified, unquantified, and uncontrolled clinical impressions. Concepts of target symptoms and psychopathological profiles were suggested to supplant general clinical descriptions. Double-blind trials, placebo controls, and random assignment of populations laid the basis for more sophisticated statistical techniques for evaluation of results and the definition of predictors. In this environment, computer techniques have been most useful in statistical t-tests; covariance and variance analyses; discriminant and canonical functions; and cluster, profile, and factor analyses. These techniques have been applied usefully in determination of the relative therapeutic efficacy of specified drugs for defined populations in interhospital collaborative studies; in the identification of drug-responsive and non-drug-responsive psychopathological symptoms; and in the development of rating scales with therapy-responsive items.

Other applications of these demographic and statistical approaches are seen in the classification of subpopulations of the mentally ill, in the training of staff members in identification of clinical symptoms, and in the trials of cluster analysis in the diagnosis of mental illnesses. Many studies of the diagnostic process in clinical medicine are providing the experience in programing for application to clinical psychiatry.

INFORMATION PROCESSING

The facility of electronic devices to transmit, shuffle (reorder), and retrieve information is great. With bulk-storage memory devices, computers scan large amounts of data, select specific examples, process sequential operations, and transmit the results rapidly. Specific applications are found in the maintenance of patient records, documentation of interview data, demographic summaries, retrieval and selective dissemination of information, and establishment of laboratory standards.

Behavioral records. Essential to the evaluation of behavioral change in patients are descriptions by staff, family, and the patients themselves. Such descriptions are generally narrative in form and are read only with difficulty. They are frequently incomplete. Various digital applications have been developed to improve this type of data collection.

Questionnaires and rating scales are widely used. The items are scored on prepared forms, and the scores are transferred to Hollerith (key punch) cards; or the items may be printed on prepared key-punched cards, and the rater simply places the individual cards into sorting bins. The clusters of cards in each bin are then scored by computer methods.

Rating scales may be completed by the examining physician, nurse, aide, or social worker; or there may be self-ratings by the patient. Many different scales have been developed, including those for the classification of the mentally ill, the evaluation of psychopathology in schizophrenia and depression, and the identification of elements of the mental status responding to treatment or useful as predictors of treatment response.

Measures of change. With many different scales as inputs, computer operations are as varied as the investigators. The items and individual scores may be sorted and listed, or the cards may be used to determine score means before and after treatment. Changes in nonhomogeneous groups may be determined by covariance and variance analyses, or more complex multivariate statistics may be used to measure score changes with various treatments. Items have been studied by factor analytic and clustering techniques to determine which elements of psychopathology vary together. Populations have been identified by the similarity of their ratings, and much recent study has been devoted to identifying the subgroups of depression and of schizophrenia.

It has become possible to bypass the stage of key-punching by the use of special rating forms that are read directly by an optical page reader and that reproduce the data in machine-assimilable form (see Figure 1, for example). Such rating scales have been translated into multiple languages, and the results of the analyses have been provided in the original language of the form and in other languages for which translation programs have been written. Such instruments have recently found special utility in international collaborative evaluation studies.

In another application, an essay type of description of a patient has been produced from his responses to a self-rating inquiry form. Such machine-programed essay reports and their questionnaires have also been translated into different formats to provide essay descriptions of the history and mental status in different languages.

Ward management. Hospital nurses' ratings, describing each patient's status each day, are completed on the ward and are immediately transferred to the computer console. Programs are of two types—comparison of the items with the patient's own record and averaging the data for the patients in one ward unit. By defining limits for changes in specified items, a computer program can rapidly determine if the patient has changed from earlier reports or, for group data, if the ward has undergone a change in scores for such items of interest as excitement, depression, or episodic impulsivity.

In another hospital application, doctors' orders, nurses' notes, measures of patient change, and laboratory data are transferred to the computer from peripheral and remote input-output units located on the wards. As

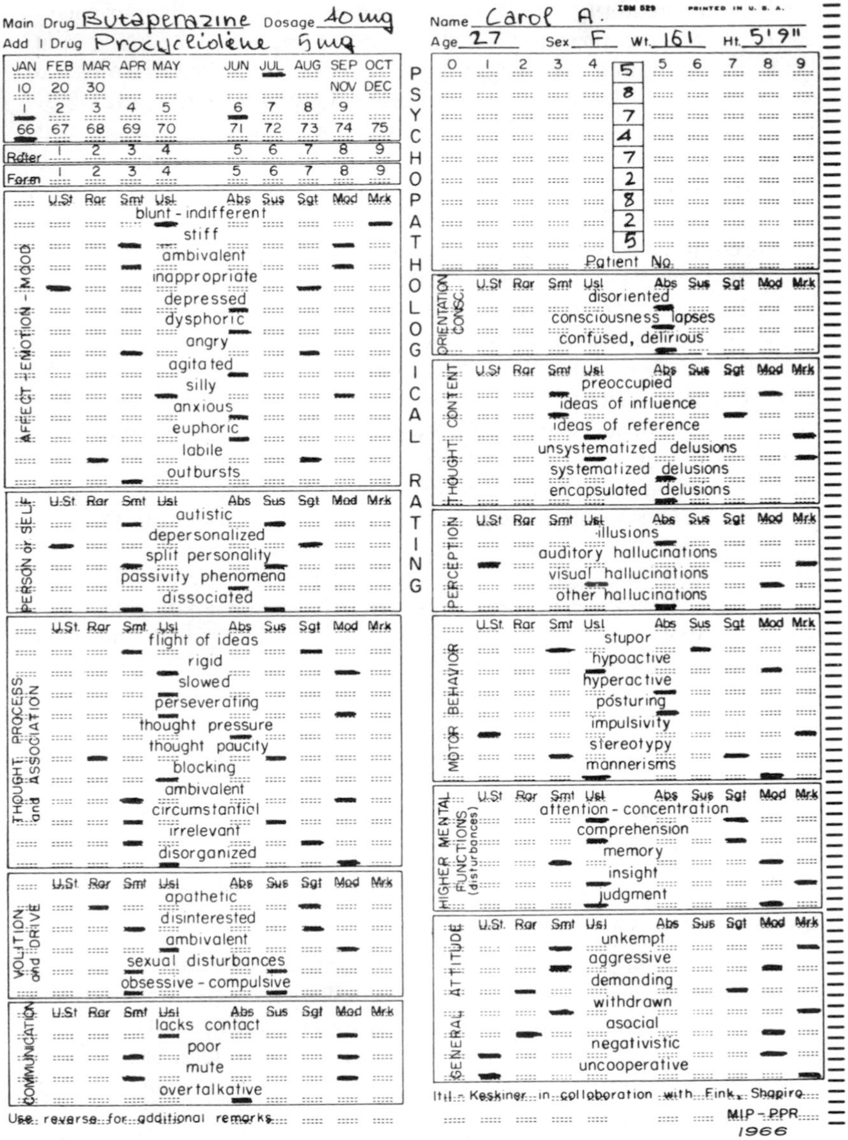

FIGURE 1. Psychopathology rating form, prepared for optical page reading. Items are rated by the examiner for incidence (rarely, sometimes, usually, only under stress) and for severity (absent, suspicious, slight, moderate, and marked). The form is completed as used in a case of hebephrenic schizophrenia. (With permission of M. Fink, T. Itil, A. Keskiner, and D. Shapiro, University of Missouri.)

the data are entered, each item is checked against established standards, providing a monitoring of doctors' orders and checking their accuracy, flagging nurses and pharmacy for the necessary supplies, scheduling treatment administration, and maintaining financial and supply records. An even more specialized use is in monitoring the physiological state of the patient and notifying the physician and the nurse when the measurements exceed predetermined limits, thus requiring immediate attention.

Information retrieval. The proliferation of large numbers of reports and studies is a special burden for the active scientist. Abstracting services have been available for decades, but only in the past few years have the storage capacity and rapid review of digital computers made large-scale retrieval and dissemination systems plausible. Present information systems use documents identified by descriptors—either allotted by specialists or derived naturally by computer programs from title, abstract, and text. Retrieval follows a scientist's inquiry for those descriptors of interest to him that have been included in the memory of the system. In the dissemination problem, the scientist is notified or sent a copy of each article that comes into the system bearing descriptors included in his individual profile of interests. These systems are, unfortunately, still unsophisticated and expensive.

With the recording and storage of psychiatrically relevant data, numerous special studies have been proposed. The demographic characteristics of populations and subpopulations may be readily defined, and members of subgroups of the mentally ill can be identified for specialized studies.

As sequential clinical studies develop large banks of data for each subject, summaries of the range and variability of individual test data provide standards specifically relevant to the subpopulations investigated. Such standards have recently been defined for the clinical laboratory test data in placebo-treated patients as comparisons for those treated with novel psychoactive drugs.

ANALOG SIGNAL ANALYSES

Changes in physiological indices are important in the study of emotions and ideation. Blood pressure, heart rate, pupillary size, and the electroencephalogram are continuously changing measures. Determination of their value requires the division of the signal into discrete samples. Such conversion from a continuous analog signal to a digital value is done by direct measurement by hand or by electronic devices.

The electronic analog-to-digital converters are voltage-measuring instruments, and any signal that is naturally electrical—EEG, electrocardiogram (ECG)—or convertible to an electrical measure—galvanic skin response, heart rate—can be sampled and its value determined. The rate of sampling is selected to provide as accurate an index of the rate of change as required by the problem. The converted signals provide the basis for subsequent analyses. Computer programs have been developed for a variety of analog signals of psychiatric interest. Thus, for the ECG, programs for pattern recognition and for frequency and variability of heart rate are available. For the EEG, many measures have been programed, including amplitude and amplitude variability, frequency and frequency variability, power spectral density and pattern (see Figure 2).

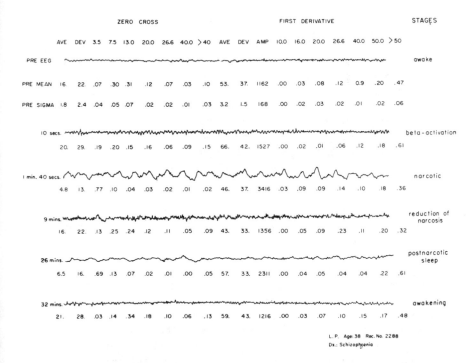

FIGURE 2. Digital computer analysis of electroencephalogram. Output of baseline, first derivative and amplitude analysis using period analysis program. Samples of EEG and measures during narcosis (intravenous Thiopental, 4 mg. per kilogram per 2 min.). Subject was a 38-year-old schizophrenic. Zero cross-bands are average (AVE), variability of average (DEV), and seven frequency bands. First derivative bands are average (AVE), variability (DEV), amplitude (AMP), and seven frequency bands. AVE and DEV in cycles a second; bands in percentage of time of sample; amplitude in units relative to calibration. Sampling rate, 320 samples a second; 30-second epochs. (Courtesy of M. Fink.)

The converted signals and their analyses provide numerical data that may be further analyzed by statistical methods. These measures have found special applications in psychopharmacology, where the EEG changes induced by psychoactive drugs have been related to the clinical efficacy of the compounds and to the type of behavioral response. The quantitative EEG measures have been suggested as a device for screening and classifying psychotropic drugs, for classifying psychiatric patients, and for measuring dose-response curves.

Such measures have recently had extensive application in the automatic classification of sleep stages and the determination of differences in sleep patterns in mental illnesses and in response to psychoactive drugs.

A special computer application in psychophysiology has been the averaging of cortical responses evoked by sensory stimuli. Such measures have been related to the psychological mechanisms of attention and anticipation and have been studied as a means of classifying the mentally ill.

These are specific applications to psychiatry today, and the instruments are also receiving extensive use in the analysis of models of neural functions, including the operations of nerve nets, firing patterns, and the interrelations of different cerebral structures. The simulation possibilities and large memory functions are useful in testing proposed models of cerebral activity and in testing neural analogs of such epistemological processes as perception, learning, calculation, and cognition. Such models of information processing are subsumed by the term "perceptrons."

AUTOMATIC PERSONALITY ASSESSMENT

The need for a rapid and concise personality description in clinical medicine and interest in psychological tests prompted various studies of digital computer uses. The Minnesota Multiphasic Personality Inventory was selected for study, for it is a simple, "yes-no" response inventory with extensive trial as a personality measure. Its simplicity and the availability of a set of defined rules for interpretation based on configural analysis of the responses led to the preparation of a mark-sense self-scoring form for use by patients. The programs developed included those for machine keypunching and the analysis of responses, and for the production of a clinical report both as numerical scores for each scale and in a simplified narrative personality description. Similar systems for the Clyde Mood Scale and Glueck Q-Sort have also been developed.

In the analysis of other psychological tests, the problems are more formidable, since operational rules for interpretation are not available. For example, in the Rorschach test, programs for the narrative interpretation of previously scored data have been described but are of limited application.

The on-line analysis of reaction-time performance tasks is yet another computer application to experimental psychology. An advantage of on-line analysis is the modification in the rate or type of stimulus presented as the responses of the subject are analyzed in real time. Concurrent analysis of the EEG provides a measure of a neurophysiological response varying with the changes in performance.

PSYCHOLINGUISTICS

Among the numerous problems of interest to language specialists for which computer methods have been programed are those of automatic translation, the development of dictionaries and concordances, automatic indexing and abstracting, and the rules of natural languages. These studies have engendered special programing languages that allow the manipulation of words as symbols according to rules that parallel the manipulations of alphanumeric symbols.

For the past two decades, the use of magnetic tape recorders of high fidelity has permitted the recording of psychiatric interviews for study. Some students have developed specialized instruments to study the formal aspects of dyadic interaction as the rate of speech, time of utterances, and pause length; others have depended on highly accurate transcriptions. These have been studied both for such formal aspects as variations in person and tense and for the more common interpretation of content. An interesting application has been the measurement of the dyadic type-token ratio (TTR)—an index of variability and repetitiveness in speech. The TTR has been shown to vary with mood and in response to the administration of psychoactive drugs.

Content analyses, although tedious and still highly subjective, provide a useful test of changes in therapist-patient interaction in psychotherapy. The need for validation and demonstration studies in psychotherapy is great, and much effort is expended in studies of the application of statistical methods to linguistic data.

A special application has been in the simulation of interviews. In an elementary form, the computer asks questions, and the patient enters responses into the console by means of a typewriter. As programs become more sophisticated, the computer's responses simulate the responses of the therapist. In addition to some practical demonstrations and their use as teaching devices, such programs are receiving intensive study to develop rules for various types of verbal interchange, including psychotherapy.

REFERENCES

Borko, H., editor. *Computer Applications in the Behavioral Sciences*. Prentice-Hall, Englewood Cliffs, N. J., 1962.

Brazier, M. A. B., editor. Computer techniques in EEG analysis. Electroenceph. Clin. Neurophysiol., 20: (Suppl.) 1961.

Pollack, S. V., and Sterling, T. D., editors. *Computers in the Life Sciences*. Columbia University Press, New York, 1966.

Siler, W., and Sterling, T., editors. Advances in biomedical computer applications. Ann. N. Y. Acad. Sci., 128: 721, 1966.

Stacy, R. W., and Waxman, B., editors. *Computers in Biomedical Research*, 2 vols. Academic Press, New York, 1965.

Whipple, H. E., editor. Computers in medicine and biology. Ann. N. Y. Acad. Sci., 115: 543, 1964.

CHAPTER 23

Experimental Neurosis

CHARLES SHAGASS, M.D.

INTRODUCTION

EXPERIMENTAL PSYCHOPATHOLOGY attempts to investigate abnormal behavior systematically under conditions that are more or less known or controlled. Controlling conditions may be introduced in many ways, such as manipulating the physical or psychological aspects of the environment, giving drugs, or ablating tissues by surgery. We shall here deal mainly with states produced by psychological forms of experimental manipulation.

Psychiatry's most urgent need is for new information about the chronic functional disorders—neuroses, personality disorders, psychoses, and psychophysiologic reactions. With the possible exception of psychophysiological reactions, the symptomatic manifestations of these disorders in man are of such complexity that they cannot be reproduced in convincing detail in any other species. In studies with animal subjects, the investigator is limited to detection of behavioral changes that *appear* similar to those occurring in human disorders. His goal is to derive laws governing the animal behavior that are applicable to man in an explanatory or predictive manner. The obvious advantage of animal experiments is that they can use procedures not permissible in humans. Even though experimentation in man promises a more convincing identification of the experimental and natural abnormal conditions, it is ethically restricted to induction of acute and reversible psychopathological states. Since the duration of mental disorders may be of crucial importance in determining their manifestations, the relevance of most human experiments is also open to question. Workers in the field of experimental psychopathology must accept these limitations, and those who study their findings must be aware of them.

EXPERIMENTAL NEUROSES IN ANIMALS

ABNORMAL ANIMAL BEHAVIOR

Criteria of abnormality may be defined in many ways, and no attempt is made here to distinguish between neurosis and psychosis in the discussion of abnormal behavioral states in animals. Although some manifestations—waxy flexibility, for example—may appear to fall more clearly into one category than the other, there are no certain criteria for making the distinction.

From a psychiatric point of view, Hebb's approach seems highly relevant. Hebb begins by defining human neurosis in behavioral terms, without use of verbal report of the subjective state, so that the definition can be used at the animal level. He distinguishes between *neurotic behavior* and *neurosis*. The former constitutes the signs of neurosis, the means by which it is recognized; the latter is the concept of a central state. Proceeding in this way. Hebb's definition is: "Neurosis is in practice an undesirable emotional condition which is generalized and persistent; it occurs in a minority of the population and has no origin in a gross neural lesion." The six essential elements in this definition are as follows: (1) undesirable, evaluationally abnormal; (2) emotional, involving emotion activity; (3) generalized, implies manifestation in a number of ways; (4) persistent, chronic to some degree; (5) occurring in a minority of the population, statistically abnormal; and (6) having no origin in a gross neural lesion.

Hebb lists three additional criteria that seem invalid to him but that have had some influence in determining what is called neurosis: (1) neurosis has no physiological basis; (2) it produces a marked change of behavior from an earlier baseline; and (3) it follows some theoretically traumatic experience, such as conflict or frustration. He regards these criteria as "not essentially true." For example, to reject physiological causes of neurosis is to deny the possibility of anything but a psychological cause. It is conceivable that neurosis may be of life-long duration, thus rendering the second criterion unessential. The third is considered unessential from the fact that neurotic behavior can result from nutritional or metabolic processes.

In his paper Hebb described spontaneously occurring neuroses in two chimpanzees that appeared to meet his criteria.

PAVLOV AND HIS SCHOOL

The term "experimental neurosis" was introduced by the great Russian physiologist, Pavlov, to describe abnormal behavior of a more or less chronic nature that is produced experimentally.

The best-known of Pavlov's experimental neuroses occurred in a dog that had been conditioned to differentiate between a circle associated with feeding (positive stimulus for salivation) and an ellipse not associated with feeding (negative or inhibitory stimulus). The original ratio of the semiaxes of the ellipse was 2 to 1. Further differentiation was attempted by approximating the shape of the ellipse to that of the circle. Differentiation progressed as desired until an ellipse with 9 to 8 semiaxes was used. After three weeks of training with this ratio, the discrimination failed to improve and even became considerably worse, finally disappearing altogether.

Simultaneously, the general behavior of the animal changed abruptly. The previously quiet dog began to squeal in its stand, he kept wriggling about, with his teeth he tore off the apparatus attached to his skin, and he bit through tubes connecting his room with the observer's room. This behavior had never previously occurred. Also new was the violent barking of the dog on being taken into the experimental room. Pavlov interpreted the behavioral changes as symptoms of acute neurosis.

Pavlov formulated three possible causes for experimental neurosis. (1) Excessive stimulation of inhibitory processes. This occurred in the experiment just described. (2) Overstrain of the excitatory process by extraordinarily strong or unusual stimuli. This is illustrated by the natural experiment occasioned by the Leningrad flood of 1924. All the animals had to swim for their lives through a storm. All their conditioned reflexes disappeared, and one of them developed a chronic neurotic condition. (3) Conflict between cortical inhibitory and excitatory processes. This mechanism is described in a dog that was able to discriminate between a positive tactile stimulus at the rate of twenty-four a minute and a negative one at the rate of twelve a minute. When one type of stimulus followed the other without a pause, the animal developed signs of a neurosis that lasted several weeks.

Pavlov's recognition of the potential significance of these observations for understanding abnormal human behavior was to have a profound influence on the focus of investigation in his own laboratory and in conditioning laboratories elsewhere. However, Broadhurst, who recently attempted to evaluate the Russian research in the light of Hebb's criteria, was forced to conclude that the Russian findings provided insufficient information about the responses of the animal outside the experimental chamber. Because of this, the results on experimental neurosis originating in Pavlov's laboratory do not convincingly meet Hebb's criterion of generalization of the abnormal behavior. It is also not clear that the behavior was statistically abnormal.

GANTT AND HIS SCHOOL

The Pavlovian laboratory at The Johns Hopkins Medical School, directed by W. Horsley Gantt, has been a principal American contributor to the study of experimental neurosis. An outstanding feature of the work is the provision of detailed case histories.

Case history of Nick. One mongrel dog, Nick, was studied for twelve years. In 1932 he was about three years old, active and playful. He appeared normal then but was more restless than most dogs during adaptation to feeding in the experimental room and slow in showing conditioned salivary response. When auditory differentiation was introduced (learning to respond to one tone and not to another), he refused food and showed a defense reaction. A rest restored food acceptance, but with an increase in difficulty of the discrimination, he again refused food and continued to do so in the laboratory for most of his life.

In the next year, all conditioned responses failed, and Nick ate more readily the farther he was away from the experimental room. In the room he showed a stereotyped restlessness whenever he was released from the apparatus. He rushed about, jumped up on the table and off it again, fumbled the uneaten food in his mouth and dropped it.

As time went on, fresh abnormalities were observed. Disturbed respiration took the form of loud, forced breathing whenever he was excited, especially when approaching the experimental room or people connected with the experiment. Gantt repeatedly noted that Nick was friendlier toward strangers than toward anyone associated with the experiment.

From the end of 1936, Nick began urinating when brought to the experimental room, with a frequency as high as twenty-five times in thirty minutes. This could not be inhibited by punishment. Concurrently, abnormal sexual excitation, as judged by penile erection, was observed during conditioning stimulation. These persistent sexual erections contrasted with the occasional short erections normally seen in young male dogs. It is noteworthy that both the urinary and sexual abnormalities occurred after a bitch in estrus had been used in the experimental situation in order to test the effect of normal sexual excitation on Nick's other abnormal signs.

Gantt observed wide generalization outside the experimental situation. He kept Nick on his farm in the country and found that the particular food given as reinforcement in the experimental situation was consistently refused there and that the signs of sexual erection, frequent urination, disturbed respiration, and a marked increase in heart rate were sometimes observed when people associated with the experiment or even members of their families approached the animal.

In relation to Hebb's criteria, Nick's behavior was frequently undesirable—for example, his refusal of food when hungry. It was markedly emotional, judging by overt signs. An autopsy report showed that he had no gross neural lesions. The persistence of the behavior pattern was strikingly well established, as was the generalization of the behavior to situations other than the experimental. The question of statistical abnormality is difficult to assess.

Schizokinesis and autokinesis. Gantt has introduced two fundamental theoretical concepts: schizokinesis and autokinesis.

Schizokinesis implies a cleavage in response between the emotional and visceral systems and the skeletal musculature. The concept originated in observations suggesting that cardiac conditioned responses are formed more quickly than motor responses, are of comparatively greater intensity, and are more resistant to extinction. Gantt considers schizokinesis to be a built-in unacquired mechanism, the function of the normal organism.

Autokinesis refers to the internal development of responses on the basis of old excitations. This is seen in the spontaneous restoration of extinguished conditioned responses and the appearance of signs of experimental neurosis long after the causal conflict has been removed. For example, new symptoms arose in Nick months or years after he was removed from the stressful laboratory environment. Moreover, although occurring much later than the original stress, the new symptoms were related to that stress, as could be seen by their ready evocation by the original environment or its elements. Gantt also distinguishes between negative and positive autokinesis. The development of new symptoms in a neurotic animal is negative, whereas improvement occurring some time after a specific therapeutic procedure, such as a drug, has been administered may be considered positive.

These concepts are primarily descriptive and rather broad; however, they draw attention to phenomena that may be of considerable importance to psychopathology.

LIDDELL AND THE CORNELL GROUP

The Cornell University group, led by H. S. Liddell, succeeded in producing chronic abnormal states in several animal species, using conditioned reflex techniques. Single animals were observed for as long as twelve years.

Anderson and Parmenter described three types of procedure: (1) difficult differentiations, (2) experimental distinctions, and (3) rigid time schedules. The first procedure is similar to that used by Pavlov in the circle-ellipse differentiation. The second consists of following the positive (food) stimulus with an exceedingly long series of negative (no food) stimuli. The third involves the use of a monotonous, lengthy routine of alternating positive and negative stimuli.

Manifestations of experimental neurosis. The many manifestations of experimental neurosis included hyperirritability, tenseness, and restlessness during the experiment; inhibitory motor reactions; change in diurnal activity cycle; respiratory and cardiac changes, recorded in the barn as well as in the laboratory; changes in micturition and defecation patterns in the laboratory; social and emotional changes.

Some of these are of particular interest. The inhibitory motor reaction in some animals involved rigidity of limbs; they could be placed in various abnormal positions, reminiscent of catatonia with waxy flexibility. Motor activity was measured by a pedometer; the daily total in neurotic animals was not significantly different from normal animals, but neurotic animals showed about as much activity during the night as during the day, whereas normal animals showed little or no activity during the night. This seems parallel to insomnia in man.

With respect to social behavior, neurotic dogs and sheep exhibited shyness, tending to remain alone and lacking normal gregariousness. They went hungry when it was necessary for them to get their food from a common source. When cornered, the shy, neurotic animals became aggressive and would bite, struggle, or kick. Neurotic sheep and goats also appeared handicapped in their ability to cope with real danger. On several occasions, dogs invaded the pasture, and each time their victim was invariably one of the neurotic animals.

Causes of abnormal behavior. Liddell did not agree with Pavlov's hypothesis that the cause of the abnormal behavior is a clash between intense cortical excitations and inhibitions. He assigned considerable importance to the factor of restraint, introduced by negative conditioned stimuli, and showed that animals allowed to run at will in a maze while attempting to solve extremely difficult problems never developed disturbances. He thought the experimental neurosis was caused by the equivalent of a human conflict situation. The animal must decide whether or not to respond; if the decision is too difficult, there is a drastic change in nervous system functioning, resulting in signs of neurosis. Other workers also found that restraint facilitated neurotic disturbances in the pig, cat, and rat.

Liddell also emphasized the importance of vigilance in experimental neurosis. The trained sheep or goat had initially struggled to escape from its restraining harness but had learned to restrict its movements to a precise limited response of the foreleg to electric shock. Its autonomic functioning, however, suggested a strong emotional undertow. On one occasion, a trained sheep was placed in the harness with electrodes attached to the foreleg and kept there for the customary hour without being given the usual signals or shocks. By the end of the hour, its breathing had become labored, and the respiratory rate had risen from 41 to 135 a minute.

Observations such as these forced Liddell to conclude that the conditioned reflex described by Pavlov was not an example of ordinary learning. He saw it as an emotionally charged episode of behavior bracketed between two primitive stereotyped reactions, the vigilance reaction and the unconditioned reaction to the reinforcement of the conditioned stimulus by food, electric shock, etc. He equated the conditioned reflex with the emergency reaction in response to danger, interpreting the waiting for the stimulus as a persisting apprehensive watchfulness in the animal.

RELATION TO CRITERIA OF ABNORMALITY

How well do the results obtained by Liddell's group meet Hebb's criteria of abnormality? It seems clear that many examples of behavior were undesirable, emotional, and persistent, and there is no evidence that they may be attributed to a gross neural lesion. However, the criterion of generalization from the laboratory to other situations is not so easily met. The fact that change in pulse and respiratory rates could be recorded from the barn can be interpreted as a conditioned response to the apparatus used for measurement. The apparently decreased capacity to cope with actual danger seems more convincing, but the finding is derived from incidental and uncontrolled observation. The issue of statistical abnormality is also difficult to decide; apparently about 25 per cent of the animals developed experimental neuroses. The Cornell animal data thus approach but do not fully satisfy Hebb's criteria.

MASSERMAN'S EXPERIMENTS

Masserman's biodynamic approach is associated with a long series of experiments in which experimental behavior disturbances were produced in conditioning situations. The basic experiment requires learning to open a food box in response to a sensory signal. Various complexities were introduced into the experiments; for example, to obtain food, animals learned to press a series of switches a definite number of times in a required order or to differentiate between printed signs. The usual technique of inducing neurotic behavior in cats, dogs, or monkeys was to present a traumatically deterrent stimulus during the execution of the well-learned response. Stimuli were electric shock, a startling air blast across the food box, or, even more effective in the case of monkeys, the sudden appearance of the head of a toy snake when the food reward was about to be taken. If the traumatic stimulus was repeated several times—two to seven in cats or dogs, generally more in monkeys—behavioral aberrations appeared.

Some of the symptoms of disturbance may be described under the interpretive headings used by Masserman.

Pervasive anxiety was indicated by low threshold of startle, persistent hyperirritability, muscular tension, body postures, mydriasis, irregularly accelerated pulse rate, raised blood pressure, and increased coagulability of the blood.

Psychosomatic symptoms included, in some animals, recurrent asthmatic breathing, genitourinary dysfunction, anorexia, flatulence, and diarrhea.

Defensive reactions included inhibition of feeding, even outside the experimental apparatus, to the point of self-starvation and serious cachexia.

Phobic aversions were observed, first to stimuli directly associated with the traumatic experiences, then spreading to other situations.

Sexual deviations included diminished heterosexual interests and accentuated homosexual activity.

Sensorial disturbances were considered present on the basis of behavior ranging from extreme sensitivity to minor changes in the surroundings to recurrent episodes of apparent disorientation and confusion. Hallucinations were thought to be present in monkeys who, although refusing food readily available in their food box, could be observed picking up nonexistent pellets and appearing to chew and swallow these.

Masserman was particularly interested in procedures for ameliorating the manifestations of the disturbances induced in his animals. He found a number effective to some degree. They ranged from petting by the experimenter to neurosurgical operations.

From the point of view of Hebb's criteria, the behavioral disturbances produced by Masserman do not easily qualify as neuroses. The behavior was not statistically abnormal, and neither its persistence nor its generalization was satisfactorily demonstrated. With respect to the animal's adjustment, it is also not clear that the behavior was abnormal.

CONDITIONED EMOTIONAL RESPONSE VERSUS SPECIFIC STATE

It has been suggested that experiments of the Masserman type, involving inhibition of feeding responses by the introduction of fear-arousing stimuli, should be regarded as eliciting conditioned emotional responses. Such responses carry no implication of a specific abnormal state. Masserman has argued against this interpretation, contending that the generalization of anxiety reactions to many other situations only remotely or symbolically associated with the original one is characteristic of *human* neurosis and not of a simple conditioned response.

The crucial issue appears to be whether the experimental neurosis can be understood in terms of general laws of learning or whether it represents a specific state requiring special conditions, such as conflict and restraint, for its production and implying some form of constitutional susceptibility to breakdown. The view that experimental neurosis is learned behavior is favored by Wolpe and is supported by the results of his experiments. These were carried out on cats in a situation like that used by Masserman but were distinguished by use of a control group, which received no initial training to feed on hearing a signal. Nevertheless, electric shock produced behavioral disturbances in all animals. These disturbances could be ameliorated by placing the hungry animal in a room enough unlike the experimental room to allow feeding and then gradually making the feeding environment more like the experimental room. Wolpe's animal studies led him to work out related procedures for treatment of human neuroses.

One striking difference between the results of Pavlov, Gantt, and Liddell on one hand and Masserman and Wolpe on the other is that all animals were made neurotic by the latter workers and only some by the former. If one scrutinizes the experimental situations for a reason, the clearly traumatic stimuli used in the Masserman procedure present an obvious difference. Pavlov and Liddell had to postulate that the apparently innocuous demands of their experimental situation for perceptual discrimination or delay of response generated conflict and strained the capacity of the nervous system. Masserman's and Wolpe's animals fed normally until exposed to stimuli universally disturbing to that species. It would appear that the need for inhibition or restraint brings out much greater individual differences in susceptibility of animals to experimental neurosis than does exposure to traumatic stimuli. One may speculate about possible parallel differences between the spontaneous neuroses of human civilian life and those that occur under war combat conditions.

Personality types. If susceptibility to experimental neurosis could be shown to depend upon constitutional factors, this would reinforce the hypothesis that they reflect a specific central state. In his writings, Pavlov paid considerable attention to possible constitutional differences between dogs. He applied the humoral classification of Hippocrates to his experimental animals, describing them as sanguine, phlegmatic, choleric, and melancholic. He noted the appearance of neurotic behavior only in dogs of the melancholic type—timid and docile with predominance of inhibitory process—or of the choleric type—aggressive and excitable with excitatory predominance. Initially well balanced animals, the phlegmatic or sanguine types, did not develop chronic disturbances in behavior. The specific state issue might be resolved if other workers could confirm these observations with more exact methods of characterizing animal personality.

Pavlov did discover a pharmacological correlate of his neurotic types. He found that temporary administration of bromides resulted in apparently permanent improvement of dogs with neuroses of the excitatory type. Treatment of the inhibitory type of neuroses was unsuccessful until he used a very small dose, only a fraction of that beneficial to the excitatory type. These observations indicate that the manifestations of a disorder are related to drug reactivity, and they favor Pavlov's theory of types, since it is easy to consider drug reactivity as an aspect of constitutional make-up. Of further interest is the fact that there are some consistent parallels between Pavlov's findings on reactivity to bromide in neurotic dogs and reactivity to amobarbital in psychiatric patients, as has been shown by Shagass.

PSYCHOSOMATIC DISORDERS IN ANIMALS

Throughout the experimental neuroses tests, various physiological disturbances were frequent accompaniments of the behavioral manifestations. Often they were the most convincing signs of disturbance, as in the case of Liddell's sheep, whose respiratory rate rose to 135 a minute. It seems clear the psychophysiologic reactions form an integral part of the picture of experimental neurosis. One could also argue that the experimental neurosis is a psychophysiological reaction, since the experimental methods are essentially similar.

GASTROINTESTINAL DISORDERS

There has been considerable work on experimental induction of functional and structural changes in the stomach. Mahl carried out a series of studies on the effects of chronic fear in dogs and monkeys and added some observations in man.

Dogs were stimulated under control conditions day and night by a twenty-second buzzer that occurred unpredictably at intervals of 5, 10, or 15 minutes. In the chronic-fear condition, the buzzer stimulation continued, and some buzzers were accompanied by a brief but painful electric shock, delivered to the animals through the grid floor of the cages. The animals developed conditioned fear to the buzzer and the cage; this was manifested by motor withdrawal activity, paralysis, trembling, widespread autonomic changes, and intense vocalization. Measurements of free hydrochloric acid (HCl) and total acidity showed significant increases in both. The dogs were then allowed a recovery period, being removed to different cages in a rest room, with no buzzer or shock stimuli. Later they were returned to the experimental cages and were stimulated for five hours with only the buzzer. During this conditioned-fear phase, there was an increase in gastric acidity. Results were similar in monkeys.

Mahl concluded that sustained fear is accompanied by increased HCl secretion in dogs, monkeys, and humans and that conditioned-fear stimuli evoked increased HCl secretion in the absence of pain stimulation. By contrast, HCl secretion is inhibited during episodic fear stimulation. Mahl found no evidence of stomach lesions in his animals.

Other investigators have been able to produce lesions and to study the relevant conditions. Weisz divided ninety rats into six split-litter groups of equal size and placed each of these in a different experimental situation. Two situations involved an approach-avoidance type of conflict; two were fear-producing, with food and water deprivation present in one but not in the other; two were control situations, involving only food and water deprivation or food and water deprivation plus the facility to see and smell food and water. Significantly more animals in the two conflict situations and in one fear-producing situation developed ulcers in the rumen of the stomach than the comparable animals in control situations.

The data suggested that severe food and water deprivation was a necessary prerequisite for the occurrence of the stomach lesions, although not sufficient in itself. Thus, this experiment showed that both conflict and chronic fear result in gastric lesions. Prolonged immobilization also produces gastric erosions in the rat, as shown in the experiments of Ader et al. The postulated chain of events is that these various stresses cause prolonged gastric hypersecretion, with increased acidity, resulting in an excessive volume of unbuffered gastric juice coming into contact with the upper portion of the stomach, which is not as well protected by mucosa as the remainder.

Porter et al. have demonstrated that experimental psychological stress may produce gastrointestinal lesions in the monkey. In eleven of nineteen animals subjected to conditioning programs directed toward a study of emotional behavior, there were lesions, which included gastric hemorrhage and erosion, duodenal ulceration, enteric intussusception, and chronic colitis. The conditioning programs differed for each animal, so comparisons for the group as a whole were not possible.

However, in two pairs of monkeys a controlled study was carried out on avoidance behavior. Two monkeys were strapped to a restraining chair, and one member of each pair was reinforced in such a way that an avoidance response was developed; the other member of the pair received just as many shocks but no specific reinforcement. The member of each pair learning the avoidance response died first and showed duodenal ulceration at autopsy; the control animals, which were killed at the same time, showed no abnormality. French et al. produced similar lesions by electric stimulation to the hypothalamic region over a prolonged period of time; this suggests that the avoidance conditioning situation may involve chronic high-level excitation of the visceral brain stem.

Asthma

It is possible to induce asthma experimentally in the guinea pig by sensitizing the animal to egg white; asthmatic attacks then occur in response to a spray of homologous antigen. The reactivity to antigen varies, but Ottenberg et al. found that consistently reactive guinea pigs displayed attacks when placed in the experimental chamber in the absence of the egg white spray. The asthmatic attacks of these animals appeared to be a conditioned response to the chamber.

The respiratory pattern associated with pain-fear response to electric shock resembles that found in experimental allergic asthma but actually involves different mechanisms. Schiavi et al. determined this by measuring several respiratory characteristics and the mechanical properties of the lungs. Under both conditions, inspiration was shortened, and expiration was prolonged. However, there was evidence of bronchiolar obstruction in experimental allergic asthma, whereas no increased airway resistance was found in the animals exposed to electric shock. This study provides an excellent example of the fact that detailed measurement and analysis of physiological functions can demonstrate that different mechanisms can be involved in an apparently similar bodily reaction pattern.

Various other physiological reactions that may be taken as representative of psychosomatic disorders have been studied in animals. The examples cited here are among the most sophisticated and give some idea of the methods and problems.

STUDIES OF NEUROSES IN MAN

A number of experimental strategies have been used to obtain observations relevant to the problems of neurosis and psychophysiological dysfunction in man. One obvious approach is to compare individuals who clearly suffer from the condition under examination with controls not so afflicted. However, although functional difference between sickness and health may be ascertained by this approach, the findings leave uncertain the antecedents of illness. For example, to show that neurotic patients have higher heart rates than healthy controls does not reveal much about the genesis of neurosis, although it may help clarify a symptom mechanism. Another approach is to attempt to reproduce the manifestations of illness in healthy subjects in a temporary and fully reversible fashion. Techniques such as hypnotic induction of conflict and emotion and the application of controlled stressful stimuli have been used for this purpose. Conditioning techniques have also been applied. In addition, a number of investigators have availed themselves of naturally occurring stress or conflict situations, such as the time preceding college final examinations, to make observations of temporary disturbances in ordinarily healthy subjects.

HYPNOTICALLY INDUCED CONFLICTS AND EMOTIONS

Prior to considering the use of hypnosis in various experimental procedures, we should draw attention to the fact that the status of the hypnotic trance as a special state is currently under active investigation and remains uncertain. The major difficulty arises from the fact that virtually all objectively observable changes that may be recorded during the trance state may also be elicited by verbal instructions or suggestions in unhypnotized subjects. However, the controversial and uncertain status of hypnosis need not prevent us from accepting the results of experiments using hypnotic methods if these methods are regarded merely as effective ways of instructing the subject.

Luria method. The Russian psychologist Luria employed hypnotic induction, together with a special method of recording motor effects, for the study of human conflicts. In a typical experiment, a story was told to the hypnotized subject; according to the story, he had committed a reproachable act, one that was contrary to his usual personality trend. A number of critical words were taken from this story and placed in a list of control words not specifically related to the story. The list was then presented as an association experiment. With each verbal response, the subject was required to press on a tambour with his preferred hand. Control sessions were carried out before and after the hypnotic experiment in which the conflict was induced and later removed. In addition to the voluntary pressure curves, verbal reaction time to the words and, in some cases, involuntary movements from the nonpreferred hand and respiration were recorded. The signs of conflict consisted of irregular hand pressures, lengthened reaction times, and, when recorded, irregular respiration.

Luria derived several laws from his numerous experiments. He used concepts reminiscent of Pavlov. For example, in his law of the decreased action of the functional barrier, the functional barrier, a cortical property involving regulation of motor activities by inhibition, was weakened by excessive emotional excitation.

Huston et al. repeated one of Luria's experiments. They used hypnosis to induce a conflict in twelve normal subjects. The story used for this purpose in one subject follows. The young man met an attractive girl who was wearing a new, brown silk dress that was very important to her. He accidentally burned a cigarette hole in her dress and allowed her to believe that she had done it herself. Words such as silk, dress, brown, cigarette, burn, and hole were selected as critical and placed in a long list of noncritical words. Apart from test responses, there appeared to be good evidence that strong emotional conflict was produced by the procedure. The conflict was not removed in this subject for twenty-four hours after the hypnotic session. That night he slept poorly, awakened with a headache that persisted until the removal of the conflicts in the afternoon, had poor appetite, was resentful and antagonistic toward the hypnotist, and was somewhat uncooperative. He was unable to give any reason for these manifestations. Throughout the day he gave away his cigarettes and apparently could not enjoy smoking. He rationalized this behavior by saying that he was giving up the habit.

In the group of twelve subjects, nine appeared to accept the story told to them as something they had done, and it produced a profound reaction in them. In six of these nine subjects, some motor aspect of the Luria technique revealed the presence of the conflict in either the hypnotic or waking states. In the hypnotic state, they tended to give verbal responses definitely related to conflict, with few nonverbal disturbances; the reverse was found in the waking state, in which there was a relative increase of nonverbal disturbances over the verbal. This suggests that if the excitation created by the conflict is not discharged verbally, there is a spread to the voluntary and involuntary motor levels.

Wittkower's experiments. The wide range of bodily functions that may be altered when hypnosis is used to produce emotional reactions is well illustrated in the monumental report by Wittkower. He was able to produce X-ray evidence of fluctuations in the size of the heart, with both enlargement and diminution of heart shadow occurring in different subjects. Salivary secretions were altered both in quantity and in chemical constitution. Gastric motility and acidity were either increased or decreased; the nature of the gastric reaction was characteristic for the individual, even with different emotions, but differed from one subject to another. Wittkower demonstrated changes in the amount of bile and the chemical constitution of bile, alterations of leukocyte counts, and changes in the serum calcium, potassium, and chloride content. He also observed changes in the urine, in the blood iodine content, and in the galvanic skin response (GSR). Wittkower's main purpose was to demonstrate the profound bodily effects of psychological states. He drew attention to the need for integrating observations of multiple reaction systems if one is to understand the total emotional reaction. Although he considered his findings to be in accord with Cannon's emergency theory, he felt that it was necessary to go beyond it and to pay attention to constitutional and experimental factors that could influence the direction and quality of the organ reaction.

The basic technique used by Wittkower has been employed in a large number of experiments with various types of physiological recording. A recent example is a study of respiratory responses by Dudley et al., which showed that increased ventilation and oxygen consumption followed meaningful hypnotic suggestions of situations eliciting anxiety, anger, exercise, and head pain. Anger, anxiety, and exercise, all of which involve an orientation toward action, were contrasted with depression, the suggestion of which resulted in no respiratory changes. Depression does not involve an action orientation. These results with respiration seem to parallel those obtained by Kehoe et al. in relation to secretion of gastric acid; the highest gastric secretory rate was associated with suggested anger and the lowest with helplessness-hopelessness. There is also some similarity to the findings with plasma hydrocortisone level, which Persky has shown to be increased by hypnotically induced anxiety.

Specificity of attitudes in psychosomatic disease.   Hypnotic techniques have also been used to provide evidence bearing on the specificity of attitude hypothesis in psychosomatic disease, which was proposed by Grace and Graham. The hypothesis states that each attitude toward a disturbing situation is associated with its own specific disease or set of physiological changes. In one study Graham et al. hypnotized normal subjects, who were told to assume attitudes that the original study had found to be associated with hives and Raynaud's disease. With the hives attitude the person sees himself as being mistreated and receiving injury, without developing even a wish to take any action himself. With the Raynaud's attitude, on the other hand, the person wishes to take some direct hostile action. Warming of the skin is part of the physiology of hives, whereas cooling is characteristic of Raynaud's disease. Skin temperatures, recorded during hypnotically induced attitudes, showed an average tendency for increase with the hives attitude and a tendency for decrease with the Raynaud's attitude. The results were taken to support the specificity of attitude hypothesis. Recent evidence indicates that similar effects can be obtained without hypnosis.

Conditioning.   Application of the method of conditioning to studies of children began in 1907. In 1925 Krasnogorski reported observations in children that seemed to be analogous to the experimental neurosis in dogs. In one child, under conditions requiring a difficult discrimination between different rates of a metronome, latent periods of the positive conditioned reflexes first increased in length. At the same time the child, who had always been easy to deal with and quiet during the experiments, became irritable and refused to go to the laboratory. The ward reported that his behavior had changed—that he had become rude, fought with other children, insisted on being discharged, and was disobedient. In the laboratory, previously accomplished differentiations were then lost, the negative stimulus was associated with yawning and sleepiness, and the child went to sleep for the first time in a period of five months of conditioning study. This child, presumably behaviorally healthy when the experiments began, thus became emotionally disturbed.

One may, of course, criticize interpretation of this reaction as experimental neurosis. It may be normal for a child required to undergo repeated exposure to a difficult laboratory situation to become upset. Furthermore, the generalization to the ward situation could have been determined mainly by anticipation of further exposure to the unpleasant laboratory situation.

More recent research in the Soviet Union, notably that of Bykov, has provided experimental demonstrations that a large number of bodily functions obey Pavlovian laws of conditioning. These experiments provide a basis for relating visceral dysfunctions to symbolic cues that have acquired meaning on the basis of previous experience. Furthermore, Razran's experiments on semantic conditioning indicate that bodily reactions may be elicited in response to verbal cues that are different in form from the initial stimuli but that have a similar meaning or a strong, previously formed, associational bond.

For example, after establishing conditioned salivation to the word "black," just as much response is obtained from its antonym, "white," whereas another color name that has low associational relationship, such as "ochre," elicits much less response. Psychotherapeutic exploration is often concerned with working out specific examples of this phenomenon—for example, when the patient reports an attack of dyspnea under particular circumstances that have only an associational relationship to symbols of previous conflict or trauma.

Mention should be made of the recent upsurge of interest in the application of conditioning techniques to comparative study of psychiatric patients and normal subjects. A detailed account of the various differences found between particular kinds of psychiatric patients and normal subjects is beyond our scope, but several books, of which Ban's is an example, have appeared recently.

EXPERIMENTAL STRESS

The idea that disturbed behavior and bodily reactions occur in response to severely taxing environmental conditions is in accord with general human experience and is widely accepted. Since environmental demands or stimuli that place strain on reserve capacities of the organism are relatively easy to produce in the laboratory, much experimental work has employed this method. Unfortunately, investigators have used the word "stress" to characterize a wide variety of experimental demands, from performing mental arithmetic tasks to exposure to severe temperature conditions or physical injury. Such indiscriminate use tends to deprive the term of its meaning.

Partial starvation. Among the most biologically meaningful procedures for studying stress are those that involve complete or partial frustration of basic organismic needs for food, sleep, or environmental stimulation.

Partial starvation over a prolonged period of time may result in various psychoneurotic manifestations. The most systematic data come from the Minnesota studies conducted by Keys et al. Thirty-six apparently normal young men, after three months of control on a good diet, were subjected to six months of semistarvation, with provision of only half of their required caloric intake. Although tests of intellectual functioning and the Rorschach projective test demonstrated no significant changes, the subjects became depressed, moody, and apathetic; felt that they were not alert mentally; and reported that they had lost ambition. The scores on the Minnesota Multiphasic Personality Inventory were in accord with these reports.

Nine of the subjects were thought to develop specific neurotic behavior and ideas. Four of these showed character disturbances, with inability to maintain their former standards of morals and honesty. One man had sensory and motor disturbances of hysterical character. One man mutilated himself twice. Bizarre behavior in connection with food was almost universal and often took the form of compulsive rituals. The subjects reported irritability and anger, which they were unable to express because of the effort involved. The disturbances were reversible with restoration of an adequate diet.

Brief laboratory stresses. The more commonly employed laboratory stress procedures are probably less biologically significant because of their brief duration. Variants of pain stimulation have been employed in several ways. Pain has proved to be particularly useful as a standardized stimulus to elicit differential physiological reactions in different types of psychiatric patients and healthy subjects.

In general, it appears that individuals with already-established illness or proneness to anxiety tend to react to moderate pain stimulation with greater physiological disturbance in various organ systems than individuals who are free of illness. Similar differentiations may be obtained by nonpainful stresses, such as those requiring the execution of difficult tasks. Furthermore, it has been demonstrated that the physiological system that is particularly responsive to experimental stress is more likely to be one habitually involved in the patient's illness—that is, one that produces symptoms. For example, headaches frequently result from sustained contraction of head and neck muscles, whereas symptoms such as palpitations, dyspnea, and precordial pain involve altered functioning of the cardiorespiratory system. By subdividing psychiatric patients, according to their complaint history, into head and heart complaint groups and subjecting them to a standard pain-stress test, it was possible to show significant differences in the affected response systems. Increased neck muscle contractions were more often elicited in head complaint group, and changes in pulse rate and respiration were more often found in the heart complaint group, even though very few of the subjects reported actual symptoms during the stress procedure. Interesting as they are, findings such as these leave unanswered the important questions concerning the events leading to symptom choice—that is, the reason for localization of dysfunction in particular organ systems.

A laboratory stress technique that has been gaining increasing favor involves the use of motion picture films, selected as being likely to induce particular kinds of emotional reactions. For example, Lazarus et al. showed subjects films of puberty rites in primitive tribes, involving incisions made in the genital area, and recorded their physiologic reactions. The powerful effects of the films were reflected in the recordings. The investigators were able to relate the nature of the reactions to some personality variables and to the kind of psychological mechanisms employed to deal with emotionally disturbing stimuli.

A further technique has been the deliberate manipulation of events in a laboratory situation in order to arouse emotions the investigator wanted to study. For example, Funkenstein et al. deliberately created a situation in which the subject was required to carry out computational problems at a very rapid rate while the experimenter became critical and demanding. The subject's behavioral reaction to this was classified as reflecting anger-in, anger-out, or anxiety. Significant differences in various cardiovascular measures were found between the anger-in and anger-out groups.

Probing interviews. Interviews that deliberately focus on emotionally charged material so that related bodily reactions may be studied represent another variant of experimental stress. This is generally not standard, although it can be made so. After a baseline interval, the topics considered emotionally relevant are introduced, and discussion centers about these. Usually there is a phase of reassurance after the emotional arousal. At times the material may be introduced after the subject has been hypnotized. Behavioral observations and physiologic recordings are made, and the various responses are correlated with the on-going stimuli. Although this procedure involves numerous methodological difficulties, it has yielded valuable data concerning the participation of physiological response systems in symptom mechanisms.

CURRENT PERSPECTIVE

It is apparent to the reader that psychiatry still lacks truly satisfactory experimental techniques for study of neurotic and psychosomatic disorders. However, the available methods do permit some insights concerning relevant mechanisms, and their use has been associated in recent years with a rather remarkable development of objective techniques for measuring numerous kinds of responses. Thus, although we are constantly working with data of limited significance, these are becoming more reliable and will provide a firm basis for future synthesis.

REFERENCES

Ader, R. Plasma pepsinogen level as a predictor of susceptibility to gastric erosions in the rat. Psychosom. Med., 25: 221, 1963.

Anderson, O. D., and Parmenter, R. A long-term study of the experimental neurosis in the sheep and dog. Psychosom. Med. Monogr., 2: 1, 1941.

Ban, T. Conditioning and Psychiatry. Aldine Publishing Company, Chicago, 1964.

Broadhurst, P. L. Abnormal animal behavior. In Handbook of Abnormal Psychology, H. J. Eysenck, editor, p. 726. Basic Books, New York, 1961.

Bykov, K. The Cerebral Cortex and the Internal Organs. Foreign Languages Publishing House, Moscow, 1959.

Dudley, D., Holmes, T., Martin, C., and Ripley, H. Changes in respiration associated with hypnotically induced emotion, pain, and exercise. Psychosom. Med. 26: 46, 1964.

French, J. D., Porter, R. W., Cavanaugh, E. B., and Longmire, R. L. Experimental gastroduodenal lesions induced by stimulation of the brain. Psychosom. Med., 19: 209, 1957.

Funkenstein, D. H., King, S. H., and Drolette, M. The direction of anger during a laboratory stress-inducing situation. Psychosom. Med., 16: 404, 1954.

Gantt, W. H. Experimental Basis for Neurotic Behavior, Hoeber Medical Division, Harper & Row, New York, 1944.

Gantt, W. H., editor. Physiological Basis of Psychiatry. Charles C Thomas, Springfield, Ill., 1957.

Grace, W. J., and Graham, D. T. Relationship of specific attitudes and emotions to certain bodily diseases. Psychosom. Med., 14: 243, 1952.

Graham, D. T., Stern, J. A., and Winokur, G. Experimental investigation of the specificity of attitude hypothesis in psychosomatic disease. Psychosom. Med., 20: 446, 1958.

Hebb, D. O. Spontaneous neurosis in chimpanzees. Theoretical relations with clinical and experimental phenomena. Psychosom. Med., 9: 3, 1947.

Huston, P. E., Shakow, D., and Erickson, M. H. A study of hypnotically induced complexes by means of the Luria technique. J. Gen. Psychol., 2: 65, 1934.

Kehoe, M., and Ironside, W. Studies on the experimental evocation of depressive responses using hypnosis. II. The influence of depressive responses upon the secretion of gastric acid. Psychosom. Med., 25: 403, 1963.

Keys, A., Brozek, J., Henschel, A., Mickelsen, L., and Taylor, H. L. The Biology of Human Starvation. University of Minnesota Press, Minneapolis, 1950.

Krasnogorski, N. I. The conditioned reflexes and children's neuroses. Amer. J. Dis. Child., 30: 753, 1925.

Lazarus, R. S., and Alfert, E. Short-circuiting of threat by experimentally altering cognitive appraisal. J. Abnorm. Soc. Psychol., 69: 195, 1964.

Liddell, H. S. A comparative approach to the dynamics of experimental neuroses. Ann. N. Y. Acad. Sci., 56: 164, 1953.

Liddell, H. S. Conditioning and emotions. Sci. Amer., 190: 48, 1954.

Luria, A. R. The Nature of Human Conflicts. Liveright, New York, 1932.

Mahl, G. F. Physiological changes during chronic fear. Ann. N. Y. Acad. Sci., 56: 240, 1953.

Masserman, J. H. Behavior and Neurosis: An Experimental Psychoanalytic Approach to Psychobiologic Principles. University of Chicago Press, Chicago, 1943.

Masserman, J. H. A biodynamic psychoanalytic approach to the problems of feeling and emotions. In Feelings and Emotions, M. L. Reymert, editor, p. 49. McGraw-Hill, New York, 1950.

Ottenberg, P., Stein, M., Lewis, J., and Hamilton, C. Learned asthma in the guinea pig. Psychosom. Med., 20: 395, 1958.

Pavlov, I. P. *Conditioned Reflexes and Psychiatry*. International Publishers, New York, 1941.

Persky, H. Adrenocortical function during anxiety. In *Physiological Correlates of Psychological Disorder*, R. Roessler and N. S. Greenfield, editors, p. 171. University of Wisconsin Press, Madison, 1962.

Porter, R. W., Brady, J. V., Conrad, D., Mason, J. W., Galambos, R., and Rioch, D. McK. Some experimental observations on gastrointestinal lesions in behaviorally conditioned monkeys. Psychosom. Med., 20: 379, 1958.

Razran, G. A quantitative study of meaning by a conditioned salivary technique (semantic conditioning). Science, 90: 89, 1939.

Schiavi, R., Stein, M., and Sethi, B. B. Respiratory variables in response to a pain-fear stimulus and in experimental asthma. Psychosom. Med., 23: 485, 1961.

Shagass, C. Sedation threshold, a neurophysiological tool for psychosomatic research. Psychosom. Med., 18: 410, 1956.

Shagass, C. Explorations in the psychophysiology of affect. In *Theories of the Mind*, J. Scher, editor, p. 122. Free Press of Glencoe (Macmillan), New York, 1962.

Weisz, J. D. The etiology of experimental gastric ulceration. Psychosom. Med., 19: 61, 1957.

Wittkower, E. Studies on the influence of emotions on the functions of the organs (including observations in normals and neurotics). Brit. J. Psychiat., 81: 533, 1935.

Wolpe, J. *Psychotherapy by Reciprocal Inhibition*. Stanford University Press, Palo Alto, 1958.

CHAPTER 24

Hallucinogens

ARNOLD J. MANDELL, M.D., and

LOUIS J. WEST, M.D.

INTRODUCTION

HALLUCINOGENS can be defined as substances that, administered in pharmacological doses (not toxic overdoses), create gross distortions in perception without significantly obtunding consciousness. These distortions frequently include hallucinations. Such compounds usually exert profound effects on mood, thought, and behavior. Such effects resemble the disturbances seen in naturally occurring psychoses. Thus, some hallucinogens have been termed psychotomimetic or psychotogenic drugs.

The psychological changes effected by these chemicals have sometimes been described as a loosening of ego structure, dissolving of ego boundaries, or disrupting of ego defenses. Such changes may include the experiencing of thoughts, feelings, and perceptions that are usually outside the individual's awareness (unconscious or repressed). Persons undergoing a psychedelic experience have also been described as being unusually suggestible, emotionally labile, and unusually aware of their own reactions and the reactions of others. Feelings of transcendence of ordinary experience and distortions in time perception have also been reported.

Hallucinogenic agents have been of growing interest to psychiatrists during recent years for several reasons: (1) Some scientists and clinicians have deliberately taken these compounds to produce psychotic-like symptoms as a means of enabling themselves to empathize better with severely ill psychiatric patients. (2) In experimental psychopathology it has been hoped that the study of chemically induced model psychoses would lead to a better understanding of those found in clinical practice. (3) Certain therapists have defined psychotogens as psychedelic or mind-realizing substances, useful to expand perceptual and experiental horizons in the treatment of a variety of patients with alcoholism, rigid personality patterns, frigidity, etc.

An increasing number of people are taking various psychotogenic substances—marihuana, lysergic acid diethylamide (LSD), psilocybin, dimethyltryptamine—frequently acquired through illegal channels and employed without medical supervision, in order to participate in special group experiences having cultlike characteristics.

Occasionally, persistent psychotic reactions and prolonged delirious reactions have followed the administration of these substances, and psychiatrists have then been called on for help.

PHARMACOLOGY

There are four major chemical classes of hallucinogens: the indole alkaloid derivatives, the piperidine derivatives, the phenylethylamines, and the cannabinols.

Indole Alkaloids

Tryptamine derivates. The simplest of these substances is tryptamine, which has no hallucinogenic effect. Its *N*, *N*-disubstituted derivatives, perhaps having easier access to the brain, constitute several active members of the series.

N, *N*-Dimethyltryptamine is found, together with bufotenine, in the Caribbean cahobe bean, chewed by certain natives to produce religious visions, and in the seeds of the domestic morning glory plant, used for hallucinatory experiences in the United States.

Various homologues have been synthesized, including *N*, *N*-diethyl-; *N*, *N*-dipropyl-; and *N*, *N*-diallyltryptamine.

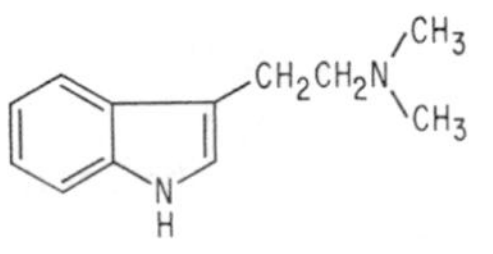

N, N - dimethyltryptamine

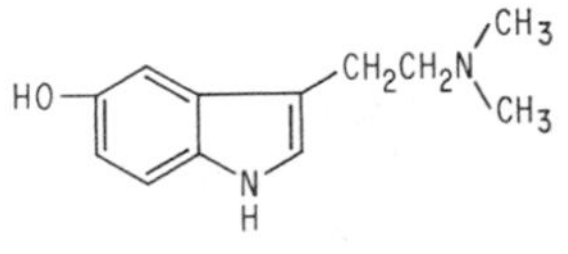

bufotenine

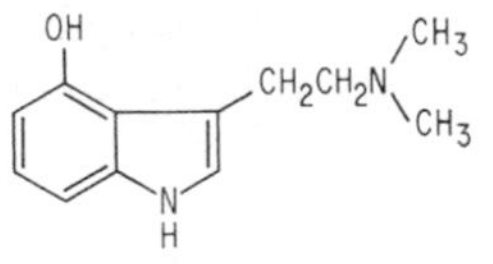

psilocin

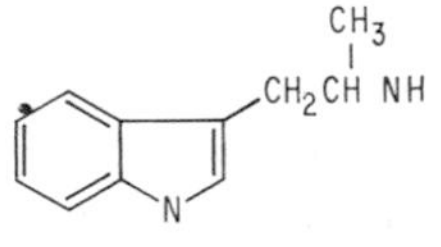

α - methyltryptamine

Figure 1. Some hallucinogenic indole amines.

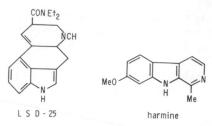

LSD-25   harmine

FIGURE 2. More complex hallucinogenic indole alkaloids.

The *hydroxylated N, N*-dimethyltryptamines are also active. Among these are the 4-hydroxy (psilocin) and its phosphorylated derivative (psilocybin, found in the ritually employed hallucinogenic mushroom *Psilocybe mexicana* of southern Mexico); the 5-hydroxy (bufotenine, originally isolated from the skin of toads) and its more active 5-methoxy derivative; and the 6-hydroxy-N, N-dimethyltryptamine.

Dimethyltryptamine is psychotogenic at 1 mg. per kilogram levels, administered intramuscularly; effective dosages of the others vary. Psilocybin and psilocin produce effects at 4 to 8 mg. in man. A recent addition to the tryptamine family is α-methyltryptamine, which has been shown to be effective at a dosage level of 20 mg. in man.

Harmine, harmaline, and ibogaine. A drug with a three-ring aromatic system (harmine) and its related dihydro derivative (harmaline) are isolated from shrubs and used by South American Indians to produce hallucinatory states. The indole alkaloids with a larger ring structure include ibogaine, used by African natives to remain motionless for as long as two days while stalking but producing confusion, drunkenness, and hallucinations if taken in large doses.

Lysergic acid diethylamide (*LSD*). The ergot alkaloids were originally isolated from a grass and rye fungus and were thought to be responsible for the convulsions, mental confusion, and gangrenous changes in the lower limbs associated with the periodic outbreaks of St. Anthony's fire caused by infected rye in the Middle Ages. All ergot alkaloids can be hydrolyzed to lysergic acid, and various derivatives of this compound have been developed. The diethylamide was synthesized by Stoll and Hofmann in 1938; in 1943 it was discovered by Hofmann to be a potent hallucinogen.

LSD is more than 8,000 times more potent on a dosage basis than mescaline. Less than 0.3 gm. has caused death in status epilepticus of a 7,000-pound elephant. This remarkable substance is by far the most powerful psychotogenic agent known, effective at levels as low as 1 μgm. (0.000001 gm.) per kilogram of body weight in man. Originally used experimentally to produce an artificial psychosis resembling an acute schizophrenic reaction lasting several hours, it has rapidly become widely employed as a psychedelic agent by a variety of practitioners and the basis for a growing cult of sorts.

The temporary psychosis caused by a dose of 100 to 500 μgm. of LSD may be accompanied by almost any type of psychopathology. Suicidal attempts have been known to occur if panic or depression is predominant. Many individuals manifest some degree of subjective euphoria and a sense of great mental clarity or comprehension after the initial marked sympathomimetic effects of the drug, although objectively they may be confused, uncoordinated, hallucinating, and disoriented. On recovery, there is often a feeling of being reborn after a profoundly moving and significant experience, and there is often a sense of deep camaraderie with others who were present and participating in the ceremony.

Overdoses of substances like LSD may produce delirium or, rarely, convulsions. The phenothiazines, especially the high-dosage group (promazine, chlorpromazine, chlorprothixine, thioridazine) are quite effective antidotes to the effects of these drugs and are preferable to the barbiturates and minor tranquilizers. Thioridazine may be the medication of choice if convulsions are feared in a given case.

Prolonged psychopathological reactions to LSD—that is, lasting more than twenty-four to forty-eight hours—are best viewed as latent psychiatric disorders precipitated or exacerbated by the drug experience. Such an illness should be treated basically the same way as in regular clinical practice.

PIPERIDINE DERIVATIVES

Both belladonna- and stramonium-containing anticholinergic compounds —such as atropine, scopolamine, and hyoscyamine—have been known for centuries to produce organic psychoses with hallucinations. Cocaine, belonging to this same family, produces hallucinations and thought disorders if taken in toxic doses. These agents are perhaps not properly termed hallucinogens as previously defined because the effects depend on overdosage. However, a number of compounds have been synthesized and tested recently by Abood and others in which the substituted glycolic acid side chains are *meta* instead of *para* to the nitrogen of the piperidine ring. These changes have resulted in a large series of psychotogens, including 1-methyl-3-piperidylcyclopentylphenylglycolate, the most powerful, and Ditran, the best known. These compounds can cause delusional thinking, disorientation, and hallucinations.

Another recently synthesized piperidine derivative that has generated

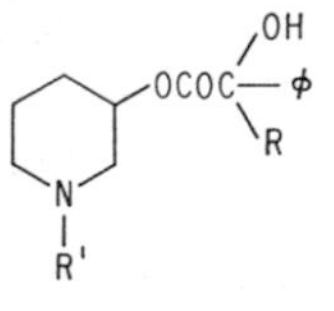

FIGURE 3. A model of the piperidine-derived glycolate series.

much interest is Sernyl. Originally, it was thought to be an analgesic or an agent that prevented sensory impulses from reaching nerve centers. Various research groups subsequently described its effects in lower doses as mimicking the primary (Bleulerian) signs of schizophrenia, including flattened affect, thought disorder, and emotional withdrawal, without the secondary signs, such as delusions and hallucinations. This was considered to be due to a peculiar effect on the sensory synapses.

More recent work has led to other reports of behavioral aberrations induced by Sernyl, including phenomena resembling those resulting from sensory deprivation.

PHENYLETHYLAMINES

Mescaline. The most significant member of this group is the trimethoxyphenylethylamine, mescaline, named after the Mescalero Apaches, who developed the cult of peyotism. Mescaline is the major active component of the buttons from the peyote cactus *Lophophora williamsii.* Today these peyote buttons are chewed by Indians of a number of tribes in the southwestern United States to induce hallucinatory states in their religious rituals. The standard employment of peyote buttons in ceremonies of the Native American Church makes control of their distribution difficult, since freedom of religion is involved.

Mescaline must be administered in high dosage to achieve a full effect, usually 0.5 to 0.6 gm. orally. The experience is usually ushered in by one to three hours of flushing, vomiting, cramps, sweating, and other autonomic phenomena, followed by several hours to days in some cases of often colorful visual hallucinations, depersonalization, and distortions of time.

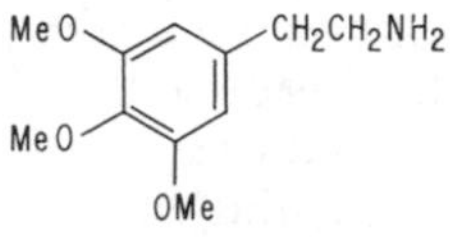

mescaline

FIGURE 4. The major phenylethylamine hallucinogen.

The remarkable sensory and introspective effects of mescaline have long fascinated psychopathologists. Both S. Weir Mitchell and Havelock Ellis reported personal experiences with it more than seventy years ago. Aldous Huxley, in his *Doors of Perception,* described mescaline intoxication as providing a voyage to the antipodes of the mind.

Amphetamines. Another phenylethylamine group, the amphetamines, should be mentioned in passing, although the therapeutic and addictive properties of these sympathomimetic amines are properly discussed more extensively elsewhere. Chronic administration of large amounts of amphetamine may result in a psychosis with delusions, hallucinations, and dangerous behavior, accompanied by distortions in reality-testing. Sleep deprivation, due to the drug's analeptic effects, may contribute to the syndrome. Such reactions usually remit promptly on withdrawal of the amphetamine, although treatment, including phenothiazine medication, may be required.

Adrenochrome. A trihydroxyindole called adrenochrome, an oxidation product of adrenaline, has been reported by some workers to be hallucinogenic in intravenous dosages of 0.5 mg. Based on these reports, including the supposed discovery of the presence of increased amounts of this and related metabolites in body fluids of psychiatric patients, an adrenochrome theory of schizophrenia was advanced by Hoffer and Osmond. More recent studies have failed to confirm the proposition that adrenochrome is an autogenous psychotogenic substance. However, other more elaborate work on the role of biogenic amines in the human brain may yet prove to be of significance in the search for hallucinogenic or psychotogenic substances related to errors of metabolism in man.

CANNABINOLS

Although they have been well known since ancient times as perceptual distorters, the members of this psychically active drug family are perhaps not properly defined as hallucinogens. Called hashish, bhang, kif, marihuana, and various other names, these hemp-derived alkaloids produce excitation, vivid imagery, euphoria, and occasionally depression and social

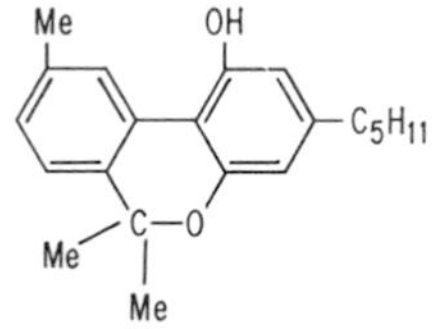

FIGURE 5. Cannabinol.

withdrawal. More major effects, such as disorientation and true hallucinations, usually occur only with overdosage or prolonged use. The smoking of marihuana, the active agent of which is tetrahydrocannabinol, in cigarette form ("sticks" or "joints") has become quite common in the United States among many groups, ranging from criminals to professional musicians to college students, who call it "weed," "pot," "tea," or "Mary Jane." A recent survey at a major university indicated that perhaps 60 per cent of the student body had used marihuana at least once during the year of the study.

MECHANISMS OF ACTION

ELECTROPHYSIOLOGICAL

Electrophysiological changes associated with the administration of psychotogens may be useful in understanding their mechanisms of action. Whether recorded from the cortex or the depths of the brain, most of the hallucinogens move spontaneous electrical activity of the central nervous system toward an alert or arousal pattern. Himwich, in a large series of studies of psychotogens, found consistent cortical alerting patterns with active congeners, but these were apparently dependent on intact lower brain stem cortical connections. The nonpsychotogenic congeners could produce an alerting effect even with these connections severed, thus suggesting action at the level of midbrain or higher sites. Adey and co-workers have shown persistent hippocampal electrical changes, resembling those seen in orienting, with low dosage of LSD. Marrazzi has employed transsynaptic excitability as a criterion, measuring evoked cortical potentials from a homologous area on the opposite hemisphere.

Many chemicals that are alerters of the electrocorticograms inhibit or reduce the transcallosal evoked potential. This suggests that what appears by some electric criteria to be an increase in excitability may actually be functional inhibition of opposing systems. Winters has described a continuum of reticular-cortical excitability from arousal to excitatory-occlusive blocking and disorganization under the influence of certain excitatory drugs, with staring and hallucinatorylike posturing of experimental animals during the maximum drug effect.

West has formulated a general theory of hallucinations that predicts their occurrence under a variety of circumstances when sensory input is impaired but arousal is increased. The combination of cortical arousal and impaired sensory input leads to the emergent awareness of on-going information processing by the brain, the so-called preconscious stream, which is then appreciated by the individual in experiences ranging from fragmentary images to well-developed scenarios. The combination of LSD's effects as a sensory poison—it alters retinal cell excitability and electrochemical activity at the sensory synapses—and as a cortical arouser may account for its hallucinogenic characteristics.

BIOCHEMICAL

Biochemical research in the area of mechanisms of action of the hallucinogens has been growing, but consistent correlates have not yet been established. This may, in part, be because one is dealing with a large number of biochemical phenomena, perhaps different for each drug in spite of similarities in their induced behavioral changes. In addition, the theoretical biochemical models being explored are not easily integrated with behavioral models; the clinician is more likely to feel comfortable when considering formulations from neurophysiology. Such words as alerting and arousal, which appear to have meaning in both the physiological and behavioral realms, even though they may refer to both related and nonrelated phenomena, are not as available in current neurochemical theory.

A number of the hallucinogens apparently undergo metabolic conversions to more active compounds in the body. Szara has done a series of studies on enzymes and urinary metabolites; his results suggest that 6-hydroxylation converts the indole alkylamines to psychoactive metabolites. Mescaline apparently is less active than the products of its oxidative deamination, the trimethoxyphenylethanol and aldehyde. Psilocybin is hydrolyzed to psilocin quite rapidly. The significance of the oxy and hydroxy metabolites of LSD has not yet been evaluated.

Effects on neurohormones. The major theme in research on the biochemical mechanisms of the action of hallucinogens centers around their effects on various postulated neurohormones, including 5-hydroxytryptamine (5-HT or serotonin), norepinephrine, dopamine, histamine, acetylcholine, and a brain polypeptide called "substance P." A series of studies of the interaction of LSD and serotonin could be used as representative of this approach.

Gaddum first reported a marked antagonism between LSD and serotonin in their effects on peripheral structures; LSD blocked the smooth-muscle contraction effect of serotonin. Because of the structural similarities of these and other substances, it was subsequently postulated by Woolley that antimetabolites of serotonin, whether naturally occurring or artificially administered, may prevent the normal functions of serotonin from being accomplished, with psychopathological results. After Brodie demonstrated that serotonin levels were not depleted by LSD and that the reserpine-produced depletion of brain serotonin was not altered by LSD pretreatment, he postulated that LSD blocked serotonin receptor sites. However, a number of more potent blockers of serotonin's action on peripheral structures were subsequently synthesized in the lysergic acid series, but these blocking agents were not hallucinogenic.

More recent studies by Freedman and co-workers showed that LSD produces a consistent increase in the particle-bound fraction of serotonin, but the nonpsychotomimetic lysergic acid congeners are not as effective. These increases are greatest in the brain stem, mesencephalon, hypothalamus, and medial thalamus. That these changes may be significant is suggested by the fact that alterations in the LSD effects on autonomic and behavioral variables are produced by pretreatment with drugs, such as monoamine oxidase inhibitors and reserpine, which respectively increase and decrease brain amines. Similar studies of drug effects on total brain levels, regional distribution, and bound-free partitioning of serotonin and norepinephrine have been carried out with the use of the indole alkylamines and mescaline.

Acetylcholine has been implicated in the action of some hallucinogens. LSD has been shown to be an inhibitor of both pseudocholinesterase and true cholinesterase. The piperidylglycolates are antagonists of the action of acetylcholine on smooth muscle and are structurally similar to acetylcholine. Histamine levels in the brain have been shown to be reduced by LSD, but the bound form appears to be increased.

Effects of methyl groups.   A recent chemical theory of psychosis and psychotogens is related to the presence of methyl groups in both mescaline (a trimethylated hydroxyphenylethylamine) and the N, N-dimethyltryptamines (methylated at nitrogen). Mescaline can be related to catecholamine metabolites, and the substituted tryptamines have the potential of coming from tryptophan. These characteristics have suggested to Smythies and others that hypermethylation of naturally occurring amines may make them more accessible to the central nervous system, which would result in the conversion of a peripherally active compound to one that, after hypermethylation, would penetrate the blood-brain barrier, becoming centrally active and perhaps psychotogenic.

The search for these hypermethylated compounds in the urine of psychotics has been unrewarding except for the recent finding by Friedhoff and Van Winkle of dimethyoxyphenylethylamine in the urine of schizophrenics in much higher incidence than in normals. They have also shown that this substance is made from dopa by liver from schizophrenic patients. Although at first reported to produce catatonia in cats, dimethyoxyphenylethylamine in rather large dosages in man did not prove to be psychotogenic, although it was *not* given in the presence of a monoamine oxidase (MAO) inhibitor, an experiment that should be attempted.

Another interesting series of experiments by Kety and others, related to the hypermethylation hypothesis, indicated that loads of methionine and other methyl donors and tryptophan after pretreatment with an MAO inhibitor produced exacerbations of symptoms in schizophrenics. Whether this was a complex, toxic psychosis instead of an exacerbation of the underlying disease remains to be fully explored.

Effects of amines.   Recent demonstrations of increased amine stores produced by hallucinogens may explain the chemical basis for their neurophysiological excitation of those brain stem and hypothalamic systems associated with arousal, information-scanning, regulation of readiness, and ability to integrate sensory information. As neurochemical horizons expand, in all likelihood such broad categories as amines and such parameters as amount will give way to more specific physicochemical findings, with behavioral phenomena being the final common pathway of a number of different underlying mechanisms.

SCREENING TECHNIQUES

The pharmacological screening techniques for potential psychotogenic compounds are of interest. The most sensitive and pertinent technique for evaluation of these substances is the response of the human experimental subject, especially if care is taken to control for placebo and mental set or suggestive effects. Other efforts to get at these phenomena in man include questionnaires, interviews, and observations by trained observers.

Animal screening tests include check lists of behavior patterns, including aggressivity, excitement, and sociability. More standardized criteria for effects on animal behavior include performance tests like rope-climbing and pole-walking; activity levels in an activity wheel; blocking of learned avoidance responses and depression of positive instrumental responses; indicators of emotionality, such as urination and defecations in a strange environment; and changes in body temperature, since some psychotomimetics produce hyperthermia. Psychotogenic substances have also been found to effect such behaviors as web-spinning patterns in spiders and swimming patterns in Siamese fighting fish.

USE OF HALLUCINOGENS
Nontherapeutic Use

The growing use of hallucinogens is worthy of special attention from the psychosocial point of view. Near many a college campus one may find small gatherings of young people in relatively characteristic costumes quietly talking of liberal causes, pop art, and avant garde theater, intermixed with periods of incoherence or sustained staring, against a background of modern rock music, while smoking "pot" or perhaps sharing a mutual semimystical experience under the influence of black market LSD. The observer wonders if this isn't a modern, secular, pharmacologically more sophisticated version of peyotism in the Native American Church, where groups of Indians under the influence of mescaline wait together through the night for intermittent religious visions.

Marihuana. This issue of marihuana is discussed in more detail in another book in this series, under drug addictions, perhaps improperly so, since it is not truly an addicting substance. Nevitt Sanford has commented, "Only an uneasy Puritanism could support the practice of focusing on the drug addicts (rather than on our five million alcoholics) and treating them as a police problem instead of a medical one, while suppressing harmless drugs such as marihuana and peyote along with the dangerous ones." On the other hand, it cannot be denied that many antisocial activities include marihuana as a partner and that the great majority of addicts to substances like heroin and many of those who now use LSD started out by using marihuana. Nevertheless, there are many who believe that marihuana should be legalized and made available freely on a commercial basis, like alcohol, for those who wish to use it.

LSD. LSD presents a somewhat different problem, one of importance to medicine and social psychiatry. The use of LSD is increasing, in spite of stringent restrictions on its distribution, since it is easily synthesized from commercially available starting materials and a growing demand exists.

The drug seems to have a particular fascination for intellectuals from the middle and upper classes, many of whom have organized a whole way of life around its use.

It would be an oversimplification to say that all those who are involved in LSD cults of one kind or another are necessarily motivated by a pathological desire to withdraw from reality. The experience is too variable and too complex for such an explanation to hold true; contacts with many LSD users convince the observer that their motives range widely. These motives may include an adventuresome desire to seek new experiences, a craving for shared forbidden activity in a group setting to provide a sense of belonging, a manifestation of adolescent and postadolescent rebelliousness, a simple search for sexual opportunities, a genuine attempt to achieve greater self-understanding and self-fulfillment, the exercise of a truly mystical bent in persons with a philosophical orientation inclined toward the transcendental, and, as Blum has described it, the search for fulfillment of a private utopian myth.

THERAPEUTIC USE

In addition, of course, there is the inevitable variety of clinical psychiatric patients who are searching for treatment or relief through the use of chemicals. Their desire may be related not only to a magical hope for cure, enhanced by the reputation of a substance as mysterious and extraordinary as LSD, but also to a very understandable human wish for a short-cut to therapeutic insight, with considerable saving of time, money, and suffering.

The physician may be tempted in some such cases to go along with the patient's request for one or more treatments with LSD. Before yielding to this temptation, however, he would do well to remember that there are other therapeutic maneuvers, such as hypnosis and the Amytal interview, which have been employed to bypass conscious resistance or temporarily modify ego structure and for which there were once high hopes indeed. Although valuable, these methods have in the long run been found to be of limited general application.

In the use of LSD, as in all instances where powerful drugs are employed, it is important for the clinician to have behind him a solid understanding of both pharmacological and psychodynamic factors, sufficient experience to evaluate the effects of the treatment, and a clear-cut formulation of clinical indications and contraindications for the use of the medication in question. There is also a question whether repeated large doses of LSD in certain individuals may lead to apparently irreversible personality changes.

In respect to indications and contraindications, the therapeutic use of LSD and other hallucinogens certainly remains unclear. Among the conditions for which LSD therapy has been tried are alcoholism, narcotic addiction, homosexuality, criminal behavior, various neurotic symptoms, schizophrenia, and resistance in psychotherapy. However, many of these experiments are characterized by vagueness of the therapeutic rationale and poorly controlled clinical conditions. This, in addition to the rare but disturbing prolonged psychotic reactions to these drugs, has led to serious questions about their usefulness in treatment and makes their place in the psychopharmaceutical armamentarium dubious to say the least. Yet the possibility remains that certain individuals may benefit from controlled psychotic-like experiences in which primary process information floods the awareness to produce a self-realizing effect. Therefore, careful clinical research on the therapeutic potentialities of LSD should continue.

REFERENCES

Abood, L. G., and Biel, J. H. Anticholinergic psychotomimetic agents. Int. Rev. Neurobiol., 4: 218, 1962.

Blum, R., editor. *Utopiates*. Atherton Press, New York, 1965.

Brodie, B. B., and Costa, E. Some current views on brain monoamines. Psychopharmacol. Serv. Cent. Bull., 2: 1, 1962.

Connell, P. H. *Amphetamine Psychosis*, Maudsley Monograph No. 5. Chapman & Hall, London, 1958.

Dahlberg, C. C. A survey of the LSD question: a review of four books. Contemp. Psychoanal., 2: 62, 1965.

Demo, P. B., and Morse, W. H. Behavioral pharmacology. Ann. Rev. Pharmacol., 1: 145, 1961.

Friedhoff, A. J., and Van Winkle, E. A biochemical approach to the study of schizophrenia. Amer. J. Psychiat., 121: 1054, 1965.

Giarman, N. H., and Freedman, D. X. Biochemical aspects of the actions of psychotomimetic drugs. Pharmacol. Rev., 17: 1, 1965.

Kety, S. S. The pharmacology of psychotomimetic and psychotherapeutic drugs. Ann. N.Y. Acad. Sci., 66: 417, 1957.

Marrazzi, A. S. The generality of cerebral synaptic drug response and its relation to psychosis. Recent Advances Biol. Psychiat., 6: 1, 1964.

Sanford, N. Foreword. In *Utopiates*, R. Blum, editor, p. xi. Atherton Press, New York, 1965.

Smythies, J. R. Recent advances in the biochemistry of psychosis. Lancet, 1: 1287, 1960.

West, L. J. *Hallucinations*. Grune & Stratton, New York, 1962.

Winters, W. D., and Spooner, C. E. A neurophysiological comparison of GHB with pentobarbital in cats. Electroenceph. Clin. Neurophysiol., 18: 287, 1965.

Woolley, D. W. *The Biochemical Bases of Psychoses*. Wiley, New York, 1962.

CHAPTER 25

Sensory Deprivation

PHILIP SOLOMON, M.D.

HISTORY

INSTANCES OF aberrant mental behavior in explorers, shipwrecked sailors, and prisoners in solitary confinement have been known for centuries. Toward the end of World War II, startling confessions induced by brainwashing in prisoners of war caused a rise of interest in the psychological phenomena brought about by deliberate diminution of sensory input in the human individual.

To test the hypothesis that an important element in brainwashing was prolonged exposure to sensory isolation, Hebb and his coworkers in Montreal brought solitary confinement into the laboratory and demonstrated that volunteer subjects—under conditions of visual, auditory, and tactile deprivation for periods of up to seven days—reacted with increased suggestibility. Some of the subjects also showed symptoms that have since become recognized as characteristic of the sensory deprivation state: anxiety, tension, inability to concentrate, vivid sensory imagery—usually visual, sometimes reaching the proportions of hallucinations with delusionary quality—and intense subjective emotional accompaniment.

Impressed by these results, Lilly went further and, in an attempt to reduce sensory excitation to as near zero as possible, immersed subjects in a tank of tepid water, having them breathe through a blacked out head mask. Symptoms occurred earlier and more intensely. At Boston City Hospital, the tank-type respirator was used to produce sensory deprivation and monotony, with the advantage that polygraphic recordings from the subject became feasible. Soon, many laboratories around the country and in Canada were setting up similar experiments, and in 1958 a national symposium on the subject was held.

EXPERIMENTATION

Interest in sensory deprivation became widespread for many reasons. It was intriguing to think that simply doing nothing and being cut off from the outside world could bring about a transient psychotic-like state. Experimental psychoses could be produced heretofore only by drugs, toxic states, or other heroic measures. Theoretical considerations led to various hypotheses of basic psychological interest that could be tested by exposure to sensory deprivation. Among the parameters studied were physiological stress, cognitive functioning, creativity, imagery, personality type, motivation, suggestibility, learning, and state of consciousness. Possible applications could be recognized in such fields as clinical medicine, psychiatry, public health, industrial psychology, and military life.

Unfortunately, from the earliest reports it became evident that there was often considerable disparity in the results from different laboratories. Prolonging sensory deprivation did or did not modify certain cognitive abilities; intensifying deprivation did or did not increase hallucinatory-like experiences; either visual, auditory, or tactile deprivation was predominantly important. Acrimony thus crept into the field.

Thoughtful workers began to study basic differences in methods. Interest focused on choice of subject (the covert selection factor in the volunteer), instructions to the subject (the role of suggestion), novelty and anxiety in the experimental set-up, breaks in sensory deprivation (feeding, talking, moving), length and type of deprivation (isolation room, water immersion, iron lung), and other variables. Attempts were made to assess the effects on the subjects of concomitant immobilization and social isolation. Efforts to use the same subject in different laboratories were of little avail. Finally, it was recognized that quantification would somehow have to be introduced before it would be possible to standardize techniques and understand the apparent discrepancies in the results of different investigators.

It may be concluded that, although much has yet to be learned about the effects of specific individual and experimental variables, sensory deprivation can definitely lead to deleterious effects on the psychological functioning of human subjects. The implications of this fact are relevant to many areas of psychiatry.

MECHANISMS OF ACTION

Two kinds of explanations are given for the phenomena of sensory deprivation—one psychological, the other physiological.

PSYCHOLOGICAL THEORIES

Psychological explanations were anticipated by Freud, who wrote: "It is interesting to speculate what could happen to ego function if the excitations or stimuli from the external world were either drastically diminished or repetitive. Would there be an alteration in the unconscious mental processes and an effect upon the conceptualization of time?" This prophetic stab is an example of Freud's extraordinary and astonishing insight and intuitive faculty. It has, indeed, developed that, under conditions of sensory deprivation, suppression of the secondary process (perceptual contact with reality) brings about emergence of the primary process (regression, confusion, disorientation, fantasy-formation, primitive emotional responses, hallucinatory activity, and pseudopathological mental reactions).

PHYSIOLOGICAL THEORIES

Physiological explanations, although they sound more scientific with their neuroanatomical terminology, are equally speculative. Presumably, the maintenance of optimum conscious awareness and accurate reality-testing depends on a necessary state of alertness, which, in turn, depends on a constant stream of *changing* stimuli from the external world, mediated through the reticular activating system. In the absence or impairment of such a stream, as occurs in sensory deprivation and in sensory monotony, alertness falls away, direct contact with the outside world diminishes, and the balance of integrated activity tilts in the direction of increased relative prominence of impulses from the inner body and the central nervous system itself.

Reverberating circuits from the association areas and proprioceptive systems, previously inhibited and kept from greater spread by the exteroceptive and activating systems, find themselves released and able to dominate the brain. The result is an increased tendency to rehearsal of memory, meditative thought, reverie, and body image awareness. Material previously repressed and relatively unconscious is given an impetus to appear in consciousness. The breakthrough, when it occurs, is thus experienced as unwilled or spontaneous, since the material involved has been stored relatively inaccessible to willful utilization.

AREAS OF APPLICATION

INDUSTRIAL AND MILITARY PSYCHIATRY

As the phenomena of sensory deprivation become more widely known, it is evoked increasingly to explain puzzling industrial and military accidents. Reference has already been made to its pertinence in brainwashing; it has also been implicated in plane crashes due to grayout and in truck crashes on long hauls over monotonous superhighways. Modern architecture applied to industrial and business plants sometimes has the deleterious effect of producing an environment devoid of sensory stimulation for workers. Assembly-line production may bring about similar results, with increased accident rates.

GENERAL HOSPITAL PSYCHIATRY

In the general hospital the psychiatrist is often consulted in reference to transient psychotic states that appear in conjunction with certain specific treatment procedures in various branches of medicine.

Neurology. Patients with respiratory paralysis treated in a tank-type respirator have long been known to experience peculiar hallucinatory states, which disappear promptly on the patient's removal from the respirator. These states are now recognized to be produced by sensory deprivation.

Medicine. Patients with so-called cardiac psychosis may be suffering from the effects of sensory deprivation. Elderly decompensated patients may be found wandering in the corridors of the hospital at night, when the wards have become quiet. They are usually confused and think they are at home. Too much rest, silence, solitude, and darkness loosen the patients' hold on reality and make them prey to fantasy. Arthritics and other chronic invalids too carefully protected from environmental stimulation may be afflicted similarly.

Ophthalmology. Black-patch psychosis, which occurs postoperatively in patients after cataract or other eye operations, is often characterized by a frenzied confusion and disorientation. Bandaging only one eye or allowing a central peephole is usually corrective or preventive.

Orthopedics. Patients in total body casts or immobilized by head tongs or other severely restricting apparatus may develop disturbing psychotic behavior. The provision of frequent visitors, radio, and television is effective in relief.

Surgery. Postoperative isolation in exaggerated form, especially in open-heart cases, can bring about the complication of postoperative psychosis. Apparently, sensory deprivation must be avoided assiduously, like wound infection.

MENTAL HOSPITAL PSYCHIATRY

The element of sensory deprivation is surely important in delirium tremens, where the best sedative is a sympathetic, attentive nurse. It is probably also a vital factor in the deterioration of the chronic back-ward inmate. When sensory deprivation is neutralized by the many attentions that accompany a new drug study, some previously neglected patients seem to get well.

DEVELOPMENTAL PSYCHIATRY

In addition to cutaneous stimuli, variegated sensory environment is necessary for the normal development of the infant. Mental retardation may be the result of sensory deprivation as well as of biochemical or physiological factors. Animal studies have shown that early sensory deprivation leads to lowered resistance to stress in later life.

GERIATRIC PSYCHIATRY

Psychological functions in the elderly may deteriorate as the result of pitiful social isolation and sensory deprivation. An increasing number of persons among the elderly live out their lives in single, desolate, barren rooms.

PSYCHIATRIC TREATMENT

Results of studies by Azima, Harris, Cohen, and other workers have shown that sensory deprivation can make some psychotic and depressed patients more susceptible to certain treatment methods. The associated regression, for example, favors the anaclitic approach.

CONCLUSION

It has been said that mankind has suffered three major mortifications in its history: Copernicus forced the realization that the earth was not the center of the universe; Darwin stung man with the revelation that he was not created uniquely but evolved from lower animals; and Freud shook man's ultimate conceit, his mind, by showing that much of its vaunted value derived from *unconscious* elements. In a sense the results of sensory deprivation studies may be considered a corollary of this last, in that even man's *conscious* mind can now be seen to be intimately dependent on continuous changing stimuli from the outside world.

REFERENCES

Azima, H., Vispo, R., and Azima, F. J. Observations on anaclitic therapy during sensory deprivation. In *Sensory Deprivation*, P. Solomon, editor, p. 143. Harvard University Press, Cambridge, 1961.

Bexton, W. H., Heron, W., and Scott, T. H. Effects of decreased variation in the sensory environment. Canad. J. Psychol., 8: 70, 1954.

Clark, B., and Graybiel, A. The break-off phenomenon: a feeling of separation from the earth experienced by pilots at high altitudes. J. Aviat. Med., 28: 121, 1957.

Kornfeld, D. S., Zimberg, S., and Malm, J. R. Psychiatric complications of open-heart surgery. New Eng. J. Med., 273: 287, 1965.

Kubzansky, P. E. The effects of reduced environmental stimulation on human behavior: a review. In *The Manipulation of Human Behavior: The Case for Interrogation*, A. D. Biderman and H. Zimmer, editors, p. 51. Wiley, New York, 1961.

Lilly, J. C. Mental effects of reduction of ordinary levels of physical stimuli on intact, healthy persons. Psychiat. Res. Rep., 5: 1, 1956.

Mendelson, J., and Foley, J. An abnormality of mental function affecting patients with poliomyelitis in tank-type respirators. Trans. Amer. Neurol. Ass., 81: 134, 1956.

Rossi, A. M., and Solomon, P. Button pressing for a time-off reward during sensory deprivation: V. Effects of relatively comfortable and uncomfortable sessions. Percep. Motor Skills, 19: 803, 1964.

Solomon, P., editor. *Sensory Deprivation.* Harvard University Press, Cambridge, 1961.

Solomon, P., Leiderman, P. H., Mendelson, J., and Wexler, D. Sensory deprivation. Amer. J. Psychiat., 114: 357, 1957.

CHAPTER 26

Concepts of Normality in Psychiatry

DANIEL OFFER, M.D., and

MELVIN SABSHIN, M.D.

INTRODUCTION

PSYCHIATRISTS HAVE always been interested in psychopathology and abnormality. Only recently, however, has there been a concerted effort to define mental health and normality. By and large, previous books on psychiatry have omitted references to normal or healthy behavior. There has been an implicit understanding that mental health could be defined as the antonym of mental illness. Given such an assumption, the absence of gross psychopathology was often equated with normal behavior. A number of recent trends have cast doubt on the usefulness of this assumption and have made it increasingly important for psychiatrists to become concerned with providing more precise concepts and definitions of mental health and normality.

As psychiatrists have moved out of their consulting rooms and hospital wards into the community, they have come into contact with segments of the population not previously seen. The broader acceptance of preventive psychiatry, including primary prevention, has necessitated reexamination of preventing *what* in *whom*. Psychiatrists have also become increasingly involved in agency consultation; they are called on to make decisions about who is healthy rather than to decide who is too sick for various positions. Interest in evaluating the outcome of psychiatric therapeutic endeavors has also brought the issue of mental health into focus. Indeed, one of the weaknesses of much work on assessing therapeutic outcome has related to lack of clarity regarding the concepts of normality and mental health.

This chapter attempts to clarify some of the conceptual issues related to normality and mental health. It cannot provide a definitive answer to the question, "What is mental health or normality?" Such an answer must evolve out of new research and new experience. It does attempt, however, to delineate the current perspectives of normality and to point to new directions that give promise of elucidating the issues still further.

FOUR PERSPECTIVES OF NORMALITY

The many theoretical and clinical concepts of normality seem to fall into four functional perspectives of normality. Although each perspective is unique and has its own definition and description, the perspectives do complement each other, so that together they represent the total behavioral and social science approach to normality. The four perspectives are: (1) normality as health, (2) normality as utopia, (3) normality as average, and (4) normality as process.

NORMALITY AS HEALTH

The first perspective is basically the traditional medical psychiatric approach to health and illness. Most physicians equate normality with health and view health as an almost universal phenomenon. As a result, behavior is assumed to be within normal limits when no manifest psychopathology is present. If all behavior were to be put on a scale, normality would encompass the major portion of the continuum, and abnormality would be the small remainder.

This definition of normality correlates with the traditional model of the doctor who attempts to free his patient from grossly observable signs and symptoms. To this physician, the lack of signs or symptoms indicates health. In other words, health in this context refers to a *reasonable* rather than an *optimal* state of functioning. In its simplest form, this perspective is illustrated by Romano, who states that a healthy person is one who is reasonably free of undue pain, discomfort, and disability.

NORMALITY AS UTOPIA

The second perspective conceives of normality as that harmonious and optimal blending of the diverse elements of the mental apparatus that culminates in optimal functioning. Such a definition emerges clearly when psychiatrists or psychoanalysts talk about the ideal person or when they grapple with a complex problem of discussing their criteria of a successful treatment. This approach can be traced directly back to Freud, who, when discussing normality, stated, "A normal ego is like normality in general, an ideal fiction."

Although this approach is characteristic of a significant segment of psychoanalysts, it is by no means unique to them. It can also be found among psychotherapists in the field of psychiatry and among psychologists of quite different persuasions.

NORMALITY AS AVERAGE

The third perspective is commonly employed in normative studies of behavior and is based on a mathematical principle of the bell-shaped curve. This approach conceives of the middle range as normal and of *both* extremes as deviant. The normative approach based on this statistical principle describes each individual in terms of general assessment and total score. Variability is described only within the context of total groups, not within the context of one individual.

Although this approach is more commonly used in psychology and biology than in psychiatry, psychiatrists have been using pencil-and-paper tests recently to a much larger extent than in the past. Not only do psychiatrists use the results of I.Q. tests, the Rorschach test, and the Thematic Apperception Test, but they also construct their own tests and questionnaires. Conceptually, the normality-as-average perspective is similar to Kardiner's basic personality structure for various cultures and subcultures. In developing modal personalities for different societies, one assumes that the typologies of character can be statistically measured.

NORMALITY AS PROCESS

The fourth perspective stresses that normal behavior is the end result of interacting systems. Based on this definition, temporal changes are essential to a complete definition of normality. In other words, the normality-as-process perspective stresses changes or processes rather than a cross-sectional definition of normality.

Investigators who subscribe to this approach can be found in all the behavioral and social sciences. Most typical of the concepts in this perspective are Grinker's thesis of a unified theory of behavior and Erikson's conceptualization of epigenesis of personality development and the seven developmental stages essential in the attainment of mature adult functioning.

NEW DIRECTIONS IN STUDIES OF NORMALITY

Although there is growing awareness of the importance of clarifying the various perspectives on normality, there is also an increasing effort to develop empirical research in this area. These new developments are seen in almost all aspects of behavioral science, but the following areas are most prototypic of the new directions: (1) psychoanalysis, (2) human development, (3) social and community psychiatry, and (4) psychiatric research.

PSYCHOANALYSIS

In addition to their growing involvement in linking normality and social process, psychoanalysts have continued their long-term interest in elucidating the vicissitudes of normal psychopathology of everyday life. Psychoanalysts have increasingly demonstrated their interest in normal adaptation to the social environment.

Hartmann has given primary leadership to this trend in his conceptualization of autonomous functions of the ego and the ego's conflict-free sphere. The concept of autonomous and conflict-free functions of the ego has intensified clinical exploration of the mechanisms whereby some individuals lead a relatively normal life in the presence of extraordinary external traumatic experiences. In discussing the average expectable environment, Hartmann has provided a framework wherein the molding of character structure for specific contexts becomes more easily understood.

Erikson's work has also served as a bridge linking developmental stages and social process. His concept of modal adaptive tasks at phase-specific stages of life not only has provided a process analysis of normal behavior but allows a cross-sectional analysis throughout life. Thus, it becomes possible to establish specific modes of adaptation.

HUMAN DEVELOPMENT

In the area of human development, Anna Freud has begun to delineate aspects of normal growth and development in children. Like Erikson, she has been interested in empirical research in helping to clarify how the child copes with a variety of adaptive tasks. The field of child development has been facilitated in its growth recently by a number of reports of longitudinal studies (Kagen). The primary point to be emphasized is that massive data are being collected regarding individual growth and development throughout life. Populations not heretofore studied have been examined with depth and precision.

The study of Offer and Sabshin (1963, 1965) on adolescents is prototypic of this trend. They have studied a group of young adolescents throughout their high school years. The group was selected by means of a questionnaire, and psychiatric interviews have been conducted with a modal sample throughout the high school years. One group of normal teenagers are being studied over a period of time. Studies like this make it possible to formulate a baseline of normal adolescent behavior and psychodynamics.

Based on their experience with a sample of adolescent subjects, the authors have formulated an operational definition of normality that is not an absolute one but is descriptive of one type of middle-class adolescent population. The criteria best describing the teenagers are: (1) almost complete absence of gross psychopathology, severe physical defects, and severe physical illness; (2) mastery of previous developmental tasks without serious setbacks; (3) ability to experience affects flexibly and to bring their conflicts actively to reasonably successful resolutions; (4) relatively good object relationships with parents, siblings, and peers; and (5) feeling a part of a larger cultural environment and being aware of its norms and values.

These authors based their conclusions on studies of typical or modal groups rather than generalizing from their experience with patients, as had been the predominant pattern in the past.

It is important to note that the developmental approach is also being used for adults. Studies of adaptation to marriage, to parenthood, to work, and to leisure activities have become increasingly prominent. Precise empirical studies are being conducted regarding developmental problems in the period of involution and decline.

The development of geriatrics has moved in a more normative direction. The deficit-focusing orientation of earlier studies in gerontology has been replaced to a significant extent by a normative framework that asks, in effect, "How do older people cope with the adaptational tasks of the sixties, seventies, and beyond?"

Social and Community Psychiatry

The rapid evolution of social and community psychiatry has given even broader possibilities to studying normative populations. As psychiatrists and their collaborators have moved into the community, they have become involved in providing services for and conducting research with populations not heretofore seen by the mental health professionals. Epidemiological investigations have become increasingly precise and sophisticated. One of the pioneering studies in the epidemiology of illness and health was carried out by Leighton et al. This attempt to ascertain the degree of sickness and health in a large population serves as a paradigm for investigations on a variety of target populations. Although a number of models for social and community psychiatry have developed over the past few years, it has become accepted that community psychiatry involves investigation and service to meet the mental health needs of a functional or geographic community.

One important model for such community psychiatry activity is carried out in the Woodlawn Mental Health Center. At this center, studies have been carried out on all of the children entering first grade in the public and the parochial schools within this geographic community. Over a two-year span, four thousand first-graders have been studied. The investigators have been interested in the ratings of adaptation and maladaptation by the teachers, the parents, and the mental health researchers for this entire population. They are also interested in carrying out follow-up studies to determine the impact of changes in experimental groups on the ultimate rating of adaptation and maladaptation.

It is impressive to note that this primary preventive approach combines the interest of child development with community psychiatry. This merging of two trends within the mental health field has great promise in helping to clarify definitions of adaptation and normality as well as maladaptation and abnormality.

PSYCHIATRIC RESEARCH

Psychiatric research has shown a resurgence of interest in the question of the use of controls for a variety of psychiatric investigations. Although a number of studies have focused on the emotional problems of volunteers for psychiatric experimentation, there is a general awareness that increased precision is necessary in selecting controls for a specific psychiatric research question. The report by the Group for the Advancement of Psychiatry has documented this specific need.

Although many investigators have become engaged in studies of controls or normal samples in the context of elucidating an experimental question regarding psychopathology, a host of new investigations have been undertaken to study normal populations as such. Grinker's presentation of a sample of homoclites is prototypic of this trend. His sample included an overwhelming number of individuals who ordinarily would not have been seen in a psychiatrist's office. They represent well-adjusted individuals whose aspirations and capacities fall within a comparable range of each other.

Psychiatrists are studying the ways individuals adapt to a variety of situational stresses. The stresses vary from adjustment to physical illness and physical hardships, such as the astronauts undergo, to adaptation to marriage, parenthood, leisure, and aging. The study by Silber et al. of the normal coping mechanisms mobilized and utilized by adolescents in the transition from high school to college is one example of such a study.

THE FUTURE

The trend toward increased study of normative populations can be equally well-documented in a variety of other mental health areas. Convergences have already begun to take place—for example, the convergence of community psychiatric studies and child development within an epidemiological framework. Increasing numbers of such convergences will probably take place during the next few decades. It is not yet possible to synthesize these multiple trends either conceptually or pragmatically. Many more studies will be necessary before such an integrating synthesis will be possible. It is likely, however, that such a synthesis will become possible within a decade, at which time the various perspectives and the various empirical studies can be put together into a more meaningful whole.

REFERENCES

Erikson, E. H. Identity and the life cycle: selected papers. Psychol. Issues, 1: 1, 1959.

Freud, A. *Normality and Pathology in Childhood*. International Universities Press, New York, 1965.

Freud, S. Analysis, terminable and interminable. In *Collected Papers*, vol. 5, p. 316. Hogarth Press, London, 1950.

Grinker, R. R., Sr., editor. *Toward a Unified Theory of Human Behavior*. Basic Books, New York, 1956.

Grinker, R. R., Sr., Grinker, R. R., Jr., and Timberlake, J. Mentally healthy young males (homoclites). Arch. Gen. Psychiat., 6: 405, 1962.

Group for the Advancement of Psychiatry. *Some Observations on Controls in Psychiatric Research*, Report 42. Group for the Advancement of Psychiatry, New York, 1959.

Hartmann, H. *Ego Psychology and the Problem of Adaptation*. International Universities Press, New York, 1958.

Kagen, J. American longitudinal research in psychological development. Child Develop., 35: 1, 1964.

Kardiner, A. *The Individual and His Society*. Columbia University Press, New York, 1939.

Leighton, A. H. *My Name Is Legion*. Basic Books, New York, 1959.

Offer, D., and Sabshin, M. The psychiatrist and the normal adolescent. Arch. Gen. Psychiat., 9: 427, 1963.

Offer, D., and Sabshin, M. *Normality: Theoretical and Clinical Concepts of Mental Health*. Basic Books, New York, 1966.

Offer, D., Sabshin, M., and Marcus, D. Clinical evaluation of normal adolescents. Amer. J. Psychiat., 121: 864, 1965.

Romano, J. Basic orientation and education of the medical student. JAMA, 143: 409, 1950.

Silber, S., Coelho, G. R., Murphey, E. B., Hamburg, D. H., Perlin, L. I., and Rosenberg, M. Competent adolescents coping with college decisions. Arch. Gen. Psychiat., 6: 517, 1961.

CHAPTER 27

Normal Psychosexual Functioning

HAROLD I. LIEF, M.D., and
DAVID M. REED, Ph.D.

INTRODUCTION

HUMAN SEXUAL BEHAVIOR is so diverse and its interrelations with almost every facet of life are so complex that a comprehensive understanding of it is extremely difficult. Understanding has been further complicated by age-old prejudices, myths, superstitions, half-truths, and erroneous theories that, under the protective mantle of "science," have bedeviled the serious investigator of human sexuality. The intense emotions surrounding sex have further hampered such investigation.

DEFINITIONS

NORMAL SEXUAL BEHAVIOR

Extreme or deviant behavior is easier to discern and comprehend than is the usual range of behavior. In sexual behavior, as in medicine, the normal has generally been extrapolated from observations of the abnormal. To deal with this problem by a different method, Kinsey et al. undertook a monumental study of representative samples of the population.

In this chapter, however, normal is not being used primarily in a statistical sense, although knowing how most people behave sexually is obviously useful, or in the sense of social norm, meaning behavior acceptable to people with average attitudes toward sex, codified by law, social institutions, or religion. In any case, the criteria for social norm based on morality, law, and social customs are contradictory. For example, coitus among unmarried partners is morally abnormal but normal by social custom, accepted by law in half the states and disapproved in the other half.

Normal is used here in the traditional medical sense of healthy or non-pathological. It signifies behavior that is adaptive not only to the requirements of society but also to the individual's needs for pleasure, growth, and self-realization or enhancement of his capacities for personality development. The difficulties in this approach are clear: (1) The needs of the individual may conflict with the needs of society. (2) The individual's pursuit of pleasure may conflict with his search for self-realization. (3) His pursuits of short-range and long-range pleasure may conflict with each other. (4) The value system used by the physician or therapist in reaching judgments of healthy or adaptive behavior is determined by his own cultural value orientation and his personal experiences. For these reasons, no one has satisfactorily delineated normal or healthy psychosexual function.

Since the delineation of normality in human sexual behavior is beset with difficulties, clinical experience suggests that any delineation should not be drawn too rigidly or too narrowly. From a clinical standpoint, sexual behavior may be considered normal even when it does not involve exclusively monogamous heterosexual intercourse or the use of stimulation techniques confined to the primary sexual organs or when it does not culminate in the achievement of mutually satisfactory orgasm. Sexual behavior that deviates widely from such delimited standards may not usefully be designated pathological unless the behavior is also compulsive, exclusive, destructive, or accompanied by much anxiety and guilt. Thus, sex outside of marriage, masturbation, and various forms of sexual stimulation involving other than the primary sexual organs may still fall within normal limits, depending on the total context.

PSYCHOSEXUAL

Further complications occur in use of the term "psychosexual." A person's sexuality is so closely entwined with his total personality—affecting his concept of himself, his relations with others, and his general patterns of behavior—that it is virtually impossible to speak of sexuality as a separate entity. The term "psychosexual" is, therefore, used here to imply personality development and functioning as these are affected by one's sexuality. It is clearly not limited to sexual feelings and behavior alone, nor is it synonymous with libido in the broad Freudian sense.

In Freud's view, all pleasurable impulses or activities are *ultimately* sexual and should, therefore, be called sexual from the start. This generalization has led not only to endless misinterpretations of Freudian sexual concepts by the laity but also to confusion of one motivation with another by psychiatrists. For example, some oral activities are directed toward obtaining food, whereas others are directed toward achieving sexual gratification, but merely because both are pleasure-seeking and both use the same organ, they are not, as Freud contended, necessarily sexual. Labeling all pleasure-seeking behavior "sexual" precludes clarification of motivation. On the other hand, a person may use sexual activities for gratification of nonsexual needs, such as dependent, aggressive, or status needs. Although sexual and nonsexual impulses may jointly motivate behavior, the analysis of behavior depends on understanding underlying individual motivations and their interactions.

SEXUAL LEARNING IN CHILDHOOD

Not until Freud described the impact of a child's experience on his character as an adult did the world recognize the universality of sexual activity and sexual learning in children. This concept has had greater effect on treatment and on education than any of the other sexual theories Freud expressed. If we put the child's learning in a transactional information (general systems theory) model, we can retain many of Freud's clinical insights while abandoning his psychic instinctual model. For example, as Gagnon indicated, the initiation of sexuality may derive not from the child's nature as much as from the sexual interests of the parents and their labeling of certain aspects of the child's behavior as sexual. Certain oral behavior and the learning of bowel control in the child can be reconceived in terms of their later effect on his sexual life without insisting that these activities are either completely sexual or protosexual from the beginning.

Most of the sexual learning experiences in childhood occur without thought on the part of the parent, but the consciousness of sex usually determines the degree of vigor of play, the frequency of father-child and mother-child contacts, the tolerance for aggression, the reinforcement or extinction of activity or passivity and of intellectual, aesthetic, or athletic interests. As Gagnon says, "The period of contact, the frequency of contact, and the psychological set of the parents can be expected to have differential consequences for gender role development."

It is clear from direct observation of children in various situations that genital play in infants is part of the normal pattern of development of the healthy child in contact with an affectionate mother. Interaction with mothers and peers is necessary for the development of effective adult heterosexual contacts in monkeys, according to Harlow, a finding that has relevance to the normal socialization of children. There is a critical period in development beyond which the infant may be immune or resistant to certain types of stimulation but during which he is particularly susceptible to the same stimuli. The detailed relation of critical periods to pyschosexual development has yet to be established; presumably Freud's stages of psychosexual development—oral, anal, phallic, and genital—are only gross approximations.

PSYCHOSEXUAL FACTORS

A person's sexuality is dependent on three interrelated factors: his sexual identity, his gender identity, and his sexual behavior. These factors affect his personality growth, development, and functioning, and their totality is here termed psychosexual. Clearly, this is something more than physical sex, coital or noncoital, and something less than every aspect of behavior directed toward attaining pleasure.

SEXUAL IDENTITY

Sexual identity refers to a person's sense of maleness or femaleness, which, in turn, depends on his biologic sexual characteristics: chromosomes, external genitalia, internal genitalia, hormonal composition, gonads, and secondary sex characteristics. In normal development these form a cohesive pattern, so that a person has no doubt about his sex.

Modern embryological studies have shown that all mammalian embryos, both the genetically male and the genetically female, are anatomically female during the early stages of fetal life. Differentiation of the male from the female results from the action of fetal androgen; the action begins about the sixth week of embryonic life and is completed by the end of the third month. Sherfey contends that these observations have "demonstrated conclusively that the concept of the initial anatomical bisexuality or equipotentiality of the embryo is erroneous." Sherfey's refutation has far-reaching implications regarding normal human sexual responsivity and alleged causes of homosexuality and other sexual deviations.

By the age of two or three years, almost everyone has a firm conviction that "I am male" or "I am female." Even if maleness and femaleness develop normally, the person still has the adaptive task of developing a sense of masculinity and femininity.

GENDER IDENTITY

According to Stoller, gender identity "connotes psychological aspects of behavior related to masculinity and femininity." Gender he considers social, whereas sex is biological; "most often the two are relatively congruent, that is, males tend to be manly and females womanly," but sex and gender may develop in conflicting or even opposite ways.

Gender identity results from an almost infinite series of cues derived from experiences with family members, teachers, friends, and co-workers as well as from cultural phenomena. Physical characteristics derived from one's biological sex—such as general physique, body shape, and physical dimensions—interrelate with an intricate system of stimuli—including rewards, punishment, and parental gender labels—to establish gender identity.

Cultural factors, as Cohen has pointed out, may establish conflicts about gender identity by stereotyping certain nonsexual behavior as masculine or feminine:

Our narrow conceptions of what is manly and hence not womanly, of what is womanly and hence not manly (conceptions which exclude large areas of thought and feeling which might appropriately be considered as human rather than narrowly sex-bound) can be seen to give rise to difficulties in our development and our relations with each other and with our children.

Artistic or intellectual interests in a boy may be regarded by his parents and perhaps himself as feminine, whereas a girl who strives for competence, intellectual development, and independence may be made to feel uneasy if these activities are labeled masculine.

The formation of gender identity is based on three factors: parental and cultural attitudes, the infant's external genitalia, and a biological force under genic influence, now identified as being physiologically active as early as the sixth week of fetal life. Whereas family, cultural, and biological influences may complicate establishment of a sense of masculinity or femininity, the standard and healthy outcome is a more or less secure sense of identification with one's biological sex, a stable gender identity.

Gender role. Related to and in part derived from gender identity is gender role behavior. This is described in the words of Money and the Hampsons as

all those things that a person says or does to disclose himself or herself as having the status of boy or man, girl or woman, respectively. . . . A gender role is not established at birth but is built up cumulatively through experiences encountered and transacted—through casual and unplanned learning, through explicit instruction and inculcation, and through spontaneously putting two and two together to make sometimes four and sometimes, erroneously, five.

The standard and healthy outcome is a congruence of gender identity and gender role. Although biological attributes are significant, the major factor in attaining the role appropriate to one's sex is learning; the influence of chromosomal and hormonal sex, for example, can be overcome by opposite-sex assignment by parents or by other learning experiences.

Gender role can appear to be in opposition to gender identity. A person may identify with his own sex but adopt the dress, hair style, or other characteristics of the opposite sex, as many of our present teenagers do. Or a person may identify with the opposite sex, yet for expediency adopt much of the behavior characteristic of his own sex.

SEXUAL BEHAVIOR

Masturbation. Masturbation is usually a normal precursor of object-related sexual behavior. In the words of Dearborn, "No other form of sexual activity has been more frequently discussed, more roundly condemned, and more universally practiced than masturbation." Research by Kinsey et al. into the prevalence of masturbation indicated that nearly all men and three-fourths of all women masturbate sometime during their life.

Longitudinal studies of development show that sexual self-stimulation is very common in infancy and childhood. Just as the infant learns to explore the functions of his fingers and mouth, so it is inevitable for him to do the same with his genitalia. Pleasurable sensations result from any gentle touch to the genital region. These sensations, coupled with the ordinary desire for exploration of one's body, produce a normal interest in masturbatory pleasure at this time. As the youngster acquires playmates, this curiosity about his and others' genitalia motivates episodes of exhibitionism or genital exploration, and such experiences, unless blocked by guilty fear, contribute to continued pleasure from sexual stimulation.

With the advent of puberty, the upsurge of sex hormones, and the development of secondary sex characteristics, sexual curiosity is intensified, and masturbation increases. The adolescent is physically capable of coitus and orgasm but is usually inhibited by social restraints. He is under the dual and often conflicting pressures of establishing his sexual identity and controlling his sexual impulses. The result is a great deal of physiological sexual tension that demands release, and masturbation is a normal way of reducing sexual tensions. An important emotional difference between the pubescent child and the youngster of earlier years is the presence of coital fantasies accompanying masturbation in the adolescent. These fantasies are an important adjunct to the development of sexual identity, for in the comparative safety of his imagination the adolescent learns to perform the adult sex role. This form of autoerotic activity is usually maintained into the young adult years, when it is normally replaced by coitus.

It is incorrect to assume that couples in a sexual relation abandon masturbation entirely. When coitus is unsatisfactory or is unavailable because of illness or absence of the partner, self-stimulation often serves an adaptive purpose, combining sensual pleasure and tension release.

Moral taboos against masturbation have generated myths that masturbation causes mental illness or a decrease in sexual potency. There is no scientific evidence to support such claims. Masturbation is a psychopathological symptom only when it becomes a compulsion beyond the willful control of the person. It is then a symptom of emotional disturbance, not because it is sexual but because it is compulsive. Masturbation is almost a universal and inevitable aspect of psychosexual development, and in most cases it is adaptive.

Orgasm. The development of adaptive sexual behavior involves an increasing interest in the opposite sex, first at the level of fantasy and dreams and then in dating and courting. Orgastic behavior for both men and women involves the sexual arousal state followed by four stages, as described by Masters and Johnson: excitement, plateau, orgasmic, and resolution phases.

The sexual motive or arousal state is affected by many factors, such as the partner, the setting, the mood, and the positive or negative effect of emotions (love, anxiety).

When the degree of motivation for orgastic release is high, excitement occurs quickly. In the male the initial physiological response to effective sexual somatogenic or psychogenic stimulation is penile erection; in the female it is vaginal lubrication. Lubrication occurs within ten to thirty seconds and is the result of a sweating phenomenon on the walls of the vaginal barrel.

If excitement is maintained, the intensity of the response usually increases rapidly, and the human male or female enters the plateau phase of the sexual cycle. The duration of the plateau phase again depends on the effectiveness of the stimuli and the strength of the drive for orgastic release.

The orgasmic phase lasts only a few seconds, during which basic responses of the body to sexual stimulation—widespread vasocongestion and generalized increase in muscle tension—are released. Both the intensity and duration of orgasmic experience vary widely in women, whereas in men there is less individual variation.

In men the resolution phase includes a refractory period that prevents restimulation until its termination. In women the potential for multiple orgastic experiences is almost unlimited.

Important findings in the research of Masters and Johnson include the following observations. (1) The nature of the orgasm in women is the same, regardless of the method or zone of stimulation, and it is as definite as it is in men. There is no such thing as a vaginal orgasm distinct from a clitoral orgasm; anatomically and physiologically there is only one type of orgasm: the rhythmic contractions of the outer third of the vaginal barrel, releasing the vasocongestion of the greatly distended circumvaginal venous plexi and vestibular bulbs surrounding the lower third of the vagina. (2) The clitoris retracts about sixty to ninety seconds before orgasm, an essential feature of a mechanism of the clitoral region, which maintains continuous stimulation of the retracted clitoris by a rhythmic pulling on the edematous prepuce during coition or by preputial friction during direct stimulation of the clitoral region. Clitoral responsivity is far more important than vaginal sensations in producing orgasm. (3) With full sexual arousal, women are normally capable of many orgasms. As many as six or more can be achieved with intravaginal coition, and many more orgasms can be obtained in an hour by direct stimulation of the clitoral region—limited only by physical exhaustion.

Sexual drive and expression is multidetermined and can be profoundly affected by physical and psychological factors. Normal strength of the sexual drive varies widely with age, sex, and the individual. The usual frequency of orgasm in mature men is two or three times a week; women have a much greater and, according to Masters and Johnson, an almost unlimited orgastic potential. It is a matter of practical importance that there is a disparity in the age-related strength of the sexual drive in men and in women. The peak of sexual drive for men occurs during late adolescence, after which it gradually declines. Women reach the maximum of sexual desire in their 30's, particularly after the birth of one or more children.

Sherfey hypothesizes that the rise of modern civilization "was contingent on the suppression of the inordinate cyclic sexual drive of women because . . . women's uncurtailed continuous hypersexuality would drastically interfere with maternal responsibilities; . . . with the rise of the settled agriculture economies . . . large families of known parentage were mandatory and could not evolve until the inordinate sexual demands of women were curbed."

Social sexual morality, operating primarily through the effect of guilty fear (a sense of wrongdoing and a fear of punishment internalized as a fear of conscience), has impaired the orgastic potential of many women. Guilty fear and other emergency emotions—such as anxiety, anger, and guilty anger—may delay or completely inhibit orgasm in the female and prevent erection or speed up orgasm in the male. Since emergency emotions increase the disparity between the time it takes to reach orgasm in men and women, hastening it in men and retarding it in women, healthy psychosexual functioning requires minimal or absent emergency emotions and is enhanced by positive or welfare emotions, such as pride, joy, and love. Of these, in the normal person, love for the partner has the greatest effect in increasing sexual pleasure and performance.

LOVE, INTIMACY, AND SEX

As we have seen, healthy psychosexual functioning depends on the development of sexual identity, gender identity, appropriate gender role behavior, and adequate sexual performance. It also requires the development of the capacity to love and to form intimate relations with a person of the opposite sex. If anything is more complex than sex, it is love. If sex is diversified and varied, love is more so; if sexual behavior is the result of the subtle interplay of multiple motivations and needs, love is more so. If man's capacity to perform sexually may be inhibited by faulty learning and the influence of emergency emotions during childhood and adolescence, even more subject to the vicissitudes of unfortunate life experiences during these formative years is man's capacity to love and to be intimate.

In a child's healthy evolution into adulthood, the potential for enjoyment of physical sexual sensations and the ability to give and to receive love have interrelated lines of development. It is as if two streams come from a similar source, the headwaters being the love of mother for child, then diverge, cross, become confluent, separate, come together again, and separate again and again until ultimately, in the state of being in love, they fuse again in a crescendo of power and fulfillment.

DEFINITION OF LOVE

A precise definition of love is difficult. Rado defines love as a sustained emotional response to a known source of pleasure. There are as many kinds of love, therefore, as there are types of pleasure, and typical of being in love is a desire to maintain closeness to the love object. This circular definition includes varieties of love besides sexual love, such as parental, filial, fraternal, anaclitic, and narcissistic love, as well as love for group, school, and country. Here we are concerned specifically with love enhanced by sex, and sex enhanced by love. The development of sexuality and the development of the ability to love have reciprocal effects on each other.

STAGES OF LOVE

As with sexuality, love evolves through a number of stages. In the beginning, since he is dominated by the wish to gratify his needs, the child loves himself. His parents are the principal instruments by which his needs are met; hence, a magical love for his parents appears, a love marked by illusions that parental figures are omnipotent, capable of immediate and complete satisfaction of the child's basic needs, and constant in their love for the child, regardless of his misbehavior. As the child becomes more and more aware of others, he learns the pleasure of object love and gradually is encouraged to feel sympathy, affection, and love toward others in various interpersonal situations. These feelings and related behavior are reinforced by love, praise, and gifts from others. The achievement of object love by the child is the goal of early acculturation, for the ability to cooperate and compromise allows the developing child to acquire satisfactory group behavior, which in turn assures acceptable social patterns in later life.

Although the influence of sex on the development of love begins with the development of early sexual identity, it becomes more evident during development of gender identity and gender role behavior. As the child is taught in many ways to discriminate between masculinity and femininity, he is also challenged to become aware of differences between men and women in their attitudes toward sex as an expression of love. Boys, for example, are encouraged to express sexual love assertively and girls more passively.

Freud made the error, in his libido theory, of thinking that there were fixed quantities of love and consequently that, as in a closed system of energy exchange, the more one loves himself, the less love he has to give another. As Fromm pointed out, however, self-love or self-regard is a fundamental requirement of the capacity to love another, and the two are not mutually exclusive.

When a person is able to give and receive love with a minimum of fear and conflict, he has the capacity to develop genuinely intimate relations with others. When involved in an intimate relation, he actively strives for the growth and happiness of the loved person. Mature heterosexual love is marked by the intimacy that is a special attribute of the relationship between a man and a woman. The quality of intimacy in a mature sexual relationship is what May terms an ability of "active receiving," wherein a person, while loving, permits himself to be loved. This capability indicates a profound awareness of love for another as well as for oneself. In such a loving relation, sex acts as a catalyst. May described the values of sexual love as an expansion of one's self-awareness, the experience of tenderness, increase of self-affirmation and pride, and sometimes, at the moment of orgasm, even loss of feelings of separateness. It is in this setting that sex and love are reciprocally enhancing and healthily fused.

The nuances of the interplay between love and sex in a heterosexual relation reflect strength, not weakness. Persons who establish alliances based primarily on sex, in which each uses the other as an object for orgastic release and little else, may soon tire of each other. At the opposite extreme, couples attracted to each other primarily for reasons of security, rather than sex, sacrifice a very important aspect of psychosexual experience.

Normal heterosexual love has three major components, called by Rado "sexual," "magical," and "sensual." Sexual love is dominated by the desire for shared orgastic release. Magical love is surrounded by the expectation that the love object is so powerful and wise that he will provide care and security as effortlessly as one's parents appeared to do in childhood. Sensual love is stimulated by an appreciation of the physical attractions of the loved one and an idealization of them on a highly subjective level. A couple may experience any of these types of love at different times and at different emotional levels, depending on the vicissitudes of life and the proclivities and interactions of the two people. A constant interweaving of the three types of love is likely to produce the most enduring and fulfilling relation.

MARITAL AND NONMARITAL SEXUAL RELATIONS

Historically, marriage has provided for the fulfillment of sexual desires, the bearing of children, and distribution of wealth. Only relatively recently in the history of man has marriage been undertaken as an act of love; in the past, most cultures arranged marriages primarily on economic grounds. American civilization, under the impact of the Judeo-Christian tradition, has been characterized by a respect for the individual person based on two dominant values, achievement and equality. The result has been the development of a social system that attaches high status and prestige to the person who realizes his highest potentials as a citizen and as a human being. At first, this attitude applied exclusively to men, but in recent generations it has included both sexes.

Indeed, the most profound change in the modern sexual revolution has been traced to the altered role of woman. Whereas woman was once expected to accept a double standard in which man alone was permitted sexual freedom, she is now challenging this male prerogative. There is a strong trend toward the dispelling of psychosexual conditioning that previously made women feel guilty and excessively inhibited in sexual matters. Many observers consider this trend indicative of a future era of sexual freedom in which both sexes will relate on a more equal basis than has been the case in the past.

CHOICE OF LOVE OBJECT

The increasing equality of the sexes profoundly affects the choice of love object. A person is attracted toward a potential mate for various reasons. One may be a purely physical attraction, which ordinarily establishes a transient relation. Another may be a magical desire to find the perfect lover, whose qualities will be reminiscent of the idealized qualities of one's parents or other sources of love and affection in the past. Other emotional reasons for choosing a mate stem from a variety of neurotic patterns in one's own personality. For example, one may take a partner to protect pride or security rather than to satisfy feelings of love. A woman who considers herself unattractive sexually may choose a mate who is passive and dependable yet sufficiently unattractive that she does not have to compete with other women. A man who has considerable doubt about his masculinity may turn to a woman who has great sex appeal on the surface but in reality may not demand exceptional sex drive or performance. Essentially neurotic themes such as these exist in all personalities and probably in all matings. When they predominate and the couple act mainly to exchange patterns of exploitation or when interlocking complementary needs fail to bring sufficient security or happiness, discomfort and anxiety occur, and a breakdown in the relation is possible.

PREMARITAL INTERCOURSE

Kirkendall noted that there is no consensus about the effects of premarital intercourse on successful marital adjustment. He found no statistical evidence in favor of premarital sex helping later sexual adjustment but pointed out that a couple's viewpoint toward premarital sex may range from a highly positive one to a very damaging and disruptive one. He also noted that the negative effects on marriage attributed to premarital sex have been exaggerated in our culture, presumably as a result of religious views that equate sex outside of marriage with sin. Just as Kinsey found that the most important social coordinate that had a negative effect on the sexual behavior of women was religion, so did Kirkendall note that those who are reared with a rigid attitude toward sex are likely to experience guilt reactions in either premarital or marital intercourse.

At this point some evaluation of cultural norms is in order. An adaptive sexual relation is possible between partners who are not married. The achievement of healthy intimacy and mutual respect cannot be traced to the ritual of marriage by itself. As many neurotic interactions occur in marriage as outside of it. In view of our cultural disapproval of nonmarital coitus, however, a large number of premarital coital acts may be nonsexually motivated; they may, for example, represent acting out of rebellion against authority. There is, thus, a somewhat greater chance that a premarital sexual relation is partly neurotic in origin than that a marriage is neurotic. This statement requires qualification, however, since certain sectors of our society permit premarital sexual relations with a minimum of guilty fear. Despite the neurotic bases of many marriages, including destructive sexual behavior, the psychological and social assets of marriage are nonetheless inestimable. Marriage can provide the structure for the maintenance of love, intimacy, sexual gratification, and development of family life over many years.

PROBLEMS OF MARRIAGE

Early problems. Many fine romances have been ruined by marriage. In the marriage act couples undertake a psychological transformation. Whereas they may be able to relate sufficiently to each other as single men and women, the moment they are married and undertake the roles of husband and wife and thereby anticipate the roles of mother and father, they encounter unconscious responses to their own parents. The girl friend who becomes a wife must start managing a house, and she usually does this by imitating her mother. In so doing, she may be profoundly influenced by her mother's attitudes toward sexuality, which were transmitted to her during her childhood. Similarly, the man who becomes a husband finds himself relying on patterns established by his father in the husband role. If there had been an intense relation between the child and parent of the opposite sex during the child's formative years, coitus in marriage may be accompanied by intense anxiety, not present in the couple's sexual relations outside marriage. One of the sources of sexual difficulties at this time is the unconscious perception of coitus with one's spouse as incest.

The marital pattern now in vogue in America is subject to certain vulnerabilities. The average age of marriage today for girls is around nineteen years; about half the teen-age marriages end in divorce, and nearly one-third are complicated by premarital pregnancy. Most observers agree that these marriages are products of a culture that has overemphasized sexual gratification and performance to the exclusion of love, intimacy, and a lasting relation. Our culture may be guilty of the mechanization of sex, of separating sex from love. With the influx of knowledge about the art of coitus and the constant emphasis on the need for adequate sexual satisfaction of one's partner, there is danger, as May pointed out, of creating a culture of sexual athletes. Such persons treat each other primarily as objects for orgastic release. They function purely on the basis of sexual love, and the relationship may deteriorate as soon as sexual tensions decline and their related needs are gratified. This outcome is the unfortunate fate of many young couples who discover too soon that the honeymoon is over.

Later problems. The passage of time brings different pressures on marriage. Early in marriage, money, sex, in-laws, and the demands for companionship are common sources of conflict and stress. Somewhat later in marriage, childbearing brings into sharp relief conflicts in gender role behavior and underlying neurotic patterns based on earlier relations with parents. A woman overly committed to her family and home during the period of child-rearing may regard eventual separation from her children as an indication of her uselessness (the empty nest syndrome). When marital, especially sexual, relations do not compensate for this loss, additional strain occurs. An aging man's preoccupation with personal success may be accompanied by fears of failing potency.

As couples grow older, sexual relations usually play an important role in maintaining marital stability. For this reason, the findings of Masters and Johnson that the sexual drive of women increases during middle age and that orgasm can be achieved during the eighth decade of life are significant in counseling the aged. These researchers point out that aging women are fully capable of achieving orgasm, particularly if they are exposed to regular and effective sexual stimulation. Aging men are usually able to continue some form of active sexual expression into the eighth and even ninth decades of life. The most important factor in maintaining effective sexuality in men of this age is consistency of active sexual expression. If a man is sexually active through the middle and involutional years, sexual gratification thereafter may be highly satisfactory.

REFERENCES

Barton, D., and Ware, P. D. Incongruities in the development of the sexual system. Arch. Gen. Psychiat., 14: 614, 1966.

Beach, F. A., editor. *Sex and Behavior*. Wiley, New York, 1965.

Brown, D. G., and Lynn, D. B. Human sexual development: an outline of components and concepts. J. Marriage Family, 28: 155, 1966.

Cohen, M. Personal identity and sexual identity. Psychiatry, 29: 1, 1966.

Dearborn, L., Autoerotism. In *The Encyclopedia of Sexual Behavior*, A. Ellis and A. Aborbanel, editors, vol. 1, p. 204. Hawthorn Books, New York, 1961.

Freud, S. Three essays on sexuality. *Standard Edition of the Complete Psychological Works of Sigmund Freud*, vol. 7, p. 125. Hogarth Press, London, 1953.

Gagnon, J. H. Sexuality and sexual learning in the child. Psychiatry, 28: 212, 1965.

Group for the Advancement of Psychiatry. *Sex and the College Student*. Atheneum, New York, 1966.

Harlow, H. F. Sexual behavior in the Rhesus monkey. In *Sex and Behavior*, F. A. Beach, editor, p. 234. Wiley, New York, 1965.

Kinsey, A. C., Pomeroy, W. B., and Martin, C. E. *Sexual Behavior in the Human Male*. W. B. Saunders, Philadelphia, 1948.

Kinsey, A. C., Pomeroy, W. B., Martin, C. E., and Gebhard, P. H. *Sexual Behavior in the Human Female*. W. B. Saunders, Philadelphia, 1953.

Kirkendall, L. A. *Premarital Intercourse and Interpersonal Relationships*. Julian Press, New York, 1961.

Masters, W. H., and Johnson, V. E. *Human Sexual Response*. Little, Brown, Boston, 1966.

Masters, W. H., and Johnson, V. E. *Human Sexual Inadequacy*. Little, Brown, Boston, 1970.

May, R. *Man's Search for Himself*. W. W. Norton, New York, 1953.

May, R. Antidotes for the new Puritanism. Saturday Rev., March 26, 1966.

Money, J. L. *Sex Research: New Developments*. Holt, Rinehart and Winston, New York, 1965.

Money, J. L., Hampson, J. G., and Hampson, J. L. Hermaphroditism: recommendations concerning assignment of sex, change of sex, and psychologic management. Bull. Johns Hopkins Hosp., 97: 284, 1955.

Rado, S. An adaptational view of sexual behavior. In *Psychoanalysis of Behavior*, vol. 1, p. 186. Grune & Stratton, New York, 1956.

Sherfey, M. J. The evolution and nature of female sexuality in relation to psychoanalytic theory. J. Amer. Psychoanal. Ass., 14: 28, 1966.

Stoller, R. J. Passing and the continuum of gender identity. In *Sexual Inversion*, J. Marmor, editor, p. 190. Basic Books, New York, 1965.

Contributors

ARTHUR J. BACHRACH, Ph.D.

Director of Behavioral Sciences Department, Naval Medical Research Institute, National Naval Medical Center, Bethesda, Maryland; Adjunct Professor of Psychology, The American University, Washington, D.C.

GUIDO M. CROCETTI, B.Sc.

Research Director, Union Project, Phipps College, Johns Hopkins Medical School, Baltimore, Maryland

WILLIAM C. DEMENT, M.D., Ph.D.

Associate Professor of Psychiatry and Head of Sleep Research Laboratories, Stanford University School of Medicine; Consultant in Psychiatry, Veterans Administration Hospital, Palo Alto, California

CYNTHIA P. DEUTSCH, Ph.D.

Research Professor, Institute for Developmental Studies, New York University School of Education, New York, New York

MARTIN DEUTSCH, Ph.D.

Professor of Early Childhood Education and Director of Institute for Developmental Studies, New York University School of Education, New York, New York

ROBERT W. DOTY, Ph.D.

Professor, Center for Brain Research; Professor of Physiology, University of Rochester, Rochester, New York

MAX FINK, M.D.

Professor of Psychiatry and Director of Division of Biological Psychiatry, Department of Psychiatry, New York Medical College; Attending Psychiatrist, Flower and Fifth Avenue Hospitals; Visiting Psychiatrist, Metropolitan Hospital, New York, New York

STEPHEN FLECK, M.D.

Professor of Psychiatry and Public Health, Yale Universtiy School of Medicine;

Psychiatrist-in-Chief, Yale Psychiatric Institute, and Connecticut Mental Health Center, New Haven; Consultant, Veterans Administration Hospital, West Haven, and Connecticut Valley Hospital, Middletown, Connecticut

ECKHARD H. HESS, Ph.D.

Professor of Psychology, University of Chicago, Chicago, Illinois

HAROLD E. HIMWICH, M.D.

Clinical Professor of Neurology and Psychiatry, Stritch School of Medicine of Loyola University, Chicago; Director of Research Division, Galesburg State Research Hospital, Galesburg, Illinois

WILLIAMINA A. HIMWICH, Ph.D.

Professorial Lecturer, Stritch School of Medicine of Loyola University, Chicago; Medical Research Adjunct Professor of Chemistry, Western Illinois University, Macomb, Illinois

E. ROY JOHN, Ph.D.

Research Professor of Psychiatry and Director of Brain Research Laboratories, Department of Psychiatry, New York Medical College, New York, New York

SEYMOUR KETY, M.D.

Professor of Psychiatry, Harvard Medical School; Director of Psychiatric Research Laboratories, Massachusetts General Hospital, Boston, Massachusetts

PAUL V. LEMKAU, M.D.

Professor and Chairman of Department of Mental Hygiene, School of Hygiene and Public Health, Johns Hopkins University, Baltimore, Maryland

HAROLD I. LIEF, M.D.

Professor of Psychiatry, Tulane University School of Medicine; Director of Hutchinson Memorial Psychiatric Clinic, Tulane University School of Medicine; Senior Visiting Physician, Charity Hospital, New Orleans, Louisiana

ROBERT B. MALMO, Ph.D.

Professor of Psychology, Departments of Psychiatry and Psychology, McGill University; Director of Neuropsychology Laboratory, Allan Memorial Institute of Psychiatry, Montreal, Quebec, Canada

ARNOLD J. MANDELL, M.D.

Professor and Chairman of Department of Psychiatry, University of California School of Medicine at San Diego; Chief of Psychiatry, University-County Hospital, San Diego; Chief of Psychiatry, Veterans Administration Hospital, La Jolla, California

DANIEL OFFER, M.D.

Associate Director of Institute for Psychosomatic and Psychiatric Research and Training, Michael Reese Hospital, Chicago, Illinois

JOHN D. RAINER, M.D.

Associate Professor of Clinical Psychiatry, Columbia University College of Physicians and Surgeons; Chief of Psychiatric Research (Medical Genetics), New York State Psychiatric Institute, New York, New York

DAVID M. REED, Ph.D., M.P.H.

Assistant Professor of Psychiatry, Family Study in Psychiatry, University of Pennsylvania School of Medicine, Philadelphia, Pennsylvania

JURGEN RUESCH, MD.

Professor of Psychiatry, University of California School of Medicine at San Francisco; Director of Section of Social Psychiatry, Langley Porter Neuropsychiatric Institute, San Francisco, California

MELVIN SABSHIN, M.D.

Professor and Head of Department of Psychiatry, University of Illinois College of Medicine; Attending Physician, Michael Reese Hospital; Consultant in Psychiatry, Presbyterian St. Luke's Hospital, Chicago, Illinois

JOSEPH J. SCHILDKRAUT, M.D.

Associate Professor, Harvard Medical School; Director of Neuropsychopharmacology Laboratory, Massachusetts Mental Health Center, Boston, Massachusetts

CHARLES SHAGASS, M.D.

Professor of Psychiatry, Temple University School of Medicine; Chief of Temple Clinical Service, Eastern Pennsylvania Psychiatric Institute, Philadelphia, Pennsylvania

IRVING SILVERMAN, Ph.D.

Assistant Professor of Psychiatry, Division of Community Mental Health, Department of Psychiatry, New York Medical College, New York, New York

CHARLES J. SMITH, Ph.D.

Associate Professor of Psychology, State University of New York at Buffalo, Buffalo, New York

PHILIP SOLOMON, M.D.

Clinical Professor of Psychiatry, University of California Medical School at San Diego, La Jolla, California

ANTHONY F. C. WALLACE, Ph.D.

Professor of Anthropology, University of Pennsylvania; Professor of Anthropology, Department of Psychiatry, University of Pennsylvania School of Medicine; Senior Research Scientist, Eastern Pennsylvania Psychiatric Institute, Philadelphia, Pennsylvania

LOUIS J. WEST, M.D.

Professor and Chairman of Department of Psychiatry, University of California at Los Angeles School of Medicine; Medical Director, University of California at Los Angeles Neuropsychiatric Institute, Los Angeles, California

Index